MEDICARE

CHANDLER PUBLICATIONS IN POLITICAL SCIENCE

Victor Jones, Editor

MEDICARE: | POLICY and POLITICS

*A Case Study
and Policy Analysis by*

EUGENE FEINGOLD
UNIVERSITY OF MICHIGAN

CHANDLER PUBLISHING COMPANY
*124 Spear Street
San Francisco, California 94105*

The painting "The Doctor" by Sir Luke Fildes is reproduced with permission of the Tate Gallery (London) and
of the New York Graphic Society, Inc.

———

FOR MY FATHER AND MY MOTHER

Contents

x | Contents

Preface

This study of medical politics and medical economics is addressed to a disparate audience. It is concerned with the struggle over government participation in the financing of medical care for the elderly that has been a major issue on the American political scene for half a dozen years. The hoped-for audience consists of three groups: those who are concerned with politics, and particularly with contemporary American politics; those who are concerned with the economics of medical care; and—closest to the author's own interests—those who are concerned with the policy output of American politics and whose interests are thus both in the process and the substantive policy areas.

The student of contemporary American politics will find here all of the characters in the modern political passion play: the influential interest group, the powerful Congressional committee chairman, the political party, the Presidential candidate. This volume shows the attempt to translate a felt need into a public policy and the response to this attempt. It deals with the creation and marshaling of public opinion, the political activities of interest groups, and the enactment of legislation. To the extent that it is successful, it should provide useful supplementary and exemplary material for the commonly offered courses in Public Opinion and Pressure Groups and the Legislative Process, as well as for the introductory course in American Government.

When I speak of those concerned with medical economics, I am thinking not only of the professional specialist, but also of the general public: my friend, a minister, who told me that he favored medicare, but didn't know how to respond to the arguments of its opponents; my physician friend who said to me: "What is the Forand bill about? I know I'm supposed to be against it, but what's in it?" I have tried, after exhausting and exhaustive examination of the literature, to select the major points at issue and to present the arguments of medicare's supporters and opponents in their own words. Additional data to help illuminate the points at issue are also presented. "Impartial" data are hard to come by; much of the "information" available is really a brief for a particular point of view. This is nowhere better illustrated than in that portion of Chapter II which deals with the financial situation of the aged.

Not only is information charged with a point of view; the very terms of the discussion also introduce a bias. One such term is "socialized medicine." This is a term which has been applied to so many different plans that it has little intellectual content, although it may have powerful emotional effect. When scholars, rather than propagandists, use the term, they usually refer to a system of state medicine, in which the government owns the medical facilities and employs the medical personnel. Because of its ambiguous meaning in general usage, however, the term is not used in this volume.

Other terms which may obfuscate more than they clarify are "compulsory" and "voluntary" medical insurance. These terms, which also have emotional impact, are frequently used to differentiate between government and private insurance programs. Yet, private insurance programs may also be compulsory: particular employers may require that their employees participate in a group insurance plan and may offer no choice as to type of plan. True, an individual who does not wish to participate in such a plan may seek other employment, but this may be no more realistic an alternative than that of jail for the individual who does not want to pay taxes for a government insurance program. Accordingly, I have tried to minimize my use of these terms, referring rather to "government" and "private" insurance.

The term "medicare" itself is somewhat ambiguous. It was first applied to a program of federally subsidized medical care for dependents of military personnel. During the discussion of proposals for hospital insurance for the aged in the last years of the Eisenhower Administration, the Secretary of Health, Education, and, Welfare, Arthur Flemming, applied the term to these proposals. Since then, the term has been used by headline writers and others to refer to a wide variety of medical-care programs, which range from the complete provision of all medical services for the entire population to the provision of selected services for a portion of the population. Because of its ambiguity, I hesitated before using the term in this volume. There is, however, a limit to the extent to which words and phrases such as "the social-security approach" and "Forand-type"[a] can be used. When I use any of these terms or "medicare," I am referring to proposals for the financing of hospital and related services for the elderly through the social-security system.

A word of explanation is in order about two other kinds of terms used in this book. All references to the "aged," the "elderly," and similar terms, mean those persons 65 years of age and over. The term "insurance" applies both to commercial insurance and to prepayment plans such as Blue Cross, except where the context indicates otherwise. Although the differences between these two methods of spreading medical-care costs are important, and are discussed in Chapter I, they can for many purposes be considered as one.

Readers may wish to learn more about particular subjects discussed in this book. Teachers may want to assign further reading to students. Students writing research papers find bibliographical suggestions helpful. To serve all three of these needs, I have tried to make this volume into a beginning guide to the literature. At the end of each chapter there is an extensive bibliography of sources particularly relevant to the subject of that chapter. Appendix A is a bibliography of sources relevant to the over-all subject of the book. The full citations for sources mentioned in the text may be found in these bibliographies.

In the selections reproduced in this book, I have generally eliminated the original footnotes. Where footnotes have been retained, they have been renumbered to run in series throughout

---

[a] After Congressman Aime Forand, one of the first sponsors in recent years of legislation providing hospital services for the elderly through the social-security system.

the selection. Occasionally, I have added explanatory footnotes to the selections; they are indicated by superior letters rather than numerals. The majority of the selection titles are my own.

Agnes W. Brewster, Wilbur J. Cohen, Ida C. Merriam, Louis Reed, and Dorothy Rice have all been helpful in suggesting material to be reviewed for inclusion in this casebook and/or in providing me with unpublished data. Robert J. S. Ross was of great assistance in finding materials for, and writing a draft of part of, Chapter III. Robert J. Myers and H. Lewis Rietz made helpful comments on an early draft of part of Chapter V. Dr. S. J. Axelrod was kind enough to read the entire manuscript and offer suggestions for its improvement. Last, but far from least, the excellently indexed library of the Bureau of Public Health Economics of the University of Michigan's School of Public Health was a treasure trove of materials on which to draw; its librarian, Jack Tobias, provided extensive aid and assistance. This casebook shows the marks of the help of all of these. I, of course, am responsible for all its faults, but I would hope that if there are any plaudits to be handed out, I may get in line for those as well.

MEDICARE

The following abbreviations are used throughout this book:

Aging	SPECIAL COMMITTEE ON AGING
AMA	AMERICAN MEDICAL ASSOCIATION
BLS	BUREAU OF LABOR STATISTICS
BOASI	BUREAU OF OLD AGE AND SURVIVORS' INSURANCE
Cong.	CONGRESS
Fin.	COMMITTEE ON FINANCE
HEW	DEPARTMENT OF HEALTH, EDUCATION, AND WELFARE
HR	HOUSE OF REPRESENTATIVES
MAA	MEDICAL ASSISTANCE FOR THE AGED
OAA	OLD AGE ASSISTANCE
OASDI	OLD AGE, SURVIVORS' AND DISABILITY INSURANCE
OASI	OLD AGE AND SURVIVORS' INSURANCE
PHS	PUBLIC HEALTH SERVICE
Sen.	SENATE
SSA	SOCIAL SECURITY ADMINISTRATION
W&M	COMMITTEE ON WAYS AND MEANS

Medical Care for the General Population

It has been said that it is only within the last fifty years that a random patient, with a random ailment, consulting a physician at random, has had a better-than-even chance of benefiting from the encounter. With the rise of scientific medicine that has made this situation possible has come rapid change in the methods of organizing and paying for medical care. The many proposals for additional changes have, in the past few years, focused on financing medical care (and especially hospital care) for those aged 65 and over. It is this problem that will be treated in this volume. The problem of financing medical care for the aged, however, does not stand alone. The aged are a special segment of the entire population, and the question of financing their medical care is part of a larger question of social policy: How shall we treat our indigents?

Economic Status and Medical Care

The bare outlines of the relationship between economic status and medical care can be simply stated. The poor—those with low incomes and few, if any, liquid assets—have greater need for medical care: they are sick more frequently and for longer periods than those who are better off financially. In spite of the fact that their need is greater, they receive less medical care. Within this pattern, there is great variation in the need for and receipt of medical care. Within each economic group, medical costs are distributed unevenly: some families have none in a given year, whereas others have costs that exceed their family income.[a]

But the crucial question is the one that concerns all scholars— causation. The relationship between economic status and receipt of medical care has been fairly clearly established; but is low income the reason for the lesser amount of medical care received, or do poor people get less medical care because of factors other than income? It is clear that one of the reasons for unmet need in any income group is the sick person's failure to recognize his need for medical care. Better-educated persons, who are disproportionately represented in the higher-income groups, are more likely to recognize such needs. Once having recognized his medical need, the sick individual may be prevented from seeking medical care by factors other than financial inability, such as fear or cultural values that inhibit consultation with physicians. Proponents of government participation in the financing of medical care usually stress the relationship between income and medical care; opponents of such government participation usually stress the non-economic factors which play a part in this relationship.

Another area of controversy between those who favor an increased government role in the financing of medical care and those who are opposed deals with the wisdom with which consumers spend their money. Opponents of an increased government role point out that the average family spends about as much for medical care as it does for liquor or tobacco. They conclude that "curtailment of luxury items in food, clothing, and shelter and reduction in expenditures for alcoholic liquors, automobile ownership and operation, tobacco and recreation would permit a material increase in medical care."[b] Thus, low-income families could afford better medical care if they gave it appropriate priority.

The opposing point of view draws distinctions between medical care and other necessities and luxuries. First, it is argued, the need

---

[a] Some of the studies which have attempted to measure the relationship among economic status, health, and medical care are cited by Anderson and Feldman, pp. 1, 2n; Davis, pp. 451-452, 457-458; Klem; Mountin and O'Hara; Serbein, chap. 1; and U.S. Federal Security Agency, pp. 22-38. Stockwell reviews the research on a closely related topic. There are a few studies whose conclusions disagree with the pattern outlined in the text; Graham's is one of these.

[b] Bachman and Meriam, p. 37.

for other necessities is more or less regular and predictable: the consumer knows that he must eat a certain number of times a day and that he needs certain kinds of clothing. The need for medical care is, in contrast, irregular and unpredictable. Second, the consumer can exercise a good deal of control over the price he pays for other necessities. His overcoat may be made of wool rather than vicuna; his dinner may be hamburger (or even vegetables) rather than steak. The costs of medical care are usually not within his control. The third, and perhaps most important, distinction between medical care and other goods or services is, in the words of one author, "the difference between a desired good and an undesired necessity."[c] Other goods and services produce enjoyment and are therefore desired; medical care is necessary, but not particularly enjoyable.

The result of these distinctions is that it is difficult for the man about to purchase a package of cigarettes to say to himself: "I better not spend this 30¢, because six months or a year from now I might need it to help pay a hospital bill." In Dr. Davis's words:

It is hard to save for what we do not want. . . . Saving for medical care . . . calls for a present sacrifice to provide for a disagreeable future contingency. Will the present sacrifice actually be required? That cannot be foretold. How much has to be saved to meet the contingency if it does occur? That is uncertain also.

There is a third area of disagreement. Those who feel that the inhibiting effect of income on the receipt of medical care is overrated sometimes argue that free and low-cost medical care are available in adequate quantity to serve the needs of low-income groups. Hospitals and charitable institutions often provide such care, and physicians traditionally set their fees in accordance with the individual patient's ability to pay. Under this "sliding scale," higher fees charged the well-to-do patients make up for the lower fees—or perhaps the free medical care—offered to poorer patients.

Those who hold the opposing point of view argue that the amount of charitable medical care that is available is small com-

---

[c] Davis, p. 19. Davis has been a leading spokesman for government health insurance; his book is an excellent presentation of this point of view; my presentation of this argument follows his.

pared to the need. More important, they find charitable medical care, even if adequate in amount, unsatisfactory: many people object to receiving charity. Rather than ask for it, they will do without needed medical care.

Those who advocate an increased government role also find the sliding scale lacking for several reasons. First, it operates to distribute the costs of medical care between the sick of different economic groups, and not between the sick and the healthy. Second, it places the responsibility on the physician for deciding the extent of the patient's ability to pay, a task for which he is not well suited. Third, it does not really operate as it is supposed to: most physicians do not have patients with a wide range of incomes, and the range of their scale is therefore not very wide.

Whatever the merits of the opposing points of view on the sliding scale, the argument is apparently being settled by the passage of time: the sliding scale seems to be disappearing from the American scene.[d]

Rising Medical Costs

The problems of financing medical care have grown more severe as medical costs have increased rapidly in recent years. Total expenditures for health care increased by about 700 per cent from 1928-1929 to 1960-1961. This has been an increase not only in absolute terms, but also in relative terms: 5.7 per cent of the gross national product was spent for health care in 1960-1961, compared to 3.6 per cent in the earlier period.[e]

About one-sixth of this spending increase reflects population increase; another sixth represents increasing per capita expenditure for health care.[f] In constant dollars, per capita spending for health care has increased 146 per cent since 1929,[g] and 39 per cent since 1948.[h]

But the rise in medical expenditures is not due simply, or even primarily, to increased utilization. Two-thirds of the increase since

---

[d] Somers and Somers, *Doctors, Patients, and Health Insurance*, pp. 53-54.

[e] "Expenditures for Health and Medical Care," pp. 1-2.

[f] *Ibid.*

[g] Sheps and Clark, p. 1411.

[h] Reed and Rice, p. 7.

TABLE 1. CONSUMER PRICE INDEXES FOR ALL
ITEMS AND FOR MEDICAL CARE[i]
(1947–1949 = 100)

	1929	1935	1940	1945	1950	1955	1960	1961	1962	1963	1964
All items	73.3	58.7	59.9	76.9	102.8	114.5	126.5	127.8	129.3	130.9	132.6
All medical care	73.5	71.4	72.7	83.1	106.0	128.0	156.2	160.9	165.0	169.1	172.5
Physicians' fees	—	73.8	74.6	86.7	104.1	123.3	145.2	148.9	153.3	156.7	160.7
Hospital daily service charge	—	47.1	50.4	64.4	114.6	164.5	223.3	240.3	257.1	273.4	287.0
All drugs	—	83.0	83.2	87.9	103.9	111.2	122.8	121.3	119.5	118.4	118.1
Prescription drugs	76.5	75.5	76.5	82.6	106.9	117.3	133.2	128.7	123.7	120.7	119.2

1928-1929 is due to an increase in the cost of medical care.[j] Highly important factors are the scientific and technological developments that have taken place. A patient who might once have died of an undiagnosable or incurable illness may survive today because his disease *can* be diagnosed and treated with drugs or procedures that were not available a decade ago. Yet these diagnostic tests, drugs, and procedures are expensive, and the patient whose life is saved may find himself with a sizable bill to pay.

These technological developments have been accompanied by a change in the style and locale of medical care. The private relationship between the individual and his physician has been changed to one that involves an increasing number of paramedical personnel. The hospital is becoming the center for medical care, bringing together the varied personnel and equipment that are characteristic of modern medical care. Although the *average length of stay* in hospitals for nonmaternity patients has decreased from 10 days in 1945 to 7½ days in 1963, the *total number of days* spent in hospitals by the average person each year has increased about 15 per cent.

The new central role of the hospital makes it particularly pertinent that hospital costs have increased much more than have other components of the medical-care dollar, with the result that

---

[i] Some of the deficiencies of the Consumer Price Index in measuring changes in the costs of medical care are discussed by Harris, pp. 4-6, 53-58.

[j] "Expenditures for Health and Medical Care," p. 2.

physicians' services, once the largest component of that dollar, have been outpaced by hospital costs. Average hospital expense per patient day was $38.91 in 1963—more than four times the expense of $9.39 in 1946. As a result, the total expense per patient stay in 1963 was almost three and one-half times that of 1946, despite the decrease in the average length of stay.[k]

A major cause of the increase in hospital costs has been increased payroll expense. Hospitals are employing more people, both because of the increased services which the hospitals provide and because of the shorter workweek. A larger proportion of their employees are skilled than heretofore. Finally, hospital wages and salaries, for both skilled and unskilled workers, always notoriously low, are being brought into line with the general wage level, although they are still well below that level. As a result, wages and salaries, which represented about half the operating costs of hospitals in 1946, make up about 60 per cent of their costs today.

The increased cost of labor has been accompanied by the cost of purchasing the expensive equipment with which the modern hospital is equipped. Costs per patient day have also increased because shorter hospital stays have resulted in a heavier concentration of services each day.

Extrapolating the effects of these factors into the future and weighing against them possible improvements in productivity, changes in the organization of medical care, and the effects of medical research, HEW Secretary Arthur Flemming concluded in 1959 that costs would probably continue to rise.[1]

The Rise of Health Insurance

One of the most striking aspects of medical-care costs is their unpredictable and uneven incidence. One recent study points out that

in one year 8 per cent of the families incurred no charges at all for personal health services, and 2 per cent of the families incurred charges in excess of approximately $1,000. . . . Another way to state this is that 46 per cent of the families incurred charges under approximately

---

[k] Sullivan and Huyck. Data for 1963 supplied by the American Hospital Association, reported in *The Wall Street Journal,* August 4, 1964.
[1] U.S. Cong. HR W&M, pp. 33-39.

$100 or none at all, accounting for 7.5 per cent of the total charges for personal health services. On the other end of the distribution, approximately 11 per cent of the families incurred charges in excess of approximately $500, accounting for 43 per cent of the total charges.[m]

If each family in the United States had to pay only the average cost of medical care, the financing of medical care would present much less of a problem. Families could budget their expenditures and save to pay their predictable medical costs; the major source of difficulty would be families with incomes too low to enable them to pay their share. It is the inequality and unpredictability of the burden which make some device for the spreading of costs very important.

One of the major changes in the way in which our medical-care bills are paid has been the rapid rise of one such device: private health insurance. As a result of the greatly increased health-insurance coverage, economic status seems to be less important today as a determinant of the utilization of medical care than it was in the past.

Although health insurance was available in parts of the United States in the 1930's, its rapid expansion did not come until World War II. The War Stabilization Board, attempting to control inflationary rises in wages and prices, exempted noncash wage supplements, or "fringe benefits," from its ban on wage increases. Trade unions and employers immediately turned their attention to these forms of compensation, and health-insurance coverage accelerated. At about the same time, the American Medical Association and many of the local and state medical societies abandoned the disapproval or, at the very least, distrust with which they had regarded the application of insurance principles to medical financing. Instead, they began to promote private health insurance as an alternative to government entry into the field of medical-care financing through compulsory health insurance of some kind.[n]

---

[m] Anderson and Feldman, pp. 36-37. McNerney *et al.*, in chapter 14, give several brief studies which help to illustrate the financial difficulties of those who are unfortunate enough to fall in the upper end of the distribution of medical expenses.

[n] For more extensive discussion of these government proposals and the reactions of the organized medical profession to them, see Chapter III.

Blue Cross and Commercial Insurance

Chart 1 shows the rapid growth of private health insurance as a vehicle for paying at least part of the individual family's medical-care bill. The great bulk of this insurance is provided by two kinds of institutions: commercial insurance companies, and the nonprofit Blue Cross and Blue Shield. Blue Cross, which covers hospital costs, is affiliated with the American Hospital Association;

Chart 1. Number of Persons with Health Insurance

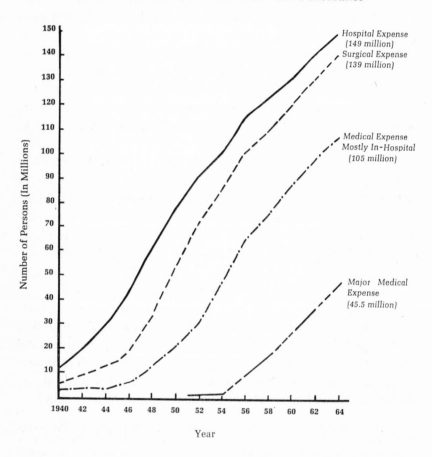

Source: Adapted from Chart I-4 of the University of Michigan's *Medical Care Chart Book.* Based on data provided by the Health Insurance Institute, an insurance-industry trade association.

Blue Shield, which covers certain medical expenses, with the organized medical profession. A major difference between the insurance offered by these two kinds of institutions is that the commercial companies customarily pay the insured a sum of cash specified in the policy, for example, $10 for every day spent in the hospital. This sum may represent more or less than the actual cost of the medical care received. The Blue plans, and particularly Blue Cross, provide service benefits; that is, the insured is covered for certain services, for example, 120 days of hospital care a year, regardless of cost. Thus, under commercial insurance, the insured may make a cash profit on his illness, or, more commonly, have additional bills to pay. Under the Blue plans, he will neither make a profit nor have additional bills for those services which are insured, although he may have other, uninsured costs.

Thus, as medical costs increase, a given commercial insurance policy covers a smaller proportion of the individual's medical bill, whereas Blue Cross absorbs the increase. It can absorb the increase only temporarily, of course, or else it would become insolvent; eventually, it must raise its premium to cover the higher medical costs. As a result, Blue Cross premiums have climbed steadily, while commercial premiums have remained the same, except insofar as their benefits have been enlarged.

Another difference, which is disappearing, between commercial companies and Blue Cross deals with the population on which actuarial computations are based. In the past, Blue Cross based its rates on the entire community, so that healthier groups within the community paid a higher rate than they would have if the rate were based on their own medical record or experience. The higher rate that they paid subsidized the less healthy elements in the population, who paid a rate lower than they would have if the rate were based on their own experience. Community rating, then, is a way of spreading insured medical costs evenly throughout the entire portion of the community which is insured. Commercial companies, in contrast, use experience rating; that is, they offer different rates to different elements of the community. The result is that it is advantageous for low-risk groups to carry commercial insurance. Most employee groups represent lower risks than the general community, and employers who pay part or all of their employees' health-insurance premiums find it profitable to leave Blue Cross for commercial insurance companies. As they do so, Blue Cross is left with a concentration of higher-risk groups, so that Blue Cross's total costs increase and it must increase its premiums accordingly. This increase drives more lower-risk groups into insuring with commercial companies, and so on. The result is indicated in Chart 2: whereas Blue Cross covered the majority of persons carrying health insurance until the early 1950's, commercial companies have taken the lead and the gap is steadily widening.

The commercial carriers are also attractive to large, national corporations because these carriers are able to provide policies

Chart 2. Number of Persons with Hospital Insurance,
by Type of Insurer
*(Excluding Independent Plans Under Which 7 Million Persons
Were Covered in 1963)*

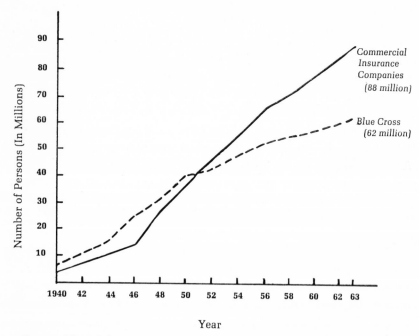

Source: Adapted from Chart I-10 of the University of Michigan's *Medical Care Chart Book.* Based on data provided by the Health Insurance Institute, an insurance-industry trade association.

with identical coverage throughout the nation. Blue Cross, which is a federation of differing regional plans, was at first not able to do this. However, in order to meet the mounting competition from commercial carriers, Blue Cross has begun to offer national insurance policies. It has also tried to meet the competition of insurance-company rates by moving from community rating to experience rating. To the extent that it does so, however, the problems of the low-income, high-risk person increase. State regulatory authorities, sensitive to these problems, have resisted Blue Cross's efforts to change its rating basis.

Comprehensive Prepayment Plans

About 5 per cent of health insurance is provided by a third kind of institution: the comprehensive prepayment plan. These plans differ from Blue Cross and most commercial plans in that the comprehensive plans cover the cost of physicians' services outside the hospital, and sometimes other medical costs as well. The usual form of operation is group medical practice, defined by the American Medical Association as the provision of medical services "by a number of physicians working in systematic association with the joint use of equipment and technical personnel and with centralized administration and financial organization." The physicians may or may not be housed in the same building; in some plans they will, in others they will not, have patients who do not belong to the comprehensive plan.° A member of the plan is, by virtue of his premium, entitled to all or most medical care either at no additional charge or, in some cases, for a slight additional fee. The growth of these plans has been much slower than that of commercial plans and Blue Cross, in part because of the opposition of the organized medical profession.

Major-Medical Insurance

Another kind of insurance which covers a wide range of kinds of medical care is major-medical insurance, which is written almost entirely by commercial insurance companies. Under a major-medical plan, the insured pays part of his medical costs, and the

---

° For a discussion of the various forms of group practice, see Somers and Somers, *Doctors, Patients, and Health Insurance,* pp. 37-43.

company the rest. The share paid by the insured is made up of three parts. He pays all of his medical costs up to a specified initial amount, typically $100 (the "deductible"). On costs above that initial amount, he pays a specified proportion, typically 25 per cent (the "corridor"). The company pays the remainder of his bills, up to a specified maximum, typically $10,000. Costs above that maximum are his to pay alone. For example, if the insured has a $500 medical bill, he pays $200 (the initial $100 plus 25 per cent of the remaining $400), and the company pays the remainder. This framework permits wide variation not only in the amount of the deductible and the corridor, but also in the period to which the deductible and the maximum are applied; that is, quite different results are obtained depending on whether the deductible is $100 per year or $100 per illness. Similarly, the maximum may apply to expenditures for a single illness or in a particular year or in the insured's lifetime.

Health Insurance and Increased Costs

Health insurance does more than spread medical costs among the insured population. It also increases these costs for several reasons. First among these reasons is the fact that both the physician and the patient need pay less attention to the cost of those kinds of medical care that are insured. This leads to increased utilization of such care. Some of this increase represents legitimate medical need, heretofore unmet because the patient could not afford the care he needed. However, some of the increased utilization is unnecessary, and represents the use of medical services simply because they are available. Insurance also affects medical costs because some physicians have increased the fees they charge insured patients. This may be interpreted as the extension of the sliding-scale principle: the insured patient is considered, by virtue of his insurance, to be better able to pay a higher fee. A third way in which insurance affects medical costs is that these now include the carriers' administrative costs and profits, which range widely— from about 5 per cent of premium income for Blue Cross to about 50 per cent of premium income for individual insurance contracts held with commercial insurance companies. The consumer does not feel these increased costs immediately, because they are initially absorbed by the insurance carriers. As a result, however, the carriers must increase their rates, at which point the consumer is likely to feel the pinch (insurance carriers obviously also increase their rates because of the increases in medical costs discussed earlier in this chapter).

Resistance to increased premiums has begun to lead to attempts by some insurance carriers to limit utilization and fees. The result is a major change in the relationship between the sick person on one hand, and the hospital and physician on the other hand. The individual patient, perhaps in a state of anxiety because of his illness, is in a poor bargaining position; not so the group of insurance-carrier representatives, who represent a market power much greater than that of the physicians and hospitals with whom they deal. (More than half of the income of hospitals and a third of the income of physicians comes from insurance carriers.) Thus, through the entry of the third party, the insurance carrier, into the doctor-patient relationship, the freedom of the physician to practice medicine and to charge fees as he sees fit is restricted.

TABLE 2. WORK STATUS OF PERSONS AGED 14 AND OVER, WITH AND WITHOUT HEALTH INSURANCE, 1958

	Uninsured population, %	Insured population, %
Currently working		
Full time	35	53
Part time	4	3
Other	3	2
	—	—
	42	58
Currently not working		
Unemployed	2	0
Retired	8	3
Disabled	3	1
Student (full time)	11	10
Housewife (full time)	33	28
Other	1	0
	—	—
	58	42
	══	══
	100	100
	—	—

Source: Adapted from "The People Without Health Insurance," p. 3.

This limitation is one reason for the organized medical profession's preference for cash, rather than service, benefits. In a service-benefit plan, the participating physician cannot charge whatever rate he wishes, but must accept the price set for that service by the insuring company.

The increase in medical costs because of health insurance affects not only the insured, but also the uninsured, who frequently have to pay higher fees without having them absorbed even temporarily by insurance. Who are the uninsured? As Table 2 indicates, one of the principal differences between the insured and the uninsured is their work status. The reason for this difference is simple: the most common method of acquiring health insurance is through one's place of employment. A very large proportion of the uninsured are not working and are therefore unable to get insurance through an employer. Of the uninsured who are employed, most work in places where health insurance is not offered to employees. People who do not get health insurance through group coverage on the job must usually get it on an individual basis. Such insur-

TABLE 3. PERCENTAGE OF VARIOUS GROUPS WITH HOSPITAL INSURANCE COVERAGE (INCOME AND EDUCATION DATA FOR 1962–1963; RACE AND RESIDENCE DATA FOR 1959)

Family income per year	
Under $2,000	34%
$2,000–$3,999	52
$4,000–$6,999	79
$7,000 and over	88
Educational level of head of household, in years	
Under 5	37
5–8	61
9–12	75
13 and over	85
Race	
Nonwhite	42
White	71
Residence	
Farm	45
Rural nonfarm	68
Urban	72

Source: Data from the U.S. National Health Survey, a federal survey conducted by household interviews of approximately 42,000 households each year.

ance is not only more expensive, but also requires positive action on the part of the individual, rather than mere acceptance of the coverage that goes with the job. One might say that these people are less accessible to the insurance companies and other insurance carriers.

This concept of accessibility can also be applied to the groups which Table 3 shows are less likely to be insured: the poor, the

Chart 3. Percentage of Population with Hospital Insurance
at End of Each Specified Time Period

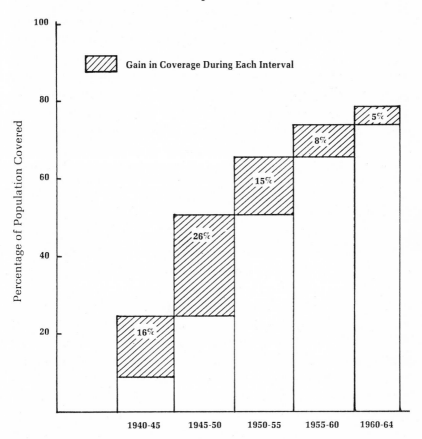

Source: Adapted from Chart I-5 of the University of Michigan's *Medical Care Chart Book*. Based on data provided by the Health Insurance Institute, an insurance-industry trade association.

uneducated, the nonwhites, and the rural population. Each for its own reason is less accessible to the insurance carriers, and it is this lack of accessibility which helps to explain the decline in the rate of growth of hospital insurance, indicated in Chart 3: those who are easy to reach have been sold insurance, and those who are still uninsured represent a much harder selling job.

Another way to measure health-insurance coverage is in terms of the proportion of the nation's medical bills which are paid by insurance. The great bulk of health-insurance premiums goes to pay for coverage of hospitalization expenses, and most of the rest for in-hospital physicians' services. As a result, about two-thirds of hospital costs and one-third of doctors' fees are paid by insurance; about 1.5 per cent of other medical-care costs are covered by health insurance. If all private consumer medical-care costs are analyzed, 28 per cent of them are paid for through health insurance. This last figure is slightly misleading, because it includes such items as nonprescription drugs and the extra costs of luxury hospital accommodations, which are not usually considered to be within the legitimate scope of health insurance. If an allowance is made for such costs, health insurance covers about a third of the potentially insurable private medical-care costs in the United States.[p]

Philosophies of Insurance

Some students of medical economics are basically happy with the status of private health insurance in the United States, which has been outlined above. Others find the existing situation unsatisfactory. The explanation for these contrasting responses lies in the different concepts of the social function of health insurance held by these two groups. Spokesmen for insurance companies and for the organized medical profession look upon health insurance as similar to other kinds of insurance: its function is simply to spread the expense of catastrophic events over that part of the population that wants to participate, rather than having the entire financial burden fall on the families who suffer the catastrophe. The opposing philosophy sees health insurance as more than a risk-spreading device; according to this point of view, health insurance should

---

[p] Reed and Rice, pp. 12-13.

be a mechanism for providing everyone, regardless of income, with the health services he needs.

The first point at issue between these two schools of thought is the extension of health insurance to more people. Both points of view advocate such extension, but the critics of the existing system are more concerned about extension than are the defenders. The critics, who want to cover everybody, emphasize those who cannot afford, or for some other reason are unable to get, the kind of coverage they want. They are particularly concerned because those who are presently not covered are, they feel, probably in greater need of the insurance mechanism. Defenders of the present system argue that almost everyone is able to get the kind of insurance he wants: the enrollment gap, they say, is due to lack of desire or need for insurance on the part of those who prefer to self-insure or who receive their medical care through the armed forces and other ways. The defenders focus their attention on the past rate of growth of health insurance, implicitly extrapolating it into the future; the critics point out that this growth rate is slackening.

The second asserted inadequacy of present health insurance is perhaps put most piquantly by Michael Davis, who objects to describing the insured as being "covered"; rather, he would describe them as being "reached." That is, he objects to the fact that only a small proportion of medical costs are insured even for those who *have* insurance. His opponents argue that not all medical costs *should* be covered by insurance; coverage should extend only to the more expensive and unexpected forms of medical care, as other forms can be budgeted for by the individual family. Moreover, even some of the kinds of medical costs that should be insured are covered by workmen's compensation, accident insurance, and life insurance (for terminal illness), and thus need not be covered by health insurance.

Public-opinion surveys have indicated interest in coverage of a broader range of services, and there are a number of indications that the average person would be willing to pay higher premiums in order to get such coverage. Whether he would be willing to pay a premium high enough to cover the costs of such insurance is another question—to which there is no answer as yet. The insurance industry has attempted to meet this demand by the introduction of major-medical insurance, which covers many kinds of medical care. The portion of the bill paid by the consumer is considered a safeguard against overutilization, and also confines the insurance coverage to major illnesses. Physicians also prefer major medical, because it provides a cash benefit, rather than a service benefit.

The critics' preferred form of insurance is the comprehensive prepayment plan because it offers a wide range of services without any additional cost, over and above the premium, to the consumer, who might be deterred by additional charges from getting the medical care he needs. They argue that deterrent fees discourage preventive and early medical care, and that in the long run medical attention may be more costly, for example, through hospitalization for an illness which could have been prevented by early care. They charge that major-medical insurance increases costs because its cash benefits encourage doctors to inflate their fees. Finally, they point out that because of its maximum limit, major medical does not cover the most catastrophic illnesses.

This chapter has described some of the problems and issues in the financing of medical care for the entire population. The balance of the book is devoted to the special problems of the aged.

SELECTED BIBLIOGRAPHY

Anderson, Odin W. *Elements of Health Insurance Today.* New York: Health Information Foundation, 1960.

———, Patricia Collette, and Jacob J. Feldman. *Health Insurance Benefits for Personal Health Services: 1953 and 1958.* New York: Health Information Foundation, 1960.

Anderson, Odin W., with Jacob J. Feldman. *Family Medical Costs and Voluntary Health Insurance: A Nationwide Survey.* New York: McGraw-Hill, Inc., 1956.

Andrews, James, Jr., and Benjamin B. Kendrick. "The Contribution of Voluntary Health Insurance," *Journal of Chronic Diseases,* III (January, February, April 1956), 25-33, 154-166, 349-359.

Association of Teachers of Preventive Medicine. Committee on Medical Care Teaching, ed. *Readings in Medical Care.* Chapel Hill: University of North Carolina Press, 1958.

Bachman, George W., and Lewis Meriam. *The Issue of Compulsory Health Insurance.* Washington, D.C.: The Brookings Institution, 1948.

Baehr, George. *Medical Care in an Affluent Society.* New York: Milbank Memorial Fund, 1960.

Barrett, Laurence. "Retreat from Idealism: Blue Cross," *The Nation,* January 9, 1960, pp. 26-32.

Becker, Harry. "The Changing Scene in Health Care Economics," *New York State Journal of Medicine,* LIX (May 15, 1959), 2044-2049.

———. ed. *Financing Hospital Care for Nonwage and Low-Income Groups.* Volume 3 of the Report of the Commission on the Financing of Hospital Care. New York: McGraw-Hill, Inc., 1955.

Becker, Harry J. "Voluntary Health Insurance," *Current History,* XLV (August 1963), 92-97.

Bressler, Marvin, ed. *Meeting Health Needs by Social Action. The Annals,* CCCXXXVII (September 1961), entire issue.

Britten, Rollo H. "The National Health Survey—Receipt of Medical Services in Different Urban Populations and Groups," *Public Health Reports,* LV (November 29, 1940), 2199-2224.

Campbell, Rita R. and W. Glenn. *Voluntary Health Insurance in the United States.* Washington, D.C.: American Enterprise Association, 1960.

Cartmill, George E., Jr. "Open Forum on Prepayment Hospital and Medical Care Plans," *Journal of the Michigan State Medical Society,* LVIII (June 1959), 949-976.

Chase, Edward T. "Can Blue Cross Survive Its Own Success?" *The Reporter,* XXI (October 29, 1959), 15-19.

Chevalier, Lois R. "They're Killing the Best Kind of Health Insurance," *Medical Economics,* XXXVII (October 10, 1960), 52-64.

Cornely, Paul B., and Stanley K. Bigman. "Prepayment for Medical Care Among a Low-Income Urban Population," *Journal of the National Medical Association,* LIV (November 1962), 684-688.

Davis, Michael M. *Medical Care for Tomorrow.* New York: Harper and Brothers, 1955.

Donabedian, Avedis, and Leonard S. Rosenfeld. "Some Factors Influencing Prenatal Care," *New England Journal of Medicine,* CCLXV (July 6, 1961), 1-6.

The Economics of Health and Medical Care: Proceedings of the Conference on the Economics of Health and Medical Care. Ann Arbor: University of Michigan, 1964.

"Expenditures for Health and Medical Care," *Progress in Health Services,* XII (January-February 1963), 1-6.

Falk, I. S., C. Rufus Rorem, and Martha D. Ring. *The Costs of Medical Care: A Summary of Investigations on the Economic Aspects of the Prevention and Care of Illness.* Chicago: University of Chicago Press, 1933.

Faulkner, Edwin J. "Health Insurance and Social Policy," in Charles C. Center and Richard M. Heins, eds., *Insurance and Government* (New York: McGraw-Hill, Inc., 1962), pp. 453-468.

Freidson, Eliot, and Jacob J. Feldman. *Public Attitudes Toward Health Insurance.* Chicago: Health Information Foundation, 1958.

The Future of the Personal Physician: The Record of a National Symposium. New York: Group Health Insurance, Inc., 1964.

Gentile, Augustine, and Earl E. Huyck. "Hospital Insurance and Proportion of Bill Paid by Insurance," *HEW Indicators,* February 1962, pp. vii-x.

Goldmann, Franz, and Hugh R. Leavell, eds. *Medical Care for Americans. The Annals, CCLXXIII* (January 1951), entire issue.

Graham, Saxon. "Socio-Economic Status, Illness, and the Use of Medical Services," *Milbank Memorial Fund Quarterly,* XXXV (January 1957), 58 ff.

Greenberg, Selig. "The Medical Care Dollar," *The Progressive,* XXV (August 1961), 18-20.

Greenfield, Harry I., and Odin W. Anderson. *The Medical Care Price Index.* Chicago: Health Information Foundation, 1959.

Harris, Seymour E. *The Economics of American Medicine.* New York: The Macmillan Company, 1964.

"Health: Are We the People Getting Our Money's Worth?" *The New Republic,* CXLIX (November 9, 1963), entire issue.

The Health Care Issues of the 1960's: The Record of a National Symposium. New York: Group Health Insurance, Inc., 1963.

"Health Insurance: Why Spending Is Soaring," *Business Week,* June 24, 1961, pp. 144-166.

Kemp, Arthur, and Walter R. Livingston. "Medical Care Costs in an Extended Inflation," *Journal of the American Medical Association,* CLXXIV (October 29, 1960), 1209-1215.

Klarman, Herbert E. "The Distinctive Economic Characteristics of Health Services," *Journal of Health and Human Behavior,* IV (Spring 1963), 44-49.

———. "Economic Aspects of Hospital Care," *Journal of Business,* XXIV (January 1951), 1-24.

Klem, Margaret C. "The Committee on the Costs of Medical Care—25 Years of Progress: 25 Years of Research in Medical Economics," *American Journal of Public Health,* XLVIII (August 1958), 63-70.

Lawrence, Philip S., and Robert R. Fuchsberg. "Medical Care and Family Income," *HEW Indicators,* May 1964, pp. xxi-xxxi.

Lear, Walter J. "Medical Care in the United States," in Karl Evang, D. Stark Murray, and Walter J. Lear, *Medical Care and Family Security* (Englewood Cliffs, N.J.: Prentice-Hall, Inc., 1963), pp. 195-344.

Lee, C. Marshall, Jr. "The Challenge of Medical-Care Insurance: An Essay on Principles, Philosophies and Practices." *New England Journal of Medicine,* CCLXII (February 18, 1960), 332-342.

MacIntyre, Duncan M. *Voluntary Health Insurance and Rate Making.* Ithaca: Cornell University Press, 1952.

McNerney, Walter J., *et al. Hospital and Medical Economics: A Study of Population, Services, Costs, Methods of Payment, and Controls.* Chicago: Hospital Research and Educational Trust, 1962.

Mountin, Joseph W., and Hazel O'Hara. "Differences in Opportunities for Health," *Public Health Reports,* LIII (April 1, 1938), 485-496.

Nelson, Russell A., John W. Paynter, and Jerome Pollack. "Three Challenges for Prepayment," *Hospitals,* XXXIV (November 1, 1960), 32-44.

New York State. Joint Legislative Committee on Health Insurance Plans. *Report.* Legislative Document #49, 1957. This report is devoted to "Gaps in coverage in voluntary health insurance" and contains an extensive bibliography on the subject.

Notkin, Herbert. *Health Research Opportunities in Welfare Records: A Preliminary Report on Illness and Economic Dependency.* Chicago: Health Information Foundation, 1959.

"The People Without Health Insurance," *Progress in Health Services,* X (October 1961), 1-6.

Pollack, Jerome. "Blue Cross and Blue Shield as Methods of Financing Health Care," *Medical Annals of the District of Columbia,* XXIX (June 1960), 351-361.

———. "A Labor View of Health Insurance," *Monthly Labor Review,* LXXXI (June 1958), 626-630.

———. "Major Medical Expense Insurance: An Evaluation," *American Journal of Public Health,* XLVII (March 1957), 322-334.

A Profile of the Health Insurance Public. New York: Health Insurance Institute, 1959.

Reed, Louis S., and Dorothy P. Rice. "Private Medical Care Expenditures and Voluntary Health Insurance, 1948-61," *Social Security Bulletin,* December 1962, pp. 3-13.

Roberts, Markley. *Trends in the Supply and Demand of Medical Care.* Washington, D.C.: U.S. Congress Joint Economic Committee, 1959.

Roemer, Milton I., and Max Shain. *Hospital Utilization Under Insurance.* Hospital Monograph Series #6. Chicago: American Hospital Association, 1959.

Rosenfeld, Leonard S., and Avedis Donabedian. "Prenatal Care in Metropolitan Boston," *American Journal of Public Health,* XLVIII (September 1958), 1115-1124.

———, and Jacob Katz. "Unmet Need for Medical Care," *New England Journal of Medicine,* CCLVIII (February 20, 1958), 369-376.

Serbein, Oscar N., Jr. *Paying for Medical Care in the United States.* New York: Columbia University Press, 1953.

Sheps, Cecil G., and Dean A. Clark. "Medical Care: Its Social and Organizational Aspects—Expenditures for Health and Medical Care in the United States," *New England Journal of Medicine,* CCLXIX (December 26, 1963), 1411-1417.

Sheps, Cecil G., and Daniel L. Drosness. "Prepayment for Medical Care," *New England Journal of Medicine,* CCLXIV (February 23, March 2, March 9, 1961), 390-396, 444-448, 494-499.

Smith, Francis R. "Why Can't the Prepayment Plans Give the Public What It Wants?" *The Modern Hospital,* XCV (December 1960), 86-90.

Somers, Anne R. "Conflict, Accommodation, and Progress: Some Socioeconomic Observations on Medical Education and the Practicing Profession," *Journal of Medical Education,* XXXVIII (June 1963), 466-478.

———, and Herman M. Somers. "Coverage, Costs, and Controls in Voluntary Health Insurance," *Public Health Reports,* LXXVI (January 1961), 1-9.

———. "Health Insurance: Are Cost and Quality Controls Necessary?" *Industrial and Labor Relations Review,* XIII (July 1960), 581-595.

———. *Doctors, Patients, and Health Insurance: The Organization and Financing of Medical Care.* Washington, D.C.: The Brookings Institution, 1961. Also available in a paperback abridged edition published by Doubleday & Company, Inc. (Garden City, N.Y.), in 1962.

Stockwell, Edward G. "Socioeconomic Status and Mortality in the United States," *Public Health Reports,* LXXVI (December 1961), 1081-1086.

Sullivan, Eugenia, and Earl E. Huyck. "Hospital Costs, 1946-62," *HEW Indicators,* February 1964, pp. xxxvii-xli.

Sydenstricker, Edgar. "Economic Status and the Incidence of Illness," *Public Health Reports,* XLIV (July 26, 1929), 1821-1833.

U.S. Cong. HR W&M. *Hospitalization Insurance for OASDI Beneficiaries,* Report by the Secretary of Health, Education, and Welfare. 86th Congress, 1959.

U.S. Cong. Sen. Committee on Education and Labor. *National Health Act of 1945: Need for Medical Care Insurance.* A Memoranda [*sic*] Prepared by Bureau of Research and Statistics, Social Security Board. Senate Committee Print #4. 79th Congress, 2nd Session.

U.S. Cong. Sen. Aging. Subcommittee on Frauds and Misrepresentations Affecting the Elderly. *Deceptive or Misleading Methods in Health Insurance Sales,* Hearings. 88th Congress, 2nd Session, 1964.

U.S. HEW PHS. *Chart Book of Basic Health Economics Data.* Health Economics Series #3, 1964.

———. *Family Income in Relation to Selected Health Characteristics: Vital and Health Statistics, Data from the National Health Survey.* Series #10, No. 2, 1963.

———. *Medical Care Financing and Utilization: Source Book of Data through 1961.* Health Economics Series #1.

———. *Medical Care, Health Status, and Family Income: Vital and Health Statistics, Data from the National Health Survey.* Series #10, No. 9, 1964.

———. *Medical Care in the United States.* PHS Publication #862, 1961.

———. *United States Statistics on Medical Economics: Present Status and Recommendations for Additional Data—Report of the US National Committee on Vital and Health Statistics.* PHS Publication #1125, 1964.

U.S. HEW SSA. Division of Program Research. *Public and Private Expenditures for Health and Medical Care, Fiscal Years 1928-29 to 1960-61.* Research and Statistics Note #22, 1962.

———. *Sources of Payment for General Hospital Care: Results from a Pilot Study in New York State.* Research and Statistics Note #6, 1958.

U.S. Federal Security Agency. Social Security Board. *Medical Care and Costs in Relation to Family Income: A Statistical Source Book Including Selected Data on Characteristics of Illness.* By Helen Hollingsworth and Margaret Klem. Bureau of Research and Statistics Memorandum #51, 1943.

University of Michigan. School of Public Health. Bureau of Public Health Economics. *Medical Care Chart Book.* 2nd ed. Ann Arbor: 1964.

Weeks, H. Ashley. *Family Spending Patterns and Health Care.* Cambridge, Mass.: Harvard University Press, 1961.

The Special Problem
of the Aged

Increasing Number and Changed Status

There were approximately 3 million persons aged 65 or over in the United States in 1900; by 1963 their number had increased five and a half times to 17.5 million. This rate of growth was almost three times that of the population as a whole, with the result that the aged today make up 9.3 per cent of the population, compared to only 4 per cent in 1900. The change from earlier times was perhaps best expressed by Senator Pat McNamara (the former chairman of the United States Senate Special Committee on Aging), who said that one-quarter of all the human beings who have ever reached the age of 65 are alive today. The proportion of elderly persons is not expected to increase greatly during the next few decades, but their number is expected to rise to 20 million by 1970 and 25 million by 1980. The aged population is not only increasing in number, but also growing older, with the highest proportionate increase in the group aged 75 and over.

Perhaps more important than the increased number of the elderly is their changed status in modern, urban industrial society. In the agricultural societies of previous centuries, the comparatively few older men retained financial independence because they owned the land on which their families lived. They were respected as the sages whose lengthy experience brought wisdom. Elderly women were able to help with the many household chores which had to be done. In an urban industrial society, however, the bulk of the population does not have the independence of self-employment and land ownership. They work for others, and their work is evaluated on the basis of their production. Older men often are unable to compete successfully with younger men in this environ-ment. Their knowledge and experience are no longer unique. The knowledge essential to the operation of a modern society is passed on through formal education to professional managers. Elderly housewives find themselves much less in demand in the smaller, modern household with its modern appliances.[a]

Greater Medical Needs

The changed position of the aged, combined with their in-creased number, creates certain social and economic problems, one of which is the question of financing their medical care. There are two major background factors that must be evaluated in con-sidering the special problems of financing medical care for the aged. The first factor, about which there is only minor dispute, is discussed in this section. It is the fact that the aged need and use more medical care than the rest of the population.

Chronic illness is the major health problem of the aged. Persons over 65 are twice as likely as those under 65 to have one or more chronic conditions. Some of these chronic illnesses are minor, but others are serious. More than half of the noninstitutionalized el-derly with chronic illness have their activity limited in some way, whereas only a fifth of younger persons with chronic illness suffer such limitation. Moreover, the incidence of chronic illness and the frequency with which activity is limited increase as a person grows older than 65. Thus, since the average age of the 65-and-over group is expected to increase in the future, the proportion of ill-ness and disability among the elderly can be expected to increase.

As might be expected from the greater incidence of illness among the elderly, their use of health facilities and medical ser-vices is also greater than that of younger persons. The elderly average about seven visits to a physician each year, compared to five for younger persons. The elderly are more frequently admitted to hospitals, and their average length of stay is about twice as long as that for younger persons. The combination of more frequent

---

[a] For more extended discussion, see Leo W. Simmons, "Aging in Pre-Industrial Societies," and Fred Cottrell, "The Technological and Societal Basis of Aging," in Tibbitts.

admissions and longer average stays resulted in total annual hospital use for the elderly about two and one-half times as great as that for those under 65—218 days per 100 persons, as compared to 85 days per 100 persons. Furthermore, 9 out of 10 persons who reach the age of 65 can expect to be hospitalized at least once during their remaining lifetime.

Medical services that are utilized must usually be paid for. Table 4 indicates that average medical expenditures by the elderly are more than double those of the rest of the population. The average expenditures of those who get medical care are, of course, higher

TABLE 4. Average Private Expenditures
for Medical Care, 1962

	All personal health services	Hospital care
All ages	$119	$33
Age 65 and over	$244	$78

Source: Estimates prepared by the Blue Cross Association; adapted from pp. 2066–2067 of the Ways and Means Committee's 1964 hearings.

than the average for *all* the elderly, which includes those who spend no money for medical care in a particular year. Total annual medical expense for an aged couple, one or both of whose members were actually hospitalized that year, amounted to approximately $1,200 at 1963 prices. Single individuals who were hospitalized could expect a total bill of well over $900.

Although there is little dispute about the greater need and demand of the elderly for medical services, there are differences of emphasis between the supporters and the opponents of federal hospitalization insurance for the aged. Supporters cite the above data as evidence of illness among the aged, while opponents place their stress on the proportion of the elderly who are *not* ill. A second difference in emphasis concerns the nature, source, and cure for the greater amount of illness among aged. Implicit in the position of supporters of medicare is the idea that the medical needs of the elderly can, or should, be met by making medical care more readily available to them. The opponents emphasize the nonmedical sources of the health complaints of the aged, and suggest that these health complaints are best met through a nonmedical attack. These two points of view are expressed in the selections that follow. The first selection is a portion of the American Medical Association's 1961 testimony before the House Ways and Means Committee. Congressman King, cosponsor of the medicare bill, responded to the AMA's testimony on the floor of the House; the appropriate portion of his response comprises the second selection.

The Health Problems of Older People Cannot Be Solved Through Legislation

AMERICAN MEDICAL ASSOCIATION

From our experience as physicians, we have learned two things:

First, the aged would rather give than get.

Second, the aged are far more concerned with the process of living than with the process of aging.

There is no doubt that *some* of our older people suffer from ill health and poverty. This group is being, and should be, helped. But most people who have passed the age of 65 are not in need of the sort of help envisioned by this measure. Although determined efforts are being made to organize the nation's elderly into a voting bloc, and to seek their political support in return for blank-check promises, these efforts have thus far failed—and for a very good reason:

The elderly are not primarily interested in more money, more benefits, more handouts.

More than anything else, today's older Americans want involvement —involvement within the mainstream of society.

They worry less about health and finances than they do about rejection. They are oppressed with the feeling of not being wanted any longer, of not being useful, of not being important. They feel that they have been stripped of their value, and hence of their dignity as human beings.

Broadly speaking, Mr. Chairman, this is the sociological problem.

With the best wishes in the world, we cannot suggest a quick, easy solution for it. But we can say that this legislation is not the answer.

Society is falling down on the job, not government.

The older person wants just about the same things that the rest of us do: to be part and parcel of his environment; to be loved; to belong; to feel that his skills and talents have value, and that they will be used and appreciated.

Congress cannot pass a law to change the attitudes of society.

From testimony at hearings on *Health Services for the Aged under the Social Security Insurance System,* held by the Committee on Ways and Means of the U.S. House of Representatives, August 2, 1961, pp. 1327-1332.

This is an age of small homes and smaller apartments; of increasingly urbanized living; of a national accent on youth. There is no need to explore, in great depth, the sociological factors involved. For the most part, they are self-evident. Children who are sometimes too concerned with raising their own families to worry about their parents; the compulsory retirement of capable, active people; the too frequent disinterest of the community in the well-being of its older citizens. These and other reasons contribute to the feeling that many of our older people have of being discards, of being obsolescent or obsolete, of being citizens emeritus.

In this golden age of medicine, we physicians have become accustomed to scientific wonders. But we do not have, and do not expect to acquire, a specific against loneliness, an antibiotic against rejection, a tranquilizer to enable human beings to live without dignity.

We have reached a point in our civilization at which industrial uselessness has not yet been offset by social adjustment. Having arbitrarily established 65 as the age of obsolescence—and we are now moving to lower that age further—we have not yet compensated the hardships of economic discard by some degree of social appreciation.

We can no more provide a statutory solution to this situation than we can legislate juvenile delinquency out of existence.

Aging is not a new problem. People have always gotten older. Our problem stems essentially from the social segregation of the aged.

As to health in its broadest sense, physicians, hospitals, nurses, scientists can go only so far alone. The rest is up to the society in which they function.

Do the people of the nation want their elders to be healthier? Then they have a job to do. They cannot discharge their responsibility by turning the problem over to the government for a quick, easy solution.

We physicians can practice preventive medicine of the highest type, seeking diligently to forestall the disabling illnesses that threaten old and young alike; but society must also take the necessary steps to meet other existing needs that are just as important. The problems of the aging must be considered and tackled in their entirety, not in terms of a single aspect.

Otherwise, we shall be taking a piecemeal approach to matters susceptible only to broad-gauge solution.

In any consideration of this subject it is essential to remember that the health problems of the aged involve far more than hospital or physician care. They involve the older person's other requirements in life, whether these be housing, recreation, community understanding and acceptance, the right to be useful, the courtesy of being treated as individuals, or the opportunity of living as self-reliant, respected members of society.

We can, for example, diagnose an illness in an older person, put him in a hospital, and in due course discharge him as cured.

But if that person cannot find an opportunity to use his skills, talents, and capabilities upon returning to his community; if he cannot obtain the emotional support he needs; if he cannot win a place of acceptance within his family or his circle of friends; it is probable that he will seek, sooner or later, a return to the only shelter available. That means the artificial haven of a hospital, a nursing home, or a mental institution.

Bearing this in mind, let us talk of health in a somewhat narrower sense.

Most older people are, in fact, in good health. The diseases to which they are susceptible are no different from the diseases to which people in any age group are susceptible. There are no diseases *of* the aged; there are simply diseases *among* the aged.

There is a greater degree of chronic illness among older people. But it is important to understand what "chronic illness" really is, for the term is generally misunderstood.

The term "chronic" refers to a recurrent condition, or one that persists over a period of time. It may, but it does not necessarily, imply disability.

For instance, a person with impaired hearing is chronically ill—although he may function normally with the assistance of a hearing aid. Similarly, a diabetic is chronically ill—although with the help of insulin he can lead a perfectly normal life. I could give you countless other examples; but I think it is sufficient to say that chronic illness should not be confused with disability.

Beethoven's deafness was not disabling. Several years ago, a diabetic represented the United States on the Davis Cup team. Franklin Delano Roosevelt was chronically ill as a result of polio. And President Kennedy's back condition qualifies him for description as chronically ill.

Yet in all of these cases, we are simply saying that certain medical conditions limit certain of the individual's capacities. These conditions do not disable, in the important sense.

I make this point in some detail because the higher incidence of chronic illness among the aged has been interpreted to mean that most older people are sick and debilitated. They are often represented to be, but they are not. I repeat, most older people are in good health. When physicians make this statement, they make it as experts. And their statements are borne out by every survey that has thus far come to our attention.

Thus, although it is true that 77 per cent of those 65 and over have chronic ailments, only 14 per cent experience any significant limitation of activity; and only five per cent have major limitations of mobility. It is equally true that nearly half those persons between the ages of 30 to 44 have chronic conditions; that more than 41 per cent of people of all ages have chronic conditions; and that nearly two out of three, between the ages of 55 and 64, have chronic conditions.

To what extent are these figures significant? Only to the extent that chronic conditions represent some loss of mobility, or limitations of activity or earning power.

Also, while it is generally recognized that the incidence of chronic illness increases with age, those 65 and over have a lower incidence of acute illness. According to the National Health Survey for the period July 1957 to June 1958, the incidence of acute conditions among the older age group was approximately three-fifths of that for younger persons.

This phenomenon is the result of one thing:

Medical science has successfully prolonged life for a significant proportion of the population, thus increasing the percentage of our older people with chronic illness and decreasing the percentage of those with acute illness.

I make this point because persons with chronic illness do not always need general hospital care or even care in nursing homes or convalescent homes, and H.R. 4222 is a measure oriented toward institutional care.

I am not stating that the aged are not more frequently hospitalized than younger groups, for they are. According to the National Health Survey, the aged receive approximately twice as much hospitalization as those under 65.

But in general, the aged consider their health to be good. According to two surveys, the aged reported their health to be poor in only 11 to 23 per cent of all cases.

In another survey, 46 per cent of the aged reported good health, 44 per cent had complaints and diseases which did not interfere with their physical functions, and only 10 per cent thought of themselves as very sick.

Just recently the National Retired Teachers' Association, with

100,000 enrolled members, and the American Association of Retired Persons, with 50,000 members, queried their enrollment along these lines. Some 87 per cent considered themselves in reasonably good health. (And 86 per cent, incidentally, reported that they were carrying medical or hospital insurance.)

Please understand, Mr. Chairman, we are not suggesting that the aged are as healthy as those in their prime—but that they are a great deal healthier than they are frequently pictured to be.

The premise that most, if not all of the aged, are in poor health is ridiculous. *Some* are in poor health. *Most* are not.

My Bill Is Not Intended to Solve All of the Elderly's Problems

CECIL R. KING

I am not aware of suggestions by any proponents of my bill that the sociological problems of older people can in general be solved through legislation nor that the health insurance proposal is in any way intended to solve all problems of aged persons. The AMA discussion seems to argue that since it is not possible to solve all sociological problems of the aged through legislation, no legislation to relieve problems of aged persons is justified. Such an argument leads to no realistic conclusion; if its efficacy in solving all problems were a test of soundness of any specific course of action, one could not, of course, find any course of action that would meet the test of soundness. Such a test would even make a case against the practice of modern medicine, since it does not appear that, with all its almost miraculous advances, medical science has been able to solve all sociological problems of the aged. The proposed health insurance benefits under OASI have not been proposed as a total solution for even the financing of medical care of aged persons but have been advanced rather as a part of the solution to the problem of providing a method of financing needed health care of the aged. Many other problems will of course remain. . . .

There is no contention that all, or most, aged persons are in poor health. If that were the case, the costs of health care would hardly be insurable. Just as the need for fire insurance does not rest on the premise that all or most owners of properties experience fires, so does the need for protection against the costs of hospitalization not depend on universal and continued experience of hospitalized illness. Rather, it is based on the fact, accepted by the AMA, that "the aged receive approximately twice as much hospitalization as those under 65" . . . , together with the contrast in incomes of younger and aged persons; these are what demonstrate a special need for such coverage as is provided under H.R. 4222.

Furthermore, the prevalence of all kinds of chronic illness is not

From "Comments on Testimony of American Medical Association," *Congressional Record*, CVIII (March 5, 1962), 3108 (daily ed.).

a fact that one would use to demonstrate the need for the health insurance benefits. The bill is directed toward meeting the costs of only those chronic conditions which require the specific types of health care outlined in the bill. . . .

On the other hand, even assuming that the overwhelming proportion of the aged were in excellent health, the inevitability of death at some age obviously suggests the likelihood of terminal illness unless aged persons were in all cases to die suddenly in the midst of good health. The high rate of hospitalization in the year of death, coupled with the overall high hospitalization rates for aged people—twice the rates of younger persons—seems adequate evidence that the great majority of the aged are not so fortunate as to escape serious illness and sizable health care costs during all of their later years.

Financial Needs

Although it is generally agreed that the aged need and use more medical care than the rest of the population, their ability to pay for this greater use is a subject of major controversy. There are two elements that go into the determination of ability to pay: the financial resources of the aged, and the demands that are made on these resources. Both of these are subjects of controversy, and will be discussed below. (The controversies over these points have the much greater significance of pointing out the dangers of using unevaluated statistics. Each side of this controversy uses or stresses those data which best support its position that the aged are, or are not, needy; each points out the limitations in the data used by the other.)

Resources

The controversy over the resources of the aged began when the proponents of federal health insurance for the elderly cited Lenore Epstein's study of Census Bureau data, showing that the majority of the elderly had annual per capita cash incomes of less than $1,000. Kemp, Martin, and Harkness responded critically to this datum, pointing out its limitations and stressing the assets of the aged. Dorothy McCamman responded in part to them. Excerpts from all three selections are reprinted below.

Opponents of health-insurance legislation also looked for other sources of data that would present what they felt to be a more accurate picture of the economic position of the aged. One of these was a paper presented at the 1960 Congress of the International Institute of Gerontologists. An article in *Science* and a letter to its editor, both reprinted below, give a picture of the controversy that arose over this study.[b]

---

[b] A revised version of the original paper was published by Wiggins and Schoeck and is cited in the bibliography for this chapter. The American Medical Association press release based on the original paper is reprinted in "Reports and Comments," *Public Health Economics*, XVII (1960), 472-473. *The New York Times'* articles of September 18 and October 2, 1960, reporting on the controversy, are also reprinted in *Public Health Economics*, XVII (1960), 473-475 and 530-532. *The New York Times* of August 25, 1960, printed a letter from one of the sociologists who discussed the paper at the gerontologists' congress, giving his criticism of the paper in some detail.

A second alternative source of data on the financial position of the aged cited by opponents of federal health insurance for the elderly was the University of Michigan Survey Research Center. On October 15, 1962, the American Medical Association issued a press release, reprinted below, giving its interpretation of data prepared for it by the Center. The Survey Research Center was responsible for the data, but not for the interpretation of it. In an interview with a *New York Times* reporter, a spokesman for the Center said that its staff had not seen the AMA press release in advance. He also said that the release's statement that "the aged as a group are substantially better off on the average than younger Americans" was open to question because the group, aged 18 to 64, to whom the aged were being compared included recent school graduates and younger families still buying household goods and raising children. Even a comparison with only those over 45 would overlook the fact that most of the aged have completed asset accumulation, a process in which the others were still engaged.[c] Nine days later, the Center released its own interpretation of the data; that release is also reprinted here.[d]

Another argument made by those who are opposed to health-insurance legislation is that the financial situation of the elderly is improving, so that any problem that exists at the present time is only a temporary one. "The Problem of the Aged in Financing Their Health Costs Is Getting Better" presents this point of view. Congressman King suggests that the income of the aged may not keep pace with increased costs in the future. "The Need for Proper Interpretation of Income Changes" presents another aspect of the question: the extent to which retired persons may be required to downgrade the standard of living to which they became accustomed while working.

---

[c] *The New York Times*, October 16, 1962.

[d] A discussion of the limitations of, and differences between, the various sources of information about income distribution appears as Appendix B of the *Background Paper on Income Maintenance* prepared for the 1961 White House Conference on Aging.

Money Income of Aged Persons

LENORE A. EPSTEIN

. . . Only about one-fifth of all aged men or less than half of those with work experience in a year, are full-time earners. Moreover, relatively few persons have assets of sufficient size to yield substantial income.

. . . About three-fifths of all persons aged 65 and over had less than $1,000 in money income in 1958 and . . . another one-fifth received $1,000-$2,000. . . . Of the men, 2 in 5 had less than $1,000 and 1 in 3 had $2,000 or more. The survey data do not include aged persons in institutions—estimated at roughly 400,000—who characteristically have incomes below the average. . . .

Such summary data on the distribution of income by size are useful indicators in planning programs relating to the needs of indigent individuals, even though they show as without money income married women who are supported entirely by their husbands.

. . . If . . . half the husband's income were to be allocated to his wife, it is probable that the majority of the wives classified as without income (about two-fifths of all aged wives) would remain at the bottom of the income range because more than half the married men received less than $2,000. . . . It is particularly significant, however, that nearly half the women classified as without income in 1956 were single, widowed, or divorced. This group, 14 percent of all aged women in 1956, must have lived with adult children, other relatives, or friends who maintained them.

From "Money Income of Aged Persons: A 10-year Review, 1948 to 1958," *Social Security Bulletin,* XXII (June 1959), 8-11. Lenore A. Epstein is Deputy Director of the SSA's Division of Research and Statistics.

Some Observations on Financial Assets of the Aged and Forand-type Legislation

ARTHUR KEMP, LEONARD W. MARTIN, AND
CYNTHIA HARKNESS

. . . A striking feature of [the report of the Department of Health, Education and Welfare to the Ways and Means Committee on medicare and of the testimony at the Committee's 1959 hearings favoring medicare] is the bias resulting from an almost complete lack of consideration of the assets of persons aged 65 and over and the almost exclusive emphasis on their cash income position.

Income—One of Many Measures

Even a cursory consideration of the problem should convince the reader that emphasis on money income tends to obscure the fact that many people aged 65 are at last reaching the time when they can retire on their savings. Why should it be difficult to understand that persons over 65 years of age, who have retired, have a lower income than those under 65 years of age who are still working and have not retired? . . .

Repeated again and again is the statement that about three-fifths of all persons 65 years or older had less than $1,000 money income in 1958. . . . This statistic, combined with the assumption that income is a sufficient measure of financial status, implies that the aged as a group suffer from poverty and privation because of their low incomes in a generally prosperous society. The implication can be questioned if one points out an equally accurate statistic, namely, that in 1957 almost one-half of all persons over 14 years of age also had incomes of $1,000 or less per year. Looking further one finds that 47% of all persons between the ages of 14 and 65 had incomes of $1,000 or less

From the article of the same name, *Journal of the American Medical Association*, CLXXI (October 31, 1959), 1228-1231. Reprinted by permission of the publisher and the authors. At the time this article was written, Arthur Kemp, Leonard W. Martin, and Cynthia Harkness were, respectively, Director, Assistant Director, and Research Assistant, Economic Research Department, American Medical Association.

per year in 1957. Yet, it also is true that the median family income in 1957 was approximately $5,000 per year. . . .

Misleading Arrangement of Data

The important fact to be remembered is that the money income figures cited by the Department of Health, Education, and Welfare and others refer to individual and not to family income. In other words, let us imagine that a club is composed of a number of persons and their respective husbands or wives and that the conditions of membership in the club are (1) that only one member of each family be an income earner and (2) that the average income per family be in excess of $20,000 per year. This is the club. By using the same statistical technique or formulation as that employed by the Department of Health, Education, and Welfare, one-half (50%) of the members of that club have incomes of less than $1,000 per year (zero incomes, in fact) and, so long as the same conditions exist, will continue to have zero incomes even though the average income per person for the club has to be, by the very conditions of membership, in excess of $10,000 a year.

All of this leads to the conclusion that money income of the aged population, arranged on a per capita basis, is an insufficient and misleading measure of financial status. An appropriate measure of the aged's financial status should include also nonmonetary income, assets, and other resources.

Growth in Assets of the Aged

An examination of the Federal Reserve Board's annual sample Survey of Consumer Finances reveals some interesting and supporting evidence concerning the aged's liquid assets and the rate at which those assets have been accumulating between 1949 and 1958. . . . Between these two years, persons aged 65 and over accumulated liquid assets faster than any other age group. . . . In 1958 nearly three out of every four persons aged 65 or over owned liquid assets in some form. In contrast the percentage of persons 55 to 64 years of age who owned liquid assets dropped to 71% in 1958, while the average for all groups between the ages of 18 and 64 years rose from 71 to 73%.

The proportion of those aged over 65 who had liquid assets of $2,000 or more increased from 30% in 1949 to 40% in 1958; for liquid assets of $500 or more, the respective increase was from 50 to 57%. It should be noted that, generally speaking, the proportion of those over 65 years of age who have liquid assets of $500 or more, $2,000 or more, and $5,000 or more is higher than for any other age group. The Federal Reserve Board's annual sample Survey of Consumer Finances also revealed that in 1958 the group aged 65 and over gained the highest median value in liquid asset holdings—$800 for all aged persons and $2,450 for the 74% holding liquid assets.

TABLE 1. DISTRIBUTION OF LIQUID ASSET HOLDINGS AND
INCOMES IN AGE GROUPS

	Early 1958	
Age of head of spending unit	*Spending units with liquid assets of more than $500, %*	*Spending units with incomes of $3,000 or more, %*
18 to 24	15	46
25 to 34	33	81
35 to 44	45	85
45 to 54	54	80
55 to 64	50	58
65 or over	56	27

It should be emphasized that these are the gross data for liquid assets only. Liquid assets, as defined by the Consumer Finances Survey, include savings accounts in banks, postal savings accounts, shares in savings and loan associations and credit unions, checking accounts, and savings bonds. Excluded are homes and other real estate, stocks, and bonds other than savings bonds. If it were possible to take into account ownership of equity securities and less liquid assets, the discrepancy in asset holdings between the aged and others probably would be even greater than the liquid asset data alone can illustrate. This observation follows from the fact that generally the aged have more of such assets than is commonly realized. Moreover, their net asset position is clearly better than that of others since their indebtedness is low and their homes are characteristically owned mortgage free.

. . . The problem of the aged is not simply one of age, or even one of money income and age. The problem is not a group problem; to the extent that it can be argued that some persons cannot afford medical care, the argument calls for either an extension of the deductible provision in income tax laws, or, at most, for some subsidization of the poverty-stricken.

Conclusions

It should be apparent that the use of money income alone in assessing the financial status of those over 65 years of age may lead to erroneous conclusions. The relatively substantial liquid assets of those over 65 years of age are of great importance. These observations raise some questions as to the desirability, and even the sincerity, of legislative proposals designed to compel those under 65 years of age to pay for the medical care costs of those over 65, regardless of financial status. Certainly, in many individual cases those over 65 are better able to afford medical care than those under that age.

Physicians and others whose efforts are devoted to providing the best quality of medical care and to preserving and extending human life should not overlook the implications of programs drawn up by an alliance of "experts" with a vested interest in governmental activities and politicians seeking election or reelection. There are indeed chronic problems of aging and the aged, but, above all else, they are individual problems of individual human beings. Moreover, if governments will refrain from engaging in activities sure to destroy the purchasing power of people's accumulated dollars, the problem, at most, is temporary. Instituting a permanent program and a new bureaucracy to provide governmental health care for the aged, regardless of need, supplies a "cure" that may be worse than the "disease" in its ultimate effects on individual freedom and a free society.

Incomes of the Aged and the Numbers Game

DOROTHY McCAMMAN

Our basic source of income data for the aged population—the U.S. Bureau of the Census—has consistently shown in recent years that more than half of all individuals aged 65 and over have cash incomes of less than $1,000 a year. This proportion was close to three-fifths only a few years ago, but has dropped gradually to 53 percent in 1960. Other studies, provided they relate to the total noninstitutional aged population and are not distorted by one means or another, have confirmed these findings.

These data on the incomes of individuals have this long-recognized drawback—they include, among the persons having "zero" income, married women who are entirely supported by their husbands, accounting in part for the fact that fewer than 4 percent of all aged men but as many as 24 percent of the women had no income in 1960. It has also long been recognized by those who work closely with these figures that the proportion of the aged population with incomes of less than $1,000 would remain about the same if half the husband's income were allocated to his wife, thus improving the position of the women but bringing some additional men into the group with less than $1,000. . . .

Against this background, we return to the example of what you can do with the "numbers game."

Several years ago, an article in the Journal of the American Medical Association attacked the Census Bureau data on the proportion of the aged with incomes below $1,000, as follows: [Here the author cites the Kemp-Martin-Harkness "club" of families with average incomes over $20,000, each of which has only one income earner.]

Thereafter, the same line of attack has been used repeatedly, but with the example personalized. There have been countless times when

From Ruth Albrecht, ed., *Aging in a Changing Society*, Gerontology Series, XI (Gainesville: University of Florida Press, 1962), 71-77. Reprinted by permission of the publisher. Dorothy McCamman is a member of the staff of the Senate Special Committee on Aging.

I have heard—and I am sure you have also heard—a doctor, an insurance company officer, or some other high-level executive refer disparagingly to these figures in the following vein: "I happen to have a very good income. I have a wife and three children (or four, or five) and they have no income of their own. Thus, four out of five of us (or five out of six or six out of seven) have less than $1,000 in income. But that doesn't really mean that my wife and children are badly off. We do very well as a family." . . .

It takes a relatively sophisticated person to recognize that one significance attaches to the fact that young wives and children who are normally dependent on the breadwinner's earnings have little or no income of their own. Quite another significance attaches to the high proportion of the aged with little or no income; here it must be recognized that the older group is heavily weighted by widows, wives of retired men, and other aged women who are no longer supported by earnings and, therefore, might be expected to have some income of their own in the form of a widow's or wife's social security benefit, for example, or from private sources.

More recently, I have seen these same Census Bureau figures attacked in another way. The attack centered on the upper end of the income distribution—the "open" end where "all the millionaires" are found. The implication of this argument was that we needn't worry about the women with less than $1,000 in income because the men at the upper end of the income scale had unlimited incomes with which to support them.

The usual distribution of the incomes of the aged starts this "open" end at $5,000. This would mean that in 1960 there were 6⅔ million women with incomes of less than $1,000 to be supported by fewer than 900,000 men with incomes of $5,000 or more, or 7½ women for every man. Even if we were to assign to the low-income women all the men with incomes of $2,000 or more, the 6⅔ million women would be feeding on a paltry 3 million men, less than half a man apiece.

. . . Newly available Census Bureau data [show that] . . . of all families with an aged head, nearly three-fourths consist of only two persons. Their median income in 1960 was $2,530, less than half that for two-person families with a head under 65 ($5,314).

Among unrelated individuals (persons living alone or lodging with nonrelatives) the economic disadvantage of the aged compared with the young is even more marked. The median income in 1960 reported by such persons aged 65 and over was only about 40 percent as large as for those under 65—$1,050, compared with $2,570.

The aged are a low income group and it is high time to stop juggling figures in the attempt to prove otherwise.

TOTAL MONEY INCOME OF FAMILIES WITH HEAD AGED 65 AND OVER
AND HEAD UNDER 65, BY SIZE OF FAMILY, 1960 (NONINSTITUTIONAL
POPULATION OF THE UNITED STATES)

Characteristic	All families	Families containing—			
		2 persons	3 persons	4 persons	5 or more persons
Median money income of family:					
Head 65 and over	$2,897	$2,530	$4,122	$6,100	$5,727
Head under 65	5,905	5,314	5,930	6,300	6,074
Percent of families with income of—					
Under $2,000:					
Head 65 and over	31.4	35.7	20.3	17.6	17.9
Head under 65	10.2	16.0	9.0	6.5	8.9
$7,000 and over:					
Head 65 and over	16.4	11.5	23.5	41.4	37.9
Head under 65	37.1	31.1	37.8	41.0	38.8
Percentage distribution by size:					
Head 65 and over	100.0	72.9	16.4	5.1	5.6
Head under 65	100.0	26.4	21.6	22.9	29.1
Average (mean) size:					
Head 65 and over	2.5	2.0	3.0	4.0	6.4
Head under 65	3.9	2.0	3.0	4.0	6.2

Source: Bureau of the Census "Current Population Reports, Consumer Income," series P-60, No. 37.

Science and Politics: AMA Attacked for Use of Disputed Survey in "Medicare" Lobbying

The American Medical Association . . . last week was under attack for its use of a survey of the aged presented before the fifth congress of the International Institute of Gerontologists. . . .

A widely distributed AMA press release said the survey "emphatically proves that the great majority of Americans over 65 are capably financing their own health care and prefer to do it on their own, without government intervention." The release said that "90 percent [of the sample] could think of no personal medical needs that were not being taken care of," and that only "a relatively small percentage of those who said they did have medical needs attributed the failure to meet these needs to lack of money." The release credited James W. Wiggins and Helmut Schoeck of Emory University as director and associate director of the study and listed 16 university sociologists from schools throughout the country as participating in the study.

The AMA endorsement and interpretation of the survey were picked up by newspapers across the country. Some papers used it as the basis for editorials opposing any large-scale federal plan for aid to the aged.

Comments on the Survey

Last week Senators Eugene McCarthy (D-Minn.) and Pat McNamara (D-Mich.) began inserting in the Congressional Record comments on the survey from the "participating" sociologists and from officials of the congress on gerontology. Here are some excerpts: From Noel Gist of the University of Missouri: "I participated in a study of aging to the extent of supervising the interviewing of a sample of rural residents in Missouri. . . . The news release, by the use of my name . . . leaves the impression that I endorse the conclusions presented. . . .

I do nothing of the sort. . . . It was quite obvious to me that the questionnaire sent to us was a very poor one, and seemed to be devised by amateurs in research. But since we agreed to do the interviewing for the project we completed the assignment."

From Clark Tibbits, chairman of the Executive Committee for the Americas, International Association of Gerontology: "I was in the audience when Professor Wiggins made his presentation. I was astonished at the data and conclusions reported. The basic figures on income, assets, and health status differ by as much as 100 percent from those reported by other studies during the past decade and from figures available through such standard sources as the Bureau of the Census, the Current Population Survey, and the National Health Survey."

From Wayne Thompson, of Cornell, a discussant of the paper: ". . . I was appalled to read the paper, which I found to be of such poor quality of scientific research technique and writing. Indeed, I regretted at that point that I had been so naive as to have accepted the paper without having seen it in advance, especially since it would be presented before an audience of internationally known scientists who might think of this as representing American sociology. . . . When the paper was actually presented, there was an immediate reaction on the part of the audience, attacking its unscientific character, and the ease with which Wiggins and Schoeck jumped to untenable conclusions. The survey was badly designed, poorly conceived and completely misleading. Not a single scientist present at the meeting rose to support either Mr. Wiggins or his paper."

The critics suggested that the questionnaire had been drawn in a way that encouraged responses that would fit the preconceptions of the planners. . . . The multiple choice question was apparently intended to discover what the aged thought should be done to make medical coverage more easily available to them, but it did not list as an alternative the widely debated plan to add medical coverage to Social Security. "This [response]," said the official AMA interpretation, "demonstrates that the vast majority of our older citizens favor voluntary programs and that only 10 percent or so support compulsory plans."

Defense of the Survey

The AMA release noted that the survey was "based on extended interviews with 1500 non-institutionalized persons 65 years of age and over . . . by trained interviewers under the supervision of professional sociologists representing more than a dozen well-known American universities and colleges." The survey critics said that in addition to aged persons in hospitals, homes for the aged, and other institutions, the survey left out all non-whites and all persons on old age assistance. One of the participating sociologists said she had been instructed to interview no one living in an apartment, thus eliminating tenement dwellers from at least this part of the sample. In general, the critics suggested the sample had been biased against those who were most likely to be having difficulty meeting medical expenses.

In defense of the paper an AMA spokesman emphasized that the survey was designed by Wiggins as a study of the "normal" segment of the aged population. Wiggins made this point in the course of the paper. But neither the title of the paper ("A Profile of the Aging: USA") nor the AMA press release made clear that the survey was less than a study of the aging population as a whole. There was no mention of the "normal" idea in the press release, and no precise definition of what Wiggins regarded as "normal" in the paper itself.

The survey was financed by a $20,000 grant from the Foundation for Voluntary Welfare. The foundation is a subsidiary of the William Volker Fund, which an AMA spokesman described as having a "conservative outlook." Wiggins is an unpaid consultant to the AMA's medical economics department.

"A Profile of the Aged" Defended

JAMES W. WIGGINS AND HELMUT SCHOECK

We excluded certain groups, chief of which were the recipients of old age assistance grants. Here we followed the precedent of the Social Security Administration, whose 1956 study excluded recipients of old age assistance unless they also received social security payments. It has been estimated that the often-quoted Social Security study *excluded* 55 percent or more of persons 65 and over. Other studies have typically excluded certain categories of the universe to be sampled, and a recently reported national study excluded "individuals in certain occupational groups and those living in institutions."

We are pleased to report that it has been unnecessary to weight any of our data to produce an artificial "representativeness" in our sample. The readers of *Science* will doubtless know that weighting of strata in sample data is a common procedure when the actual sample is found not to be representative of the population sampled. . . . We do not wish to be understood as criticizing these weighting procedures. Rather, we invite attention to their being commonplace, and to the high representativeness of our own sample, which made weighting unnecessary. . . .

Considerable attention has been given to our findings, with the statement or inference that they are inaccurate. As a matter of information only, it can be reported that the findings of the Steiner-Dorfman study were called "controversial." Ethel Shanas's National Opinion Research Center study also created considerable discussion. Her report of income for the aged was higher than U.S. census estimates, and she reported that 60 percent of the aged are either as well off economically after age 65 as before, or are better off after 65. In spite of the generally recognized fact that census figures for income are some 20 percent too low, Shanas's findings were attacked again in the "Background Paper on Income Maintenance," prepared for the 1961 White House Conference on the Aging. . . .

From a letter to the editor of *Science*, 133 (May 19, 1961), 1625-1626. Copyright 1961 by the American Association for the Advancement of Science. Reprinted by permission of the publisher and the authors.

48

From the latest data available, it is illuminating to examine the income of the aged. The "Chart Book" for the White House Conference on Aging states that federal programs provided $17 billion in benefits and services to the aged population. The "Background Paper on Income Maintenance" reported that the federal programs provided between one-third and two-fifths of the total income to the aged. Assuming the lesser total income, we reach a gross income for 17 million aged of $42.5 billion. Simple arithmetic reduces this to an average per capita income of $2500. The median aged respondent in the "Profile" study reported income between $2,000 and $3,000.

Our findings in the field of health produced some comment. We found that 90 percent of our respondents had no unmet medical needs that they knew of. It has been suggested that all kinds of people know more about an older person's health than he does. In any case, a considerable number of studies by state or region, and most national studies, have assumed that the respondent has a fair idea whether he is sick or not.

Ninety-six percent of our respondents reported no medical debts, and exactly the same percentage was found by Steiner and Dorfman for 1951.

The most recent study of medical expenses of the aging known to us is based on data collected through the National Opinion Research Center. Odin W. Anderson, Patricia Collette, and Jacob J. Feldman, in "Family Expenditures for Personal Health Services" (Health Information Foundation, 1961), present findings comparable to our own. The "Profile" study showed that 97 percent of respondents had expenditures for physicians below $50 for one month, and that 2 percent had expenses above $50 but below $100. Anderson *et al.* found that 86 percent of their aged respondents had expenditures for physicians below $100 for an entire year. The "Profile" study showed that 95 percent of the respondents had no hospital expenditures in one month and that 3 percent had hospital expenditures below $100. Anderson reports that 86 percent of his aged respondents had no hospital expenditures in a year, and that 5 percent had hospital expenditures below $100. According to the "Profile" study, 98 percent of the aged had expenditures for medicines of less than $50 in a month, while Anderson reported that 88 percent had spent less than $100 for (prescribed) medicines in a full year.

If a few of our regional associates in the study, in response to a request from a subcommittee of the United States Senate, have felt it their duty to support the subcommittee, we may expect the data to be biased in favor of universal misery. If, in spite of the data they delivered and certified to us, some associates wish to believe that the aging are in a grave plight, it is a tribute to their professional competence and scholarly objectivity that they furnished the data as obtained by the interviewers. It has often been said that a chief mark of the scientist is that he even reports findings he does not like.

The Aged as a Group Are Substantially Better Off Than Younger Americans

AMERICAN MEDICAL ASSOCIATION

A new survey of the economic condition of American families, made by the University of Michigan Survey Research Center, proves again the injustice of forcing higher payroll taxes on the nation's workers to buy health care for the aged.

The statement was made by George M. Fister, M.D., president of the American Medical Association, in a news release accompanying an evaluation of the Michigan survey.

"Analysis of the survey findings once again demonstrates, as other studies have, that the aged as a group are substantially better off on the average than younger Americans," Dr. Fister said.

"It proves that the proposed program of nationalized health care for the elderly would be an intolerably unfair burden on wage earners by forcing them to pay health-care bills for the aged, the vast majority of whom are well able to take care of themselves.

". . . As shown by the findings of the University of Michigan survey, aged families, far from destitute and impoverished, actually own considerably more assets and owe fewer debts than younger families. Corresponding evaluation of cash incomes reveals that because of tax exemptions and credits, size of families, and other advantages enjoyed by persons over 65, the gap in income per family member between aged and younger families is relatively small."

Dr. Fister said "the conclusion is irresistible" that the campaign for government controlled health care for the aged "is built on a monstrous fraud.". . .

Dr. Fister said that "the most striking and most significant disclosure, in view of the agitation for nationalized health care for the elderly, is the fact that 96 per cent of the aged interviewed did not owe a single penny to a hospital, a physician or a dentist."

"Furthermore," he said, "the evidence is overwhelming that paying for medical care is not a pressing problem for the vast majority of Americans, since 90 per cent of families under 65 had no debts to

Press Release, October 15, 1962.

physicians, dentists or hospitals, and only 1 per cent of all families, including those over 65, owed $500 or more to these providers of medical services.

"Part of the answer obviously lies in the spectacular growth of health insurance, which now covers . . . more than 9½ million . . . elderly, . . . 68 per cent of everyone over 65 who either needs or wants health insurance.

"It must be concluded that the push for federalized health care for the aged is not just a simple fraud, but what's worse, it's a fraud being perpetrated for political purposes. The aged are being exploited for political power and the taxpayers are being hoodwinked for the same purpose."

Dr. Fister said the survey shows:

1. The median value of total assets owned by families with the head of the family over age 65 was $8,349 in 1960, almost twice as much as the $4,839 which was the median value of total assets of all other age groups as determined by the study. . . .

2. The median value of equity in a home for the over-65 families was $4,559, almost 4½ times as much as the $1,028 reported for younger families.

3. The median value of liquid assets was almost 2½ times as great for the over-65 families—$1,012 compared with $460.

4. Sixty-four per cent of the aged families are home owners, and 53 per cent of these own their homes free of mortgage. In contrast, 53 per cent of younger families are home owners and only 18 per cent have no mortgage indebtedness.

5. Sixty-three per cent of over-65 families own assets valued at $5,000 or more compared with 47 per cent of younger families. And 41 per cent of the aged hold assets valued at $10,000 or more, compared with 27 per cent of younger groups, while 18 per cent have assets of $25,000 or more, contrasted with only 9 per cent of younger families.

6. Among aged families, 74 per cent had no personal debt, compared with 34 per cent of younger families, and 86 per cent reported no installment debt, compared with 48 per cent of all other age groups.

Dr. Fister said that "proponents of government controlled medicine try to paint a picture of economic wretchedness as a universal condition of the aged by citing income alone and ignoring the favorable asset and debt position of the aged."

"But using income alone as a test of economic condition," Dr. Fister said, "is misleading when it ignores the substantial tax relief given those over 65 through double income tax exemptions, retirement income credit, full medical expense deductions and exemption of benefits from social security, railroad retirement and other pensions, annuities and dividends, as well as size of family and other factors.

"Median income for families under 65, according to U. S. Census Bureau statistics, was $5,905 in 1960, compared with $2,897 for families over 65.

"But adjustment for tax and other advantages enjoyed by the aged, together with fewer family members and family obligations, reveals that family income per member was only about $248 less for aged families in 1960 than for younger families.

"And when the 524,000 aged families who get medical care under the old age assistance program are removed, the gap is reduced to $148."

Dr. Fister added: "Some aged obviously need help and they should be helped, but it is equally obvious that with private health insurance doing such a remarkable job and the Kerr-Mills Law available for those truly in need, a new back-breaking compulsory tax program to purchase health care for the aged regardless of need is not called for."

The Economic Condition of the Aged

UNIVERSITY OF MICHIGAN

New and detailed data on the economic condition of the aged have been collected in the 1962 Survey of Consumer Finances, conducted by the Survey Research Center (SRC) of The University of Michigan. . . .

Among the older units (65 and over), 71 per cent had a disposable income of less than $3,000 and 10 per cent had more than $5,000 in 1961. (In the 55-64 year group, figures were 34 and 38 per cent respectively).

Not only do older units have substantially lower incomes than younger ones, but low incomes are commonly temporary among younger families and permanent among the aged. On the other hand, the number of persons included in a spending unit (family or individual) decreases with age; therefore, the age differences in per capita income are smaller than in spending unit incomes. . . .

The distribution of assets among the spending units 65 years and over is much more unequal than among younger units. The average asset data are greatly influenced by the small proportion of aged with sizable asset holdings. While the average assets of those 65 and older are similar to those 55 to 64 years old, 34 per cent of the former have practically no liquid assets at all (less than $100 in bank deposits and bonds) as against 28 per cent of the latter. Net worth data, including home ownership and investments and deducting debt, show that 23 per cent of those 65 and over have net worth under $1,000 as against 14 per cent in the 55 to 64 years group.

Consumer debt is less common among the aged than among middle-aged or young people because the latter are much more frequent purchasers of automobiles and appliances.

Forty-three per cent of spending units over 65 reported having had what they called large medical expenses for doctors, nurses, and hos-

Press Release, October 24, 1962.

pitals in 1961 against 36 per cent in the 55-64 age group and 39 per cent among all those between 35 and 64.

These data consider only aged people with some income, who form independent spending units. In addition, there are about 2 million aged individuals excluded from the tabulation because they have no income and form a part of the spending units of their children or other relatives. Many other older people are excluded because they live in institutions.

Altogether there are approximately 9½ million spending units in which the head is 65 years of age or older. . . . Among these older

DISTRIBUTION OF INCOME AND ASSETS BY AGE (PERCENTAGE DISTRIBUTION OF SPENDING UNITS)

	Age of head of spending unit			
	35–44	*45–54*	*55–64*	*65 and over*
Disposable income in 1961*				
under $3,000	14	22	34	71
$3,000–4,999	25	21	28	19
$5,000–$7,499	33	27	22	4
$7,500 and over	28	30	16	6
	100	100	100	100
Liquid asset holdings early in 1962**				
Under $100	36	31	28	34
$100–$999	36	28	20	14
$1,000–$4,999	22	26	36	27
$5,000 and over	6	15	16	25
	100	100	100	100
Net worth early in 1962***				
Under $1,000	26	19	14	23
$1,000–$4,999	21	15	17	14
$5,000–$24,999	39	41	47	44
$25,000 and over	14	25	22	19
	100	100	100	100

* Spending unit annual income minus Federal income taxes.

** Deposits with banks, savings and loan associations, and credit unions, and U.S. Government savings bonds.

*** Liquid assets plus investments in stocks and bonds, farm, livestock and equipment, other real estate, business, plus equity in owner-occupied home, minus debt. The most frequent assets are liquid assets and home ownership.

spending units, those with relatively high income tend to have sizable assets, while those with low income tend to have small assets. It appears that there are close to 4.5 million spending units 65 and older who had a 1961 disposable income of less than $2,000 (including social security benefits). Forty per cent of these units have practically no assets, and most of them have no medical insurance either.

The Problem of the Aged in Financing Their Health Costs Is Getting Better

AMERICAN MEDICAL ASSOCIATION

Those who favor a national compulsory health plan for the aged not only argue that most of this group are unable to pay the costs of their own health care, but they carry this fallacy one step further. They claim that whatever financial capabilities the aged may have to finance health costs are diminishing day by day and that this segment of our population is rapidly approaching a time of crisis. Thus, if something is not done right away the elderly will lose whatever precarious ability they may presently have to pay for health services.

Thus runs the argument. Here again, it is an emotional approach designed for maximum appeal to decent instincts, but serving to play down the inconveniently obtruding facts which contradict its thesis. The strategy is aimed, apparently, at the creation of a synthetic atmosphere charged with crisis in which Congress can be pressured into hasty, ill-conceived action.

Just what are the facts?

1. Retirement plans, supported by private industries, are rapidly increasing the degree to which they help support the over-65 population. At present, total annual income to the elderly from this source is roughly $1 billion, according to the estimate of the planning committee for the White House Conference on Aging.

However, private pension plans have only been established in fairly recent years. As a consequence, many of the currently retired were either not included in such plans, or their period of contribution was too short to return them sizable benefits.

But this picture is changing rapidly. The Securities and Exchange Commission estimated total investments in pension plans of all types, public and private, at $74.2 billion at the end of 1956. Of this total, $28.9 billion was in private funds. Thus it is clear that within the

From testimony at hearings on *Health Services for the Aged under the Social Security Insurance System,* held by the Committee on Ways and Means of the U.S. House of Representatives, August 2, 1961, pp. 1335-1338.

next couple of decades a much higher percentage of persons retiring at age 65 will have substantial income assistance from pension funds.

2. The planning committee for the White House Conference also estimated the total income of our over-65 population from all types of private investments at from $4.3 to $8.3 billion a year. This includes dividends, interest on savings, annuities, rents, royalties, and so forth. It does not include such non-income producing assets as homes occupied by the elderly, nor the value of business in which the over-65 group are still actively engaged. At a conservative estimate, therefore, older people appear to own between $75 and $150 billion worth of income producing assets.

There is every reason to believe that the numbers of older people with private investments will expand markedly within the years ahead. To support this assertion, home ownership has increased rapidly; bank savings have gone up; and the number of individual investors in corporate securities and income producing bonds has risen sharply. We have had twenty years or so of nearly uninterrupted prosperity, with almost full employment and constantly rising incomes; and these factors are reflected in the steadily increasing worth of private investments.

3. In the years ahead, more and more people reaching retirement age will be covered by OASDI. More than 90 per cent of those now working are eligible for retirement benefits under Title II of the Social Security Act, as compared with fewer than seven per cent in 1940; 26 per cent in 1950; and 68.9 per cent in 1960. By the same token, the percentage of older people on Old Age Assistance has been decreasing steadily over the years—from 22.8 per cent in 1940; to 22.5 per cent in 1950; to 14.1 per cent in 1960.

4. According to the Health Insurance Institute, nearly 132 million Americans, or 73 per cent of the civilian population had some form of health insurance through voluntary insurance organizations at the end of 1960.

The Institute estimates that half the aged had some form of health insurance in 1960 and that, by 1970, nine out of ten persons reaching age 65 who desire coverage will have it on a voluntary basis.

The Health Insurance Institute reports that seven out of every ten workers covered under group health insurance policies issued during 1960 have the right to retain their protection when they retire. The greater availability of coverages that continue into retirement is shown by contrasting the 1960 data with findings at the end of 1959.

In 1959 only 55 per cent—or about five out of every ten workers—had the right either to continue or convert their coverage upon retirement.

Having carried health insurance during their working lives, Americans have learned to value its protection and to continue that protection after retirement.

. . . Some 290 voluntary health-insuring organizations are now issuing hospital or surgical policies to the elderly; and in rapidly expanding variety, policies are now available to everyone. Further, aware of the great potential of this 65-and-over market, aggressive companies are lowering premiums to levels which are within the reach of persons with low or modest incomes.

To sum up, then: by whatever yardstick we choose to measure the present needs of the elderly, we come up with the same answers. Some are in financial difficulties, most are not; some are in very poor health, the vast majority are not.

Finally, in the years ahead the problem—to the extent that a problem presently exists—will decrease in magnitude. Scientific advances in medicine will enable us to safeguard the health of the elderly with increasing efficiency. The financial status of the aged—now relatively favorable for the majority—will continue to improve.

No permanent, irreversible Federal governmental program, of the sort proposed in H.R. 4222, is therefore needed to solve a temporary problem affecting a minority of the aged. And H.R. 4222, if enacted into law, would be both permanent and irreversible: not only because this is the nature of such programs, but because its very passage would destroy the resources now available for doing the job.

The Problem of the Aged in Financing Their Health Costs Will Get Worse

CECIL R. KING

. . . There is every reason to believe that the problem faced by the aged in financing health costs will, in the absence of Federal action, get worse. Although the costs of health care—increasing more rapidly than costs of all consumer items and substantially more rapidly than the income of aged persons—cannot be predicted with precision into the distant future, it would seem highly unrealistic to assume any immediate sharp reversal of the upward trend in such costs that has continued over decades. The official cost estimates for my bill, incidentally, assume such substantial further increases in costs.

Unless income and resources increase in direct ratio to any increases in medical care costs, it is obvious that the aged will face an increase in the difficulty of financing needed health care. It is quite likely that the financial resources of aged persons will increase somewhat as time goes on. Allowing for increases in monthly OASI benefits, in earned income, and in the limited amounts paid by private health insurance, and assuming increases in all of these amounts in the future, we are still left with the question of how these resources could grow at a rate equal to or faster than the justifiable costs of health care we must expect as medical science continues its phenomenal progress toward improving health and increasing longevity for all of us.

The AMA statement, in discussing the future sources of income of the aged, quotes some current figures on income from these sources and suggests that they are already substantial. Of course, billions of dollars sounds like a great deal of money, but the present total income to the aged from private pension plans quoted by the AMA—$1 billion annually—does not sound so impressive when divided among total present aged persons—a per capita figure of less than $60 per year. The same situation appears with regard to the $4.3 to $8.3 billion estimated as total annual income of the aged from private investments . . .

From "Comments on Testimony of American Medical Association," *Congressional Record*, CVIII (March 5, 1962), 3109 (daily ed.).

which would provide a per capita figure of about $250 to $490. It would seem a mathematical certainty that not all our aged citizens can be receiving very substantial income from these sources.

The Need for Proper Interpretation of Income Changes

... One major flaw characterizes much of the ordinary discussion about the income status of our aged citizens. This is the failure to reckon with the dynamic nature of the problem. For example, when it is said . . . that the median money income of aged family heads as a percentage of the median income of all families dropped from 60 percent in 1949 to 52 percent in 1959, there seems to be a tacit assumption that the aged of 1959 are the same people as those aged in 1949, but they are not exactly the same. The 4.8 million men and 5.5 million women aged 65 to 74 in 1960 were not "aged" in 1950, for example.

The crucial question is, what change takes place in the incomes of a given age group as it moves into retirement status? When we say that between 1949 and 1959 the income of the male "aged" increased 55 percent, we are really not talking about the same intact population. In reality, the median income of men aged 55 to 64 in 1949 was $2,366, but by 1959, these same men (minus those who died, etc.) experienced not an increase in their median income but a decrease.

More specifically, the best data available on this point are provided by the Bureau of the Census, in its January 1961 report on 1959 incomes. The median income of men born in March 1895, and earlier was $1,710 in 1949; 10 years later, the median income of the *same* group had *decreased* 8 percent, to $1,576. These figures, moreover, are in current dollars and not constant ones: an analysis using constant 1959 dollars would reveal that this group of men suffered an approximate 33 percent *decrease* in real income from 1949 to 1959, while during the same period of time, the real median income for men aged 24 to 34 in 1949 *increased* by approximately 57 percent; for men aged 34 to 44 in 1949, the increase was approximately 34 percent.

The same analysis can be applied to the changes in assets and savings. In all of these trends, it is important to recognize another aspect that is too often neglected, namely, the effect of rising expectations in the general population—expectations which do not automatically abate

From *Action for the Aged and Aging*, a report of the U.S. Senate Committee on Labor and Public Welfare, made by its Subcommittee on Problems of the Aged and Aging, 87th Congress, 1st Session, Senate Report #128 (March 28, 1961), pp. 71-72.

upon retirement. This aspect further aggravates the problem of an adequate income for future generations of retired Americans. An increasing number of such persons will be more insistent on an adequate level of living than past generations of retirees. The younger Americans of today will carry into their own retirement of tomorrow many expectations and aspirations that cannot be met if their retired income status is no better than that of the aged of the present time.

Financial Needs (continued)

Demands

The other aspect of the controversy over the financial needs of the elderly is the demands on their resources. What are their material needs? Even if their income *is* lower than that of the rest of the population, this is not too significant if their needs are *correspondingly* lower. One measure of need is the budget prepared by the Bureau of Labor Statistics to provide a "modest but adequate" standard of living for a retired couple. In the selections that follow, Commissioner Clague describes the characteristics of this budget, and Margaret Gordon compares its cost with the incomes of elderly persons.[e]

What about the fact that many elderly persons do not live by themselves, but rather with their children, and thus have lower living costs? What about those who live in their own homes, and thus have no rent to pay? What about noncash income? Morgan and David give a description of the economic condition of the elderly that takes account of these and other factors.

Related to the question of financial need is the question of how the elderly meet their medical costs. "Methods of Paying for Medical Care" provides some answers. It is based largely on two 1957 surveys: a Health Information Foundation Survey of a random sample of all elderly persons who were not in institutions, and a survey of social-security beneficiaries and their families.

---

[e] The needs of the elderly, as shown in this budget, are compared to the needs of the general population, as shown in the similar budget prepared by the BLS for an urban worker's family of four, in the Special Committee on Aging's publication, *Background Facts on the Financing of the Health Care of the Aged*, pp. 41-42.

The Budget for a Retired Couple Prepared by the U.S. Bureau of Labor Statistics

EWAN CLAGUE

. . . The "budget family" consists of a husband and wife, aged 65 or over, who maintain their own 2- or 3-room rented dwelling in an urban area. The couple are assumed to be self-supporting, in reasonably good health, able to take care of themselves, and manage the home. The budget is designed to represent a level of living which provides the goods and services necessary for a healthful, self-respecting mode of living, and allows normal participation in community life according to standards prevailing in large cities or their suburbs in the United States. It provides a "modest but adequate" level of living—not a luxurious level but one adequate to provide for more than the basic essentials of consumption. . . .

The home is assumed to be equipped with the furnishings and mechanical equipment usually considered to be household necessities, such as a gas or electric cooking stove, mechanical refrigerator, and small electrical appliances. . . . The wife does all of the cooking and most of the cleaning and laundry. The budget, however, does allow for part of the laundry to be sent out and for occasional paid help.

The goods and services provided by the budget for both housing and food conform with scientific standards of adequacy and also reflect actual choices of large-city families of this type. For other goods and services, where scientific standards do not exist, the budget level was determined by analyses of the purchasing pattern of retired elderly families.

. . . There is no provision for life insurance or income taxes. This assumes that payments on life insurance policies have been completed before retirement, and that most of the income of retired couples at this level is tax exempt because of source and the remainder insufficient to require payment of taxes.

From a statement at hearings on *Retirement Income of the Aging* before the Subcommittee on Retirement Income of the U.S. Senate Special Committee on Aging, July 13, 1961, pp. 88-91. Ewan Clague is the United States Commissioner of Labor Statistics.

. . . The . . . budget provides for the use of an automobile by about one-fifth of the families . . . .

The total annual cost of the . . . goods, rents and services at autumn 1959 prices in 20 large cities ranged from $2,641 in Houston to $3,366 in Chicago. . . .

Since the retired couple's budget is designed to measure the cost of a specified standard of living for a retired couple residing in a rental dwelling in a large city or its suburbs, estimates of its total cost provide a useful tool for measuring changes in the standard of living of such couples, for evaluating the adequacy of their income, and for measuring differences in living costs between cities or among different family types. As such, it is an important benchmark statistic in social and economic research, and in welfare legislation and administration. However, there are important limitations on the use of the budget which arise from its concept, definitions and the assumptions on which it is based. These must be kept in mind and evaluated in relation to the conditions of the problem being considered.

One important limitation results from the fact that the budget housing costs are limited to rentals for a 2- or 3-room dwelling, although a majority of retired couples live in owned homes, most of which are free of mortgages. . . . A very rough estimate based on an analysis of expenditure data was made which indicated that homeowner costs, assuming there is no mortgage, would be about one-fourth to one-third less than the cost of rent, heat, and utilities in the budget, and that cost in the budget ranged from $595 at the low point to $1,067 at the high. . . .

Another limitation of the budget is that it applies to a retired couple who live alone and in a large city. Thus, it does not provide a measure of living costs for the substantial number of aged who are not married, or who live with other relatives. Furthermore, only about one-half of all aged persons live in large metropolitan areas. A scale developed from expenditure data indicates that a single aged person living alone would require about 60 percent of the cost of the budget for the retired couple. . . .

The budget has been priced only in 20 large cities, and cost estimates are not available for other cities or States, nor for the U.S. average. The budget costs given in this report, therefore, are not representative of the costs in all large cities or of those in cities of other sizes and economic characteristics.

Measuring the Adequacy of Retirement Income

MARGARET S. GORDON

. . . [The Steiner-Dorfman study] utilized 1951 income data . . . and also developed estimates of budgetary requirements for elderly couples and individuals with a variety of living arrangements in both urban and rural areas. Their results indicated that 44 percent of the elderly couples and a substantially larger proportion of the men and women without a spouse had total receipts that were below the amounts needed to maintain a modest but adequate level of living. More serious was the fact that more than a quarter of the couples, about a third of the men without a spouse, and approximately half of the women without a spouse, had less than the amounts required for a bare subsistence level of living.

Although in some sectors of the aged population the proportion with inadequate incomes has probably decreased since 1951, it is not at all clear that this is true for all, or even the most important, sectors of the population aged 65 and over. Budgetary data recently published by the Bureau of Labor Statistics . . . provide an indication of the extent of the rise in living costs of elderly couples during the 1950's. They show that, if no allowance is made for changes in patterns of expenditures during the 1950's, the living costs of elderly couples in the 20 large cities were, on the average, 57 percent higher in the autumn of 1959 than they had been 9 years earlier. In other words, this was the average increase, between 1950 and 1959, in the cost of the goods and services included in the original elderly couple's budget that had been developed by the Social Security Administration in the late 1940's. If, however, allowance is made for changes in patterns of expenditures, and the cost of the revised budget in 1959 is compared with the cost of the original budget in 1950, the increase amounted to 71 percent. These heavy increases were especially attributable to sharp

From a statement at hearings on *Retirement Income of the Aging* before the Subcommittee on Retirement Income of the U.S. Senate Special Committee on Aging, July 1961, pp. 182-183. Margaret S. Gordon is Acting Director of the Institute of Industrial Relations of the University of California.

upward movements in the costs of medical care, transportation, and other services.

How much did the money incomes of elderly couples increase during the same period? Although appropriate data are not available for 1950, families headed by an individual aged 65 and over in urban areas experienced an increase in median income between 1951 and 1959 amounting only to 27 percent. In rural nonfarm areas, such families fared much better, experiencing a rise in median income of 68 percent, while in rural farm areas the corresponding increase amounted to 62 percent.

These data suggest that, at least for elderly couples living in rented quarters in large cities, money income may have risen substantially less than living costs during the 1950's. Probably homeowning couples fared somewhat better than renters. The BLS Consumer Price Index indicates that housing costs have risen less for homeowners than for renters, and this is probably particularly true for the elderly, since most aged homeowners own their homes free and clear and thus have not been affected by the increase in mortgage costs. But it should be kept in mind that, although the proportion of elderly couples who own their own homes is high for the country as a whole, it is not as high in very large cities like New York and Chicago as it is in smaller communities.

The Aged and Their Economic Position

JAMES MORGAN AND MARTIN DAVID

Background

This statement contains data on a representative sample of the U.S. population. The data were collected by personal interviews taken during March and April of 1960. . . . The sample is not large, and the sampling error attaching to any absolute statement about the aged may be as high as 10 percent. However response errors are held to the minimum by using a highly trained staff of professional interviewers. Moreover, the data disclose with relative accuracy relationships between age and other characteristics of these families. . . .

Income of the Aged

Our data are for the noninstitutionalized population; information on the aged in institutions does not appear in any available survey data, except those from the decennial censuses.

A clear picture of the economic status of the noninstitutionalized aged must take account of the following:

(a) Some of the aged live in the homes of relatives. . . .

We deal with this problem by treating as a separate unit each adult 18 or older, with his spouse and minor children, if any. This requires estimating the transfers that pass from one adult unit to others living in the same family, so we imputed the value of the free food and rent received by dependent adult units. Where the dependent unit also received clothing, transportation, and other aid, we may have understated its economic position somewhat, but we did include the two items that should account for the bulk of the transfers within the family.[1]

From the authors' statement at hearings on *Retirement Income of the Aging* before the Subcommittee on Retirement Income of the U.S. Senate Special Committee on Aging, July 1961, pages 188-189. The footnotes have been renumbered. At the time this study was conducted, James Morgan and Martin David were, respectively, program director and study director at the Survey Research Center of the University of Michigan.

[1] We estimate that there are 10.3 million adult units in the United States not in institutions, where the head of the unit is 65 or older. Of these, some 200,000 units are dependent on relatives with whom they live and another 60,000 units keep separate finances but live in a relative's home.

(b) Income in kind and irregular gifts, in addition to those received as a result of living with relatives, may comprise an important source of sustenance for some aged persons and couples.

We have attempted to include these nonmoney incomes by including the value of free medical care received by the unit, the money saved by home production of food and home repairs, and by estimating the imputed rental income earned on the net equity in an owned home.

(c) Many of the aged have fewer requirements for food, housing, and clothing because they are older and not working, and because their families are smaller.

We deal with this problem not only by looking at the total real income but by relating it to an estimate of needs based on family budget standards.

The tables that follow build up a picture of the income situation of the units in various groups, giving the average incomes including more and more components. . . . The first column in table 1 shows the average wage income of adult unit heads who are not farmers or self-employed businessmen. The average is calculated on the basis of all adult units in each age group, even though some may not have any wage income.

The second column adds to this the average earnings of the wife and children under 18, the estimated earnings (net of a return on capital invested) of farmers and self-employed businessmen, and the value of home-produced food and home repairs. Column 2 is an estimate of the income earned by the labor of all earners in the adult unit.

The third column adds to the real earnings the average income from property. This includes money income and imputed return on equity in an owner-operated business, farm, or the unit's own home.

The fourth column adds average transfer incomes, including estimates of free food and rent received by those living with relatives, and free medical care, as well as alimony, irregular gifts, veteran's benefits, unemployment compensation, social security, retirement pensions, and public welfare. At the same time an estimate of the adult unit's Federal income taxes is deducted.[2] . . .

It is clear from table 1 that adult units whose heads are 65 and older average less income from earnings than adult units in any other age group. Their gross factor income averages less than any group except adult units whose heads are 18 to 24. Income from property is about the same for units whose heads are aged 55 to 64 and units whose

---

[2] We take account of the double exemption available to each person over 65.

heads are 65 to 74; income from property for units whose heads are 75 and older is substantially smaller.

The fifth column adds no income components—gross disposable income includes all income components except capital gains, which we did not try to measure—but transforms the measure into one which takes account of differences in family composition and needs. To do this we divide gross disposable income by an estimate of the income required to support such an adult unit at some fairly low but arbitrary level.

The standard budget which was used for this calculation was prepared by the Community Council of Greater New York and is used as a basis for administering assistance to needy families in New York City. The absolute level of the standard is conservative. For an elderly retired couple the standard is nearly $600 less than the $3,044 budget allowed by the Bureau of Labor Statistics for aged couples in the New York area. As prices vary from New York City to other areas of the country the budget cannot reflect accurately the well-being of all families in the sample. Therefore a ratio of 100 percent (income equal to budget requirement) should be thought of merely as one point along a scale rather than a well-defined boundary between adequacy and inadequacy. . . .

TABLE 1. Cumulative Adult Unit Income Components, within Age of Adult Unit Heads (Mean for Adult Units)

Age of adult unit head	Percent of all adult units	(1) Average wage income of adult unit head	(2) Average real earnings of adult unit	(3) Average gross factor income of adult unit	(4) Average gross disposable income of adult unit	(5) Average value of welfare ratio of adult unit[1]
18 to 24	13	$1,939	$2,294	$2,326	$2,602	100
25 to 34	19	4,457	5,677	5,915	5,562	150
35 to 44	20	4,836	6,336	6,967	6,441	160
45 to 54	18	4,357	5,862	6,741	5,977	170
55 to 64	14	3,669	4,826	5,891	5,306	180
65 to 74	10	983	1,472	2,524	3,452	140
75 and older	6	141	271	868	1,935	90
Total, all adult units	100	3,486	4,560	6,258	4,986	150

[1] Adult unit gross disposable income as a percent of the budget requirement.

[Table 2 and pertinent text have been omitted.]

One of the most revealing calculations on the economic position of the aged is displayed in table 3. We show in the stub the gross disposable income of the adult unit as a percent of the budget requirement of the unit, for the aged population. Nearly a third of the units with a male head 65 or older have less than 90 percent of the income necessary to meet the modest budget standard. More than three-fifths of the units headed by women 65 or older have income less than 90 percent of their estimated needs. For the national population of all ages, including the aged, 28 percent of adult units have incomes less than 90 percent of their budget requirement.

TABLE 3. DISTRIBUTION OF ADULT GROSS DISPOSABLE INCOME AS A PERCENT OF ADULT UNIT BUDGET REQUIREMENTS, BY SEX OF HEAD*

(Percentage distribution of adult units 65 and older)

Adult unit gross disposable income as a percent of adult unit budget requirements	*Sex of head*	
	Male	*Female*
	Percent	*Percent*
80 percent and less	32	63
90 to 100 percent	11	7
110 to 120 percent	8	12
130 to 150 percent	11	8
160 to 200 percent	17	5
210 percent and greater	21	5
Total	100	100
Interpolated median	130	60

* Abridged from the original.

Table 4 shows distributions of dollar amounts of some types of income, by sex, of the adult unit head, for adult units whose heads are 65 and older. The differences here may exaggerate the inferior status of aged women because they are usually in single-person units, whereas many of the aged men have wives. Table 3, with its adjustment for needs according to the number of people in the unit, is a better measure.

It is interesting to note that adding nonmoney components of income, including imputed rental income, home production, free medical care, and food and housing contributed by relatives, increases the average by only $300 or $400, but reduces substantially the proportion receiving less than $2,000. It is also important to note that more than a third of the adult units headed by males report no social security

TABLE 4. Some Types of Adult Unit Income for 1959,
by Sex of Adult Unit Head

(Percentage distribution of adult units whose heads are 65 and older)

Amount of income	Social security benefits		Other pensions and annuities		Total money income		Gross disposable income	
	Male	Female	Male	Female	Male	Female	Male	Female
None	38	57	68	85			0	1
$1 to $499; negative	9	14	6	2			3	6
$500 to $999	19	23	12	6			10	33
$1,000 to $1,999	30	6	7	4			22	39
Under $2,000	96	100	93	97	46	89	35	79
$2,000 to $2,999	4	0	4	3	19	6	19	15
$3,000 to $4,999	0	0	2	0	16	4	25	5
$5,000 to $7,499	0	0					11	0
$7,500 to $9,999	0	0	1	0	19	1	3	1
$10,000 to $14,999	0	0					4	0
$15,000 and over	0	0					3	0
Total	100	100	100	100	100	100	100	100
Interpolated median	$740	0	0	0	$2,210		$2,790	$1,260
Mean					$3,582	$1,019	$3,880	$1,462

income, and 57 percent of the females report none. Only a combination of transfer incomes, money income, and nonmoney incomes makes the economic position of the aged as satisfactory as it is, and none of the three appears predominant. . . .

Tables 5-8 and pertinent text have been omitted.

Living with Relatives and Dependency among the Aged

The proportion of adult units who are living in a relative's dwelling, and thereby receiving some transfer income, is high at both ends of the age scale:

Age of head of adult unit:	Proportion of units living in a relative's dwelling
18 to 24	61
25 to 34	14
35 to 44	6
45 to 54	6
55 to 64	8
65 to 74	16
75 and older	29

Some of these units are not dependent upon their relatives, but are secondary spending units who have income, keep separate finances, and may even pay rent to the relatives with whom they live. . . .

. . . On the average the incomes of families in this country are more than sufficient to provide for dependent aged.

Not all the dependent adult units are aged persons living in the home of younger relatives. About a sixth of the family heads over 65 themselves provide housing for their relatives. For them, sharing a home with other units works two ways. They provide housing, and sometimes food and other things for relatives, at the same time these relatives may have income of their own. . . . When older people provide housing for relatives, they add on the average 1⅔ additional people to the family, but also add nearly $2,000 to the total family income.

. . . Both the host unit and the dependent units have lower average incomes than families which do not include more than one unit. The total family income of multiple-unit families is higher on the average in each age group than single-unit families, but the income per person is smaller, and the average incomes both of the adult units who house relatives, and the adult units who live with relatives are lower in each age group than the average income of the adult units who live alone.

It is not sufficient to look merely at the financial results of living with relatives; there are also some psychic costs involved. Part of a family's real income is its privacy. We asked two questions to obtain attitudes toward living with relatives and toward relatives' responsibilities for older people:

"Some older people move in with their children, others try hard to keep a separate household even when it means pinching pennies. Do you think it is a good idea or a bad idea for older people to live with their children? Why is that?

"If the older people don't have enough money, do you think their relatives should support them, or should the Government take care of them, or what? Why do you say so?" . . .

We found a sizable majority of spending unit heads are opposed to having older people live with their children. We infer that living with relatives may solve certain problems of economic maintenance, but it is not a generally popular or desired solution. However, a majority feel that relatives rather than the Government should take major responsibility for the support of older people who cannot support themselves. The inference is that if existing contributory programs are not sufficient, most people feel that relatives have some responsibility.

This does not mean that people are opposed to governmental responsibility for the aged. Only 30 percent said that relatives should be solely responsible, and even they probably interpreted the question to mean that relatives should be responsible where social security and private pensions are inadequate.

The greater the financial capacity of the respondent, the more opposed he was to units living together, but the more willing to accept the idea of some financial responsibility on the part of relatives.

Savings and Retirement

The income figures which we have presented understate the economic well-being of some of the aged. Some persons aged 65 and older have substantial resources in bank accounts, savings accounts, or Government bonds. Table 9 indicates that about a fifth of these spending units whose heads are 65 and older have $5,000 or more in these liquid assets. . . .

TABLE 9. Amount of Liquid Assets Held by Spending Units*

Amount of liquid assets held by spending units		Percentage of spending units whose heads are 65 and older
$5,000 or more		22
$1,000–$4,999		27
$500 to $999		8
Less then $500		37
Had $500 or more within the last 5 years	10	
Did not have $500 within the last 5 years	23	
Not ascertained whether had $500 within last 5 years	4	
Not ascertained		6
Total		100

* Abridged from the original.

By and large the retired do not draw on their savings to pay for living expenses after retirement. . . .

It seems likely that these savings are considered a basic reserve, not to be used except in the most dire emergency, and that being forced to use them would be a traumatic experience for an aged person.

Summary

We have shown that more careful inclusion of nonmoney incomes of the aged makes the welfare position of some look dismal. However, taking account of aged people who live with relatives, and who generally have low incomes even when we include the transfers of free food and housing, increases the estimated number of needy aged.

When we discover also that living with relatives is an almost universally disliked solution, with psychic costs, the problem of the dependent aged living with relatives becomes even more important.

While some of the aged have assets, it is clear that they cling to them, and are generally unwilling to use them for living expenses.

Finally, a substantial fraction of the aged report disabilities of one kind or another which may represent a large financial burden and which would interfere with any effort to find work and thus supplement income from pensions and assets.

No single source of support is predominant for older people, and only the combination of social security, earnings, income from capital (particularly the home), free room and board, and other transfers allows them to get along.

Methods of Paying for Medical Care

Using Own Resources

A 1957 study for the Health Information Foundation (HIF) on resources to pay for health services among those aged 65 and over reported as follows:

In early 1957 the older population could be divided into three groups: Those who had resources from which they could meet a medical bill as large as $500; those who had no ready resources for meeting such a bill; and a small amorphous middle group whose position cannot be clearly ascertained . . . . No categorical statement can be made to summarize how older people said they would meet a large medical bill. Some felt they could pay a medical bill as large as $500 from a combination of current income and savings. This group included roughly 6 of every 10 couples, 5 of every 10 unmarried older men, and 4 of every 10 unmarried older women. On the other hand, some older persons would have to mortgage property, borrow on life insurance, ask help from their children, turn to public assistance or charitable aid, or say in despair, "No one would charge me that . . . I just couldn't pay it." This group included about 3 of every 10 couples, 4 of every 10 unmarried older men, and 5 of every 10 unmarried older women.

The HIF study asked people how they thought they would handle a large bill. The OASI survey in the same year obtained fairly comprehensive data on the means by which aged persons actually met their medical emergencies. More than two-fifths of the couples and roughly three-fifths of the nonmarried beneficiaries studied who spent some time in a general (or short-stay special) hospital in 1957 did not meet all the year's medical costs out of their own income, assets, and health insurance. Almost all beneficiaries hospitalized paid some of their medical bills from their own income and savings, but those with very long stays were least able to stretch their resources to cover all costs. For example, 78 percent of the nonmarried beneficiaries in a general hospital longer than 60 days did not assume responsibility for all

From U.S. Senate Special Committee on Aging, *Background Facts on the Financing of the Health Care of the Aged: Excerpts from the Report of the Division of Program Research, Social Security Administration, Department of Health, Education, and Welfare,* 87th Congress, 2nd Session, 1962, pp. 51-55.

their own medical costs for the year, compared with 55 percent of those hospitalized for shorter periods.

Medical debts were incurred—or increased—by 21 percent of the couples and 12 percent of the nonmarried beneficiaries with a hospital episode during the year. (For all the beneficiaries, whether or not hospitalized, the proportions were much smaller—7 percent and 3 percent, respectively.) And this does not count the cases where a doctor, for example, reduced his fees because he knew that the patient could not pay. Moreover, a considerable number of the beneficiaries who had more unpaid medical bills at the end than at the beginning of the year got help from outside as well.

Help from Others

Fifteen percent of the couples and 29 percent of the nonmarried beneficiaries who had a hospital episode relied for at least part of their medical care on public assistance agencies, hospitals, or other public and private health and welfare agencies. Less than half as many of the nonhospitalized beneficiaries had to turn to welfare agencies.

The number receiving help from relatives in one form or another was at least as large. When beneficiaries were asked how they met their medical bills, 15 percent of the couples and 26 percent of the nonmarried with one or more hospital episodes reported that relatives helped pay for them. (Less than half as many of the other beneficiaries had to turn to relatives.) Some additional beneficiaries with hospital bills in effect received as much or more help with their medical costs from relatives who helped support them either by sharing their home or by paying other regular living expenses.

The longer the period of hospitalization the more frequently relatives contributed to help out with expenses. Most of the relatives who were contributing to an aged person living in the household were themselves in the middle or lower end of the income scale.

. . . The aforementioned study by the HIF asked the persons 65 and over to whom they would turn (other than their own husband or wife) in event of illness. More than 6 in 10 named a son or daughter or the spouse of a son or daughter. Those designated were described as follows:

Those to whom older people would turn for help in a health crisis were already involved with many family responsibilities. If these individuals were sons or daughters of older people they were usually young or middle-aged adults. Three of every four among them (73 percent) had children of their own . . . . The relatives to whom older people without children would turn for help were themselves likely to be in the older age groups, and many of these were over 65 years of age; also, many were widowed or single.

When asked how they would pay a medical bill of $500 or more, about one-fourth of the aged women who were widowed, divorced, or single, and about one-eighth of the men who were not married, said they would turn to children or other relatives. Fewer of the married persons—1 in 13—mentioned relatives as a resource presumably because those still married tend to be younger and to have more income and savings than the widowed.

Medical Need and Public Assistance

The exact number of aged who must seek public assistance because of medical need cannot be measured with exactitude. Depending on facilities available for the medically indigent and on local assistance practices, as well as on personal differences in reaction to a means test, some come for help at the time of medical need while others come to seek help in meeting daily living expenses only after using up their resources to pay their medical bills.

For example, the 1957 BOASI survey found that among all aged beneficiaries who incurred medical costs during the survey year, about 1 in 14 of the couples and 1 in 8 of the nonmarried were on public assistance at some time during the same 12-month period.

An analysis of the reasons for approving old-age assistance grants in about half the States in January–June 1961 shows that nearly 1 in 3 recipients needed assistance, at least in part, as a result of health problems in the 6 months preceding. . . .

The Role of Hospital Insurance

Were it not for health insurance many more aged persons would have to turn to relatives or welfare agencies, or both, to meet their pressing medical needs.

LENGTH OF STAY AND PORTION OF BILL COVERED

Data from the National Health Survey for 1958–60 reveal that for half the short-stay hospital episodes of aged persons during a year health insurance paid no part of the bill.

Even when insurance was available to the aged it was less effective for long than for short stays, defraying three-fourths of the hospital bill for 47 percent of the stays lasting over a month compared with 60 percent of those lasting no more than 30 days. . . . Although the average elderly patient in a general hospital who leaves the hospital alive does so within 15 days, nearly 1 in 10 remains a month or longer. The longer his hospitalization lasts the more likely it is the aged person will have to seek help from others to pay for his care.

The OASI beneficiary survey also provides a measure of the degree to which insurance met hospital costs of aged patients. About 1 in 5 married beneficiaries and 1 in 4 of the nonmarried with insurance found it met all of the hospital charges. On the other hand about 5 percent of those with a hospital insurance policy found it did not cover any of the costs of their care in a nongovernmental general hospital (table 35).

TABLE 35. Insurance Coverage of Hospital Costs of OASI Beneficiaries: Distribution of Aged Beneficiaries in General Hospitals
according to Proportion of Costs Paid by Insurance, by
Marital Status and Hospital Ownership, 1957

Proportion of general hospital costs paid by insurance[1]	*Married couples*[2,3]		*Nonmarried beneficiaries*	
	Total	*Non-Gov-ernment*	Total	*Non-Gov-ernment*
Total hospitalized	100	100	100	100
With no hospital insurance	43	39	48	41
With some hospital insurance	57	61	52	59
With some hospital insurance	100	100	100	100
No costs met by insurance	7	6	9	5
Less than 25 percent met by insurance	7	8	4	3
25 to 49 percent met by insurance	18	20	6	5
50 to 74 percent met by insurance	22	22	29	30
75 to 99 percent met by insurance	20	19	21	23
100 percent met by insurance	19	19	24	27
Unreported amount met by insurance	6	6	6	7

[1] Excludes surgeons' and inhospital physicians' fees. In the case of married couples, with both members hospitalized, represents hospital costs for the couple. (General hospitals include short-stay special hospitals.)

[2] Insurance status for married couples refers to the hospitalized person. If both were hospitalized, but only one insured, the couple is classified in the "with insurance" category and by the proportion of total general hospital costs for the couple which was met by the insurance.

[3] Aged beneficiary and spouse, whether or not entitled to benefits; spouse may be under 65 years of age.

Source: Bureau of Old-Age and Survivors Insurance, Social Security Administration, *1957 National Survey of Old-Age and Survivors Insurance Beneficiaries.*

AMOUNT OF INSURANCE AND AMOUNT OF HOSPITAL UTILIZATION

Aged persons having insurance against costs appear to enter a hospital with greater frequency but have a shorter average stay than those with no insurance protection. Those with a higher benefit policy use the hospital more often than those with a lower benefit policy.

SELECTED BIBLIOGRAPHY

Becker, Harry, ed. *Financing Hospital Care for Nonwage and Low-Income Groups.* Volume 3 of the Report of the Commission on the Financing of Hospital Care. New York: McGraw-Hill, Inc., 1955.

Brewster, Agnes W. "Meeting the Health Needs of the Aged," *The Annals,* CCCXXXVII (September 1961), 114-125.

Campbell, Rita R. and W. Glenn. *Voluntary Health Insurance in the United States.* Washington, D.C.: American Enterprise Association, 1960.

Corson, John J., and John W. McConnell. *Economic Needs of Older People.* New York: Twentieth Century Fund, 1956.

Epstein, Lenore A. "Income of the Aged in 1962: First Findings of the 1963 Survey of the Aged," *Social Security Bulletin,* XXVII (March 1964), 3-25.

———. "State Variations in Income of the Aged," *Social Security Bulletin,* XXVI (January 1963), 3-9.

Financing Health Care of the Aged: A Study of the Dimensions of the Problem. Chicago: Blue Cross Association and American Hospital Association, 1962.

Goldmann, Franz, et al. "Financing Medical Care for the Aged," *American Journal of Public Health,* XLIX (February 1959), 161-185. A symposium giving a variety of viewpoints.

Harrington, Michael. *The Other America: Poverty in the United States.* New York: The Macmillan Company, 1962.

Kreps, Juanita M. "Aggregate Income and Labor Force Participation of the Aged," *Law and Contemporary Problems,* XXVII (Winter 1962), 52-66.

"Medical Care Costs of Aged OASI Beneficiaries: Highlights from Preliminary Data, 1957 Survey," *Social Security Bulletin,* XXII (April 1959), 3-9.

Orbach, Harold L., and Clark Tibbitts. *Aging and the Economy.* Ann Arbor: University of Michigan Press, 1963.

Rimlinger, Gaston V. "Health Care of the Aged: Who Pays the Bill?" *Harvard Business Review,* XXXVIII (January-February 1960), 108-116.

Rosow, Irving. *Old Age—One Moral Dilemma of an Affluent Society.* Washington, D.C.: Washington Center for Metropolitan Studies, 1961.

Shanas, Ethel. *Family Relationships of Older People: Living Arrangements, Health Status and Family Ties of Those Aged 65 and Over, As Re-*

ported by the Aged, the Persons to Whom They Would Turn in a Health Crisis, and the General Public. Chicago: Health Information Foundation, 1961.

———. *Financial Resources of the Aging: Reported Resources Available to Those Aged 65 and Over in Meeting Medical Costs Up to $500.* Chicago: Health Information Foundation, 1959.

———. *The Health of Older People: A Social Survey.* Cambridge, Mass.: Harvard University Press, 1962.

———. *Medical Care Among Those Aged 65 and Over: Reported Illness and Utilization of Health Services by the "Sick" and the "Well."* Chicago: Health Information Foundation, 1960.

Spiegelman, Mortimer. *Ensuring Medical Care for the Aged.* Homewood, Ill.: Richard D. Irwin, Inc., 1960. This book should be read in conjunction with the critical review by Jonas N. Muller which appeared in the *Milbank Memorial Fund Quarterly,* XXXIX (January 1961), 163-171.

Steiner, Peter O., and Robert Dorfman. *The Economic Status of the Aged.* Berkeley: University of California Press, 1957.

Stotz, Margaret S. "The BLS Interim Budget for a Retired Couple," *Monthly Labor Review,* LXXXIII (November 1960), 1141-1157.

Tibbitts, Clark, ed. *Handbook of Social Gerontology: Societal Aspects of Aging.* Chicago: University of Chicago Press, 1960.

U.S. Cong. Joint Committee on the Economic Report. *Making Ends Meet on Less than $2000 a Year: Case Studies of 100 Low-Income Families.* Senate Document #112. 82nd Congress, 2nd Session, 1952.

———. Subcommittee on Low-Income Families. *Characteristics of the Low-Income Population and Related Federal Programs.* Committee print. 84th Congress, 1st Session, 1955.

———. *Low-Income Families and Economic Stability: Materials on the Problem of Low-Income Families.* Senate Document #231. 81st Congress, 2nd Session, 1950.

———. *Low-Income Families: Hearings.* 81st Congress, 1st Session, 1949; 84th Congress, 1st Session, 1955.

———. *A Program for the Low-Income Population at Substandard Levels of Living.* Senate Report #1311. 84th Congress, 2nd Session, 1956.

U.S. Cong. Joint Economic Committee. *The Low Income Population and Economic Growth.* Study Paper #12 of the Study of Employment, Growth, and Price Levels. By Robert J. Lampman. 86th Congress, 1st Session, December 1959.

U.S. Cong. Sen. Committee on Labor and Public Welfare. *Studies of the Aged and Aging: Selected Documents.* 85th Congress, 1st Session, 1957.
Vol. 1: *Federal and State Activities*
Vol. 2: *Health and Health Services*
Vol. 3: *Income and Income Maintenance*
Vol. 4: *Employment*

Supplement to Vol. 4: *Employment*

Vol. 5: *Public and Private Services for Older People*

Vol. 6: *Care of the Aging by the Veterans Administration*

Vol. 7: *Guide to Significant Publications* (an annotated bibliography)

Vol. 8: *Population: Current Data and Trends*

Vol. 9: *Research, Demonstration and Training*

Vol. 10: *Surveys of State and Local Projects*

———. Subcommittee on Problems of the Aged and Aging. *Action for the Aged and Aging: A Report.* Senate Report #128. 87th Congress, 1st Session, March 28, 1961.

———. *The Aged and Aging in the United States: Summary of Expert Views.* 86th Congress, 1st Session, June 1959.

U.S. Cong. Sen. Aging. *Background Facts on the Financing of the Health Care of the Aged: Excerpts from the Report of the Division of Program Research, Social Security Administration, Department of Health, Education, and Welfare.* 87th Congress, 2nd Session, 1962.

———. *Developments in Aging, 1959 to 1963.* Senate Report #8. 88th Congress, 1st Session, 1963.

———. *Health and Economic Conditions of the American Aged: A Chart Book.* 87th Congress, 1st Session, June 1961.

———. *New Population Facts on Older Americans, 1960: A Staff Report.* 87th Congress, 1st Session, 1961.

U.S. HEW Library. *Selected References on Aging: An Annotated Bibliography Compiled for the Special Staff on Aging.* 1959.

U.S. HEW SSA. *Hospitalization and Insurance Among Aged Persons: A Study Based on a Census Survey in March 1952.* By I. S. Falk and Agnes W. Brewster. 1953.

———. *Income Security Standards in Old Age.* By Lenore A. Epstein. Research Report #3, 1963.

———. Bureau of Old-Age and Survivors Insurance. *Hospital Insurance Coverage of Aged Beneficiaries.* By Charlotte Ellis. 1957 National Survey of Old-Age and Survivors Insurance Beneficiaries Highlight Report #8, 1962.

———. *The Impact of Hospitalization Costs on Aged Beneficiaries.* By Edna C. Wentworth. 1957 National Survey of Old-Age and Survivors Insurance Beneficiaries Highlight Report #6, 1961.

U.S. HEW SSA. Division of Program Research. *The Financial Position of the Aged.* By Lenore A. Epstein. Research and Statistics Note #1, 1962.

———. *The Health Care of the Aged: Background Facts Relating to the Financing Problem.* 1962.

———. *Money Income of Aged Persons, Mid-1960.* By Lenore A. Epstein. Research and Statistics Note #28, 1960.

U.S. HEW SSA. Division of Research and Statistics. *Estimated Expenditures for Medical Care of Persons Aged 65 and Over.* Research and Statistics Note #3, 1963.

——. *Health Costs of the Aged: A Source Book on the Use of Hospital and Medical Services and on Health Insurance and Other Methods of Financing Medical Care Among the Aged.* By Agnes W. Brewster and Dorothy McCamman. 1956.

——. *Health Insurance of the Aged: Quality of Coverage.* By Paul Ahmed. Research and Statistics Note #3, 1965.

——. *Retirement Income and Measures of Need.* By Lenore A. Epstein. Research and Statistics Note #2, 1964.

Wiggins, James W., and Helmut Schoeck. "A Profile of the Aging: USA," *Geriatrics,* XVI (July 1961), 336-342.

The Legislative History of Medicare

Legislation providing health insurance for social-security beneficiaries was first introduced in Congress in 1952. It first attracted extensive public attention seven years later, when Congressman Aime Forand for the second time introduced legislation that provided hospitalization insurance for the elderly through the social-security system. By 1961, the Forand bill had evolved into the King-Anderson bill, the official proposal of the Kennedy and Johnson Administrations to meet the special problems of the aged outlined in Chapter II.[a]

Early Efforts

The Forand and King-Anderson bills, as well as the various other bills that have proposed alternative methods of paying for the elderly's medical bills, had their predecessors in the proposals for government-financed medical care for the entire population that were put forth in the United States from time to time during the first half of the twentieth century. In the selection that follows, Odin Anderson outlines the major developments in the movement for such legislation before 1950.[b]

---

[a] A summary of the 1965 version of the King-Anderson bill appears in the appendix. A general discussion of its provisions and of other legislation proposed to deal with this problem appears in this chapter.

[b] The reader who is interested in greater detail about the proposals discussed by Dr. Anderson and their fates should consult the two Social Security Administration booklets cited in the bibliography for this chapter.

Compulsory Medical Care Insurance, 1910-1950

ODIN W. ANDERSON

The agitation for and against the adoption of a compulsory system of medical care insurance in the United States began shortly before World War I. . . . The first period, 1910–20, reached the legislative stage in several states, but no bills were passed. Action for compulsory medical care insurance appeared to be ill-prepared and hasty, and subsided abruptly as soon as unexpected opposition mustered its forces effectively. The second period, 1921–33, was a quiet one devoted to study of basic facts and problems only superficially comprehended in the first period. The third period, beginning in 1933, has been characterized by action similar to that of the first period, but on a much broader base of support and opposition, and in a profoundly different social, political, and economic context.

First Period, 1910–20

During the first period the American Association for Labor Legislation (AALL) was the chief group calling attention of the problem of medical care insurance and making concrete suggestions for its solution. The AALL was organized in 1906 by a handful of prominent economists. By 1913 it had over 3,300 members consisting of economists, lawyers, political scientists, historians, and members of other fields concerned with social problems. It passed out of existence in 1942.

It is important to note that the AALL was dedicated to the improvement of various phases of society within the contemporary economic and social structure and ideology. The organization was primarily interested in the effects of industrialization as seen in industrial accidents, occupational diseases, and general working con-

From *The Annals of the American Academy of Political and Social Science*, CCLXXIII (January 1951), 106-113. Footnotes have been renumbered. Reprinted by permission of the author and of the publisher. Odin W. Anderson is currently Research Director of the Health Information Foundation, an organization established by executives in the pharmaceutical and related industries. When this article was written, Dr. Anderson was Associate Professor in Charge of the Social Aspects of Medicine, University of Western Ontario.

ditions. Workmen's compensation was greatly emphasized and pushed as the prime method of reducing industrial accidents and diseases and protecting the earning power of the workers. In this regard the AALL was very effective, because workmen's compensation laws were enacted in thirty states by 1915. The AALL was thus flushed with a seemingly easy victory and was looking over the social scene for some other problem to attack.

Medical care insurance was selected as the next logical step for action. Workmen's compensation protected the workers against the economic loss of accidents and illness arising out of employment, while medical care insurance was designed to cover workers for illnesses and accidents not related to employment.

In 1912 the AALL established a Committee on Social Insurance, the first of its kind in the United States, which in the next few years carried the main burden of medical care insurance study and activity. Three of the members of the committee were also members of the Social Insurance Committee established by the American Medical Association (AMA) in 1915. They were Alexander Lambert, I. M. Rubinow, and later S. S. Goldwater, all physicians. . . .

In 1914 a subcommittee of the Committee on Social Insurance was appointed to draft a bill in preparation for an active campaign in the states and in Congress. By the end of 1915 a model bill was drafted to be introduced in several state legislatures in January 1916. At the same time it was reported that the AMA had appointed a committee to co-operate with the Committee on Social Insurance "in putting the finishing touches on the medical sections of the bill." Also, several other important organizations appointed committees early in 1916 to study the proposal of the AALL. The Secretary of the AALL optimistically wrote in the annual report: "The opportunity now appears good for a big educational campaign for the conservation of health, with fair prospects for legislative commissions to investigate in 1916 and for compulsory health insurance legislation in this country in 1917."

OPPOSITION AROUSED

So far so good for the protagonists, but opposition emerged very rapidly after the AALL had unstrategically exposed itself completely. It was naively assumed that a reform which they thought should be deemed good by everyone would triumph on its own merits.

As long as medical care insurance was discussed without relation to specific and concrete actions, the potential opponents apparently were not aware of its implications. However, when ten state commissions were established to study the subject and make recommendations, and bills were introduced in sixteen state legislatures, the proponents were surprised at the opposition's vehemence and gathering strength. . . .

By 1918 the movement had reached its peak as represented by activities of state commissions in the state legislatures. The most intense activity was found in California and New York. At this point the seemingly favorable attitude of organized medicine turned into vigorous opposition. Simultaneously, pharmaceutical companies, accident and health insurance companies, companies selling industrial insurance, and healing cults proved to be too much for the proponents of compulsory medical care insurance. Furthermore (and this was a dismaying discovery for the AALL), Samuel Gompers, president of the American Federation of Labor, was very outspoken in his denunciation of government-operated social insurance schemes. Numerous state federations of labor supported the AALL proposal, particularly in New York State, but their support came too late and Gompers' prestige was too great.

AMERICAN MEDICAL ASSOCIATION

It appears to be coincidental that the prominent physicians in the American Medical Association were able to have a committee established in 1915 to study the issues of medical care insurance and report to the House of Delegates from time to time. The apparent purpose was not to advocate any compulsory insurance, but, according to I. M. Rubinow who became the executive secretary of the committee, "to bring about friendly understanding between all parties concerned and to protect the legitimate economic interests of the profession."

A few months before Rubinow's statement, the *Journal of the American Medical Association* ran an editorial regarding the model bill of the AALL: "It is hoped that physicians will take advantage of this opportunity [of studying the AALL bill] and that it will be possible to avoid that lack of co-operation between physicians and legislators which, for a time, marred some of the foreign legislation."

By 1920 officials of state medical societies were reacting vehemently against any deliberation on compulsory medical care insurance, particularly in New York, Michigan, Illinois, and California. A powerful group of delegates assembled at the annual session of the AMA in New Orleans in 1920 "to get Lambert," as they put it, who was then president of the association.

At the same session, the House of Delegates established a basic policy which has not been revised to the present day, and expressed it in the following resolution:

The American Medical Association declares its opposition to the institution of any plan embodying the system of compulsory contributory insurance against illness, or any other plan of compulsory insurance which provides for medical service to be rendered contributors or their dependents, provided, controlled, or regulated by any state or Federal government.

The end of the controversy over compulsory medical care insurance was just as abrupt as the foregoing resolution was final.

Second Period, 1921–33

After the emphatically worded resolution in 1920, the American Medical Association at several annual meetings considered resolutions concerned with definitions of "state medicine" and similar forms of medical care organized and operated by government.

In 1921 the Sheppard-Towner bill to provide grants-in-aid to states for maternal and child health programs was up for consideration in Congress. The bill aroused bitter controversy at the hearings, and many physicians testified in opposition. Although the bill was not proposing a system of compulsory medical care insurance, physicians regarded it as an entering wedge for encroachment of government in private practice. Nevertheless, the Sheppard-Towner Act was passed in 1922 with active support from citizen's groups. The act was disapproved officially by the House of Delegates at the annual meeting of the AMA in 1922.

Problems regarding the economic and social aspects of medical care were discussed on several occasions in 1925 and 1926 at conferences attended by physicians, members of the public health professions, and economists. These conferences were called to formulate plans for a study of the structure of medical services of the country, especially the economic aspects. As a result of the deliberations of these conferences, the Committee on the Costs of Medical Care (CCMC) was established. Its work was financed by six foundations. . . .

The committee consisted of 42 persons—14 private practitioners of medicine, 6 from public health, 8 from institutions interested in medicine, 5 economists, and 9 persons representing the general public.

From 1928 to 1932 the CCMC released twenty-eight reports on the incidence of illness, the cost of medical care, and related aspects of health. The period of study seemed to be one of watchful waiting. The AMA editorialized: "Most physicians and most economists and most social workers are willing to wait until the Committee on the Costs of Medical Care, a group with which the medical profession is co-operating wholeheartedly, has brought into the situation, data on which to base reasonable action for the future."

The effect of the final report dealing with recommendations for action on the basis of findings was immediate. Majority and minority reports split the CCMC and supporters of its objectives into factions. The lead in opposition to the majority report was taken by the AMA and some of the physician members of the CCMC.

The majority of the members of the committee were of the opinion that "medical service, both preventive and therapeutic, should be furnished largely by organized groups of physicians, dentists, nurses, pharmacists, and other associated personnel" and that "the costs of medical care be placed on a group payment basis," through the use of insurance, taxation, or both.

The minority group, while agreeing with the majority report in many matters, objected to the proposal for group practice and the adoption of insurance plans unless sponsored and controlled by organized medicine.

The editorial response of the AMA to the majority report has become a classic, and was presumably directed at the aspects of the report dealing with group practice and areas of government responsibility, and not at voluntary insurance, as such, if sponsored and controlled by organized medicine. The editorial read:

The alinement is clear—on the one side the forces representing the great foundations, public health officialdom, social theory—even socialism and communism—inciting to revolution; on the other side, the organized medical profession of this country urging an orderly evolution guided by controlled experimentation which will observe the principles that have been found through the centuries to be necessary to the sound practice of medicine.[1]

Third Period, Beginning 1933

The recommendations of the Committee on the Costs of Medical Care and the reactions to them formed the base of the third period of the compulsory medical care insurance movement. The main issues and factions were brought to the surface as the movement gained momentum and breadth during the following years. It will be recalled that the American Association for Labor Legislation, an organization composed chiefly of professional people, was the group most instrumental in initiating interest in and action for some type of

---

[1] *Journal of the American Medical Association,* Vol. 99 (Dec. 3, 1932), p. 1952.

compulsory medical care insurance in the first period; but during the third period, beginning in 1933, which has not yet ended, the Federal Government, through official committees and legislative activity, and later state governments, have been the agencies which spearheaded the reopening of the issue of government-sponsored medical care insurance. What government has done during this period has conditioned the attitudes and actions of other groups which feel that they have a stake in the future of medical care. There has been general agreement that a problem exists, and the depression made it more acute; but there has been profound disagreement as to what should be the solution.

The depression and the deliberations over the nature and scope of the impending social security program provided the framework for discussions and action regarding compulsory medical care insurance. The precedent-setting Federal *Rules and Regulations No. 7* of 1933 defined policies and procedures under which medical care might be given to those receiving unemployment relief in the states. Representatives of the American Medical Association participated in the formulation of the rules and regulations and gave their sanction. Access to medical care was now recognized by government as a basic minimum right together with food, clothing, and shelter.

COMMITTEE ON ECONOMIC SECURITY

In 1934 the President appointed the Committee on Economic Security to make recommendations for a program "against misfortunes which cannot be wholly eliminated in this man-made world of ours." In addition there were numerous committees established as advisory to the Committee on Economic Security, with a very broad range of representation of fields of interests and organizations. The research duties of the committee were divided into several problem areas; among them, medical care.

Medical care insurance was given short shrift, however, inasmuch as Edwin E. Witte, executive director of the Committee on Economic Security, reported that medical care insurance could not even reach the research stage, not to mention its incorporation in the social security program. He wrote:

When in 1934 the Committee on Economic Security announced that it was studying health insurance, it was at once subjected to misrepresentation and vilification. In the original social security bill there was one line to the effect that the Social Security Board should study the problem and make a report thereon to Congress. That little line was responsible for so many telegrams to the members of Congress that the entire social security program seemed endangered until the Ways and Means Committee unanimously struck it out of the bill.

As a corollary, the AMA was also the object of pressure. Its *Journal* editorialized, on November 24, 1934:

The headquarters office of the American Medical Association has been besieged with telephone calls, telegrams and letters on this subject. . . . Some physicians are apparently opposed to all change and feel that the American Medical Association should officially make itself felt in opposition to the entire program of the government.

FOLLOWING THE SOCIAL SECURITY ACT

The Social Security Act was passed in 1935. Thereafter the Government sponsored a series of activities which either deliberately or coincidently resulted in the introduction of the first compulsory medical care insurance bill in Congress to attract any widespread attention, the so-called Wagner bill of 1939 (S. 1620).[2] The series of activities was as follows:

1. The National Health Survey was made in 1935-36—a large-scale study of the incidence of illness and the underlying social and economic factors.

2. In 1935 the President appointed the Interdepartmental Committee to Coordinate Health and Welfare Activities, entrusted with the task of making sure that the provisions of the Social Security Act were being effectively applied, and suggesting improvements. One of the chief interests of the committee was the problem of medical care.

3. Out of the Interdepartmental Committee was created the Technical Committee on Medical Care in 1937, consisting chiefly of experts from the Federal agencies concerned in whole or in part with health.

4. Early in 1938 the Technical Committee recommended, among other things, that there was a need for a general program of medical care and insurance against loss of wages as a result of illness.

5. Thereupon, the Interdepartmental Committee called the National Health Conference held in Washington, D.C., in July 1938, to discuss the findings and recommendations submitted by the Technical

---

[2] Actually, the first medical care insurance bills in Congress were those introduced by Senator Capper of Kansas in July 1935 (S. 3253) and in January 1937 (S. 855); but they received little attention.

Committee. Invitations were sent to a large representation of people from the medical profession, from agencies working in health, and from labor, industry, agriculture, and other groups of citizens. The purpose of the conference was to clarify issues and stimulate constructive criticisms. No specific recommendations were expected from the conferees.

SUCCESSION OF BILLS

The Wagner bill of 1939 was followed by: the Capper bill in 1941 (S. 489); the Eliot bill in 1942 (H. R. 7354); the Wagner-Murray-Dingell bill in 1943 (S. 1161); a reintroduction of S. 1161 by Representative Dingell, Michigan, early in 1945 (H. R. 395); and in November of the same year, a new Wagner-Murray-Dingell bill (S. 1606). In 1947 there appeared the first counterproposal to compulsory medical care insurance in the bill (S. 545) sponsored by Senator Taft and others to assist states in providing medical care for the indigent. The opposite type of bill was introduced in the same year by Senators Murray, Wagner, and others (S. 1320).

In May 1948 another health conference, the National Health Assembly, was held in Washington, attended by 800 professional and community leaders. Again all phases of the problem of medical care were examined. The Medical Care Section of the assembly unanimously agreed that the *principle* of contributory insurance should be the basic method of financing medical care for the large majority of the American people, but differed in their views on the method of implementation. Independent of the National Health Assembly, the Federal Security Administrator, Oscar R. Ewing, recommended a compulsory system, and in the report to the President marshaled a great array of data in an attempt to justify his conclusions.[3]

In 1949 bills in Congress on medical care became so numerous that they were difficult to follow, but two bills emerged as the focus of the conflict over compulsory medical care insurance—the administration bill, S. 1679, and the opposition bill, S. 1970. The latter bill proposed a "voluntary" approach by providing for Federal grants to the states to assist co-operating voluntary prepayment plans to make their services generally available to those wishing to utilize them. The difference between the two bills reflects diverse philosophies.

Because of the intense and prominent activities on the Federal level, parallel actions on the state level have been overlooked or discussed

---

[3] Oscar R. Ewing, *The Nation's Health, A Ten Year Program: A Report to the President*, Washington, D.C.: Federal Security Agency, 1948, 186 pp.

as of little importance, except in California. However, since 1935 compulsory medical care insurance bills have been introduced in over a dozen states, and in some of them repeatedly. In California, by law of 1949, compulsory insurance against the cost of hospitalization was introduced for all persons covered by compulsory unemployment insurance.

As stated previously, it appears that government activity was the stimulus for counteractivity on the part of proponents of voluntary health insurance. Today these plans are widespread.

DEVELOPMENT OF ISSUES

To close the discussion of the third period let us trace the development of issues to the present time, so that we can be assisted in delineating current issues. Not until the National Health Conference held in Washington in 1938 did the issue of compulsory medical care insurance become a national issue in the sense that a great variety of groups throughout the country became aware of the problem and acted accordingly.

The shifts in issues since 1933 may be broadly indicated as follows:

1. In 1933 medical care insurance, regardless of type of sponsorship, was an issue.

2. By 1939 insurance as a device to spread the economic risk of illness ceased to be an issue. The hospitals had for several years supported insurance plans pertaining to hospitalization, and the AMA recognized them and began to direct attention to medical plans along similar lines.

3. Also by 1939 an insurance system covering the Nation regardless of type of sponsorship was an issue.

4. By 1946 both the American Hospital Association and the AMA subscribed to a nation-wide system sponsored and operated by themselves.

5. The remaining basic issue has become a national compulsory medical care insurance system or a national voluntary system. There are important subissues, such as the questions of scope of service, extent of coverage of population, and pace of development.

Basically the AMA is in the forefront of the chief opposition group, and organized labor—the CIO and the AFL—is spearhead for some form of compulsory insurance. It will be recalled that the collapse of the movement for compulsory medical care insurance in the first period was partly due to the lack of effective support from organized labor; but the reverse is true today.

BASES OF AGREEMENT

So much attention is being paid to disagreements between opposing factions that bases of agreement are ignored. The bases of agreement holding all parties and individuals within sparring distance of one another is the consensus that all should have access to medical care irrespective of income. Given this consensus, the next step is the struggle over means. The means is insurance, but there is disagreement as to sponsorship and control.

Another common orientation is that groups on both sides of the question of compulsory medical care insurance have a basic faith in the present political and economic institutions. The individuals and organizations supporting compulsory medical care insurance are not necessarily revolutionary; nor are those opposing such a system necessarily reactionary. As specific objects of a reform movement, physicians are naturally very much affected, and to them it seems a revolutionary step; but in the perspective of a deep-seated and world-wide movement gaining momentum in the United States with the Social Security Act in 1935, compulsory medical care insurance is a rounding out of a broad social program.

The exact form a national medical care insurance program might take would probably depend on the ability of the Blue Cross and Blue Shield plans to modify and deflect an all-out Federal state compulsory medical care insurance system, and on the as yet unclear trends of the burgeoning union health and welfare plans. In other words, the third period of the medical care insurance movement in the United States is by no means over. . . .

Efforts since World War II

Proposals for government health insurance have had rough going. As Anderson points out, even in 1935—perhaps the time when public support for social services and welfare legislation was highest—Congress struck from the social-security bill a line directing the Social Security Board to "study" health insurance. The movement for compulsory health insurance of the 1930's was halted by the concerns of World War II and by the demise of New Deal political ascendancy. In the postwar period, despite continued demands for social reform, support for the Wagner-Murray-Dingell bill was not enough to overcome Congressional allegiance to "traditional forms of medical practice"—as these were defined by the medical profession.

This bill (really a series of bills) was the Truman Administration's proposal for government health insurance for the entire population. It would have set up a state-administered system with federal financing. Since the bills were health measures, rather than tax measures, the exact method of financing was not specified, although it was clear that revenues would come primarily from payroll taxes. The types of medical care to be covered included almost all physicians', dental, and home nursing services; 60 days of hospital services a year; and certain auxiliary services and drugs. To be covered were almost all those employed in the private sector of the economy, all the self-employed, federal civilian employees and annuitants, persons entitled to Old Age, Survivors' and Disability Insurance (OASDI) benefits (the technical name for what is commonly referred to as "receiving social security"), and their dependents. Those who were not covered, such as the unemployed and persons receiving public assistance (i.e., "on relief") could be insured for any period for which payments were made by or for them, or were guaranteed by a local, state, or federal agency. Federal grants were to be made to the states, which would contract with providers of care and fix rates of payment. The states could use nonprofit, voluntary prepayment carriers as their agents, and physicians could choose the method by which they would be paid—either fee-for-service (the traditional method under which a physician is paid a fee each time he renders a service) or capitation (an annual fee for each patient).

Republican liberals and Democratic moderates responded with proposals of their own. They attempted to meet a widely felt need while at the same time attempting to avoid a compulsory program and charges of "socialism." Prominent among these proposals were the Flanders-Ives bills, which would have indirectly subsidized nonprofit private carriers through state plans. Participation would have been voluntary. Funds would have come both from subscribers' premiums, set to a sliding scale on the basis of income, and from state and local subsidies. Federal grants would have reimbursed each state for from one-third to three-quarters of its subsidy payments, the proportion depending on the state's per capita income. Regional health authorities would have determined the kinds of medical services to be provided in their local area. These bills were first introduced in 1949 by Ralph Flanders and Irving Ives in the Senate and by Clifford Case, James Fulton, Christian Herter, Jacob Javits, Thruston Morton, and Richard Nixon in the House. Hearings were held on these bills in 1949, but not in the later years in which they were introduced. Nevertheless, much of the thought that went into them was to become relevant in the 1960's as Jacob Javits, now in the Senate (as were several of the other sponsors), formulated the liberal Republican response to the Forand and King-Anderson bills.

The major role in defeating these postwar proposals was played by the American Medical Association.[c] The organized medical profession had engaged in extensive lobbying and public-relations efforts to defeat proposals for government health insurance in the 1930's and 1940's. The efforts of the National Physicians' Committee in this regard had begun to run down by 1948, when Harry Truman's election to a Presidential term in his own right surprised the nation. Truman had supported proposals for government health insurance, and his election presented the danger that his proposals, or some modification of them, might be enacted.

In 1945, Earl Warren, then Governor of California, had pro-

---

[c] An excellent description of the AMA's efforts is Kelley, Chapter III, "Medical Economics and Doctor Politics." The following description of AMA activities is drawn from Professor Kelley's work.

posed a statewide scheme of government health insurance to the California Legislature. The bill had failed after a campaign waged on behalf of the California Medical Association by Whitaker and Baxter, a public-relations firm which specialized in political campaigns. In 1949, Whitaker and Baxter, with a staff of thirty-seven, went to work for the American Medical Association on a National Education Campaign against the Truman proposals. Almost $5 million was spent in the next three and a half years on the campaign, a large part of it as seed money designed to encourage and inspire expenditure and activity by others. The campaign emphasized grass-roots publicity, rather than traditional direct contacts with legislators, although it did encourage lobbying of Congressmen by their personal physicians.

A principal element of the campaign was the solicitation of endorsements from other organizations. State and county medical societies compiled lists of organizations in their areas. These organizations were called on by local physicians and by members of the Whitaker and Baxter staff. Form speeches were prepared for use by physicians in addressing meetings of these organizations, and form resolutions were provided the organizations for their endorsement. Ten thousand such endorsements were secured. Each endorsement was sent to the President, members of Congress, state legislators, and the press. Groups making endorsements were asked to distribute literature to their members, publish news and editorials on the issue in their publications, and use their influence to get endorsements from other organizations.

Announcement of such endorsements was one way of getting publicity in the press for the AMA point of view. Statements by spokesmen for the medical profession provided another. To get still more publicity, Whitaker and Baxter collected material for use by newsmen in writing feature and other special articles. These articles, once published, were reprinted and circulated by Whitaker and Baxter. A firm which prepared editorials for publication by rural newspapers was paid to circulate editorials presenting the AMA point of view. In an attempt to get a more favorable reception for AMA press releases, physicians spoke to editors of their acquaintance. From 40 to 50 million pieces of literature were distributed each year by doctors, dentists, druggists, insurance men, and others.

All of this activity reached a peak during the 1950 Congressional election. The AMA was successful in making government health insurance a key issue in the election, in which its position was supported by the Republican party, while the Democratic party was divided. The high point of the AMA election effort was a $1 million advertising campaign concentrated in two weeks in October. A 70-column-inch advertisement went into each of 11,000 newspapers, while spot announcements were placed on over 1,000 radio stations. Tie-in advertisements for use by service clubs, civic groups, trade associations, medical-care plans, insurance companies, dairies, restaurants, druggists, and other small businessmen were prepared. Letters were sent to the presidents of 25,000 business firms, asking them to participate in the campaign. The National Retail Dry Goods Association sent similar letters to 7,000 retail stores. Mats for the advertisements were sent to newspaper advertising directors, pointing out the opportunity offered them to sell advertising. This effort brought forth $2 million worth of tie-in advertising by 65,000 advertisers, in addition to the AMA's own expenditures of half that amount.

The AMA campaign did not discuss the content of the Truman Administration proposals or of the compromise proposals made by others. Rather, it was a broad attack on "socialized medicine," which would result in deterioration of the high quality of American medical care and was an attempt on the part of the government "to assume control not only of the medical profession, but of hospitals—both public and private—the drug and appliance industries, dentistry, pharmacy, nursing and allied professions." Supporters of the scheme were listed: "The Federal Security Administration. The President. All who seriously believe in a Socialistic State. Every left-wing organization in America. . . . The Communist Party." The alternative was "The Voluntary Way"—"If a family can afford a daily pack of cigarettes or a Saturday night movie, that family can afford to buy Voluntary Health Insurance."[d] A

---

[d] Quotations are from a National Education Campaign release, quoted by Kelley, pp. 74-75.

central theme of the campaign was Fildes' painting of a doctor at the bedside of a sick child. The text underneath read:

KEEP POLITICS OUT OF THIS PICTURE!

When the life—or health of a loved one is at stake, hope lies in the devoted service of your Doctor. Would you change this picture? Compulsory health insurance is political medicine. It would bring a third party—a politician—between you and your Doctor. It would bind up your family's health in red tape. It would result in heavy payroll taxes —and inferior medical care for you and your family. Don't let that happen here!

The AMA's campaign was successful: neither the Administration proposals nor any of the other legislative alternatives were enacted during Truman's second term. In the fall of 1952, the National Education Campaign wound up its work, and the National Professional Committee for Eisenhower-Nixon was organized. Its officers represented several professions, but its chairman was the chairman of the National Education Campaign, its managers were Whitaker and Baxter, and its staff was identical with that of the National Education Campaign. Its techniques were similar to those of the Campaign, although its themes were the broader ones of the Eisenhower campaign.

The Early 1950's

The election of Eisenhower and a Republican majority in both houses of Congress in 1952 ended whatever hopes liberals might have had for a large-scale federal solution to problems of medical-care financing. The Democrats regained control of both houses of Congress in the 1954 election, but their leadership, House Speaker Sam Rayburn and Senate Majority Leader Lyndon Johnson, were not active supporters of liberal causes.

Moreover, the political debates of the 1950's took place in a world different from that of 1935 or 1948. In contrast with the 1930's, the national mood in the 1950's was one of satisfaction and conservatism.[e] Another source of difficulty for proponents of national health insurance was the increasingly critical and sometimes

---

[e] Eric Goldman's *The Crucial Decade—And After: America, 1945-1960* (New York: Vintage, 1961) evokes and describes this mood well.

"The Doctor," a painting by Sir Luke Fildes, in the Tate Gallery.

hostile view held by the public and by Congress of organized labor and its concerns and proposals.

Needs were still felt, however, and numerous Congressional proposals attempted to attack the problem of the financing of medical care. The legislative proposals through the early and middle 1950's ranged from the perennial reintroduction of the Wagner-Murray-Dingell type of compulsory national health insurance for the entire population to programs for the subsidization of private health-insurance plans. Although none of them became law, they provided a backdrop of experience with the issue for the public and Congressional debates of the late 1950's and early 1960's.

The Forand Bill

From 1957 on, Democratic Representative Aime J. Forand of Rhode Island introduced versions of what came to be known as the Forand bill. As a social-security measure, it was referred to the Committee on Ways and Means. Congress operates largely through its committees. Indeed, it has been said that the Congress is really a collection of largely independent committees, which meet together occasionally to ratify one another's actions. Both houses, and particularly the House of Representatives, rarely act on legislation that has not been approved by the appropriate committee. Most of the bills that are introduced in Congress never emerge from committee. If a bill is to emerge, or at least to receive serious consideration, the committee will normally hold a public hearing on it. In 1958 the Ways and Means Committee held hearings on various bills amending the Social Security Act, including the Forand bill. The bill was not reported out of the Ways and Means Committee, but it did provoke the beginning of the present controversy about medical care for the aged. The principal interest group in favor of the Forand bill was the AFL-CIO. The American Medical Association, the American Dental Association, the American Hospital Association, and the American Nursing Home Association formed a joint council to encourage the writing of private health insurance for the aged.[f] On the floor of the Senate,

---

[f] *Congressional Quarterly Almanac,* 1958, p. 321.

Wayne Morse of Oregon moved an amendment to the social-security bill which would have provided for health insurance. It failed by voice vote on August 16, 1958.

Not until 1959, when Forand reintroduced his proposal, did health care for the aged begin to become a significant political issue. The Ways and Means Committee held five days of hearings on it in July, at which HEW Secretary Arthur Flemming indi-

---

SUMMARY 1: Forand Bill (H.R. 4700, 86th Congress)

The principal features of this bill were as follows:

Eligibility. Included all persons 65 or over who were eligible for OASI benefits, even if employed and therefore not receiving those benefits; excluded persons receiving old-age assistance.

Benefits. *Hospitalization:* 60 days per year.

Nursing homes: 120 days per year or 2 days for each unused hospital day; available only upon transfer from hospital.

Home health services: None.

Surgeons' fees: Full payment.

Laboratory and X-ray services: Full payment for hospital inpatients; no coverage for outpatients.

Drugs: Full payment for hospital inpatients; no coverage for outpatients.

Method of financing. Additional social-security tax of ¼ of 1 per cent of first $4,800 of wages to be paid by employee, and equal amount by employer; self-employed persons were to pay ⅜ of 1 per cent of first $4,800 of earnings.

---

cated the Administration's strong opposition to the compulsory social-insurance method of financing. Recognizing that "a satisfactory solution to the problem of paying for adequate medical care for the aged will become more, rather than less important," Secretary Flemming went on to outline the Administration's objections to the Forand bill's proposed solution. He pointed out that, in his belief,

enactment of a compulsory hospitalization insurance law would represent an irreversible decision to abandon voluntary insurance for the aged in the hospital field and would probably mark the beginning of the end of voluntary insurance for the aged in the health field generally. The pattern of health coverage of the aged would . . .

become frozen in a vast and uniform governmental system [involving] governmental intervention into arrangements that on the whole are better left within the framework of nongovernmental action.

Flemming was joined in his opposition by representatives of the medical profession, of business groups, and of the insurance industry. Some of the opposition were opposed to any federal action whatsoever, while others were opposed only to federal action through the social-security system. Those favoring the Forand bill were representatives of organized labor, social workers, and prepaid group medical-care plans, together with the American Nurses Association and some rebel physicians' groups. After conclusion of the hearings, further action was put off until the next session of Congress in 1960. Meanwhile, the medical profession began to survey its chances of blocking the Forand measure in the Ways and Means Committee.[g]

1960: Proposals and Politics

The several major legislative proposals that emerged in 1960 centered primarily around three basic positions. The first was that embodied in the Forand bill, which would have financed hospitalization, surgical, and other medical-care benefits by means of a $\frac{1}{4}$ of 1 per cent increase in the social-security tax paid by workers and a similar increase in the matching tax paid by their employers.[h] Eligible for benefits would be those eligible for existing OASDI benefits. Variations on this approach were introduced by several Democratic Congressmen and Senators, all retaining the basic social-security approach to financing; eligibility and benefits varied among the proposals.

The second approach was embodied in the Javits proposal and in the Eisenhower Administration's recommendations. The Javits bill would have authorized federal grants to states which helped subsidize the cost of health insurance for those 65 or over. Participating states would either set up an insurance carrier for the purpose or contract with private carriers to supply health insurance. Individual participation would be voluntary, and premiums would

---

[g] See "The Forand Bill: The Inside Story on Its Chances."

[h] All references to the rate of social-security taxation are to the rate paid by the employee or the employer, rather than to the sum of the two.

vary with income. The difference between premiums and cost would have been made up by the states, while the federal government would reimburse the states in shares ranging from one-third to three-quarters. The state plans would have to offer a choice between cash benefits or payment for specific services regardless of cost ("service benefits"). The Administration offered no proposal in 1959 and early 1960. Then on May 4, 1960, Secretary Flemming presented an Administration program that was also based on federal grants to the states, but which would have restricted eligibility to those with less than a certain income.

The third approach was embodied in the legislative result of the second session of the 86th Congress (1960), the Kerr-Mills Act. This Act followed neither of the two basic lines discussed above, but rather was an extension of public assistance. It satisfied neither the liberal Democratic supporters of the Forand bill nor the moderate and liberal Republican supporters of voluntary health insurance. It was the product of a struggle, resulting in a stalemate for some of the political actors and in a major victory for others, which involved four kinds of politics:

1. That created by the forthcoming 1960 Presidential and Congressional campaigns. The prospects and plans of each of the Presidential aspirants—Richard Nixon, John Kennedy, Lyndon Johnson, Hubert Humphrey, and Stuart Symington—influenced both their strategies and their positions.

2. That within the Eisenhower Administration itself. Within the Administration were moderate and liberal viewpoints as well as more conservative ones. Internal disagreements were the source of the Administration's slowness in joining battle and its seeming indecisiveness once it did formulate its own proposals. Vice-President Nixon's Presidential hopes were important to these maneuvers within the Administration; and the President's power to veto legislation was influential in determining Congressional action—especially among moderates of both parties.

3. That of pressure-group action. The two major organizations in the struggle—the AFL-CIO supporting the Forand bill, and the AMA opposing it—attempted to, and did, exert great pressure on Congressmen and Senators; they also acted to gain mass support

for their positions, with the hope of turning this support into political pressure on Congress.

4. That of the Congress itself. Within both houses, certain Representatives and Senators, powerful through committee chairmanships and/or through their influence among their colleagues, were the ultimately decisive factors in producing or frustrating legislation.

The first two kinds of politics underlay the confusing series of public statements begun in February by President Eisenhower and HEW Secretary Flemming. On February 3, 1960, the President said the Administration was considering raising the OASDI payroll tax by 1/4 of 1 per cent to provide health care for the aged, especially for catastrophic illness, but he did not indicate that any conclusions had been reached, and nothing further was ever heard from the Administration about this suggestion. The proposal had been made at the urging of Vice-President Nixon, who felt the need for some Administration plan that he could use to counter Democratic proposals in the Presidential election in which he hoped and expected to be the Republican candidate. Though not enthusiastic, Eisenhower was allowing Nixon "full scope for his own views in the coming campaign." The situation was complicated by Flemming's search—as an ally of Nixon's against the more conservative of the GOP leaders—for a plan acceptable to Budget Bureau Director Maurice Stans and Secretary of the Treasury Robert Anderson.[1]

The day after President Eisenhower made this statement about the Administration's interest in using the payroll tax to finance health care for the aged, Secretary Flemming reemphasized the Administration's opposition to the Forand bill's compulsory, government-operated features. He also outlined the Administration's disapproval of two alternatives frequently suggested. Increasing public-assistance grants to the states for medical care would cost too much, he said, and would require a "means test." He also spoke of the "admitted failure" of voluntary health-insurance plans to cover catastrophic illness.

Fast on the heels of these statements a major boost for the social-

---

[1] *The New York Times*, February 21, 1960, and March 18, 1960.

security approach was provided by the report of the Special Sub-committee on Problems of the Aged and Aging of the Senate Committee on Labor and Public Welfare. This subcommittee, chaired by Pat McNamara, Michigan Democrat, had been established early in 1959 to conduct a study of the major problems of the aged. It held hearings in seven communities throughout the country and its activity was one of the major contributions to public consciousness of the health problems of the aged. The subcommittee report (released on February 23, 1960, but reported in *The New York Times* of February 9, 1960) strongly urged social-security financing of medical care for the aged. The subcommittee's Republican members, Senators Barry Goldwater of Arizona and Everett Dirksen of Illinois, dissented, warning against disrupting traditional American medical practice.

In the House, the Ways and Means Committee went into executive (closed) session on March 14 to consider the social-security amendments of 1960, and there it stayed until June 13. Medical care for the aged was the major item of debate. Speaking to the committee on March 23, Secretary Flemming made it quite clear that the Administration would oppose any compulsory health program that would, in his opinion, "stifle private initiative." He said that the Administration was still studying alternative proposals.

The day before his statement to the committee, Flemming had been defeated at a White House meeting with the President and Republican Congressional leadership. *The New York Times* of March 23 reported on this meeting, at which Flemming could not get support from the President for a "subsidized system of voluntary health insurance for the aged." The President sided with Congressional leaders who called for further study. Although Nixon again stated he was against a "negative approach," he was "agreeable to reasonable delay." Reports of this meeting led Senator McNamara to claim that Flemming's statement to the Ways and Means Committee showed he had been "effectively stymied" by the "Republican high command." At this point, reports seemed to indicate that the issue would die until after the 1960 campaign.[j]

However, another set of pressures on the Congress got under

---

[j] *The New York Times,* March 25-27, 1960.

way at that time. On March 23 in New York City, 6,000 people attended a rally for the Forand bill—the start of similar activity across the nation. Forand himself had begun circulating a petition to discharge his bill from the Ways and Means Committee—a procedure he never completed. And on March 27, the whole set of Democratic Presidential hopefuls endorsed the Forand bill's principles at a rally in Detroit of 12,000 retired members of the United Automobile Workers.

Impatient with the Administration's delay, three liberal Republican Senators, seemingly in opposition to the President's wishes, announced that they were drafting a voluntary program involving federal matching grants to states and financed out of general revenues. These Senators were Javits of New York, Hugh Scott of Pennsylvania, and John Sherman Cooper of Kentucky. The bill, known as the Javits bill (S. 3350), was introduced on April 7 without Administration backing. On April 11, Secretary Flemming said the bill was a "step in the right direction" but did not proffer Administration support. This softening of Administration resistance to a large-scale federal program was reported by *The New York Times* of April 6 to be the result of a White House meeting on the preceding day. At that meeting, the combination of Vice-President Nixon's presence (he had been away at the time of the meeting on March 22) and the impending Javits action convinced the Republican leadership of the necessity of presenting some Administration alternative to the Forand bill, rather than trying to fight something with nothing. New York Governor Nelson Rockefeller's announced support of health insurance through social security may also have been on their minds, as he was the liberal Republican challenger to Nixon for the Presidential nomination.

But the Forand bill's chances had again become dim. The Ways and Means Committee had rejected it 17-8 on March 31. The committee had also rejected, by a vote of 16-9, a compromise which included only hospitalization and nursing-home care. Moreover, there was speculation about the prospects of a Presidential veto of Forand-type legislation (which President Eisenhower had called a "definite step toward socialized medicine").[k]

ᵏ *Congressional Quarterly Almanac*, 1960, p. 154.

The Democratic leadership now began the hunt for votes which was to characterize its operations for the next five years. House Speaker Sam Rayburn and Senate Majority Leader Lyndon Johnson combined forces to convince the Ways and Means Committee —that is, to convince its chairman, Wilbur Mills of Arkansas—to accept a more limited bill which would still retain the social-security financing mechanism. Because of his post as chairman of the Ways and Means Committee, Mills' opposition was the greatest barrier faced by supporters of Forand-type legislation.

The power of Congressional committees is, for the most part, concentrated in the hands of the committee chairmen. The chairman is the member of the majority party in his house who is senior in terms of service on the committee. Chairmen are always men of great influence among their colleagues, and especially their committee colleagues. This stems, first, from the prerogatives that accompany the chairmanship. Although there is some variation among committees, a committee chairman has the primary voice in determining when and if the committee shall meet and what it will do when it does meet. He can keep a bill in committee if he wants it killed; he and the ranking minority member of his committee usually control access to the floor when a bill gets there; when he is friendly to a Congressman, he can be instrumental in getting favors written into bills which affect that Congressman's district. Second, as a senior member of his committee and of Congress, a committee chairman possesses expertise, both on specific legislation and as a parliamentarian, which assures his counsel of a hearing and usually of adherence.

Wilbur Mills, chairman of one of the House's most powerful and prestigious committees, is one of the most powerful men in Congress. Johnson and Rayburn calculated—correctly—that if they could get his support for a compromise, he could get committee votes to report out the bill and floor votes for its passage. Committing themselves to the OASDI mechanism, they offered a plan to limit benefits to hospital and nursing-home care and not medical or surgical expenses. According to numerous sources,[1] this effort was an attempt on Rayburn's part to boost the chances

---

[1] See, for example, *The New York Times*, April 17, 1960, and *Social Legislation Information Service*, April 25, 1960.

of fellow-Texan Johnson for the Presidential nomination at the coming Democratic Convention.

On April 20, *The New York Times* reported that Chairman Mills was working for the Rayburn-Johnson plan and was attempting to win over the five other Democrats who had joined him in defeating a similar proposal in committee. At a meeting of the five and himself, the *Times* of April 21 reported, Mills had moved to an "option" plan, by which beneficiaries could get either insurance or an increase in cash benefits to help pay for private health insurance. AMA President Louis Orr opposed a compromise of this kind. Secretary Flemming rejected such a proposal in a closed session with the Ways and Means Committee, and a Presidential veto of a bill embodying such a plan was considered "not unlikely." However, the Democrats were willing, it was rumored, to use such a veto as an issue in the fall campaign.[m]

Finally, on May 4, 1960, the Administration revealed its proposal for meeting the health needs of the aged. Using the term "medicare" for the first time in this context, Secretary Flemming proposed a system of federal grants to the states to help finance two alternatives to be offered potential subscribers. Eligible were only those 65 and over who did not pay an income tax in the preceding year or whose total income, including OASI benefits, railroad retirement, and veteran's pensions, did not exceed $2,500 ($3,800 for a couple). The first $250 ($400 for a couple) of medical expenses would not be covered. Beyond that, the program would pay 80 per cent of the cost of hospital care up to 180 days, nursing-home and home-care services, surgery, diagnostic tests (up to $200), physicians' and dentists' services, prescribed drugs (up to $350), and auxiliary services. In lieu of this program, eligible persons could elect to have the government pay 50 per cent of the cost of a private major-medical insurance policy (up to $60 a year). Participants would pay an annual fee of $24 and the federal government would reimburse the states for from one-third to two-thirds of the remaining costs.

Neither the supporters nor the major opponents of the Forand bill were favorably inclined toward the Administration's proposal.

---

[m] *The New York Times,* April 17, 1960.

Liberals and conservatives alike said it would cost too much; and liberals disliked the means test. Governor Rockefeller criticized it along these lines and called for a system containing an option, but retaining social-security financing.

Two days later, Senator McNamara, for himself and eighteen other Democratic senators, introduced a bill (S. 3503) based on the social-insurance mode of financing, but containing features designed to overcome some of the Republican objections to the Forand bill. Chief among these objections was the argument that the Forand bill would exclude that quarter of the aged population who were not covered by OASDI, while at the same time including employed persons who were eligible for social security, but who were presumably less needy financially because they were still working. McNamara's bill offered coverage to all retired aged, with the non-OASDI eligibles to be financed from general revenues. Vice-President Nixon was among those who had criticized the Forand bill because it left out those not covered by OASDI. Senator McNamara, because of the inclusion of *all* retired aged in his bill, challenged the Vice-President to support it.

The Kerr-Mills Bill Emerges

As the legislative proposals proliferated in the Senate, the Ways and Means Committee continued its closed sessions in an attempt to reach some sort of compromise. Hard on the heels of a rally in New York City in May of 12,000 persons for Forand-type legislation, *The New York Times* reported that the Ways and Means Committee was still split among three groups: Democrats for the Forand bill; Republicans for a proposal similar to the Administration's; and Southern Democrats, who were against any legislation at this time. Mills, it was reported, had been given a free hand by Rayburn, but was not committed to the Forand bill or to the social-insurance approach. At the end of May, he gave the committee a proposal to establish a system of federal grants to the states to pay part of the cost of medical services for the needy aged. Each state would decide whether to participate and would determine standards of eligibility and types of services to be provided, within broad limits. The federal share of costs would be between 50 and 65 per cent. In addition, federal participation in existing public-assistance medical care would be increased somewhat.

On June 13, Ways and Means reported out H.R. 12580, a bill containing a number of amendments to the Social Security Act, including Congressman Mills' medical-care proposal. H.R. 12580 came before the House under a closed rule which permitted no amendments from the floor, as is customary for social-security and tax legislation. It was debated on June 22 and passed the next day by a vote of 381-23.

With this House-passed legislation before the Senate's Finance Committee, the focus of the politics of financing medical care for the aged shifted to the Senate. Another reason for this shift of focus was the presence of all the Democratic Presidential aspirants, as well as Vice-President Nixon, in the Senate, where most were principals in the fight.

Although Rayburn had failed with Mills in the House, liberals were counting on Majority Leader Johnson to get Forand-type legislation passed by the Senate. A conference committee would then be charged with reaching a compromise between the House and Senate bills; it was the liberals' hope that Mills' vote in the conference committee could be won over at that time. At this point Mills' chief ally in the Senate, Robert Kerr of Oklahoma, became a crucial figure. Although not chairman of the Senate Finance Committee, Kerr was the next-ranking Democratic member, and he had enormous prestige and power in the Senate. According to *The New York Times* of June 24, Johnson had unsuccessfully attempted to get Kerr and Clinton Anderson of New Mexico to draft a compromise for the Finance Committee. As Congress recessed for the party conventions, Anderson, who was a strong supporter of the social-security approach, introduced a plan before the Finance Committee which included that mechanism, but with more moderate coverage than either the Forand or McNamara bills. Anderson's plan was said to have Johnson's tacit support.[n] On the same day, the Governor's Conference voted 30-13

---

[n] *The New York Times,* June 30, 1960.

for a resolution supporting the social-security approach; and a day later, Republican Senator Leverett Saltonstall introduced the Administration proposals as S. 3784. Of all these proposals, Anderson's became the center of debate.

On July 12, the Democratic National Convention adopted its platform statement, calling for health care for the aged financed through the social-security system, and without a means-test requirement. The Republicans, on July 17, called for health care for the aged through a "contributory system," thereby straddling the conflict between Rockefeller and the Administration.

In August, Congress resumed its deliberations. The liberal Democrats had first opposed the rump August session, believing—with some accuracy—that it was an attempt by Johnson and Rayburn to strengthen Johnson's Presidential appeal at the Democratic convention. As things turned out, Republican Senator Thruston Morton of Kentucky had predicted most accurately what would happen: Johnson accepted the Vice-Presidential nomination, and the Kennedy-Johnson team returned to Capitol Hill with Johnson attempting to produce a Democratic record they could campaign on, while Kennedy launched his Presidential electioneering. However, legislative results were minimal, both on medical care and on other issues.

On August 13, the Senate Finance Committee defeated the Anderson proposal, despite pressure from the Democratic leadership and Presidential nominee Kennedy, and approved a proposal by Senator Kerr that was similar to the House bill. The medical-care provisions approved by the Senate Finance Committee, by a 12-5 vote, were similar to those drafted by Mills, though with more liberal provisions for the matching formulas in federal-state grants. Observers in Washington reported that the plan had had President Eisenhower's express backing; supporting materials and estimates that were not even available to Finance Committee Republicans were said to have been made available to Kerr by HEW. Of the six Democrats who supported the plan, four—Byrd (Virginia), Smathers (Florida), Long (Louisiana), and Talmadge (Georgia)—were Southerners, who joined with the six Republicans to pass the bill. Five senators voted against it, saying they would take the fight for social-security financing to the floor.

The AMA quickly supported the Kerr-Mills proposal; Eisenhower reiterated his opposition to a compulsory system if one were enacted on the Senate floor, but the possibility of a veto was seen by the liberals as a good campaign issue. AFL-CIO President George Meany said the labor movement would settle for nothing less than the social-security approach. And on August 17, Kennedy and Anderson announced they planned to cosponsor and fight for an amendment embodying various compromises in coverage, but financed through the social-security payroll tax.

After the Finance Committee had reported to the Senate, the liberal and moderate Republicans attempted again to take what Vice-President Nixon had called a "positive approach." A compromise between the Javits and Administration bills was introduced by the New York Senator and eight other Republicans, and was supported by Nixon and Flemming.

This Javits amendment never was a real political alternative and was beaten 67-28 on August 23 by a party-line vote joining liberal and conservative Democrats against it. The defeat, however, forced the liberal Republican sponsors to choose sides in the vote on the Anderson-Kennedy amendment. In the final Senate vote on that amendment, only one Republican, Case of New Jersey, joined with the supporters of social-security financing; it was defeated 51-44. Of the 51 votes against, 19 were Democrats, 32 Republicans. Of the 19 Democrats voting against, only 3 were from non-Southern states. These were Frear of Delaware, and Kerr and Monroney of Oklahoma.

The final result passed the Senate 91-2. The conference-committee report was accepted by the House on August 26 by a vote of 369-17, and by the Senate 74-11 on August 29. The Kerr-Mills proposal became law on September 13, when President Eisenhower signed it without comment. Both Vice-President Nixon and Senator Kennedy were disappointed. Nixon thought the Kerr-Mills Act was "most inadequate";[o] Kennedy had insisted all along that only the social-security method of financing was sound. Governor Nelson Rockefeller did "not regard it as any real solution to the great human problem."[p]

[o] *The New York Times,* September 25, 1960.
[p] *The New York Times,* September 20, 1960.

New Frontiers for the Aged

In November 1960, Senator John F. Kennedy was elected President by the narrowest of margins. Pledged to take America to new frontiers, he included medical care as one of them, and the early days of the Kennedy Administration saw "medicare" a prominent issue.

The opening act of the 1961 drama was the White House Conference on Aging, held by the lame-duck Eisenhower Administration during the second week in January. Before the conference convened, social-security expert Wilbur Cohen, then Professor of Public Welfare Administration at the University of Michigan and later to become Assistant Secretary for Legislation of Health, Education, and Welfare, wrote conference chairman Robert Keane that he would not participate. He claimed that the conference had been stacked by the AMA and its allies in the insurance industry in order to reject all endorsement of social-security financing of health care for the elderly. The medical profession was heavily represented in the Income Maintenance Section of the conference, where the issue would arise; about half of the medical-care work group consisted of representatives of the medical profession and the insurance industry. *The New York Times* of January 9 reported the conference as an "immense battleground" for the issue.

Cohen and other Forand-bill supporters were to be surprised. On January 10, Marion B. Folsom, Flemming's predecessor as Eisenhower's HEW Secretary, advocated the social-security system as the appropriate financing mechanism for health care for the aged. Folsom's reputation and experience as an expert on social security and pension plans, and his status as a prominent business executive, lent added weight to his words. Then, that night, Arthur Larson, Under Secretary of Labor and speech writer in the Eisenhower Administration, also spoke in favor of the social-security approach. He, too, was known as an expert in the field. With two such prestigious Republicans for it, the social-security approach received serious consideration from many who had previously dismissed it, and was endorsed 97-77 by the Income Maintenance Section.[q] The conference statement that the social-security

---

[q] For a discussion of the conference action on financing medical care for the aged, see "Aging Parley Bows to Social Security," *Washington Post,* January 13, 1961.

mechanism should be the basic means of financing health care for the aged was backed up by President Kennedy's task-force report on the issue, which came to the same conclusions.

In his message to Congress on February 9, 1961, John Kennedy, now President of the United States, renewed his attempt to secure social-security financing for medical care for the aged. His pro-

SUMMARY 2: 1961 King-Anderson Bill
(H.R. 4222 and S. 909, 87th Congress)

This bill differed from the Forand bill (H.R. 4700, 86th Congress) in the following respects:

Eligibility. Also covered persons eligible for railroad-retirement benefits.

Benefits. *Hospitalization:* Period of insurance changed from year to "benefit period": to start first day person received hospital benefits and end 90 days after he ceased being inpatient at hospital or nursing home. ◆ Provided 90 days of hospitalization per benefit period. ◆ Included deductible of $10 daily for first 9 days of hospitalization, with minimum deductible of $20.

Nursing homes: 120 days per benefit period plus extra 2 days for each unused hospital day; total per benefit period not to exceed 180 days; available only upon transfer from hospital (as under Forand).

Home health services: Intermittent nursing care, therapy, and homemaker services for up to 240 visits per year.

Surgeons' fees: None.

Laboratory and X-ray services: Full payment for hospital inpatients (as under Forand); covered outpatient services with deductible of $20 for each diagnostic study.

Method of financing. Taxable earnings base increased from $4,800 to $5,000.

posal was more limited than either the Forand bill or his own bill of the preceding year, and the President was criticized for this watering-down by many supporters of the social-security approach. Their criticism was to be repeated by supporters of other social legislation in the ensuing years of the Kennedy Presidency: the President, they said, was too eager to compromise with the opposition. He watered down his proposals in the vain hope of placating the opposition; whereas if he were to fight vigorously for all that he (or, perhaps more accurately, his liberal critics) wanted, he might have more success.

Wilbur Mills, in contrast, had no comment on the President's recommendations, but refused to introduce the Administration bill, even as a courtesy to the Democratic leadership. The bill was introduced in the House as H.R. 4222 on February 13 by Representative Cecil King of California, and in the Senate as S. 909 by Senator Anderson. It differed from the preceding year's Forand bill primarily in that it excluded surgeons' fees and required that beneficiaries pay $10 a day for their first 9 days of hospitalization. Only OASDI eligibles were covered, working or not. H.R. 4222 was referred to the Ways and Means Committee, and Senate action waited on that committee.

Outside the halls of Congress, the grass-roots campaign for and against the social-security approach continued. On February 15, *The New York Times* reported a new AMA campaign against the King-Anderson bill. As the year wore on, with the bill still awaiting Ways and Means action, opinion polls indicated a national majority for the social-security approach.[r]

Finally, at the end of July, the Ways and Means Committee held hearings on H.R. 4222. The hearings lasted from July 24 to August 4, but the committee did not report out a bill. The Administration didn't press the committee very hard to do so, as the President was more concerned about the antirecession measures and tax revisions he had recommended to Congress, many of which were also in the hands of the Ways and Means Committee. That so much of his program was before Ways and Means made it difficult for the President to press the committee to take action on financing medical care, a matter he considered of lower priority. Moreover, the HEW staff, which would have to carry the ball for the Administration on medicare, was busy fighting and losing the battle for federal aid to education.

Other reasons for Administration hesitancy became apparent later. King-Anderson proponents were not sure they had enough votes on the House floor to pass the bill if it were reported out of committee. This insecurity was attributed partly to the fact that

[r] *The New York Times,* April 30, 1961.

visible public support for the measure seemed to be decreasing from the peak it had reached early in 1960. Also, Chairman Mills, who did not support King-Anderson, was influential beyond his own committee. With the situation so close in the House, the Senate Democratic leadership stopped a move to add medicare to a House-passed bill in the Senate. For this strategy to succeed, the House Rules Committee would have had to permit a conference to compromise the House and Senate versions. The results of the conference would have had to be successful, and the conference report would then have had to be passed by the House. All this was quite doubtful, especially because the House was jealous of its constitutional prerogative in initiating tax measures. With the vote as close as it seemed, the Administration did not choose such a risky procedure.[s] Instead, on August 31, President Kennedy and HEW Secretary Ribicoff pledged to fight "across the land" for the bill's passage at the next session. The hope was that election-year pressures would get the bill through. If not, then it would at least be an issue in the election.

1962: House Inaction and Senate Action

However, in order for the bill to get through, or to fail of passage and be used as an issue, it had to be gotten out onto the floor. From January to June of 1962 the legislative controversy over medical aid for the aged was once again focused on the Ways and Means Committee. With a majority of the committee against the King-Anderson bill, both the Administration and the press turned their attention to committee members who might be induced either to support a compromise or to vote to allow the bill to reach the floor of the House.

On January 31, anticipating the failure of that strategy, Senator Anderson moved, at a meeting of the Senate Finance Committee, that hearings on his bill (S. 909) be held by April 1, regardless of Ways and Means action. Anderson's motion was defeated, 10-7.

In the meantime, the American Hospital Association, which had been an opponent of social-security financing, changed its position. It announced that the means of financing a government hospital-insurance program were not its concern, so long as the

---

[s] See *The New York Times,* September 1, 1961.

federal government did not administer the program, but rather placed its operation in the hands of a private organization, such as Blue Cross. With the AHA ambivalent and pressure for the King-Anderson bill coming from organizations like the 300,000-member National Council of Senior Citizens for Health Care Through Social Security (founded by retired Representative Forand), the medical profession continued to organize politically at the local level in order to sway the votes of Congressmen then in office and to influence the elections of 1962.

The American Medical Political Action Committee (AMPAC) was founded to devote research and financial resources to the support of candidates who shared the medical profession's view of King-Anderson and similar proposals. For tax purposes, it was independent of the AMA, but the overlap of leadership and point of view made it clearly a political-action extension of that organization. In each state, HOPE (Health Organization for Political Education) groups were formed with an organizational perspective extending to the precinct level; the movement was spearheaded by the wives of medical doctors, and the AFL-CIO's Committee on Political Education was the model used. As the Congressional session drew on to summer, Drew Pearson reported that AMPAC and the state medical organizations contributed heavily—both financially and in human resources—in the primary campaigns of key Congressmen on the Ways and Means Committee.

Both Democrats and Republicans realized that even if Ways and Means kept the bill in committee, the issue would loom large in the 1962 campaign. There were two principal Republican responses. On March 28, Representative Frank Bow of Ohio introduced H.R. 10981, which would have granted a tax credit of up to $125 to persons aged 65 or over who purchased private health insurance. Persons who did not pay a federal income tax would receive a grant of $125 from the federal government toward the cost of private health insurance; those who paid a federal income tax of less than $125 would get a grant of the difference between the amount of tax that was due and $125.

The Bow proposal was immediately supported by Representative William Miller of New York, the Republican National Chairman. Miller sent letters to House Republicans urging their support for the bill as a solution to the inadequacies of the Kerr-Mills Act. Miller's action was little appreciated by the House Republican leadership, which felt that he had undercut their argument that no additional legislation was necessary. This was not a split between liberal and conservative Republicans. Miller, Bow, and House Republican leader Charles Halleck were all conservatives. Among the supporters of the Bow measure was Edgar Hiestand, one of the two members of the House of Representatives who admitted to being members of the John Birch Society. The controversy over the Bow proposal was, rather, a manifestation of the difference in orientation between the GOP's national leadership and its Congressional leadership. The former is somewhat more attuned to general public demand and national issues, while the latter is more narrowly local in orientation, as well as being more responsive to rural pressures and outlook.[t]

The second Republican alternative was proposed by the liberal Republicans. Representative John Lindsay of New York, acting in part as Governor Rockefeller's spokesman, introduced H.R. 11253, which would have used social-security financing, but would also have offered, to those who did not want to participate, an option of receiving cash benefits they could use to pay private health-insurance premiums. There were a number of other Republican proposals, all of which encouraged King-Anderson supporters, who considered the Republican attempts to find alternatives as evidence that their program was likely to pass.

Meanwhile, King-Anderson supporters were attempting to formulate a compromise both to attract Republican votes and to get Ways and Means approval. The compromise was reportedly to be financed through social security, without any option, and was to have an emphasis on catastrophic illness.[u] Through the beginning of May, the prospects of a Ways and Means majority report containing the social-security approach seemed good; on May 8, President Kennedy told the United Automobile Workers conven-

---

[t] For a discussion of the Republican split over the Bow proposal, see "GOP Leaders in House Split in Fight Against Kennedy Medical Plan," *The Wall Street Journal*, April 11, 1962.

[u] For discussions of possible compromise strategies, see "Aged Care Bills Chances Change From Bad to Good," *The New York Times*, April 15, 1962, and "Kennedy Backers Have Compromise Medical Aid Plan," *The Wall Street Journal*, May 4, 1962.

tion that his hospitalization-insurance program would be enacted that year. Soon afterward, however, these prospects once again died out.

On May 26, *The New York Times* told of the 13-12 defeat of a compromise put before the Ways and Means Committee. In June, only 10 sure votes for King-Anderson could be counted on in the committee. The Administration was reluctant, as in 1960, to push Chairman Mills too hard, as he had served well on the President's top-priority Trade Expansion Act. HEW Secretary Abraham Ribicoff continued to seek a compromise plan; at a private White House meeting the idea of administration by a private group was brought out. But Mills once more put it off for the next year, with reform of his own Kerr-Mills Act a part of his program.

In this period the flow of public opinion was important. On May 20, President Kennedy had spoken to a mass rally at New York's Madison Square Garden. This was one of 32 rallies across the country linked by closed-circuit television. The television stations carried the President's talk as a "public service." The next day the AMA paid for a nationwide television hook-up to answer the President. AMA President Leonard Larson, together with one of the Association's most articulate spokesmen, Dr. Edward Annis, spoke—from a symbolically empty Madison Square Garden—of the doctors' hard-pressed fight to get their point of view across. The AMA apparently had the best of the exchange, as support for King-Anderson seems to have fallen off thereafter.ᵛ By late June, the program was killed for the year, as far as the Ways and Means Committee was concerned.

As failure in Ways and Means became clear, the "Senate-first" tactic began. The public-welfare bill, despite Secretary Ribicoff's misgivings, was chosen as the vehicle. Though a fight for medicare as an amendment to the welfare bill entailed the risk of delaying the bill or even jeopardizing its passage, the liberals stuck with their choice. This was decisive—a decisive error.

The amendment was formulated on the initiative of Democratic whip Hubert Humphrey of Minnesota. Anderson and Humphrey, seeking from 6 to 10 Republican votes, compromised with the

---

ᵛ *The Wall Street Journal,* June 11, 1962.

liberal Republicans by covering persons not eligible for OASDI or railroad-retirement payments; by providing an option for private insurance; by permitting the use of private organizations to administer the system; by establishing a special Health Insurance Trust Fund into which social-security taxes for health care were to be paid; and by providing additional assurances against federal control over the providers of medical services.ʷ

On June 29, Anderson and 23 other sponsors introduced his amendment. The Republican cosponsors were Jacob Javits, John Sherman Cooper, Kenneth Keating, Clifford Case, and minority whip Thomas Kuchel of California. Though Senate approval was predicted, little chance was seen for ultimate passage. First, the House Rules Committee was not likely to grant a rule permitting a House-Senate conference. Second, since the conferees would have been the senior members of the Ways and Means and Finance Committees, there would not have been many supporters of the social-security approach among them.

Meanwhile, the summer of 1962 had brought to public and Congressional attention the possibility that American physicians would refuse to treat patients under the King-Anderson bill if it were enacted. In May, 44 physicians on the staff of a hospital in Point Pleasant, New Jersey, had signed a statement that they would "refuse to participate in the care of patients under the King-Anderson bill or similar legislation." The doctors stated that they would continue to treat patients who paid their own bills or whose bills were paid by insurance and that they would treat indigent patients free of charge. The King-Anderson bill, of course, did not cover doctors' fees. The physicians' plan was to make it impossible for their hospital to render care under King-Anderson; if enough hospitals were in this position, the program would not be able to operate. Indeed, as a result of the doctors' action, the hospital trustees had informally declared that, since the hospital staff would not participate, the hospital would not be able to provide care under the King-Anderson bill if it were enacted. The Point Pleasant idea received support from doctors elsewhere in New Jersey and in the United States, and a bill was introduced in the

---

ʷ More information about the contents of this amendment and of others offered in this Senate debate may be found in Cohen and Ball's 1962 article.

New Jersey Legislature that would make it illegal to refuse to treat a patient solely because of the method by which he proposed to pay for his medical care.

On July 1, the Canadian province of Saskatchewan put into effect a system under which the government would pay the medical bills for the entire population. The Saskatchewan medical

SUMMARY 3: Anderson-Javits Bill (S. 3565, 87th Congress)

This bill differed from the 1961 King-Anderson bill (H.R. 4222 and S. 909, 87th Congress) in the following respects:

Eligibility. Also covered persons not eligible for OASI or railroad-retirement benefits, but who reached 65 before 1967, or who reached 65 in 1967 or later and had three quarters of OASI coverage for each year after 1965 and before they reached 65.

Benefits. Offered choice between federal insurance which provided following benefits or private insurance which included them.

Hospitalization: Private insurance compelled to offer choice between 90 days per benefit period with deductible of $10 daily for first 9 days (minimum deductible of $20) or 45 days per benefit period with no deductible. No choice offered in federal insurance, which remained the same as under King-Anderson. ◆ Definition of "benefit period" changed: to start first day person received hospital benefits and end after he had not been an inpatient for 90 days out of any period of 180 days. (In other words, beneficiary no longer had to be out of hospital or nursing home for 90 *consecutive* days in order to begin new benefit period, but merely 90 days out of any 180-day period.)

Nursing homes: Home had to be affiliated with hospital. HEW Secretary was required to study ways of increasing availability of skilled nursing homes and could authorize participation of nursing homes not affiliated with hospitals if they were operated under conditions assuring good-quality care—provided such action did not create or increase actuarial imbalance in hospital-insurance trust fund.

Laboratory and X-ray services: Covered hospital outpatients with deductible of $20 for services furnished within 30-day period.

Method of financing. For OASI eligibles: financing was the same as under King-Anderson, except that taxable earnings base increased to $5,200. ◆ For non-OASI eligibles: financed from general federal revenues. ◆ Established separate hospital-insurance trust fund. ◆ Costs incurred by state agencies for planning and other coordination attributable to program to be shared by federal government.

Administration. Limited HEW Secretary's authority for prescribing conditions for hospital participation in addition to those in bill: these conditions could not be more strict than those required for accreditation by Joint Commission on Accreditation of Hospitals. ◆ Required HEW Secretary to assist providers of medical care, insurance carriers, and other public and private organizations to develop and make available supplementary private insurance for aged. ◆ Authorized providers of medical care to designate organization of their own choice to act as intermediary in financial dealings with government.

profession responded by refusing to provide medical care except at designated emergency-treatment centers. Although the Saskatchewan legislation was starkly different from the King-Anderson bill, the possibility of similar action on the part of American physicians was called to public attention.

In late July, the Louisiana State Medical Society presented to the AMA House of Delegates a resolution that supported the plan of the Point Pleasant physicians. The House sidestepped the issue, reaffirmed its opposition to King-Anderson, and noted that the AMA's ethical code already directed physicians not to practice under conditions which interfered with their free exercise of medical judgment. This presumably left it to the individual physician to decide whether King-Anderson, if enacted, would so interfere.

As the debate continued, chances for Senate passage of the Anderson amendment dwindled. Some Senate Democrats did not like the unusual procedure, while some of the liberal Republicans were balking at the contents of the measure. On August 17, the amendment failed 52-48; 43 Democrats and 5 Republicans backed the plan, while 31 Republicans and 21 Democrats opposed it. In fact, the amendment lost because it was tied to the public-welfare bill. The crucial vote came on a motion to table the amendment. Senator Jennings Randolph of West Virginia, a strong supporter of the King-Anderson bill, voted in favor of tabling it; that is, he voted against the amendment. If he had voted against tabling it, the over-all vote before the last person voted would have been 50 votes for tabling, and 49 against; that last person was Carl Hayden of Arizona, who, because of an expected strong conservative attack in his coming attempt at reelection, had pledged his vote only if it were needed. Hayden, faced with a 50-49 tally, would have voted against tabling, thus tying the vote and thereby defeating the motion to table.

Randolph explained his vote immediately after the total had been announced.[x] He said that the attempted amendment was a "futile gesture" which could have jeopardized 12,500 West Virginia families whose relief payments had been cut off on June 31, when the programs covered by the public-welfare bill had expired. Observers added comments about his "close personal relationship with Senator Kerr. The Oklahoman campaigned personally for Mr. Randolph in 1958 and had cooperated closely with him as a fellow member of the Senate Public Works Committee."[y] There were also speculations about provisions in the welfare bill favorable to West Virginia which Kerr—its floor manager—had aided Randolph in inserting.

Two Southerners who didn't support the President, Richard Russell of Georgia and Lister Hill of Alabama, were said to have opposed the bypass of the Finance Committee because it provided a precedent for bypassing the Judiciary Committee on civil-rights legislation.[z] Only 4 Southern Democrats supported the amendment, and 10 out of 16 committee chairmen voted against it.

The 88th Congress

During the summer of 1962, the Democrats hoped to make medicare the major issue of the coming Congressional election, but during the campaign the impact of the issue became cloudy. Often it was overshadowed by local issues or confused by Republicans who had not voted for the Anderson amendment but stated that they supported medical care for the aged. George Gallup found that many voters had lost interest during the period between the bill's Senate defeat and the election.

---

[x] See the *Congressional Record,* July 17, 1962 (daily ed.), pp. 12924-12925.

[y] *The Wall Street Journal,* July 18, 1962.

[z] *The New York Times,* July 18, 1962, and *The Wall Street Journal,* February 25, 1963.

What can be said is that no Democratic incumbent who supported the Administration proposal lost; and that the Democrats reversed a 28-year trend by keeping their midterm losses negligible. In the Senate, the Democrats picked up four seats, and on the House floor, the "bare majority for the King-Anderson plan has probably increased," speculated *The New York Times.*[aa]

The King-Anderson bill that was introduced in the 88th Congress, like the 1962 Anderson-Javits amendment, provided coverage for those elderly who were not entitled to OASDI or railroad-

SUMMARY 4: 1963 King-Anderson Bill (H.R. 3920 and S. 880, 88th Congress)

This bill differed from the Anderson-Javits bill (S. 3565, 87th Congress) in the following repects:

·**Benefits.** No private-insurance option.

Hospitalization: Offered choice between 90 days with deductible of $10 daily for first 9 days (minimum deductible of $20) or 45 days with no deductible or 180 days with a deductible of average cost of 2½ days of hospital care.

Nursing homes: 180 days.

retirement benefits. Like the amendment, it permitted the use of private organizations to administer the system, established a Health Insurance Trust Fund, and provided additional assurances against federal controls. The Anderson-Javits amendment, however, had made one major change in the 1961 King-Anderson bill which did not appear in the 1963 version: the option for private insurance. In introducing the 1963 bill, Senator Anderson explained that he had dropped that option because it raised administrative difficulties while not at the same time placating the opposition to the social-security approach. Senator Javits stated his opposition to the Administration bill without the private-sector option, although he expressed the hope that he and Senator Anderson would again be able to reach a mutually satisfactory compromise.

When the 88th Congress convened in January 1963, it was faced

---

[aa] For a discussion of the role of the hospitalization-insurance issue in the 1962 election, see "Aged Care Issue Credited in Vote," *The New York Times,* November 11, 1962, and Donald B. Johnson, "The Congressional Campaign and the Off-Year Elections of 1962," in Jack W. Peltason, ed., *American Government Annual, 1963-1964* (New York: Holt, Rinehart and Winston, Inc., 1963), pp. 68-70.

with two closely connected organizational problems, both of which were related to the medical-care battle. The first of these was the size of the House Rules Committee. The second was the filling of two Democratic vacancies on the Ways and Means Committee.

Usually, when a controversial bill is reported out by the legislative committee that has been considering it, it does not go directly to the House floor. Rather, it goes to the Rules Committee, which issues a "rule," setting the procedure under which the bill will be debated. If the committee refuses to issue a rule, the bill usually dies at that point, even though a legislative committee has recommended "that it do pass." Circumventing the Rules Committee is possible, but very difficult. (Since the late 1930's, the conservative majority of the Rules Committee has used its power to block a good deal of social-welfare legislation.)

Although having their bills in the Rules Committee's power was upsetting to the liberals, House Speaker Sam Rayburn was not too concerned, because he could usually get measures in which he was really interested through the committee. Matters came to a head in the 86th Congress, and particularly in the portion of the session which followed the political conventions. The Speaker was no longer able to exercise much influence on the committee, which did not endear itself to the Democratic Presidential candidate by undercutting his campaign promises during that August session. As a result, at the opening of the 87th Congress in January 1961, the House, by a vote of 217-212, enlarged the committee to permit the addition of two Democrats who were more amenable to the desires of the party leadership.[bb] This enlargement was a temporary one, for the duration of the 87th Congress only. When the 88th Congress convened in January 1963, the President and the House

---

[bb] For a detailed study of the struggle to enlarge the committee, see William R. MacKaye, *A New Coalition Takes Control: The House Rules Committee Fight of 1961,* Eagleton Institute Case in Practical Politics #29 (New York: McGraw-Hill, Inc., 1963), or Milton C. Cummings, Jr., and Robert L. Peabody, "The Decision to Enlarge the Committee on Rules: An Analysis of the 1961 Vote," in Robert L. Peabody and Nelson W. Polsby, eds., *New Perspectives on the House of Representatives* (Chicago: Rand McNally & Company, 1963). See also H. Douglas Price, "Race, Religion, and the Rules Committee: The Kennedy Aid-to-Education Bills," in Alan Westin, ed., *The Uses of Power* (New York: Harcourt, Brace & World, Inc., 1962), and Robert L. Peabody, "The Enlarged Rules Committee," in Peabody and Polsby, cited above.

Democratic leadership fought successfully to keep the committee at its new size. This enlarged committee was essential if the President was to get his program to the floor of the House. In order to ensure the support of the Georgia delegation in the Rules Committee fight, Representative Phil Landrum of Georgia was promised one of the two Democratic vacancies that existed on the Ways and Means Committee.

The two vacancies had been created by the retirement of one opponent of the King-Anderson bill and the primary defeat of another. The House leadership and the President had resolved to fill their seats on the Ways and Means Committee with Congressmen who would vote for the social-security approach to financing hospital insurance for the aged. Having won the Rules Committee fight with the help of the Georgia delegation, the Democratic leadership supported Landrum and Representative Bass of Tennessee for the Ways and Means Committee vacancies. Landrum, although opposed to the social-security approach, had pledged to vote to allow the bill, lodged in committee for over four years, to go to the House floor if he became a member of the committee. Bass was a supporter of the program.

However, the Democratic caucus upset the House leadership's plan. Southern Democrats were resentful of Landrum's trading Georgia's votes in the Rules Committee fight for the promise of leadership support for the Ways and Means seat. Northern liberals preferred a man of more liberal leanings, Representative Jennings of Virginia, a supporter of the King-Anderson bill. The two groups, voting together for quite different motives, defeated Landrum and elected Jennings and Bass to the committee. The Ways and Means Committee was thus almost evenly divided, with the majority still opposed to the Administration's medicare proposals. This left decisive leverage in the hands of Chairman Mills. He and the two Democratic committee members who continued to oppose King-Anderson were the objects of repeated compromise overtures.

In the Senate the prospects for passage had also improved. Senator Kerr's death left the Senate without its most powerful and articulate opponent of the Administration's program. And the election of additional Democratic Senators pledged to that program gave forecasters a total of 52 favorable votes for medicare. A majority of the Senate Finance Committee was still against the King-Anderson bill. However, a Senate committee can be more easily bypassed than can a House committee. The Finance Committee's opposition was thus not as significant as the opposition of the Ways and Means Committee in the House.[cc]

King-Anderson's improved prospects faded when the President made it clear that, once again, the bill did not have top priority. That position in 1963 was reserved for his tax program. His tax recommendations gave the Ways and Means Committee a massive job—one which it could not finish until far into the summer. And so, financing medical care for the aged was once more put off.

Then came the outburst of civil-rights demonstrations in the late spring and early summer of 1963. Civil-rights legislation clearly displaced everything else on the Administration priority lists, although Administration spokesmen contended that tax legislation shared the top position. Congress, however, took little action on these—or any other—measures that summer and fall. Even bills appropriating funds for the fiscal year that had begun in July remained unpassed, as Congress ground slowly to a halt. There were a number of reasons for this inaction, but one of the principal reasons was an effort by Southern members of Congress to put themselves in a better bargaining position on civil-rights legislation. If there were a large backlog of "must" legislation, the Administration would be less willing to risk the further delays of a long civil-rights filibuster, and so would be more willing to reach an accommodation with the Southerners.

Against this background of stalemate, a subcommittee of the Special Senate Committee on Aging issued a report in October that was highly critical of the Kerr-Mills program. Senator Mc-Namara, who had introduced several bills providing for medical care financed through social security, had formerly been chairman of the full committee and of its predecessor, the Special Subcommittee on Problems of the Aged and Aging of the Senate Labor Committee. Under his direction, the Special Committee on Aging

---

[cc] For a discussion of King-Anderson prospects in House and Senate, see "Medical Care Plan Again Depends Mainly on House Ways-Means Unit," *The Wall Street Journal*, February 25, 1963.

and its predecessor had from time to time held hearings and issued reports which provided ammunition for supporters of medicare. However, with Senator Kerr's death at the beginning of the 88th Congress, Senator McNamara had become the senior Democrat on the Senate Public Works Committee. Senate practice did not permit him to be chairman of two committees, and so he had given up his chairmanship of the Aging Committee to become chairman of the Public Works Committee. The choice was a natural one, as Public Works is a legislative committee through whose hands pass the authorizations for pork-barrel legislation, and its chairman is therefore a person of political power and prominence. However, McNamara's successor as chairman of the Committee on Aging was George Smathers of Florida, an opponent of medicare. From that point on, the Aging Committee's activities on behalf of medicare were no longer visible, if they existed. Senator McNamara, however, was chairman of one of the Aging Committee's subcommittees, the Subcommittee on Health of the Elderly. It was this subcommittee which, in October 1963, issued the report attacking the Kerr-Mills program.

In November a new element entered the picture. Five days before the Ways and Means Committee was once again to hold hearings on medicare, the National Committee on Health Care for the Aged proposed a compromise that would use both government and private insurance. The committee, chaired by former HEW Secretary Arthur Flemming, was a 12-man private group that had been organized at the suggestion of Senator Javits after the Senate had rejected the Anderson-Javits proposal a year earlier. Its compromise called for government hospitalization insurance to be financed by a specifically designated social-security tax. This measure was to be accompanied by Congressional action exempting private insurance companies from the antitrust laws so that they could join together in developing special programs to cover other medical costs for the aged. These programs would be exempt from taxation, nonprofit, and open to all without restrictions based on the condition of the insured's health. Programs that met these requirements were to be publicly endorsed by the government. The committee recommended that insurance companies develop methods for prepaying the cost of this insurance during the insured's active working life.

President Kennedy praised the committee's report, but hopes that it might provide the basis for a compromise were dimmed by the American Medical Association's denunciation of the report as providing nothing new "except for a few gimmicks."

On November 18, the Ways and Means Committee began, in the words of *The New York Times*, "listening to familiar witnesses present familiar arguments" on medicare. The committee planned to end its hearings ten days later, but they were brought to an abrupt halt by an event which had entered into no one's strategic calculations—President Kennedy's assassination.

Lyndon Johnson Takes Over

When President Johnson addressed a joint session of Congress a few days later, he called for action on almost every point in the Kennedy program, including "the dream of care for our elderly." It was clear, however, that the tax and civil-rights bills were the legislation in which he was most interested.

In January the Ways and Means Committee resumed—and concluded—hearings on medicare, and President Johnson predicted its enactment in 1964, saying that he had "just begun to fight." The spring of 1964 was spent waiting for something to emerge from the Ways and Means Committee. The committee began work in executive session on April 9. In April, also, Senator McNamara's subcommittee held public hearings on the costs and adequacy of private health insurance for the aged. The hearings had no discernible effect on the Ways and Means Committee, which continued its executive sessions.

Rumors about possible compromises abounded. President Johnson, facing an election campaign that fall, was clearly eager to strengthen his image as a man who could deal successfully with Congress. Observers speculated about how much of a compromise he would be willing to make in order to get a bill labeled "medicare" enacted. He had shown himself adept in cajoling and persuading key Congressional leaders on other issues, such as his tax proposals, which were enacted early in 1964. Would he be successful in applying "the treatment" to Wilbur Mills?

There wasn't much time—Congressmen wanted to adjourn by July so that they could attend the national conventions of their respective parties and then begin campaigning for reelection. The Senate had been tied up since early March with a filibuster over the civil-rights bill, and it could not be expected to shake loose until June. Administration spokesmen talked of recessing for the Republican convention in July, reconvening until the Democratic convention the following month, and then reconvening again in September. Although possible, it was doubtful that Congressmen could be kept in Washington very far into the campaign season. Chances for enactment of medicare—and the rest of the Johnson program—faded.

Meanwhile, Congressman Mills' strategy became clear. He proposed increased federal grants to states that would relax the eligibility rules and provide broader services in their Kerr-Mills programs. This would weaken the charge that Kerr-Mills was inadequate. At the same time, he proposed increased *cash* benefits for social-security beneficiaries. Such increased benefits were desirable, it was argued, because there had been a 7 per cent increase in living costs since 1958, when the level of benefits was last set. At the same time, the increase in social-security contributions necessary to finance the higher cash benefits would presumably result in taxpayer resistance to further increases in these contributions for medicare.

Mills was not able to get his committee to agree on the liberalization of the Kerr-Mills program. However, he was successful on the increase of cash benefits. On July 7, the Ways and Means Committee reported out a bill which provided a 5 per cent increase in cash benefits and expanded social-security eligibility slightly. These changes would have increased monthly social-security payments to individuals by $1-$6, for a total annual cost of $1.5 billion. To pay for this increase, the wage base on which social-security taxes are paid would have been raised from a maximum of $4800 to a maximum of $5,400, and the rate of taxation from $3\frac{5}{8}$ per cent to 3.8 per cent. Social-security taxes had previously been scheduled to increase gradually to $4\frac{5}{8}$ per cent by 1971, and the committee bill brought the scheduled increase by that year to 4.8 per cent. Thus the increased cash benefits would bring the level of social-security taxes dangerously close to the 5 per cent that was sometimes cited as the level beyond which increases would meet insuperable taxpayer resistance.

In the background, the McNamara subcommittee continued its work for medicare. In mid-July, it released a report based on the previous spring's hearings and on staff research, attacking the adequacy and cost of private insurance for the aged and alleging that insurance enrollment figures had been inflated by the insurance industry to make medicare appear less necessary. The Republican members of the subcommittee—including Presidential candidate Barry Goldwater—attacked the majority report as an attempt to distort the "record of progress" of private insurance.

As is customary for legislation reported out by the Ways and Means Committee, the social-security bill came up on the House floor under a closed rule—that is, a rule which permitted no amendments. The bill was passed 388-8 on July 29 and was sent to the Senate Finance Committee.

A medicare amendment could be added to the bill in the Senate, but this maneuver would be only the first step in getting medicare enacted. The bill would then go to a conference committee made up of the senior members of the Ways and Means Committee and the Finance Committee, the majority of whom were opposed to medicare. It did not seem likely that a bill carrying medicare provisions would emerge from such a conference, and there was something to be lost by trying: a deadlock in the conference committee would jeopardize the increase in cash benefits, something which Congressmen were reluctant to do in an election year. Nonetheless, medicare supporters decided to try.

The majority of the Finance Committee, like the majority of the Ways and Means Committee, was opposed to medicare. Unlike House procedure, however, in the Senate the bill could be amended on the floor. However, the members of the Finance Committee who favored medicare knew that a floor amendment would be subject to the objection that it had not been considered by the Finance Committee and that such a complex matter should not be legislated without committee action. Accordingly, they proposed that the committee hold hearings on medicare, even though this meant that no bill could be reported out until just before the

Democratic National Convention at the end of August. The committee agreed to hold hearings on medicare.

At the hearings, HEW Secretary Anthony Celebrezze said that the House bill had ignored the "most critical need," and urged that the cash increase be replaced by medicare. Former HEW Secretary Ribicoff, now a member of the Finance Committee, attacked the House bill as a "mess of pottage, a snare and a delusion." While the Finance Committee was conducting its hearings, the Senate, having only recently undergone the filibuster against the Civil Rights Act, found its time occupied with another filibuster—this one unexpected. Senator Dirksen had offered a rider to the foreign-aid authorization bill which would have delayed, and in the long run probably stopped, court-ordered reapportionment of state legislatures. A small group of Senate liberals took up the cudgel against the Dirksen rider. As their filibuster continued, the Finance Committee, as expected, reported out the social-security bill without attaching a medical-care amendment. Floor action was not possible because of the reapportionment filibuster, and a few days later, Congress recessed for the Democratic convention.

When Congress reconvened, the reapportionment filibuster had been temporarily suspended, and the social-security bill was up for discussion. Proponents of medicare were prepared to offer an amendment to the bill when they were thrown into confusion by Senator Russell Long of Louisiana, an opponent of medicare. He offered an amendment to increase social-security benefits by 7 per cent, increasing taxes to the magic 5 per cent point to finance them. This was clearly a move to prevent the enactment of medicare at any future time, although Long described it as a measure to "put some protein on the table, some bacon on Wednesday, and some chicken on Saturday, and some fish on Friday."

Senator Paul Douglas of Illinois held the Senate floor to delay action on the Long amendment, while the pro-medicare forces retreated to the majority leader's office to redraft their amendment to the bill so that it would be germane as an amendment to Long's amendment. The proposal with which they emerged was introduced by Senator Albert Gore of Tennessee. It encompassed most of the benefits of the King-Anderson bill, plus a $7 increase in monthly benefits. It was to be financed by increasing the social-security wage base to $5,600, and the tax rate to 5.2 per cent by 1971. The Gore amendment would be voted on before the Long amendment, as it was technically an amendment to the Long amendment.

Several of the Senators who had previously filibustered against the Dirksen reapportionment proposal realized that once action was taken on medicare, the Dirksen proposal would come up again. To prevent this recurrence, they began to prolong their discussion of the medicare bill. Thus, the fates of four different types of legislation were momentarily tied together: medicare, the social-security cash increases, the reapportionment proposal, and the foreign-aid bill which the latter amended.

This knot was untied in private negotiations, and on September 2, the Gore amendment came to a vote. At first, the vote resulted in a 42-42 tie. Before this result could be announced, however, 9 additional Senators entered the chamber and announced their votes. Presumably they had been subject to cross-pressures, and were waiting to see if their votes would be necessary. The final vote was 49 for the amendment to 44 opposed; 44 Democrats and 5 Republicans had voted for the amendment. The Republicans, led by Senator Javits, had been won by the addition to the Gore amendment of a modified form of one of the recommendations of the National Committee on Health Care for the Aged. This was the proposal for antitrust exemption for private insurance companies so that they could develop common programs for the aged.

The 44 opposition votes consisted of 28 Republicans, 15 Southern Democrats, and Democrat Frank Lausche of Ohio, who often votes with his Southern colleagues. Among those voting against the Gore amendment was Senator Goldwater, who had interrupted his Presidential campaign planning in Phoenix and flown to Washington so that he might cast his vote on this issue. Of those Senators voting in 1964 who had also voted in 1962, 4 Democrats and 2 Republicans had switched their positions—4 so as to favor medicare, and 2 in the opposite direction.

Clearly, those who voted for the Gore amendment did not expect it to emerge from the House-Senate conference intact. Rather, they were merely trying to establish as strong a bargaining position as possible. It was widely rumored that the position to which they expected to fall back in conference, and which they hoped would be satisfactory to Wilbur Mills, was a proposal that had been formulated earlier by Senator Ribicoff. This measure called for offering the elderly a choice between a cash-benefit increase of $7 a month or a smaller cash increase plus medicare, perhaps with reduced benefits to keep down the cost.

The following day, the Senate passed the entire social-security bill by a vote of 60-28 and returned it to the House. The next step whenever the two houses pass different versions of a bill is normally a joint conference committee which attempts to reach a compromise. However, it was clear that the majority of the conferees from both houses would be opposed to medicare. The Senate conferees were honor-bound to support the bill as passed by the Senate (although it was unknown for how long and with what enthusiasm they would do so). The majority of the House conferees, on the other hand, could be expected to oppose medicare with vigor. Therefore, medicare proponents planned to try a rarely used method of removing discretion from the conferees: a motion of the House of Representatives instructing its conferees to accede to the Senate medicare amendment. This was a potentially dangerous tactic, as defeat of the motion could be cited by Mills as a mandate to stand fast against medicare.

Before a conference can be held, it must be authorized by unanimous consent of the entire House of Representatives. Without such consent, the Rules Committee must offer a rule authorizing the conference; the rule must then be approved by a majority vote of the House. The House Republican leadership, aware that the Democratic leadership intended to offer a motion to instruct the conferees, warned that unanimous consent would not be forthcoming so long as this was the plan. The Democratic leadership was thus forced to take the Rules Committee route. There was some concern that Rules Committee Chairman Smith might attempt to block the conference, as he had done on occasion in the past with legislation that he opposed. However, in this case he seemed to be cooperative. Despite this cooperative spirit, it was not possible to get a quorum of the Committee for two weeks because of heavy Congressional absenteeism as the election drew closer.

During this period, Congressman King attempted to line up support for his forthcoming motion instructing the conferees. Although the heavy absences made it difficult to count noses accurately, it seemed that many Congressmen who favored medicare were unwilling to violate normal procedure. Realizing that he could not obtain a majority for a motion to instruct the House conferees, Congressman King suddenly shifted strategy and dropped the plan to do so. Republican leaders then withdrew their objections to sending the bill to conference, and it was sent to conference by unanimous consent on September 15.

The conferees set to work the following day. Attempts to reach a compromise on the medicare issue failed, as the Senate conferees—to the surprise of many—held fast for medicare. The question then was whether there was to be an increase in cash benefits. Proponents of medicare were opposed to the increase, for fear that the concomitant increase in social-security taxes would prevent later Congressional action on medicare. Moreover, they hoped that a Democratic election landslide would strengthen their hand in the next Congress. Congressman Mills argued for enactment of the cash increase, promising that the following year the Ways and Means Committee would take up the problem of easing medical-care costs for the aged. However, the majority of the Senate conferees, with some prompting from President Johnson, held firm.

The stalemate continued into October, as Congressmen grew more and more restless to return home for the election campaigns in which their opponents were already hard at work. The leadership finally was compelled to accede to their demands, and Congress adjourned one month before the election, letting both medicare and the cash increase die, as well as other legislation. The promedicare forces had suffered a defeat in that medicare was not enacted. However, they also had a partial victory in their ability to hold off the cash increase.

Early in 1964, in his New Hampshire primary campaign, Barry Goldwater had suggested making social security voluntary. The proposal was apparently poorly received by the voters, and the Democrats kept reminding them of it. Senator Goldwater was therefore delighted at the opportunity to attack the Democrats for letting the increases in social-security cash benefits die. Within hours after Congress adjourned, he was telling his audience, "Now you know who the friends of social security are . . . ."

The stage seemed to be set for medicare to become a major issue of the Presidential campaign. Goldwater's flight to Washington to vote against it clearly indicated his position. Johnson emphasized his position by promising that medicare would head his list of must legislation if he were reelected. The American Medical Association spent $1 million on an advertising campaign praising Kerr-Mills; its political arm spent half that amount on 150 Congressional contests. Despite all this activity, medicare never became an important issue in the Presidential campaign, which was instead fought on a much more general level.

November 3 was a Democratic triumph. Not only was Lyndon Johnson elected President in his own right, but the Democrats increased their margin in the House of Representatives by 38 seats; the new House would be Democratic by better than two to one. The Senate in the previous Congress had already had a two-to-one Democratic majority; the Democrats picked up still another seat there. The 89th Congress would be the most heavily Democratic Congress since Franklin Roosevelt's 1936 sweep.

Even more significantly for medicare, the Democratic losses were concentrated in the South, where anti-medicare Democrats were replaced by anti-medicare Republicans. In the North, however, antimedicare Republicans were replaced by promedicare Democrats. The National Council of Senior Citizens estimated that medicare proposals would be able to muster 54 votes in the new Senate and a House majority of as much as 60. The Ways and Means Committee might still present a problem, but medicare supporters might even be able to muster enough signatures on a discharge petition to get medicare out of the committee if it should prove recalcitrant.

The first sign that the committee would not be recalcitrant came a week after the election. Wilbur Mills announced that he was ready to bring up medicare in the Ways and Means Committee immediately after Congress convened in January if the President wanted him to. The President did not respond immediately, as he had not yet decided which he wanted Ways and Means to go to work on first: medicare or his proposals to cut excise taxes. He soon made up his mind and met with House leaders to urge them to press for quick action on medicare.

On November 30, the House of Delegates of the American Medical Association, made up of delegates from the state medical societies, held its regular semiannual meeting. The Michigan and District of Columbia societies offered proposals for compromise with the Administration, neither of which, however, would have involved social-security financing. AMA President Donovan Ward acknowledged that "the outlook is neither pleasant nor easy," recognizing that the election meant a "significant loss of votes" for the AMA in Congress on the medicare issue. However, he opposed the Michigan and D.C. proposals, saying, "We do not, by profession, compromise in matters of life and death. Nor can we compromise with honor and duty." The House of Delegates followed suit and rejected the proposals, giving the AMA trustees full authority to spend the amount they considered necessary to fight medicare.

The picture began to look even blacker for the AMA. Amid predictions from medicare supporters that their bill would be enacted by Easter, Congressman Mills said he would support a program of hospitalization insurance for the aged that was administered by the Social Security Administration, as long as it was financed through a separate tax. He also wanted a separate trust fund for medicare, something which had been included in the Kennedy Administration's proposal. The separate tax and trust fund were to make clear the cost of medicare and insure that general social-security funds were not applied to medicare in the event that its costs exceeded advance estimates. Just after the beginning of the new year, the Social Security Advisory Council, a group of nongovernmental experts appointed to advise the trustees of the social-security system, recommended that such a separate payroll tax be used to finance medicare. They suggested that the program be administered, however, as part of the social-security system, using the same records and personnel. The following week, President Johnson sent a health message to Congress, giving first priority to medicare, which he described as "of utmost urgency." In his message, he endorsed the idea of a separate trust fund for medicare, and Congressman Mills said that the President's proposal met with his approval.

SUMMARY 5: 1965 King-Anderson Bill (H.R. 1 and S. 1, 89th Congress)

The medical-care provisions of this bill differed from the 1963 King-Anderson bill (H.R. 3920 and S. 880, 88th Congress) in the following respects:

Benefits. *Hospitalization:* 60 days per benefit period with deductible of national average cost of 1 day of hospital care.

Nursing homes: 60 days per benefit period.

Laboratory and X-ray services: Set deductible for outpatient services at ½ national average cost of 1 day of hospital care.

Method of financing. For OASI eligibles: provided for increasing taxable earnings base to $5,600 and for the following increases in social-security tax rates:

	Employee	Employer	Self-employed
1966	0.30%	0.30%	0.45%
1967-1968	.38	.38	.57
1969 and after	.45	.45	.675

Administration. Authorized creation of associations of private insurance carriers, exempt from antitrust laws to sell, on nonprofit basis, approved policies covering those health costs not included in this bill.

Medicare legislation had already been introduced by Congressman King and Senator Anderson and had been symbolically designated "H.R. 1" and "S. 1"—the first bills to be introduced in both houses of Congress. The new King-Anderson bill included a 7 per cent increase in cash benefits, as well as other changes in the social-security system. Its medical-care benefits were similar to those of the social-security bill passed by the Senate in 1964: 60 days of hospitalization (with a 1-day deductible), 60 days of nursing-home care, home health services (such as a visiting nurse) up to 240 visits a year, and outpatient hospital diagnostic services. It did not include a separate payroll tax, but was to be financed by the allocation of a specified proportion of social-security contributions to a separate hospital-insurance trust fund. The bill authorized private insurance carriers to pool their resources for the purpose of making low-cost supplementary health insurance available to the elderly. In return for the inclusion of this provision, Senator Javits and two other Republicans cosponsored the bill in the Senate.

Medicare's path in the 89th Congress was further eased by changes in the composition of the Ways and Means Committee and in the rules of the House of Representatives. The committee division which had previously been 15 Democrats to 10 Republicans was changed to 17 Democrats and 8 Republicans. In addition to the two new Democratic vacancies, there was a third to be filled because one member had been elected to the Senate. Congressman Landrum was elected to one of the vacancies, with the understanding that he would not prevent medicare from coming to the House floor; the other two vacancies were filled with medicare supporters.

The changes in the House rules weakened the ability of the Rules Committee to obstruct legislation. The new rules permitted the chairmen of the legislative committees, if recognized by the Speaker, to call up bills that had been stalled before the Rules Committee for 21 days or longer. A second change permitted a bill to be sent to conference by a majority vote, rather than the unanimous consent that had been necessary in the absence of clearance from the Rules Committee.

The path seemed to be clear for medicare's enactment in the 89th Congress.

1965: Medicare Enacted

Before the Congressional machinery could start action on medicare, the AMA early in January offered an alternative—"eldercare." In 1964, the Association had suggested that the Kerr-Mills legislation be amended to permit the states to buy private health insurance for the needy aged. This proposal was transmuted, with public fanfare, into eldercare. Under eldercare, the elderly would buy private health insurance, with the premium to be based on the purchaser's income. The federal government would subsidize premiums for the needy, but the program was to be administered by the states. A bill authorizing the eldercare program was introduced by two Ways and Means Committee members, Republican Thomas Curtis of Missouri and Democrat A. Sidney Herlong of Florida.

The announcement of the eldercare program followed the theme of the AMA's earlier promotion of Kerr-Mills, stressing the potential availability of comprehensive benefits, in contrast with the limited benefits available under the King-Anderson bill. A "national education campaign" to carry this theme to the public was announced, and a rarely held special meeting of the AMA House of Delegates was called for the second week end of February to discuss eldercare. At this meeting, there was some grumbling over the cost of the campaign, but the delegates endorsed eldercare and empowered the AMA's trustees to conduct a "vigorous" campaign in its behalf. The AMA later filed a report, as required by the Federal Regulation of Lobbying Act, indicating that it had spent $951,570 to "influence legislation" during the first quarter of 1965. The bulk of this sum—by far the largest quarterly expenditure ever reported under the Act—was spent on the eldercare campaign. This sum did not include expenditures by state and local medical societies.

Meanwhile, on January 27, the Ways and Means Committee began its hearings on the King-Anderson bill. The Republican members of the committee had called for public hearings. Chairman Mills, however, argued that adequate public hearings had been held in the past, so the hearings were closed. He promised final committee action by mid-March. Whether it was because the hearings were closed or because it was generally accepted that medicare would be enacted or for some other reason, the content of the hearings was quite different from that of previous years. The majority of the witnesses engaged in serious discussion of technical details of the bill, and there was much less propagandistic posturing than in the past.

Shortly after the hearings began, Congressman Byrnes of Wisconsin, the senior Republican on the Ways and Means Committee, offered his own bill, which provided a voluntary program, two-thirds of which was to be paid for from the general revenues of the federal government. The remainder was to be financed by premiums ranging from $4 to $11.50 a month. The amount of premium to be paid by a particular beneficiary would depend on the size of the social-security pension he was receiving. The program would pay for the first $1,000 of hospital room and board charges, plus 80 per cent of additional hospital room and board charges. It would also pay 80 per cent of other medical expenses, after the insured paid a deductible of $50. There would be a lifetime limit of $40,000 in benefits paid on behalf of any person. The program would presumably be administered by private agencies, which would pay claims and be reimbursed by the federal government.

The Byrnes bill was endorsed by the new House Republican leader, Gerald Ford of Michigan. Although there was little, if any, chance that it would be enacted, it was proffered in accordance with Ford's announced policy of devising constructive alternatives to Administration proposals in order to improve what he described as the Republican Party's negativist image. Inasmuch as it was unlikely to be enacted, it could be drafted, in the words of *The Wall Street Journal,* "for maximum political contrast with the limited benefits of medicare."

The contrast was too stark for some Democratic members of the Ways and Means Committee. Chairman Mills came up with a solution: add a voluntary insurance program, similar to the one in the Byrnes bill, to the Administration proposal. This addition was made, and on March 23 the Ways and Means Committee reported out the bill by a straight party vote. The committee bill, H.R. 6675 (the Mills bill), replaced the King-Anderson bill as the vehicle for medicare. Its basic program was similar to, although somewhat less extensive than, the King-Anderson program. To this program was added a supplementary voluntary provision which would pay 80 per cent of the cost of physicians' services and a variety of other medical services. The supplementary program, which had an annual deductible of $50, would be financed by a monthly premium of $3, to be matched by an equal sum from general revenues.

There were no doubts that the bill would pass the House. Rules Committee Chairman Howard Smith indicated that he was resigned to its passage, and his committee granted the closed rule sought by Mills. The closed rule meant that no amendments could be offered on the House floor, but that the House would get the opportunity to vote on one alternative offered by the opposition. Since the spokesman for the opposition would be the senior Republican on Ways and Means, John Byrnes, it would be his bill that would be offered as the alternative, and the House would not have the opportunity to vote on eldercare.

House debate began on April 7, and on the following day, to no one's surprise, the bill was approved by a vote of 313 to 115. Supporting the bill were 189 Northern Democrats, 59 Southern Democrats, and 65 Republicans. Opposing it were 2 Northern Democrats, 40 Southern Democrats, and 73 Republicans.

The real test, however, came not on the vote to pass the Mills bill, but rather on the preceding motion to replace it with the Byrnes bill. Here the margin was closer, although still comfortable. Voting for the Byrnes bill were 3 Northern Democrats, 60 Southern Democrats, and 128 Republicans, for a total of 191. Against it were 188 Northern Democrats, 38 Southern Democrats, and 10 Republicans. Thus, almost all Republicans and a majority of Southern Democrats preferred the Byrnes bill; nevertheless, when it was defeated, enough voted for the Mills bill to give it the support of the majority of the Southern Democrats and almost half the Republicans. Republican switches were encouraged by Congressman Ford's announcement before the vote was taken that the House Republican Policy Committee had endorsed the Byrnes bill, but had taken no position on the Mills bill.

The Senate Finance Committee, which had been waiting for the House to complete action, opened its (public) hearings at the end of April. The first witness, HEW Secretary Celebrezze, lauded the Mills bill. He had, however, one suggestion for changing it. The King-Anderson bill, in addition to paying for hospital room and board charges, would also have covered the fees of certain medical specialists when their services were used by the hospital patient and included in his hospital bill. The Mills bill did not cover the charges for these services in the basic plan, although they were covered by the supplementary plan. Celebrezze urged the Finance Committee to amend the Mills bill to cover these charges in the basic plan where the practice of the hospital involved was to include them in its bills. In those relatively few cases where these specialists' fees were not normally included in the hospital bill, coverage should be provided by the supplementary plan.

Celebrezze's suggestion touched a sensitive nerve. The manner of payment for these services, provided by anesthesiologists, radiologists, pathologists, and physiatrists (specialists in physical medicine), had long been an issue in the health professions. In most cases, the fees for these services are included in a patient's hospital bill. The hospital, in turn, pays the specialist either a percentage of the income of his department or a salary. The American College of Radiology and the College of American Pathologists have opposed this kind of arrangement as the corporate practice of medicine, to which the medical profession has been strongly antagonistic since the 19th century. Corporate medical practice is also illegal in some states, because it provides an element of lay control over the physician, which assertedly results in poorer medical care. The American Hospital Association, on the other hand, sees nothing unethical or illegal in current practices. For the hospitals it is not a matter of lay control of the physician, but rather of the hospital taking responsibility for the services offered to the patient on its premises by physicians whom he has not chosen.[dd]

Obviously, the provisions of the medicare bill would play a major part in determining the outcome of this conflict. The American Hospital Association saw the struggle in even broader terms. It argued that if these specialists were to break away from the hospitals, the contemporary concept of the hospital as the "central institution in our health service system" would be destroyed. AMA President Donovan Ward responded that it "is not the . . . purpose or . . . function" of hospitals to be the central institution for the provision of medical care. "The hospital is primarily a place where medical care is provided to patients. Medical care is the responsibility of physicians, not hospitals." The AMA, taking up the cudgel for the specialists, urged state and local medical societies to put forth an "all-out campaign" to prevent any change in this aspect of the House bill. In response

---

[dd] See Somers and Somers, *Doctors, Patients, and Health Insurance,* pp. 79-83, for a discussion of this issue.

to the AHA assertion that the exclusion of these specialists' services would "tend to increase the overall cost of care to aged persons," Ward asserted that physicians "have a far better record than hospitals in keeping the price of their services within bounds." He also charged the hospitals with excessive charges for their laboratory and X-ray services.[ee]

Celebrezze's proposal, formally offered for Finance Committee consideration in the form of an amendment sponsored by Senator Paul Douglas of Illinois, was one of the two principal issues discussed by the committee. The other issue was posed by Senator Long of Louisiana, the second-ranking Democrat on the Finance Committee and newly elected Senate Democratic whip. Long had formerly opposed medicare. His new role as a member of the Senate Democratic leadership, however, put pressure on him to support it. His resolution of this problem was the suggestion that the medicare program be changed from a program offering limited benefits at the same cost for all the aged to one concerned primarily with catastrophic illness, offering broader benefits at a cost based on the recipient's income. He proposed eliminating the time limits on the use of hospitals and nursing homes. To offset the cost of these additional benefits, patients would pay a larger proportion of their bills, with the amount to be paid by the patient based on his income. The effect of the payment scale would have been to eliminate any financial benefit for those with an income over $10,000 unless they had above-average hospital costs; almost all patients would have had to pay more under the Long plan than under the Mills bill.

The first issue was resolved early in June, when the Finance Committee approved the Douglas amendment, including services provided by the four categories of specialists within the basic plan. In mid-June, the committee approved the Long plan. Voting for it was a mixed group of medicare supporters and opponents, with several committee members absent. The suggestion was made that the proxies of some of the absent members might have been mis-

---

[ee] See the exchange of letters between the presidents of the AMA and the AHA, originally printed in the *AMA News* of June 14, 1965, and reprinted in *Public Health Economics*, XXII (July 1965) 477-479. Other information about this controversy appears in the aforementioned issue of *Public Health Economics*, pp. 473-477; the 1965 Ways and Means Committee Hearings, pp. 230-236; and the 1965 Finance Committee hearings, pp. 298-303, 611-612.

used, and Administration leaders said they would try to have the committee reconsider its action, arguing that the Long proposal violated "the principle of Social Security."

The committee took up the Long plan again the following week. AMA lobbyists were reported to be urging its retention, in the hope of causing a deadlock in the conference committee and thus preventing the enactment of medicare. On June 23, the committee, by a vote of 10-7, scrapped the original Long proposal. In its place the committee, on Long's motion, added another 60 days of hospital care and other benefits if the patient paid part of the cost. The following day the committee approved H.R. 6675 by a vote of 12-5. The only Democrat to oppose the bill was committee chairman Harry Byrd of Virginia; 2 Republicans voted with the other 10 Democrats on the committee to approve the bill. The Finance Committee version of H.R. 6675 differed from the House-passed version primarily in the inclusion of the Long and Douglas amendments.

While the Finance Committee was considering H.R. 6675, several physicians' organizations began to call for a physicians' boycott of medicare if it were enacted. When the AMA House of Delegates convened for its regular meeting on June 20, eight state societies introduced boycott resolutions. The mildest of these proposals called on doctors to continue to treat elderly patients, but to refuse to sign forms attesting to this treatment, so that the patients would have to pay for the care themselves rather than being reimbursed by the government. The more extreme proposals suggested that physicians refuse to certify patients for admission to hospitals if their bills were to be paid by medicare.

The new AMA president, James Z. Appel, in his inaugural address on the first day of the meeting, rejected such boycotts as unethical and bad citizenship. He urged instead that physicians participate actively in the development of medicare rules and regulations so that these might be more to their liking. He also suggested a campaign to amend medicare legislation so that it would more closely resemble AMA proposals. Appel was quite obviously assuming that medicare would be enacted, whereas his predecessor had refused to admit the inevitable.

Boycott supporters, however, continued to press their resolutions. The committee to which the resolutions were referred recommended that no action be taken on them until medicare legislation was passed. The committee also proposed a resolution urging the government to seek AMA advice on medical-care legislation and to appoint physicians to all advisory committees dealing with health care.

The AMA House of Delegates generally followed this tack, neither approving nor disapproving of boycotts and leaving the decision up to the individual physician. It postponed action on the boycott resolutions, but reaffirmed policy statements of previous years to the effect that a physician should not work under conditions "which tend to interfere with or impair the free and complete exercise of his medical judgment and skill, or tend to cause a deterioration of the quality of medical care." Another resolution offered to meet with President Johnson to discuss medicare, although a resolution "petitioning" for such a meeting was rejected.

On July 6, the Senate opened debate on H.R. 6675. Approved by voice vote was an amendment proposed by Senators Hartke and Long to eliminate the time limit for hospital care, with the patient paying $10 per day after the first 60 days. The bill was passed on July 9 by a vote of 68-21. Northern Democrats voted solidly for it; Southern Democrats split 12-7 in its favor; and Republicans divided about evenly, 13-14. Seven Democrats and 8 Republicans who had previously voted against medicare changed their positions. The only direct test of the medicare portion of the bill came on a motion by Senator Curtis to kill only that portion of the bill; this move failed by a vote of 64-26. The losing side was made up of 18 Republicans and 8 Southern Democrats.

The conference committee quickly agreed to retain part of the additional hospital, nursing-home, and home-visit benefits contained in the Senate bill. A week later, the conferees agreed to retain the House provisions for the coverage of care by radiologists, pathologists, anesthesiologists, and physiatrists under the supplementary plan rather than the basic plan. The House approved the conference committee report on July 27 by a vote of 307-116; the Senate acted the following day, approving the report 70-24.

On July 29, President Johnson had what was described as a "friendly" meeting with 11 AMA leaders. The AMA representatives agreed to cooperate in administering medicare and said that the meeting had done much to alleviate their suspicions about federal intentions with respect to the medical profession. Johnson asked them to meet with HEW staff on the development of rules and regulations for the medicare programs and stated that no regulations would be enacted without providing the AMA the opportunity to recommend changes.

The following day, Johnson flew to Independence, Missouri, to sign the medicare bill at the Truman Library. The signing took place in former President Truman's presence, thus recognizing his efforts to have government-financed medical care enacted when he was President.

Within a few days, the Association of American Physicians and Surgeons, a group formed in the 1940's to fight the socialization of medicine, urged its members to refuse to cooperate with the medicare program in any way. The AMA officers, in their first official statement since the enactment of medicare, responded by telling physicians that they could boycott the program individually, but that they might be violating the antitrust laws if they did so in concert through professional organizations.

And so the legislative battle over medicare came to an end, at least temporarily. Still in the future are the battles over the implementation of the program—battles which, although less public perhaps than the legislative struggle, are likely to be no less important.

SUMMARY 6: A Comparison of 1965 Health-Insurance Legislation at Various Stages (Basic Program and Supplementary Program)

BOTH PROGRAMS

Eligibility

Eligibility for benefits under all versions of the legislation was essentially the same, although there were slight differences. Eligibility for both the basic program and the supplementary program was essentially the same, although there were minor differences. ◆ Eligible are: (1) persons 65 or over who are entitled to monthly social-security benefits or to annuities under the Railroad Retirement Act; this group constitutes 93 per cent of persons reaching age 65 at present; (2) persons aged 65 or over who are not eligible for social-security or railroad-retirement benefits; in the future, fewer and fewer persons will reach age 65 without being eligible for social-security or railroad-retirement benefits, so that this group will gradually disappear.

Benefits—Period

The benefit period was the same under all versions of the legislation: to begin when individual enters a hospital and end when he has not been an inpatient at a hospital or nursing home for 60 consecutive days.

BASIC PROGRAM

Benefits—Hospitalization

King-Anderson bill (H.R. 1 and S. 1). Inpatient hospital services for up to 60 days per benefit period, with deductible equal to national average cost of 1 day's hospitalization. ♦ Did not include tuberculosis or psychiatric hospitals. ♦ Included all hospital services ordinarily furnished by hospital to inpatients. Hospital services of physicians covered only in case of (1) interns or residents in training, and (2) radiologists, anesthesiologists, pathologists, and physiatrists whose services are provided under arrangement with hospital.

Mills bill (H.R. 6675) as passed by House. Inpatient hospital services for up to 60 days per benefit period, with deductible of $40. This deductible amount would be increased if necessary, but no earlier than 1969, to keep pace with increases in hospital costs. ♦ Included tuberculosis hospitals. ♦ Included all hospital services ordinarily furnished by hospital to inpatients. Hospital services of physicians covered only in case of interns or residents in training.

H.R. 6675 as recommended by Senate Finance Committee. Inpatient hospital services for up to 120 days per benefit period, with deductible of $40 for first 60 days and $10 for each additional day. These deductible amounts would be increased if necessary, but no earlier than 1968, to keep pace with increases in hospital costs. ♦ Included tuberculosis and psychiatric hospitals, but with lifetime limit of 210 days' benefits in psychiatric hospitals. ♦ Included all hospital services ordinarily furnished by hospital to inpatients. Hospital services of physicians covered only in case of (1) interns or residents in training, and (2) radiologists, anesthesiologists, pathologists, and physiatrists whose services are provided under arrangement with hospital and billed through hospital.

H.R. 6675 as passed by Senate. Unlimited inpatient hospital services, with deductible of $40 for first 60 days and $10 for each additional day. These deductible amounts would be increased if necessary, but no earlier than 1968, to keep pace with increases in hospital costs. ♦ Otherwise, similar to H.R. 6675 as reported by Finance Committee.

H.R. 6675 as enacted into law. Inpatient hospital services for up to 90 days per benefit period, with deductible of $40 for first 60 days and $10 for each additional day. These deductible amounts will be increased if necessary, but not earlier than 1968, to keep pace with increases in hospital costs. ♦ Includes tuberculosis and psychiatric hospitals, but with lifetime limit of 190 days' benefits in psychiatric hospitals. ♦ Includes all hospital services ordinarily furnished by hospital to inpatients. Hospital services of physicians covered only in case of interns or residents in training.

Benefits—Nursing Homes

King-Anderson bill (H.R. 1 and S. 1). Up to 60 days per benefit period; available upon transfer from hospital.

Mills bill (H.R. 6675) as passed by House. Up to 20 days per benefit period, plus 2 additional days for each unused day of hospital benefits, with maximum of 80 additional days; available only upon transfer from hospital.

H.R. 6675 as recommended by Senate Finance Committee. Up to 100 days per benefit period, but after first 20 days would pay daily deductible of one-eighth of deductible for first 60 days of inpatient hospital care; available only upon transfer from hospital.

H.R. 6675 as passed by Senate. Similar to H.R. 6675 as reported by Finance Committee.

H.R. 6675 as enacted into law. Similar to H.R. 6675 as reported by Finance Committee.

Benefits—Home Health Services

King-Anderson bill (H.R. 1 and S. 1). Intermittent nursing care, therapy, part-time home health aid services, services of interns and residents under approved teaching program of hospital with which home health agency is affiliated furnished in patient's residence under plan established by physician, for up to 240 visits per calendar year.

Mills bill (H.R. 6675) as passed by House. Similar to King-Anderson, but coverage on post-hospital basis, for up to 100 visits in year after hospital discharge. Patient must be homebound except that he could be taken to hospital, extended-care facility, or home health agency to receive services requiring equipment that cannot readily be taken to patient's home.

H.R. 6675 as recommended by Senate Finance Committee. Similar to House bill, but coverage for up to 175 visits.

H.R. 6675 as passed by Senate. Similar to H.R. 6675 as reported by Finance Committee, but coverage for up to 175 visits per calendar year and need not be on post-hospital basis.

H.R. 6675 as enacted into law. Similar to House bill, but coverage for up to 100 visits per benefit period.

*Benefits—*Outpatient Hospital Diagnostic Services

King-Anderson bill (H.R. 1 and S. 1). As required, but subject to deductible equal to average cost of ½ day of inpatient hospital care for services furnished within 30-day period.

Mills bill (H.R. 6675) as passed by House. Similar to King-Anderson, except that deductible was $20 (subject to increase, as was deductible for hospitalization) for each diagnostic study, i.e., for services furnished within 20-day period by same hospital.

H.R. 6675 as recommended by Senate Finance Committee Similar to House bill, except program would pay only 80 per cent of costs above deductible amount.

H.R. 6675 as passed by Senate. Same as H.R. 6675 as recommended by Finance Committee.

H.R. 6675 as enacted into law. Same as H.R. 6675 as recommended by Finance Committee.

Financing

King-Anderson bill (H.R. 1 and S. 1). By allocating to separate hospital-insurance trust fund the following proportions of wages taxable under social security:

	Employee	Employer	Self-employed
1966	0.30%	0.30%	0.45%
1967-1968	.38	.38	.57
1969 and after	.45	.45	.675

Earnings base of $5,600. ◆ Costs of paying benefits for persons not entitled to monthly OASI or railroad-retirement benefits financed from federal general revenues. ◆ Authorized Secretary of Treasury to require that W-2 forms show proportion of total social-security tax withheld for financing hospital insurance.

Mills bill (H.R. 6675) as passed by House. By separate payroll taxes paid to separate hospital-insurance trust fund. Contribution rate, the same for employees, employers, and self-employed, as follows:

1966	0.35%
1967-1972	.50
1973-1975	.55
1976-1979	.60
1980-1986	.70
1987 and after	.80

Earnings base of $5,600 from 1966 to 1970; thereafter, $6,600. ♦ Costs of paying benefits for persons not entitled to monthly OASI or railroad-retirement benefits financed from federal general revenues. ♦ Required that W-2 forms show proportion of total payroll tax withheld for financing hospital insurance.

H.R. 6675 as recommended by Senate Finance Committee. By separate payroll taxes paid to separate hospital-insurance trust fund. Contribution rate, the same for employees, employers, and self-employed, as follows:

1966	0.325%
1967-1970	.50
1971-1972	.55
1973-1975	.60
1976-1979	.65
1980-1986	.75
1987 and after	.85

Earnings base of $6,600. ♦ Costs of paying benefits for persons not entitled to monthly OASI or railroad-retirement benefits financed from federal general revenues. ♦ Required that W-2 forms show proportion of total payroll tax withheld for financing hospital insurance.

H.R. 6675 as passed by Senate. By separate payroll taxes paid to separate hospital-insurance trust fund. Contribution rate, the same for employees, employers, and self-employed, as follows:

1966	0.325%
1967-1970	.50
1971-1972	.55
1973-1975	.65
1976-1979	.70
1980-1986	.80
1987 and after	.85

Earnings base of $6,600. ♦ Costs of paying benefits for persons not entitled to monthly OASI or railroad-retirement benefits financed from federal general revenues. ♦ Required that W-2 forms show proportion of total payroll tax withheld for financing hospital insurance.

H.R. 6675 as enacted into law. By separate payroll taxes paid to separate hospital-insurance trust fund. Contribution rate, the same for employees, employers, and self-employed, as follows:

1966	0.35%
1967-1970	.50
1971-1972	.50
1973-1975	.55
1976-1979	.60
1980-1986	.70
1987 and after	.80

Earnings base of $6,600. ◆ Costs of paying benefits for persons not entitled to monthly OASI or railroad-retirement benefits financed from federal general revenues. ◆ Required that W-2 forms show proportion of total payroll tax withheld for financing hospital insurance.

Administration

King-Anderson bill (H.R. 1 and S. 1). HEW Secretary authorized to use appropriate state agencies and private organizations to assist in administration. State agencies under an agreement would be used to determine and certify eligibility of providers to participate. Hospitals and other providers of services could nominate public agencies or private organizations to receive and pay bills in lieu of dealing directly with government. Secretary could delegate additional administrative functions to designated organizations.

Mills bill (H.R. 6675) as passed by House. Similar to King-Anderson; differed mainly in that Secretary required to use state agencies in determining eligibility of providers of services to participate.

H.R. 6675 as recommended by Senate Finance Committee. Same as House bill.

H.R. 6675 as passed by Senate. Same as House bill.

H.R. 6675 as enacted into law. Same as House bill.

SUPPLEMENTARY PROGRAM

Benefits

King-Anderson bill (H.R. 1 and S. 1). No supplementary program.

Mills bill (H.R. 6675) as passed by House. Annual deductible of $50. Then plan would cover 80 per cent of patient's bill (above deductible) for following services: (1) physicians' and surgeons' services, whether furnished in hospital, clinic, office, home, or elsewhere; (2) inpatient psychiatric hospital services of up to 60 days per benefit period, with lifetime limit of 180 days; outpatient psychiatric treatment limited to $250 per calendar year or 50 per cent of expenses, whichever is smaller; (3) home health service (with no requirement of prior hospitalization) for up to 100 visits during each calendar year; (4) diagnostic X-ray and laboratory tests, and other diagnostic tests; (5) X-ray, radium, and radioactive-isotope therapy; (6) ambulance services; (7) surgical dressings and splints, casts, and other devices for reduction of fractures and dislocations; rental of durable medical equipment such as iron lungs, oxygen tents, hospital beds, and wheelchairs used in patient's home; prosthetic devices (other than dental) which replace all or part of an internal body organ; braces and artificial legs, arms, eyes, and so on.

H.R. 6675 as recommended by Senate Finance Committee. Similar to House bill, except that : (1) inpatient psychiatric hospital services covered under basic plan, rather than supplementary plan; (2) chiropracters' and podiatrists' services covered; (3) services of radiologists, pathologists, anesthesiologists, and physiatrists covered only when not billed through hospital.

H.R. 6675 as passed by Senate. Same as H.R. 6675 as recommended by Finance Committee.

H.R. 6675 as enacted into law. Similar to House bill, except that inpatient hospital services covered under basic plan, rather than supplementary plan.

Financing

King-Anderson bill (H.R. 1 and S. 1). No supplementary program.

Mills bill (H.R. 6675) as passed by House. Persons who elect to enroll would pay monthly premiums of $3, to be matched by federal government with payment from general revenues. ◆ Individual and government contributions would be placed in separate trust fund for supplementary plan. All benefit and administrative expenses under supplementary plan would be paid from this fund. ◆ Premium rates for enrolled persons (and matching government contribution) would be increased from time to time if program costs rise, but not more often than once every 2 years.

H.R. 6675 as recommended by Senate Finance Committee. Same as House bill.

H.R. 6675 as passed by Senate. Same as House bill.

H.R. 6675 as enacted into law. Same as House bill.

Administration

King-Anderson bill (H.R. 1 and S. 1). No supplementary program.

Mills bill (H.R. 6675) as passed by House. HEW Secretary required, to extent possible, to contract with carriers to carry out major administrative functions relating to medical aspects of program, such as determining rates of payments and holding and disbursing funds for benefit payments.

H.R. 6675 as recommended by Senate Finance Committee. HEW Secretary authorized to enter into contracts with carriers and, with respect to functions involving payment for physicians' services, Secretary required, to extent possible, to enter into such contracts.

H.R. 6675 as passed by Senate. Same as House bill.

H.R. 6675 as enacted into law. Same as House bill.

INCOME-TAX PROVISIONS

King-Anderson bill (H.R. 1 and S. 1). None.

Mills bill (H.R. 6675) as passed by House. Under income-tax law in effect before passage of medicare, persons under 65 could deduct only medical expenses in excess of 3 per cent of their adjusted gross income, while persons over 65 could deduct all medical expenses. Mills bill removed this special treatment for those over 65. In its place, the bill added a special deduction of one-half of medical-insurance premiums for taxpayers of all ages who itemize their deductions. This deduction limited to $250 per year.

H.R. 6675 as recommended by Senate Finance Committee. Eliminated changes made in House bill.

H.R. 6675 as passed by Senate. Same as H.R. 6675 as recommended by Finance Committee.

H.R. 6675 as enacted into law. Same as House bill, except that special deduction limited to $150 per year.

SELECTED BIBLIOGRAPHY

Anderson, Odin W. "Health Insurance in the United States, 1910-1920," *Journal of the History of Medicine and Allied Sciences,* IV (Autumn 1950), 363-396.

Burrow, James G. *AMA: Voice of American Medicine.* Baltimore: Johns Hopkins Press, 1963.

Cohen, Wilbur J., and Robert M. Ball. "Public Welfare Amendments of 1962 and Proposals for Health Insurance for the Aged," *Social Security Bulletin,* XXV (October 1962), 3-22.

———. "Social Security Amendments of 1965: Summary and Legislative History," *Social Security Bulletin,* XXVIII (September 1965), 3-21.

Davenport, Russell W. "Health Insurance Is Next," *Fortune,* XLI (March 1950), 63 ff.

"The Forand Bill: The Inside Story on Its Chances," *Medical Economics,* XXXVII (January 18, 1960), 217 ff.

Goldmann, Franz. "Labor's Attitude Toward Health Insurance," *Industrial and Labor Relations Review,* II (October 1948), 90-98.

Kelley, Stanley, Jr. *Professional Public Relations and Political Power.* Baltimore: Johns Hopkins Press, 1956.

"Many Interests Involved in Fight Over Aged Health Care," *Congressional Quarterly Weekly Report,* November 15, 1963, pp. 1991-1996.

Maslow, Harold. "The Background of the Wagner National Health Bill," *Law and Contemporary Problems,* VI (August 1939), 606-618.

Mitchell, William L. "Social Security Legislation in the Eighty-sixth Congress," *Social Security Bulletin,* XXIII (November 1960), 3-29.

Reed, Louis S. "Legislative Proposals for Compulsory Health Insurance," *Law and Contemporary Problems,* VI (August 1939), 628-644.

Rorty, James. *American Medicine Mobilizes.* New York: W. W. Norton Company, Inc., 1939.

U.S. HEW SSA. Division of Program Research. *Health Insurance and Related Proposals for Financing Personal Health Services: A Digest of Major Legislation and Proposals for Federal Action, 1935-1957.* By Agnes W. Brewster. 1958.

———. *Major Legislative Proposals for Financing Personal Health Services for the Aged, 1939-1961.* 1962.

U.S. Library of Congress. Legislative Reference Service. *The Administration's Health Reinsurance Proposal.* By Helen E. Livingston and Frederick B. Arner. October 17, 1955.

Witte, Edwin E. *The Development of the Social Security Act.* Madison: University of Wisconsin Press, 1962.

Alternative Solutions for the Aged

A major point at issue was the question of whether there were other methods that could and would meet the special needs of the aged as effectively as, or more effectively than, the Administration's proposals. Opponents of medicare pointed to three other mechanisms which, they said, together could "do the job that needs to be done": efforts by private organizations and individuals, including physicians; voluntary health insurance; and public assistance ("relief"), as liberalized by the Kerr-Mills law.

Private Efforts[a]

The first selection below is a discussion by the American Medical Association of the efforts of the medical profession and other private individuals and agencies to meet the problems of the elderly. In addition to the offer of free medical care for the needy made in this statement, the AMA also, on February 5, 1962, called on physicians to lower their fees for aged patients of modest means. In the subsequent selections, Congressman King and Dr. Mazique take issue with the American Medical Association, and Dr. Dixon discusses the impact that free care has on the hospital that provides it.

---

[a] Estimates of the monetary value of medical services provided through the efforts of private individuals and organizations appear in HEW's *Medical Resources Available to Meet the Needs of Public Assistance Recipients*, pp. 64-70.

Private, Voluntary Efforts and Those of the Medical Profession

AMERICAN MEDICAL ASSOCIATION

The range of private voluntary efforts is tremendous—from community "meals on wheels" programs to the construction of great hospitals through philanthropic grants. It includes the contribution you give to your Community Chest, as well as the work you do in your home town for a national program on, say, heart disease. For these activities, although general in nature, certainly include the elderly.

The private citizen, working at the local level, is the very backbone of our humanitarian yet realistic system of helping those who need help.

Perhaps we would only realize the full impact of voluntary, private, unselfish efforts on the local level, if suddenly they were to stop. We would be hard put to replace them, if, indeed, we even could.

Through cooperation at the community level, new chronic disease centers and referral centers are being built in substantial numbers, as are retirement villages and new nursing homes. Recreational facilities are being set up, home care activities are expanding, and research programs are becoming more extensive and more intensive. As the importance of rehabilitation becomes more evident, such plans are expanding rapidly.

Contributions to the health of the aged, made by private citizens through their religious, fraternal, civic, and philanthropic groups are immeasurable. I understand that this Committee has heard or will hear direct testimony on these activities from other witnesses, so I shall leave the details and most of the statistics to them.

However, I would like to point out that the Roman Catholic Church—with more than 39 million members—alone has established 314 homes for the aged which care for some 28,000 persons. And the Protestant Episcopal Church operates or is associated with 74 homes

From testimony at hearings on *Health Services for the Aged under the Social Security Insurance System,* held by the Committee on Ways and Means of the U.S. House of Representatives, August 2, 1961, pp. 1369-1377.

for the elderly, caring for 2,250 persons. These are but two of many examples.

As I indicated earlier, there are many efforts not designed especially for the aged, which nonetheless benefit them greatly—sometimes more so than they benefit the general population.

I am talking about such diverse programs as housing and recreation center developments; our ever-expanding corps of hospital volunteers; Community Chests and United Funds; and broad campaigns like those for mental health which carry special significance for the aged who occupy so much space in our mental institutions—often on a custodial care basis.

Imagination is at work, too, on the local level. New approaches in hospitals and nursing homes are emerging, such as progressive patient care, which moves the patient through successive stages of increasing self-help as his ailment improves. Thus, the hospital or nursing home can effect a financial savings while giving the patient better care, in this case a program of rehabilitation.

Another new technique is "hospital-in-the-round," which provides better patient supervision with less personnel. This is accomplished by constructing circular floors or wards and placing a supervising nurse at the hub.

And so, one quite properly asks whether passage of H.R. 4222 will damage private voluntary efforts to help the elderly. One also asks whether H.R 4222 will hamper the motivation for charitable contributions, whether it will discourage citizens from giving of their time and talent, whether it will stunt imagination in devising new ways of helping our elderly.

We believe it will—in every case mentioned above.

In short, we believe—and have so stated before—that legislation such as H.R. 4222 has many ill effects going beyond the intrinsic provisions of the bill. Such legislation would in our opinion curb community incentive to support hospitals, nursing homes, health campaigns and health centers; it would discourage at the community level freedom to experiment with new techniques, such as home care programs, homemaker services, progressive patient care, new concepts for treatment through outpatient departments and doctors' offices and the like; it would usurp—albeit inadequately—the magnificent role played by our fraternal, civic, religious, and philanthropic groups in the care of the aged.

Mr. Chairman, I think it is imperative that this Committee bear in mind not only what H.R. 4222 purports to accomplish, but also what it would damage, if not destroy.

What the Medical Profession Is Doing

. . . Without intending to "sing the praises" of the medical profession too loudly, I believe it is important to note that the value of medical care donated by private practitioners in the United States is now estimated to total $658 million a year. Admittedly, this figure is difficult to document. But we believe, in all sincerity, that it is conservative.

. . . Our profession has stated again and again that medical care is readily available to every citizen of this country, regardless of his age, and regardless of whether he is able to pay for it.

On behalf of the nation's physicians I make this statement again, confident that we can back it up.

Cases undoubtedly exist where this guarantee by the medical profession is not known to the potential patient. We want to know about these cases. I invite members of this Committee to inform us of any instances which come to their attention where it appears that inability to pay the cost of needed health services has resulted in failure by the nation's health professions to take appropriate action.

As the Committee may know, the American Medical Association formed a Committee on Geriatrics which met for the first time in 1955. At its first meeting, the Committee decided that the word "geriatrics" in its title was improper; for there are no diseases *of* the aged, but simply diseases *among* the aged. Accordingly, the Committee changed its name to the Committee on Aging.

I feel it is in order at this point to tell what this Committee, the American Medical Association generally, and state and local medical societies have been doing in this field since I last appeared before the House Ways and Means Committee in 1959.

1. *Regional Conferences on Aging.* During 1959-60 the AMA's Committee on Aging and 48 state medical associations sponsored nine regional conferences on aging, involving both lay and professional leaders from diverse fields of interest.

These conferences focused widespread attention on the need for a broader understanding of the true needs, the health status and the capabilities of older people. . . .

2. *State Medical Association Activities.* All state medical associations and more than 100 county societies have active committees on aging. Their activities include: sponsorship of conferences on aging for both lay and professional leaders; promotion of health maintenance pro-

grams; special surveys of older people, their needs, and the resources available in the community and state to meet these needs; the sponsoring of voluntary health insurance and prepayment programs for persons over 65; testimony before Federal and State government committees holding hearings on aging; improvement of state and local indigent care programs; stimulation of nursing home construction; promotion of homemaker services, home care programs, rehabilitation services in nursing homes, and other special health care programs; educational programs to acquaint the public with medicine's continuing positive programs on behalf of older persons; leadership in formation of state joint councils to improve the health care of the aged; special articles or issues by state medical journals devoted to aging; and in many states extremely active participation in state and local activities related to the 1961 White House Conference on Aging. . . .

3. *White House Conference on Aging.* Staff and Committee on Aging members served as consultants to the sections on Health and Medical Care, Research in Gerontology, Medical and Family Life at the White House Conference on Aging held in January of this year. Two hundred and eighty-eight of the 2,700 delegates were physicians and dentists. . . .

4. *Committee Papers.* To further the work accomplished at the nine regional conferences on aging, the Committee is undertaking an expanded educational program, based on a booklet entitled *Medicine's Blueprint,* to stimulate a broader understanding of the ways in which all groups and individuals will be affected by improved health and longer life expectancy. Plans are being made for meetings with such groups as educators, business and labor, the health professions and others, to explore the implications posed for each by the new era of aging. Through these meetings and through Committee publications, attention will be focused on such areas as education of today's youth for a longer, healthier life; development of health maintenance programs by individuals of all ages; more realistic employment and retirement policies; new emphases needed in care of the sick; the changing roles of physicians, dentists and other health professionals; and community programs for older people. . . .

5. *Inter-Professional Post-Graduate Training.* State and county societies, through their committees on aging, are sponsoring scientific programs and articles to acquaint physicians with new discoveries and techniques in the care of the older patient. The AMA's Committee on Aging also sponsors such scientific programs at the Association's Annual and Clinical Meetings.

6. *Committee Publications.* "*Medicine's Blueprint for the New Era of Aging: A Positive Health Program for Older Persons*"; "*Health Aspects of Aging*"; and "*Report of the Regional Conferences on Aging*" have been distributed widely to individuals and groups interested in the field of aging. In addition, the AMA Council on Medical Service, of which the Committee on Aging is a component, publishes two bi-monthly newsletters entitled the "Chronic Illness Newsletter" and "Homemaker Service Bulletin". These are mailed, without charge, to approximately 9,000 persons. . . .

7. *Joint Council to Improve the Health Care of the Aged.* This national Joint Council was established in October, 1958, by the American Medical Association, American Hospital Association, American Dental Association, and American Nursing Home Association. The major purposes of the national Joint Council are to encourage and assist affiliates in establishing state joint councils; to develop patterns for joint effort and planning; and, as the principal purveyors of health care for the aged, to establish liaison and cooperative relationships with other organizations working with similar purposes in: identifying and analyzing the health needs of the aged; appraising available health resources for the aged; fostering effective methods of payment for the health care of the aged; developing community programs to foster the best possible health care for the aged; fostering health education programs of the aged; and informing the public of the facts related to health care of the aged.

To achieve these goals the national Joint Council sponsored its first national conference in June, 1959. The second national conference will be held December 14-15, 1961 in Chicago. Thirty-three states have active Joint Councils. . . .

8. *Current Association Projects.* At the present time, the staff of the AMA is gathering data in the following areas: (a) economic resources among older people; (b) the effect of reduced employment opportunities on health of older persons; and (c) the relative ability of persons under and over 65 to pay for hospital care. . . . Data obtained thus far concerning the ability of those under and over 65 to meet hospital expenses indicates that less than 5 per cent of the over 65 group have unpaid bills, in contrast to approximately 14 per cent of those under 65 with unpaid bills.

Finally, Mr. Chairman, I should like to outline the American Medical Association's policy on aging as adopted by the House of Delegates at its Clinical Session in 1960. This policy has served as the guidepost for action by the individual physician; our state and county medical societies; and the AMA itself.

1. *Older Individuals Should Not Be Isolated:* The medical profession and others interested in aging should resist any effort to break up the family into groups because of arbitrary differences such as age. Instead they should strive to keep the unit together by placing emphasis on their similarities.

The stimulation of a realistic attitude toward aging should be a major educational goal for medical societies and other groups or individuals because of its vital importance to the health of older people. This educational effort should emphasize: (a) the capabilities of older people, and the contributions they can make if their potential is used properly; (b) the importance of physical, mental and financial preparation for later years by each individual; (c) the fallacy of forced retirement based on chronological age and recognition instead of the ability and desire of the older person to continue working; (d) the need to end discrimination in initial employment on the basis of age, with employers and employees cooperating to develop full and part-time opportunities for persons unable to continue their normal job activity.

2. *A Health Maintenance Program Is Necessary for Every Individual:* The physician has a key role in encouraging his patients to follow a health maintenance program. The individual has primary responsibility for maintaining his own health, however, and must do certain things for himself. These include: (a) attention to proper diet, exercise and living habits in earlier years to ensure healthier later years; and (b) regular physical checkups and early treatment of disease or disability which may prevent the latter's progression. . . .

3. *Voluntary Health Insurance and Prepayment Plans Can and Should Provide the Basis for Meeting Health Care Costs for Most People:* State and county medical societies should continue leadership in encouraging development of voluntary health insurance plans for older persons, both employed and retired. Particular emphasis should be given to the development of health insurance and prepayment policies tailored to meet the needs of patients requiring long-term nursing home and home-centered care.

While personal health care is primarily the responsibility of the individual, when he is unable to provide this care for himself, the responsibility should properly pass first to his family, then the community, then the state, and only when all these fail, to the Federal

Government. Religious and fraternal groups are especially suited to provide the first support in the event of impaired ability of individual or family.

4. *More Persons Interested in and Working with the Older People in Medical and Other Professional Fields Are Needed.* . . .

5. *More Adequate Nursing Home Facilities Are an Urgent Health Need for Some Older People in Many Communities:* Constituent and component medical societies and individual physicians should cooperate with nursing homes, hospitals and other community leaders in effective efforts to improve nursing home standards and to expedite construction of new nursing home facilities where needed.

6. *Further Development of Services and Facilities Are Required:* This includes: (a) such home-centered services as home care programs, homemaker, and visiting nurse services to provide a basis for improved health care of many older persons; (b) experimentation in such other new methods of providing better health care as rehabilitation education services in nursing homes, chronic illness referral centers, and progressive patient care in hospitals; and (c) an increasing number of community councils on aging and special study projects. Because health receives so much emphasis in all these activities, it is imperative that the medical profession provide its special knowledge to such programs and vigorously make its leadership felt.

7. *Extension of Research in Both Medical and Socio-economic Aspects of Aging Is Vital.* . . .

8. *Local Programs for Older Persons, Especially Those Which Emphasize the Importance of Self-help and Independence by the Senior Citizen, Should Be a Major Concern of Medicine, Both Collectively and Individually:* The Association endorses community activities for older people such as may be found in churches, senior achievement groups, "Golden Age Clubs" and day centers. Emphasis in all such programs and activities should be placed on active, day-by-day integration of the older person with the community as a whole, encompassing all age groups, and not just those in later years.

9. *Local Medical Society Committees, along with Other Leaders in Community Service, Should Be Equipped to Appraise the Advantage or Disadvantage of Proposed Housing for Older People:* In evaluating all kinds of "senior citizen" housing, recognition should be given to the need for older people to continue as active, independent, integral parts of community life as long as possible. As an alternative to institutional care of the extremely old person, the development of special housing facilities with medical supervision and other supportive services should be encouraged by medicine at all levels.

My Bill Would Not Damage Voluntary Community Efforts or Those of the Medical Profession

CECIL R. KING

The AMA . . . advances the preposterous argument that H.R. 4222 will damage or destroy such varied activities as community meals-on-wheels programs, construction of hospitals through philanthropic grants, community chest activities, and voluntary efforts to build chronic disease centers, retirement villages, church homes for the aged, and nursing homes.

It is true of course that if the bill is enacted, individuals and voluntary organizations will be relieved, to a large extent, of one burden they now carry: If the bill is enacted, many thousands of older Americans will no longer have to seek charity from voluntary organizations when they become ill. I know that both the charitable organizations and the aged will look upon this as a blessing. . . . The enactment of my bill would enable charity organizations to devote their energies and resources to meet more completely the varied needs of the community. For example, voluntary hospitals, or nursing homes that are constantly in financial difficulty because they must accept older people who cannot pay for the care they receive would be relieved of this problem. The funds that are released would be available for improving the services these hospitals and nursing homes give to their patients; or the funds would be available to reduce the rates that now have to be charged to paying patients.

If H.R. 4222 is enacted, community chests and other large and small voluntary organizations that contribute to support hospitals and nursing homes will of course benefit in the same way. These organizations will then be able to devote more of their resources and energies to building retirement villages, meals-on-wheels programs, and a myriad of other needed services.

From "Comments on Testimony of American Medical Association," *Congressional Record*, CVIII (March 5, 1962), 3112-3113 (daily ed.).

The AMA has described in detail the efforts that many American doctors and medical organizations are voluntarily making to meet the health problems of older Americans. I was impressed primarily with the wide range of activities that physicians carry on in order to advance science, promote better public understanding of the problems of aging, and encourage better medical, public health and rehabilitation services for aged people. I think it is also important to point out, however, that the bill would not alter or in any way affect these activities of physicians.

I would like to add that whatever progress has been made in improving the medical and vocational services available to older people has been due not only to the efforts of physicians but also to the efforts of Americans in many different occupations who have joined in bringing to bear their energies, their different skills, and their money to common purposes. Also, it is fair to point out that the Federal Government has played an important and active part in these achievements.

The AMA rightly emphasizes that there still remains a great need for additional hospitals, nursing homes and other community health facilities. . . . H.R. 4222 would assist . . . by enabling the aged to pay for the health care they receive. It is common knowledge that providing free care and below-cost care for the aged has placed a considerable financial strain on hospitals that has impeded improvements in hospital care. Obviously, the inability of aged people to pay for needed health care has also hampered the development of facilities designed to meet the health needs of old age. The current low level of care in nursing homes is a good example of the quality of the health care the aged now get through present financing arrangements. When provision is made so that the aged are able to finance the care they need, facilities will be constructed to provide that care.

Can Charity Fill the Vacuum?

EDWARD C. MAZIQUE

I bitterly disagree with one of my colleagues' announced alternative of a few days ago that doctors will gladly give their services to those unable to pay. First, diagnosing and prescribing is but one aspect of medical need; the aged require medicine, nursing care and at times, more often than the general population, require hospitalization and surgery. I have yet to locate the drug firm with free or marked down prescriptions for the aged. In my case, I could very well spend all my time calling on the aged and aging or at least a significant portion to the neglect of other patients and my bills. No allowances are made by bill collectors for the charity doctor. Moreover, for the Negro physician, because of the peculiar historic relationship of his patients to the American economy, the problems of the aged and aging is often more serious than that of the general population. . . .

Governmental insured medical care for the aged will mean more hospitals, more remuneration for physicians, better health for the Nation as a whole. Only the Government can provide necessary capital to construct adequate clinics and schools needed to generate medical capital out of the physical and intellectual surplus now lying idle. We have enough girls and boys to serve as nurses and doctors to staff adequate health centers. We have untapped resources to compound prescriptions enough to allay the pains of every one of the aged. We have the manpower and bricks and other building materials to house the ailing senior citizens. When delivery of the mail and education of children became too complex to be democratically handled by private interests the Government stepped in and administered these programs and so it is today in modern society as regard our aged and aging.

From a statement at hearings on *Health Needs of the Aged and Aging* before the Subcommittee on Problems of the Aged and Aging of the U.S. Senate Committee on Labor and Public Welfare (86th Congress, 2nd Session, April 12, 1960), pp. 232-233. Dr. Mazique is President of the National Medical Association, an organization of physicians whose membership is predominantly Negro.

Unreimbursed Hospital Care for the Needy Endangers the Entire Hospital System

JAMES P. DIXON

During the fiscal year just ended, our 58 member hospitals located in Pennsylvania rendered over 1 million days of inpatient care to the needy at an average ward cost of $20 per patient day or a total cost of over $20 million. An entire third of this cost represented unpaid care rendered to persons on social security.

Toward this $20 million of free care, the city of Philadelphia contributed $10 million, the State of Pennsylvania granted $4.4 million, and the United Fund contributed an additional $1.3 million. Our hospitals were thus required to provide nearly $5 million in free care from their own resources. This deficit is up nearly half a million dollars from the previous year and is rising steadily.

Unrestricted endowments in most hospitals have long since been swallowed up by these deficits, and ward bed endowment no longer attracts private philanthropy.

We are caught in yet another squeeze between our traditional charity standards and our traditionally low wage standards. Philadelphia hospitals are currently undergoing a union organizing drive under the slogan that hospital employees should not be required to subsidize community hospitals through substandard wages. As this situation resolves itself, it will undoubtedly add to our financial crises, since wages and salaries make up about 80 percent of hospital operating costs.

Unpaid care has become such a drain on the resources of our hospitals that the quality and the availability of hospital services are seriously threatened. Every possible resource is poured into free care; funds are lacking to modernize or replace outmoded buildings and equipment; services have been reduced substantially in several hospi-

From a statement at hearings on *Hospital, Nursing Home, and Surgical Benefits for OASI Beneficiaries* held before the Committee on Ways and Means of the U.S. House of Representatives (86th Congress, 1st Session, July 13, 1959), pp. 47-49. At the time this statement was made, Dr. Dixon was a director of the Hospital Council of Philadelphia. At present, he is President of Antioch College.

tals and others are on the verge of doing so. The hardest hit are inevitably those carrying the heaviest charity load. . . .

We cannot realistically expect State and local governments and the public assistance program to meet the total free care burden, or even a much larger portion of it than the 45 percent now covered in Pennsylvania. Large sums of new money will have to be made available from some new source if the situation is to be improved.

Persons receiving benefits from the old-age, survivors, and disability insurance (OASDI) constitute the largest single segment of people receiving this unpaid care. There are currently about 250,000 people on social security in the five counties of southeastern Pennsylvania, and these people use about 36 percent of all free care given in the area's 58 hospitals. If these beneficiaries were covered by hospital insurance, a third of our free care deficits would be wiped out. State and local grants could then be applied to the remaining two-thirds, and hospitals would be financially able to devote a much larger portion of their income to improvement of services and the raising of wages.

We have undertaken to determine whether the situation in Pennsylvania and in our region is similar to the situation in the country as a whole.

We have found ample evidence, both from earlier reports of this committee and from other sources, to indicate that the problem of hospital care for older people is inadequately met on a national basis, and, furthermore, that the extent of the problem, both in terms of numbers to be served and costs of necessary services, is rapidly expanding.

Private Health Insurance

Chapter I pointed out the connection between work status and health-insurance coverage. Most of the elderly are not employed; consequently, it has been difficult for them to get health insurance. As attention was called to this problem by the efforts to enact hospitalization insurance based on social security, the insurance industry began to make new efforts to sign up the elderly. Emphasis was placed on mass enrollment during limited time periods, in this way cutting overhead and reducing the possibility that only bad risks would sign up. Blue Cross had traditionally permitted a person, on retiring, to convert the group insurance he had at work to an individual policy, at higher cost. The commercial insurance companies began to follow suit. Some firms continued group coverage of their retired pensioners.

The most striking development, however, was the issuance of individual insurance to persons over 65 who had not been previously insured, something which was largely unheard of until the late 1950's. These policies are provided by individual insurance companies and by groups of companies banded together under special, permissive legislation to offer "65 Plus" coverage. They are noncancelable and require no medical examination, although preexisting conditions are not covered for the early period of the policy's life, and benefits are more limited than those provided by other insurance policies. Although the individual insurance companies offering special policies for the aged expect to make a profit, the intercompany pools, according to *The Wall Street Journal*, "generally hope merely to break even."

As a result of these efforts, health-insurance coverage of the elderly has increased markedly, although it still remains less than coverage of the rest of the population. Today, from 54 to 60 per cent of the elderly have health insurance, compared to about 75 per cent of the younger population. As might be expected, the low-income elderly are less likely to have insurance than the better-off—about two-fifths of those earning under $2,000 a year, compared to three-fourths of those earning $10,000 and over, have insurance. The sick are less likely to have insurance than those who are well. The health insurance carried by the elderly is primarily hospitalization insurance, and the elderly who *do* carry insurance have policies which pay a smaller proportion of their hospital bills than do the policies carried by younger elements of the population. There is some controversy over the extent of private insurance coverage of the elderly. Late in 1963, the Under Secretary of Health, Education, and Welfare charged that the insurance industry was intentionally inflating the number of aged who carried health insurance in order to substantiate arguments against King-Anderson.[b] The Senate Aging Committee's Subcommittee on the Health of the Elderly inquired into this charge at its April 1964 hearings. The subcommittee's report, issued in July, supported the Under Secretary's charge, although with a vigorous dissent by three of the four minority members of the subcommittee.

But the real issue is not the extent of *present* coverage of the elderly. Rather, it is the extent of the potential for future coverage. Supporters of medicare say that private insurance cannot meet the needs of high-risk, low-income groups, such as the aged. They agree that the new devices and harder selling efforts of the insurance industry have increased the extent of aged coverage considerably. However, they say that most of the elderly covered so far are working, have higher incomes, and/or are in better health. The needs of the remainder cannot be met by private insurance, which cannot overcome the basic obstacles of high medical needs and low income of the aged. Because of these obstacles, they say, the special insurance programs for the elderly are often priced beyond the reach of the bulk of the elderly and/or provide benefits that are too small to meet their needs. Despite such limitations, these special programs are losing money; the New York State pool, for example, lost over $2 million in its first 14 months of operation. Both the individual insurance companies and the intercompany pools announced or requested substantial rate increases in the past two years. For this reason, medicare's supporters allege, special programs for the aged are not offered by the

---

[b] His statement is reprinted at pp. 1508-1510 of the Ways and Means Committee's 1964 hearings.

better insurance companies, but rather by "second-string companies."ᶜ

Advocates of medicare argue further that private health insurance, because it cannot handle the load of the elderly, is not doing
as good a job for the rest of the population as it otherwise could.
Thus, they say, removal of the need to take care of the aged will
enable private health insurance to do a better job for the rest of
the population, thereby strengthening the private, voluntary insurance mechanism in our economy. Because the elderly will have
only part of their medical costs covered by medicare, there will
still be a market for supplementary private insurance.

Opponents of medicare agree that health insurance has not
been readily available to the aged in the past. However, this situation has changed. Such insurance is now available, they say, and
the bulk of the aged who want and need health insurance now
have it. Most of the aged can afford private health insurance; the
minority that cannot afford it can be taken care of through other
means, such as public assistance or charity. Thus, private health
insurance can meet, and is meeting, the needs of the elderly. The
adoption of federal hospitalization insurance for the aged, they
say, will mean the end of private health-insurance underwriting.
Why should anyone pay for private insurance in addition to the
public insurance he is required to pay for?

The two selections which follow present these opposing points
of view.

ᶜ Statement of Dr. Paul Hanchett at the April 1964 hearings of the Senate Subcommittee on the Health of the Elderly, pp. 225-229.

Advancements of Private Insurance and Prepayment Mechanisms

AMERICAN MEDICAL ASSOCIATION

... I have pointed out the vital role played by private health insurance and prepayment plans in helping the aged cushion the financial shock of illness. Half the aged are now covered. And in the years ahead, an increasing percentage of older people will reach retirement age with health insurance coverage *if*—and I stress the word "if"—measures like H.R. 4222 are not enacted into law.

The passage of such legislation would unquestionably undermine private health insurance. It would substitute a compulsory system of health care financing for a voluntary system that has proved its ability to do the job that needs doing beyond any measure of doubt. It is realistic, in our opinion, to predict the decline, if not the demise, of private health insurance if H.R. 4222 were passed, for those compelled by law to carry the cost of a national compulsory "health" plan would be neither able nor anxious to carry private health policies as well.

The American Medical Association is convinced that private health insurance and prepayment plans constitute the most effective device available to the elderly for the financing of health care. Yet the proponents of compulsory national health plans are fond of claiming that persons over 65 cannot get private health insurance or that if they can, the insurance is inadequate. "Voluntary health insurance will never do the job of the elderly," they affirm.

This is a different statement than they were making on this subject at the time of the Murray-Wagner-Dingell legislation controversy. At that time, the same people were saying that private health insurance could never do the job for the population as a whole. The record disproves this, as some of the proponents of a compulsory national health plan for the elderly now admit. They now assert that, although private health insurance is doing the job of providing coverage for the

From testimony at hearings on *Health Services for the Aged under the Social Security Insurance System,* held by the Committee on Ways and Means of the U.S. House of Representatives, August 2, 1961, pp. 1382-1388.

vast majority of Americans of all ages, it does not and will not provide effective protection for the elderly.

A look at the record will again prove enlightening.

It is no overstatement to say that the growth of private health insurance since World War II has been phenomenal. . . .

Perhaps the pertinent fact here is that the amount of health insurance owned by the aged is growing at a faster rate than that owned by the population as a whole.

In March of 1952, only 26 per cent of persons 65 and older had health insurance coverage of any kind. But by the middle of 1961 more than 50 per cent owned some kind of coverage, according to estimates of the Health Insurance Association of America. By contrast, 59 per cent of persons of all ages were covered as of 1952, while an estimated 73 per cent are now covered.

This means, then, that while coverage for the number of persons of all ages rose 14 per cent from 1952 to 1961, coverage for our aged citizens showed an amazing jump of more than 50 per cent.

It should also be remembered that our aged population increased significantly during that period. Thus, the 26 per cent covered in 1952 represented 3.4 million persons, while the current figure of more than 50 per cent represents over eight million persons.

We know, moreover, that perhaps 25 to 30 per cent of the aged are not in the market for health insurance because their medical care is provided through Old Age Assistance Programs or other means. Therefore, we can safely conclude that 70 per cent of the aged who are in the market for voluntary health insurance now have it.

The rapid increase in coverage of those 65 and over can be expected to continue. HIAA[d] estimates that by the end of 1965, 80 per cent of the aged needing and wanting protection will be insured. The figure is expected to climb to 90 per cent by 1970.

In short, private health insurance in this country is well on the way toward accomplishing near-universal coverage of the entire population. And that coverage is versatile enough, adequate enough, and available enough to meet the needs of this nation.

As the Committee is aware, Mr. Chairman, many factors enter into establishing fees for professional services. The ability of the patient to pay is only one of them. Nonetheless, in December of 1958, the AMA House of Delegates adopted a report which reiterated this well-established principle and further encouraged the development of low-

---

[d] The Health Insurance Association of America, an insurance-industry trade association.

cost health insurance and prepayment programs for persons who were over 65 and in modest circumstances.

The response to this re-statement of policy was immediate from state medical societies and their Blue Shield plans. . . .

At present, there are 51 plans in 41 states and the District of Columbia offering non-group coverage to persons over 65; and 11 additional plans under development in four states. This compares with 40 plans in 37 states last year.

Some 240 voluntary health-insuring organizations—including Blue Cross and Blue Shield—are now issuing hospital or surgical policies to the elderly.

Aware of the great potential market in insurance for those 65 and over, aggressive companies are continually driving premium costs down.

The Blue Cross Association reported recently that 1960 was its biggest year. Representing some 79 health and hospital plans across the nation, Blue Cross membership reached 56,063,215 in 1960—a gain of 1,041,382 over the previous year.

In reviewing the year, the Association's president James E. Stuart, had this to say:

"The quality and quantity of hospital care measures up to the standards required by medical progress: that constantly improving hospital care can be made accessible without hindrance to all who need it."

Benefits for the elderly are provided in a number of different ways. Without exception, older active workers are continued in group insurance plans. Most new group plans provide for the continuation of benefits to retiring workers; other group plans allow retiring workers to convert their insurance to individual policies; and paid-up-at-age 65 policies are now available.

The Health Insurance Institute[e] reports that seven out of every ten workers covered under group health insurance policies issued during 1960 have the right to retain their protection when they retire. The greater availability of coverages that continue into retirement is shown by contrasting the 1960 data with findings at the end of 1959.

According to HII, in 1959 only 55 per cent—or about five out of every ten workers—had the right either to continue or convert their coverage upon retirement.

By and large, the majority of insured individuals continue into their

---

[e] An insurance-industry trade association.

later years individual contracts issued at younger ages. As I have pointed out, this number is increasing rapidly. As to policies especially designed for older persons, many of them do not require evidence of good health as a condition of eligibility. After a short probationary period, these policies pay benefits for losses due to pre-existing conditions.

I should like to stress here that insurance companies are constantly bending their efforts to develop new ways of helping the aged obtain the protection they need.

For example, a number of insurers are now setting up group plans for such associations of older people as Golden Age Clubs.

As an instance of the fresh, creative thinking that is being done throughout the country in this field, insurance carriers from Connecticut are joining together in order to offer major medical and hospital insurance programs to senior citizens at the lowest possible premium. In its initial stages, the program will be experimental and confined to the state of Connecticut, but eventually this approach may well spread throughout the country. . . .

Efforts in Pennsylvania are also noteworthy—to cite just one other state. The Pennsylvania Medical Society has provided the stimulus for a Blue Shield Senior Citizen program recently approved by the state insurance commissioner. The Senior Citizen Program is being offered to Pennsylvanians age 65 and older who are not already Blue Shield subscribers.

Under the plan, these older persons are permitted to buy prepaid medical care insurance regardless of age or the condition of their health.

In addition, there are opportunities for persons over 65 to obtain insurance protection through such plans as Continental Casualty's 65-Plus Plan, the Senior Security Plan of Mutual of Omaha, the 65/1 Plan of Firemen's Fund, and the like.

In view of this record, it is difficult to see the basis on which claims are made that privately purchased health insurance is of little or no help to the aged in helping cushion the costs of illness.

Yet those who favor a compulsory national health plan continue their charges that the voluntary health insurance system is ineffective.

For example, the Committee may have heard it stated that our voluntary health system offers no protection to 28 per cent of the civilian population, or 49 million persons. The reason why this is true, it is said, is because the 49 million people involved simply cannot meet the premium rates. And why not? Because these unprotected members of the population are the aged, the disabled, the low-income workers, and the unemployed.

Is it true—as is sometimes alleged—that 49 million people do not have voluntary health insurance because the cost of the premium is beyond their means?

The Health Information Foundation[f] has examined data on those of the aged with, and those without, voluntary health insurance. Of all the aged surveyed, less than three per cent had tried to obtain health insurance and been turned down. Of those uninsured at the time of the survey, about one-half said they could not afford or could not get health coverage; one-fourth said they had never thought about health coverage; and most of the remaining fourth said they did not want coverage.

Frankly, Mr. Chairman, there has been a concerted and deliberate effort to discredit voluntary health insurance. To state that voluntary health insurance is beyond the ability to pay of 49 million people is either evidence of bias or an inability to draw logical conclusions from plain facts. It may be true that 49 million do not have voluntary health insurance. It is not true that all of them are unable to afford the premiums—as the survey of the Health Information Foundation shows.

Another criticism in the campaign to discredit voluntary health insurance is that relatively few of the aged obtain benefits through it. This is usually presented as an indictment; however, it may be interpreted more appropriately as evidence that the aged are in good health—and particularly the insured aged.

The fact that one is lucky enough—or better, healthy enough—to escape the need for using health insurance certainly does not mean he has been inadequately covered. He bought, paid for, and received protection of a certain type for a certain period of time. That in itself is value received. Just the same, let us look briefly at another example of how statistics on health insurance are misinterpreted.

The Social Security Administration's Bureau of Old Age, Survivors and Disability Insurance reached the following conclusion after conducting a survey of insurance beneficiaries in 1957:

"Relatively few—14 per cent of the couples and nine per cent of the non-married beneficiaries—had any of their [total medical care] expenses covered by insurance."

---

[f] A research organization established by a number of executives in the pharmaceutical and related industries.

Now, it is a feature of all health insurance that one must use medical care in order to receive a benefit. But apparently this axiom has eluded some of the experts.

It should further be pointed out that hospital insurance is far and away the most common type among insured persons. Therefore, in a survey such as the above, many persons failing to be hospitalized during their illness would be counted among those who received no benefits from their policies.

Analysis of the data yielded by the survey reveals that 79 per cent of all OASDI beneficiary couples and 84 per cent of all OASDI non-married beneficiaries surveyed did not enter a hospital during the survey period. The data are not arranged to indicate whether those who were hospitalized had health insurance and received hospitalization insurance benefits. Nor is it clear whether the 14 per cent of the couples who had some of their medical care expenses covered by insurance received hospitalization benefits only, or received hospitalization plus other benefits.

Nonetheless, the data suggest that a possible 65 to 70 per cent of the beneficiary couples who did use the hospital *could* have obtained aid in paying the cost. This performance of voluntary health insurance is extremely good.

The multiplicity of plans, coverages and rates is sometimes referred to as a weakness by critics of voluntary health insurance. I feel, however, that this is one of the greatest strengths of the voluntary mechanism.

Is is a strength for the simple reason that it permits the individual a wide variety of choices in the selection for a health care plan. He can select the plan that is uniquely best for him, the plan tailored to his need.

Even assuming that most people prefer a particular kind of plan—whether it be employee benefits, with or without Blue Cross or Blue Shield or some other device—there is still available to them a wide variety of health insurance programs.

Let me sum up this discussion by pointing out that the performance of voluntary health insurance is one of the great arguments against a national compulsory "health" scheme for any segment of the population.

Voluntary health insurance has done a remarkable job in its brief history. It is capable of doing an even more remarkable job in the years ahead, not only in terms of the steadily increasing percentage of our population that will be covered, but in the quality of the coverage that it will provide.

In addition, use of voluntary health insurance assures free choice by the individual buyer of the coverage best suited to his particular requirements.

Under H.R. 4222, choice of coverage would be eliminated. In its place would be substituted a rigid, inadequate pattern of benefits imposed on the aged by the government, regardless of individual needs or wishes in the matter.

Private Insurance Cannot Provide Adequately for the Aged

CECIL R. KING

In the AMA statement, the supporters of H.R. 4222 are accused of being opposed to the development of private health insurance for the aged. . . . Nothing could be further from the truth. And the allegation —presumably attributed to me and to the supporters of my bill—that 49 million people cannot afford health insurance is something I never heard of before. . . . I accept the AMA's proof that this allegation, which I presume was originated by the AMA, has no base. I have watched with interest the growth of health insurance for the younger population and hoped that their coverage would be paralleled by comparable coverage for the aged, which would have helped solve their health care cost problems. However, this has not occurred—less than 50 percent of the aged have any kind of insurance and much of it is completely inadequate for their health care needs.

Now, it should be made clear that I do not criticize the Blue Cross plans nor the insurance companies for this. On the other hand, I applaud their commendable efforts and ingenuity and I admire, along with the AMA, the noteworthy recent efforts of the Connecticut insurance companies and the Pennsylvania Medical Society to provide adequate insurance for the aged. . . .

The AMA, after "adjusting" the figure on aged people without health insurance to take out the people on public assistance, proudly announces that "We can safely conclude that 70 percent of the aged who are in the market for voluntary insurance now have it." . . . Since illness and high-health-care costs are major reasons for applying for assistance and many of these people would not be on assistance if they had health insurance, it is remarkable that the AMA chooses to count those on assistance as "not in the market." They, like all the low-and-moderate-income aged, are "not in the market" for adequate commercial insurance in the same sense that they are not in the market for automobiles—they cannot afford them. This kind of measurement

From "Comments on Testimony of American Medical Association," *Congressional Record*, CVIII (March 5, 1962), 3114-3115 (daily ed.).

is appropriate for market research purposes but not for the purpose of determining the need for health insurance for the aged.

Furthermore, it is not enough to provide figures on how many aged persons are covered; it is important to note the characteristics of people who do not have insurance, a subject which the AMA statement avoids. According to the National Health Survey, in 1959 health insurance coverage was carried by only 33 percent of the aged in families with less than $2,000 yearly income, by only 42 percent of the retired aged, and by only 30 percent of the aged unable to work or keep house due to chronic conditions. Thus, extension of insurance coverage to the aged who are not insured becomes increasingly difficult to achieve because they are more likely to be persons in the low-income and poor health-risk groups who cannot afford insurance and are poor prospects from a commercial insurance point of view.

In view of these facts, I am not impressed with the AMA figures on the number of insurance plans offering health insurance to the aged or on the number of workers with insurance that could continue into retirement. . . . It would be more significant if the AMA would provide data on the premium costs of adequate insurance for the aged and the number of aged persons who could afford to pay these costs.

I have several times referred to the inadequacy of insurance for the aged, a subject on which the AMA statement does not provide the facts, and I would like to offer some specific information about this matter. The Department of Health, Education, and Welfare has provided me with the following information which is based on the Health Insurance Institute's 1960 report on "Health Insurance Plans and Policies of Insurance Companies Available to Americans 65 Years of Age and Older." . . .

It is instructive to compare the premiums of the policies with broader coverage—though all are quite limited—to the median income of an aged person, namely, about $1,000. Such policies do not provide payment for nursing home care, home health services, outpatient diagnostic procedures, physician home and office visits, drugs, dental care nor eyeglasses; the payments provided for hospital room and board are far below the usual charges to the patient, and those for miscellaneous extras would rarely cover all the charges for operating room, recovery room, laboratory, and special diagnostic services; but the premiums run as high as $122 for an individual, which would amount to over 12 percent of income for aged persons with average income.

Even Blue Cross often does not provide coverage for some of the aged subscribers equal to that which it offers to the younger members. Senior certificates typically provide for no more than 31 days of hospital benefits and many provide limited allowances—$7 to $10 a day—toward the cost of room and board, or provide for a deductible or for coinsurance. In most cases there is an exclusion or limitation on hospitalization coverage for preexisting conditions.

The AMA statement says that the passage of H.R. 4222 "would unquestionably undermine private health insurance." I think the AMA is unquestionably wrong on this point. The proposed health insurance benefits would not cover the younger group who number nine-tenths of the population; nor would they cover all the health care costs of the aged. Many aged persons will want to buy insurance protection against the costs of drugs, medical appliances, and physicians' services and will in fact be encouraged to do so by reason of having the basic coverage of health service costs under the bill.

In a speech before the last annual meeting of the Health Insurance Association, Frederic M. Peirce, president of General American Life, although opposed to the administration's bill, stated that such a program would not end private health insurance. He pointed to the growth of life insurance since enactment of the Social Security Act, and went on to say, "It is a record which provides a fitting analogy and a sound precedent upon which to base the expectation that the health insurance business will continue to grow and prosper despite the advent of Government-provided health insurance, if that unwelcome development should come to pass." Many other spokesmen for commercial health insurance agree with Mr. Peirce. Why should the allegations of the AMA then, that health insurance would be undermined, be given credence?

I was amused by the AMA's fumbling attempt to discredit a statement taken, out of context, from a report submitted to the Committee on Ways and Means by the Department of Health, Education, and Welfare in 1959. The statement excerpted from the report is:

Relatively few—14 percent of the couples and 9 percent of the nonmarried beneficiaries—had any of their [total medical care] expenses covered by insurance. . . .

The AMA would have us believe that the small proportion of the aged with medical expenses covered by insurance is proof that the aged are healthy. This must be the case, they imply, since "one must use medical care to receive a health insurance benefit." . . . This is a fantastic extreme of misinterpretation. The part of the report from which the AMA lifted its quote had reference to "beneficiary groups incurring medical costs." The report brought out that of those incurring costs relatively few had any of their costs covered by insurance. Far from saying that few of the aged received medical care or had medical expenses, the report brought out that actually only 3 percent of the aged couple beneficiaries and only 8 percent of the nonmarried aged beneficiaries in the survey had no medical expenses during the survey year.

The AMA statement places much emphasis on the multiplicity of plans and "the wide variety of choice in the selection of a health plan." . . . Let me point out that, with the small incomes of aged people, choice is limited to what can be afforded. The services covered under the bill are basic ones. With the coverage of these basic costs, then aged people will really be able to choose among the additional benefits available under private health insurance.

Public Assistance

Approximately 2¼ million elderly persons—about 13 per cent of the aged population—receive old-age assistance. The proportion of the aged population receiving such assistance varies from state to state; it is generally higher in rural Southern states and lower in the industrial Northeast. The extremes are Louisiana, where 51 per cent of the elderly population receive old-age assistance, and New Jersey and Delaware, where only 3 per cent do so.

Most states make some provision for medical care for persons receiving old-age assistance. A few provide, in one way or another, all needed medical care; some provide virtually none, assuming that medical-care needs will be met in other ways. Since the 1930's, the federal government has paid part of the cost of such medical care, as it has paid part of the cost of old-age assistance generally. At first, the federal share of the medical-care dollar was small, but it has been increased through a series of amendments to the Social Security Act that liberalized federal participation in state old-age assistance programs. One part of the Kerr-Mills legislation, enacted in 1960, was another in this series of liberalizing amendments. It provided federal funds for medical care (up to $12 a month per recipient of old-age assistance) in addition to the maximum of $65 a month for all living costs that the federal government was already paying the states for each such recipient. This is the old-age assistance, or OAA, portion of the Kerr-Mills law.

In addition to the OAA program, the Kerr-Mills law also provided a new program of medical assistance to the aged, or MAA. Under this program, the federal government repays a portion of state expenditures for the medical care of "medically indigent" persons—those who are not receiving old-age assistance, "but whose income and resources are insufficient to meet the costs of necessary medical services." The federal share of MAA costs ranges from 50 per cent for states with per capita income equal to or greater than the national average, up to 80 per cent for states with lower per capita income; this is one of the most generous of the various federal matching grants to the states. There is no dollar ceiling on the federal share; the amount of federal expenditure is governed by the extensiveness of the state programs. The state determines who is eligible for the MAA program and what kinds and amounts of medical care will be provided; if a state wishes, it may cover virtually all medical-care costs. No state need participate in the program if it does not wish to.

Most of the discussion of the Kerr-Mills program has been directed at the MAA program. This is to be expected, as it is the most significant portion of the Act, and the major reason for its enactment. The OAA portion of the Act, unlike MAA, does not represent a new departure, but is merely a continuation of an earlier program on a broader scale.

Those who favor federal hospitalization insurance argue that Kerr-Mills is desirable as a *supplementary* means of meeting the medical-care costs of the needy aged. However, they are opposed to it as the *principal* governmental means for doing so. Most of those opposed to federal hospitalization insurance find Kerr-Mills preferable as the major governmental activity to meet this problem. There have been two kinds of controversies over the Kerr-Mills programs as the principal governmental means of meeting the medical-care costs of the needy aged. The first has been over the *desirability* of this means of meeting these costs; the second has been over the extent to which the Kerr-Mills programs have been *effective* in meeting these costs. The following selection, "Public Welfare Programs," explains why the American Medical Association finds this means a more desirable method. Congressman King responds. One of the principal objections raised against the use of public assistance as a means of supplying medical care is the "means test," which is discussed in the two succeeding statements.

The controversy over the effectiveness of the MAA program turns on a simple point: the extent of a state's Kerr-Mills programs is determined by that state. Thus, although a state's MAA program *could* cover all of the elderly not receiving old-age assistance and *could* pay for all of their medical care, none actually does so. Opponents of medicare focus on the *potential* of the MAA programs, promising to help broaden the actual programs where necessary; those who support medicare focus on the *actual* programs that have been enacted by the states. A more muted strain of this controversy stems from the variation in the MAA programs of the various states: critics of the program tend to favor a national standard, whereas admirers of the program point to the variation as evidence of the flexibility of the program in dealing with local needs. "Advantages of the Kerr-Mills MAA Method" discusses the potential of the program and the reasons why the American Medical Association feels these potentials have not been realized. Congressman King finds other reasons for this failure.

To what extent has the potential of the MAA program been realized? There are three aspects to this question: the number of states participating, the persons eligible in those states, and the kinds of medical treatment covered. There has been some confusion as to just how many states are participating. Proponents of Kerr-Mills, eager to show its rapid implementation by the states, combined data for both OAA and MAA programs and issued the total as the number of states having adopted Kerr-Mills programs. Although this figure was technically correct, it confused those whose attention was focused on the MAA program, which had a much smaller number of adoptions than did the OAA program, especially at first. This discrepancy was understandable, inasmuch as MAA was a new program, whereas OAA was simply an expansion of an already existing program. Another source of confusion was the fact that some states had passed legislation permitting participation in the MAA program, but had not provided funds for such participation. As of December 31, 1964, 39 states had MAA programs in operation. Two states (Indiana and New Mexico) had had their plans approved, but their programs were not yet in operation. Two states (Georgia and Mississippi) had enacted authorizing legislation, but failed to provide funds for operation of the program. Texas had enacted a constitutional amendment to permit participation in the program, but still needed enabling legislation. In 6 states (Alaska, Arizona, Missouri, Montana, Nevada, and Ohio), enabling legislation had been rejected. The District of Columbia, Puerto Rico, Guam, and the Virgin Islands all had programs in operation.

What kinds of eligibility requirements are set by the states that have MAA programs? How many of the aged are eligible? For what kinds of medical treatment? Helen Martz's review of the first three years of MAA describes these aspects of the programs.

Public Welfare Programs

AMERICAN MEDICAL ASSOCIATION

It is . . . necessary to point out the existence of a number of well-established welfare programs . . . designed to help the aged—and others in need—to obtain necessary medical care . . . .

The existing programs I have mentioned spread the cost of medical services across the entire community to assist those unable to pay. In what way would a Federal program be an improvement, with its complete absence of individual or community decision as to which costs are to be met and which institutions are to be paid? The individual taxpayer is already contributing to these programs at the community level and the state level—programs which will be available to him *in time of need,* programs in which he has a much greater voice, through local supervision and local elections.

The medical profession has no desire to "pauperize" the aged— nor does it believe that the majority of state and local governments, and state and local welfare officials, have such an aim. It does believe, however, that a Federal medical care program, cutting across and in conflict with existing, operating programs, can only be uneconomical, inefficient, confusing, and, in the end, destructive of good medical care.

Today, every state in the Union has an Old Age Assistance program, designed to provide a basic income for those over 65 who are unable, without help, to meet the costs of daily living. In January, only seven of those states did not have a formal vendor payment medical care program[g] for OAA recipients, and those seven either provide medical care through some other program or include amounts in the cash grant for the individual to purchase his own care. . . .

This is the basic resource for the needy aged. And it should be pointed out that a number of these states will accept over-65 appli-

---

From testimony at hearings on *Health Services for the Aged under the Social Security Insurance System,* held by the Committee on Ways and Means of the U.S. House of Representatives, August 2, 1961, pp. 1378-1381, 1395-1398.

---

[g] A program providing direct payments to the suppliers ("vendors") of medical care.

cants for Old Age Assistance "for medical care only"—will enter them on the rolls and pay their medical bills for as long as they need this type of help.

Every state also has General Assistance programs, financed either by the state and local communities in cooperation with, or entirely by, local action to provide help for those not eligible for the federally-aided Public Assistance programs. Frequently, these programs are the resource of those only temporarily in need of help—but they provide a considerable amount of medical care. Incomplete figures for January 1961 indicate almost $9 million spent on medical care through General Assistance programs, compared with $24.6 million through OAA. Many of the medically indigent are helped through General Assistance; a few states also have programs designed specifically for this purpose.

The other three public assistance programs also provide resources for the aged, although the natural tendency is to provide most of the help for the aged through OAA. In Aid to Dependent Children, the child's guardian receives some aid; in Aid to the Blind, and Aid to the Permanently and Totally Disabled, there is also a comparatively limited number of the aged receiving help. Most of the states have incorporated medical care in these programs, as well as in OAA.

These are not the only resources available. Many states and communities have erected their own hospitals, which provide needed care for those unable to pay. Over three-quarters of the psychiatric and tuberculosis hospital beds and roughly two-thirds of the long-term hospital beds are supported by state and local governments.

A number of other state and local programs, though not strictly welfare programs, touch on the medical problems of the aged. Some may receive help through vocational rehabilitation programs, some through various programs administered by state and local health departments—such as heart, cancer, and mental health clinics. . . .

Finally, even at the Federal level there are existing programs which help the aged belonging to specific population groups.

Federal hospitals provide a health resource for retired personnel of many Federal services, particularly the armed forces; the Public Health Service assumes responsibility for care of the Indian population; and the Veterans' Administration offers complete medical and hospital care for veterans with service-connected disability, and for veterans with non-service-connected conditions who are unable to pay. Since some two million veterans are now over 65 years of age, this provides a resource for a considerable portion of the aged population.

We do not claim that this spectrum of local, state and Federal programs and facilities has reached perfection in all parts of the nation or that every program provides all the services an aged person might need. We do not claim that every such program sets a completely realistic standard of need for eligibility.

However, we do believe that these local and state programs represent the *natural* development and the *natural* implementation of the community's responsibility for its members. They recognize the individual's right to call upon his neighbors for help when he needs it; they do not force upon him a specious promise of protection in which he has no choice and which bears no necessary relationship to his real problems.

We also believe that these programs have been improving rapidly, with the basic aim of equating medical services with the needs of the community served, within the limits of medical resources which are available and which can be made available to the community's residents. We in the medical profession have been working towards this end, and we feel that, in many areas, we have achieved considerable success.

Passage of this bill can have little effect except a crippling one on these programs. The existence of the Federal-state public assistance programs has placed a continually increasing pressure on locally-financed general assistance programs to allow the incursion of Federal money into these programs, also. The passage of a wholly Federal medical assistance program will place a similar pressure for abolition on "competing" Federal-state programs.

For example, the existence of a Federal program providing hospital, nursing home, and home health services will place pressure on state agencies not only to avoid duplication of these services in programs in which state funds are involved, but will also bring pressure to use the Federal rather than the state program wherever feasible. It is quite conceivable that this could lead to postponement of needed treatment for those nearing the eligible age when pre-65 treatment requires the expenditure of state funds and post-65 treatment does not.

In addition to the economic pressure on the states to force as many patients as possible within the framework of the Federal program, there will be a corresponding psychological pressure on the patient himself. The propaganda for the Federal approach as the more humane has, in effect, made it more difficult to provide community assistance in a dignified fashion. The patient has been told that, if he fits his illness within the hospital-nursing home framework of this bill, he is receiving care in a dignified respectable fashion—while if he receives help locally from his neighbors, he is being degraded. Obviously, he will tend to postpone treatment until he can take advantage of the former mechanism.

Finally, what about the development of medical facilities and services which are truly suitable to the community's needs and resources? Local programs, locally administered, are tremendously flexible; they can take into account topography, nearby general facilities and statewide specialized resources. They can consider local standards of income, local availability of professional personnel, travel patterns of residents, the character of the population—all those factors, extraneous to the science of medicine itself, which help determine the *pattern* of medical care best suited to the community.

This, no purely Federal program can possibly accomplish. The bill in question notably demonstrates this by fixing a master-pattern of health services for the aged throughout the entire nation. How can this master-pattern take account of what facilities are actually available; or make allowance for local determination; or allow local appeal from Federal rulings? It cannot.

Far too little consideration has been given, in our opinion, to the damaging effect this bill will have on existing aid programs. It would be much more effective, much more economical, and far better for the health of the nation if, instead of enacting an experimental Federal medical program which cuts across, and is in conflict with, operating programs across the nation, the energy expended in promoting this bill were spent, instead, on improving those programs and mitigating those flaws which are offered as reasons for short-circuiting the whole complex of state and local programs.

The Medical Assistance for the Aged program inaugurated last year (PL 86-778) is, for example, one of these *natural* developments of state and local programs—a way of extending community assistance to those who have no permanent necessity for help, but who do need aid when confronted with a medical problem beyond their ability to finance. . . .

Flexibility vs. Conformity

Besides its merits in maintaining individual responsibility for personal health services, we believe that the MAA program has a further advantage in the great flexibility of action it allows, and which is inherently impossible in a Federal direct service plan such as proposed by H.R. 4222.

The pressure for some special medical care financing plan for the aged is, in terms of legislative history, a comparatively recent thing—the result of a complex of forces, including the increased proportion of the voting population over 65, the increasing difficulty of older people in obtaining employment, and major advances in the science of medicine. As a result, we do not believe that there is truly enough evidence for Congress to say, "Here—in a 90-day hospital program, plus limited nursing home care, plus home health services and help in paying for some medical and outpatient diagnostic care—lies relief from worry for the older citizen."

Yet it should be obvious that, if this bill is passed, a staggering and probably fatal blow may be dealt to any alternative approach. The economic pressure focused on these four facets of care for the aged will be so heavy that there will be little practical possibility of comparing its effectiveness with other methods. And past experience with Federal programs indicates that the tendency, when a program fails to meet the need for which it was established, is to expand it rather than to take a different direction.

The MAA program, on the other hand, allows each state to choose its own method of operation and its own scope of benefits. As for those covered, it may set its sights a little above the present level for Old Age Assistance or it may include every resident over 65 meeting the states' definition of "medically indigent." Programs may be varied to suit the medical resources already available in the state, instead of promoting a forced growth of particular types of services not now generally available.

Thus, the Federal government participates in the cost of the program within each individual state, but otherwise exercises little control. The relationship here is precisely of the sort spelled out in the clear language of the Tenth Amendment. As the distinguished members of this Committee know, this Amendment states that "the powers not delegated to the United States by the Constitution, nor prohibited by it to the States, are reserved to the States respectively, or to the people."

There is another advantage to the MAA program:

Its future growth would be based on the actual experience, of not one but of fifty plans; not of one administrative mechanism but of many; not of one fixed and limited schedule of benefits but of many and varied schedules.

Agreed, some of our aged population have difficulty financing medical care and a larger number are apprehensive over possible future difficulties. The best solution must be based on accurate information as to the extent and areas of need as they vary from state to state, with assistance programs scaled to meet problems. This is infinitely wiser than setting up a fixed national program, into which all these individual problems are to be forced, whether they fit or not.

Social Insurance Is Preferable to Public Assistance

CECIL R. KING

The tenor of [the preceding AMA statement] is that the programs now providing assistance to some of the needy people who cannot meet the costs of their medical care have been ignored by the advocates of the social insurance approach; . . . that these programs represent a satisfactory method of dealing with the problems the aged have in meeting these costs; . . . that setting up a health insurance program under social security would conflict with, and perhaps even destroy these programs, substituting for them an inferior one; and that the public has a greater voice in other programs than in a Federal one. None of these things is the case. . . .

The supporters of my bill have not ignored the existence of public and private welfare programs that now help to meet the costs of medical care of some of the needy aged. In the absence of a social insurance program these programs serve an essential function; and even when health insurance is added to social security they will continue to exist and perform an important function.

There is no conflict between these programs and health insurance under social security, just as there is now no conflict between old-age assistance and old-age and survivors insurance. In fact the effectiveness of old-age and survivors insurance in preventing poverty among the aged has enabled public and private welfare programs to deal much more adequately with the declining residual need than would have been possible if the welfare programs were mistakenly relied upon to do the whole job. Similarly, when hospital insurance for the aged is added to the social insurance program, the Federal-State assistance programs and the other public and private welfare programs mentioned in the statement of the AMA . . . will be able to meet the cost of residual medical needs much more adequately than they are able to meet these needs at present.

The AMA speaks of "fixing a master-pattern of health services for

From "Comments on Testimony of American Medical Association," *Congressional Record*, CVIII (March 5, 1962), 3113-3116 (daily ed.).

the aged throughout the entire Nation" as if this were a bad thing. . . . I do not believe that it is a bad thing to provide basic protection against hospital costs for the aged person no matter where he lives. This is what my bill would do. What we have at present is a situation where a person in Massachusetts or New York who needs hospital care for a given condition and for a given period of time can get assistance while a person in Kentucky, Tennessee, or Mississippi with exactly the same need cannot get assistance. This may seem a desirable situation to the AMA because it reflects the income and resources of the States but it does not seem so to the residents of Kentucky, Tennessee, and Mississippi who need the care but cannot pay for it. A Federal program can reflect fully the needs of local communities through local offices, consultation with the States, and use of State officials to perform appropriate parts of the administration of the program. Under H.R. 4222 all these things would be done. One of the advantages of the Federal program is that it would not be bound by the limited resources of the low-income States.

The AMA makes much of the idea that State and local assistance programs "represent the natural development and the natural implementation of the community's responsibility for its members." . . . The implication must be that in some way a national social insurance program like we have today is unnatural. How the AMA reaches this conclusion is beyond me. It is natural and highly desirable that the mind of man devise better solutions to his problems as time goes on. There is practically universal agreement that so far as income maintenance is concerned social insurance is the preferred approach over public assistance; surely it was natural, then, to turn to the insurance approach. So, too, it is quite natural for our people to prefer social insurance against the costs of medical care in old age to the inferior method of assistance, which requires people to exhaust their resources and declare themselves unable to meet their own needs before they can get help.

The AMA says it has no desire to "pauperize" the aged. . . . Of course it does not desire to do so and would not do so. Nevertheless, the end result of the program it advocates would be that many older people would be pauperized. Any program relying on a means test—any program that, as the AMA advocates, helps only those who establish inability to care for themselves—is by definition a program that requires older people to exhaust their resources before they can get help. If exhaustion of resources is not pauperizing people, what is it?

The AMA makes the preposterous suggestion that the only reason why people prefer insurance to assistance is "propaganda for the Federal approach." . . . I find it hard to deal with this suggestion seriously. Does the AMA really believe that the only reason why people do not want to subject themselves to an examination of their and their children's income, resources and other personal circumstances—that the only reason why they do not want to declare themselves incapable of meeting their own needs—is that they have been propagandized into this attitude? Of course the AMA does not believe this. The fact of the matter is that a means test approach to any problem requires the division of people into two groups—one labeled "successful" and the other "unsuccessful." It is innately distasteful to any man who has supported himself and his family throughout his entire working life to have to come, hat in hand, to the welfare agency in his old age and say: "I have failed. I cannot pay my bills. Please give me help." This is the reason why the American people overwhelmingly prefer the insurance approach, and why the present complex of assistance programs, helpful and necessary as it may be, is not a satisfactory approach to the problem.

The provision of health insurance benefits at age 65 is attacked by the AMA because it might encourage people to defer treatment until age 65. . . . Social insurance proponents do not argue that the protection provided under the program will cover all problems. Because it does not try to cover all problems, social insurance can concentrate on the problems of the aged, among whom the need for protection is most acute. But is the AMA concerned because medical assistance for the aged and old-age assistance are available only after 65, and is it concerned because such help as the States offer to persons below age 65, for whom there are no Federal grant-in-aid programs, is even more woefully inadequate than the help offered to the aged? . . .

Then, let us not overlook the fact that whether a person qualifies under medical assistance for the aged depends upon whether he meets the State definition of "need." In other words what a person can get under medical assistance for the aged depends upon what the State sets as the requirements of "medical indigence," and what, even after the person meets these requirements, the State can afford to provide for him in the way of medical services. The whole point is that one does not know what, if anything, will be done. Some States will be in a position to do very little and then for only those who have very little.

The Emotional Predisposition
Against Means Tests

AMERICAN MEDICAL ASSOCIATION

After examining all the arguments against MAA (aside from those stemming from automatic preference for *any* Federal program over a local or Federal-state-local program), we believe that many prefer the H.R. 4222 type of mechanism to the Public Assistance method because of an emotional predisposition against means tests. The benefits listed under H.R. 4222, they argue, are available to anyone over 65 who is entitled to OASDI benefits, while, under the MAA program, he must show need.

We believe that there is a great deal of inconsistency in this argument and that it does nothing to better our older citizens' situation. The means test came into being as a method whereby the taxes could be conserved for use where they were most needed. Basically, a means test is simply a comparison of an individual's resources and his needs, aimed at determining whether he must have help to meet those needs.

This is precisely the basis on which the adherents of OASDI-oriented plans have supported them. In fact, the entire prologue of H.R. 4222 *is* a means test, in which the resources of the entire aged population have been weighed in the balance against their medical needs, and, in the opinion of the measure's drafters, found wanting.

Plainly, H.R. 4222 requires a legislative assumption that everyone past the age of 65 is—without exception—medically indigent; and that a compulsory program of Federal payment of a limited amount of medical, hospital, nursing home, and home health service charges is necessary to meet these costs. Such an assumption is the basis of any OASDI-oriented program. The American people may accept Social Security in the form of a retirement cash income program, vaguely related to their tax contribution to the program, but they are unlikely to accept a federally-subsidized medical *service* program, bearing no relation between benefits and the amount the individual has con-

From testimony at hearings on *Health Services for the Aged under the Social Security Insurance System*, held by the Committee on Ways and Means of the U.S. House of Representatives, August 2, 1961, pp. 1395-1396.

tributed, unless they are convinced it serves a special need which cannot be met through any other mechanism.

Yet the program proposed by H.R. 4222, which assumes that all the aged need help to meet their medical expenses, would cover only those eligible for OASDI benefits; in other words, those who have been employed in "covered" occupations for a sufficient length of time to build up an insured status. In Old Age Assistance programs, the state is required to take into consideration the applicant's income and resources—although the major part of the Old Age Assistance load consists of those not eligible for OASDI benefits, those who, throughout their lives, have generally had less opportunity to save for their own old age.

Those over 65 on OASDI are *automatically* labelled "medically indigent" on the basis of their age alone; those over 65 not on OASDI must present evidence, depending on the individual state's requirements, of their need for help.

The controversy comes down to this: those supporting H.R. 4222 agree that there should be a means test to determine an individual's eligibility for tax-supported aid in meeting his medical bills—only they believe that the test should be based on age and OASDI-insured status. We believe it should be based on the individual's resources and needs. In our opinion, the latter formula is far closer to American ideals of independence, self-sufficiency, and personal responsibility.

The so-called "degradation" of the means test is not inherent in the test itself, but in its administration, which is, in turn, dependent on local public feeling concerning the program. There has, for instance, been little outcry that the means test required for non-service-connected care in Veterans Administration hospitals is "degrading," or that reducing or withholding payments under OASDI to beneficiaries who earn more than a specified amount each year creates a "stigma." Indeed, investigation of resources is commonplace in today's installment-payment culture.

If MAA is designed and administered, as the medical profession has recommended, as a support to the ordinarily self-sufficient person, to help preserve his independence, and if it is permitted to exist without constant attack as an attempt to "pauperize" the elderly and without constant allegations that this method of providing community assistance is "demeaning," we believe that the program can successfully operate without lowering the individual's self-respect.

On the other hand, we believe that it is equally possible for a program to become demeaning and degrading in which every OASDI beneficiary is considered medically indigent; in which he becomes a ward of the Federal government for medical, hospital, nursing home, and home care and subject to Federal regulation as to which hospitals and homes will admit him; in which admission will be subject to scrutiny by utilization committees organized in accordance with Federal directives; and in which everyone over 65 is considered incapable of providing for his own needs.

In fact, we believe such a program to be even more demeaning because it is based on the assumption that the aged, as a group, cannot pay their own way, instead of on the more honorable belief that even the most provident person may, at times, be faced with health expenses beyond his ability to finance.

The Means Test

WILLIAM TOLLEN

. . . Physicians are most familiar with the type of means test they themselves apply to some of their patients. This is at best an informal, almost casual, not too probing procedure, in which considerable weight is attached to the appearance and manner of the patient or of his relatives; at worst, a highly inaccurate and rather inequitable method of assessing degree of ability to pay.

Such a means test is a far cry from the procedure that any responsible public agency must follow, with its accountability to public auditors, legislative committees, and taxpayers in general. The public agency is expected or required by law to assure itself that only those who meet defined eligibility conditions receive the benefits of its program. It must request the applicant to specify in writing the nature and amount of his income and resources. It must require a sworn statement, with legal penalties for false representations, or conduct an investigation to verify the applicant's statements, or do both. The applicant is aware that his economic status will be measured against a standard; that the service he needs and has requested will be granted him only if that standard declares him needy or medically indigent; and that at least his economic life history will be entered upon a public record.

Implicit in the conviction of the American Medical Association that a publicly administered medical program for the aged should be concerned with and benefit only the needy, and therefore must be based on a means test, is the presumption (a) that submission to the means test is not or need not be humiliating; or (b) that if submission to the means test does offend the feelings of some old people, the number affected constitutes only a small minority; or (c) that their gratitude for the life-prolonging medical service freely provided outweighs any temporary embarrassment that may be experienced by

From William B. Tollen, "Financing Medical Care for the Aged," *Social Work,* Vol. 6, No. 2 (April 1961), p. 10. Reprinted by permission of the publisher. William Tollen is Commissioner of Public Assistance of the State of Pennsylvania.

aged beneficiaries of public medical programs obliged to undergo a means test. To make any of these assumptions is to misread the temper of the times. In a society in which material wealth is a mark of success, old people consider it offensive to be obliged to undergo a means test, particularly at a time when they and their families are already distressed by illness, because to them a means test represents a public confession of their failures and inadequacies. The aged prefer social security insurance benefits to public charity because acceptance of these benefits involves no social stigma. To dismiss the feelings of the aged themselves because the number adversely affected by a means test may be small, or because the time period during which their feelings are aggrieved is relatively short, is inconsistent with the objectives of an enlightened democracy.

Advantages of the Kerr-Mills MAA Method

AMERICAN MEDICAL ASSOCIATION

The [MAA] program, as enacted in Federal law, is in close accord with the policy adopted by the American Medical Association in June, 1960: it recognizes the responsibility of the individual and his family to finance his health services, and where they are unable to do so, the Federal government acts only *through* the state and local governments and in cooperation with them. The states retain the prerogative of deciding both who needs help and how much and what type of help shall be given.

Potentially—depending on how it is implemented by the states—this program is capable of financing whatever health services are needed for any individual over the age of 65 who cannot pay for these needed services himself. The medical profession believes that this potential should be realized to the fullest possible extent, and has worked and will continue to work to achieve this goal. We believe it would be foolish and wasteful, a usurpation of state and local responsibility, and a destruction of individual responsibility to destroy this program by enacting H.R. 4222. Further, the Medical Assistance for the Aged program has had some chance to prove itself.

Potential vs. Real

The AMA recommendations for MAA programs adopted in November, 1960, envision state programs which could provide any help *needed* to anyone over 65 *needing* help and which enable him to retain his self-sufficient status at the conclusion of treatment. The specific policy statements follow:

"Medical Assistance for the aged [should] not be limited to the group within some fixed income-and-resources level, but should be based on the individual applicant's medical needs and his ability to pay for care without compromising those resources essential to his retaining self-supporting status after completion of treatment.

From testimony at hearings on *Health Services for the Aged under the Social Security Insurance System*, held by the Committee on Ways and Means of the U.S. House of Representatives, August 2, 1961, pp. 1391-1395.

"In Medical Assistance for the Aged, any type of treatment or facility medically necessary to the individual's care [should] be included within the possible range of assistance, but that aid [should] be provided in meeting only the costs of those services which are beyond the individual's means rather than all treatment costs for each case."

This is the goal towards which the American Medical Association and the state medical associations have been striving since the enactment of Public Law 86-778, last year, with varying degrees of success. Some states have established programs which will provide both a comprehensive range of services and a flexible standard of eligibility, balancing the cost of services needed against the individual's income; some have comprehensive services, but for a more limited group of residents; some have broader eligibility requirements but pay for only a few types of services; and some are limited both as to services and the group eligible for help. Most important, it must be realized that in the opinion of some states the law is not required and thus they have wisely not implemented it.

The admitted fact that the potentials of this program have not yet been fully implemented, even in those states which have passed their own MAA programs, does not, however, mean that these potentials *cannot* be achieved. Some of the states which began MAA programs last fall have or are already considering the liberalization of benefits and the expansion of the eligible group. We believe that this trend will continue in other states until the program reaches its full possibilities, if it is allowed to follow a natural course.

We must point out that it has *not* been allowed to develop naturally thus far. Some of the states with limited programs have established these limits out of laudable fiscal caution. Statistical estimates concerning the number of aged who need help, the type of help they need, and its cost have varied so widely that state legislatures, especially those with little experience with formal statewide vendor payment medical care programs, wish to gain some valid experience with the program before expanding.

However, since Congress passed this program there has been a campaign of active disparagement of MAA, hampering its implementation. The very people who support H.R. 4222 have been most active in this campaign. They have categorized MAA as "an administrative monstrosity," a "pork barrel," a program to "pauperize" the aged, and so on. Further, they have done this even before most states had determined who would be eligible and how the program would be administered.

It is obvious that if the Kerr-Mills Law could be put into full, effective operation before H.R. 4222 was considered by Congress, the success of MAA would, in itself, constitute a powerful argument against the Social Security financing method. Hence the widespread campaign to discredit the present law before it can be given a fair chance of proving its effectiveness.

In addition to the campaign *against* MAA, there has been the correlative claim that it would be "outmoded" by an OASDI-oriented program such as H.R. 4222 in the 87th Congress. Some state legislatures, as a result, have been reluctant to devote state funds to MAA on the grounds that it might be superseded—and some state officials have opposed MAA in order to give more strength to the case for OASDI-"insurance." . . .

Despite the concerted effort to slow down the implementation of Public Law 86-778, exceptional progress has been made. . . .

It is patently wasteful and foolish to destroy the steps taken toward implementing this program before its full worth in meeting the medical problems of the needy aged can possibly be judged, and without giving Congress the benefit of the factual data on the medical needs of the aged which can be derived from its operation.

Criticisms of MAA

This program has been called an "administrative monstrosity"; it has been claimed that it cannot be afforded by the states . . .

Since administration of the program is by the individual states, it is obviously impossible to attack the administrative mechanism at the Federal level unless all Federal grant-in-aid programs are at fault. At the state level, a catch-all labeling of all state plans as "monstrosities" before the mechanism of many of these plans is even decided on is ridiculous. Inherently, this program need not be any more difficult to administer than any other statewide aid program; indeed, with the greater leeway allowed the states by PL 86-778, it contains possibilities for simpler administration than the other public assistance programs.

The argument that the states cannot afford this program is another which has little factual basis; without knowing the demand on the program and its costs, it appears fanciful to classify it as too expensive. Further, of course, the medical profession does not understand how the nation can "afford" H.R. 4222, but not MAA. Does not *all* the money spent by the Federal and state governments come from the same place—the pocket of the taxpayer?

Many States Have No MAA Program Because of Their Financial Situation

CECIL R. KING

The AMA admits that the medical-assistance-for-the-aged programs "have not yet been fully implemented," and offers as an explanation the "laudable fiscal caution" exercised by States that have established limited programs because of a lack of information on the cost of such programs. . . .

The misinformation of the AMA's hard-sell advertisement, published in a large number of newspapers on April 19, 1961, which said about the Kerr-Mills program of medical assistance for the aged, "it is now being put into operation in 46 states"—actually, even as of mid-August only 14 States had programs in effect—has now been replaced by a newer soft-sell approach—one presenting somewhat less in the way of outright misinformation. However, it is common knowledge that the reason that so many States have no programs is not because of some abstract laudable fiscal caution but because State and local taxes in many parts of the country have reached the outer limits of practicability and painful searches for new tax sources have met with frustration. It is not surprising that States, wishing to compete with their neighbors for new business, are unable—not that they are unwilling—to embark on a brand new welfare program when in State after State existing State and local services are starved for adequate support.

In explaining why States without any medical-assistance-for-the-aged program have not acted, the AMA statement refers to a "campaign of active disparagement of medical assistance for the aged, hampering its implementation. The very people who support H.R. 4222 have been most active in this campaign." . . . It is strange that laudable fiscal caution is used to explain the severe limitation found in some of the handful of existing medical-assistance-for-the-aged programs but not to explain why the majority of States have taken no

From "Comments on Testimony of American Medical Association," *Congressional Record,* CVIII (March 5, 1962), 3116 (daily ed.).

action. In any case, I will take this opportunity to point out that I as well as the other advocates of H.R. 4222 have for many years worked hard to bring adequate public assistance to the needy aged. I might add that organized medicine did nothing to help to create the assistance programs, including the vendor payment program for medical care under old-age assistance. I also know the California Medical Association opposed the start of the vendor payment program under old-age assistance there, and called the program socialized medicine, until it seemed good tactics to support public assistance as part of an attempt to defeat what they feel is a greater evil—the King bill. I am delighted at the AMA's change of heart and their support of medical assistance for the aged, in spite of their motives. I am disgusted, however, at their allegations that people who have always supported public assistance have changed their minds. I believe that medical assistance for the aged and H.R. 4222 are both necessary, as do all the supporters of H.R. 4222 I am acquainted with. Thus, nothing could be farther from the truth than the impression given by the AMA that those recommending enactment of H.R. 4222 are in favor of destroying the medical-assistance-for-the-aged programs. . . . H.R. 4222 and medical assistance for the aged are not alternatives, as the AMA suggests, any more than the existing public assistance and social insurance programs are alternatives.

One of the most startling contradictions in the entire AMA testimony appears on page 79 of the statement. Previously, the AMA has declared that its official policy is to give full support to the Kerr-Mills program and the passage of State legislation to put that program into effect. . . . Now, two pages later, we are astonished to find the AMA saying: "Most important, it must be realized that in the opinion of some States the law is not required and thus they have wisely not implemented it." Is this the way that the AMA gives full support to the development of the Kerr-Mills program? Is the AMA now suggesting that in some of the States without such a program older persons should not even have help through the Kerr-Mills legislation? Or that in some States no aged persons outside of those receiving old-age assistance have a problem of meeting health care costs? One must wonder whether the AMA really is sincere in its professed support of the Kerr-Mills legislation or is merely using that legislation to attempt to confuse the issue and thus delay enactment of H.R. 4222.

One reason the AMA gives for the lack of State action to implement medical-assistance-for-the-aged programs is that:

Some State legislatures . . . have been reluctant to devote State funds to medical assistance for the aged on grounds that it might be superseded [by H.R. 4222.]

It should be obvious that there is a need for medical assistance for the aged that is separate and apart from the need for H.R. 4222. If such were not the case, the States might be expected to abandon cash payments under their existing public assistance programs, because of the existing OASDI program. On the contrary, at least one State, West Virginia, adopted a fuller medical-assistance-for-the-aged program—as a temporary expedient in anticipation of Federal health insurance legislation—than it really could afford to carry on a continuing basis, counting on passage of the insurance program to reduce the assistance program to manageable proportions. . . .

It is the AMA, not the sponsors of H.R. 4222, who are the Johhny-come-latelies in supporting medical assistance. The sponsors of H.R. 4222 recognize that the medical-assistance-for-the-aged plans will do a more effective job if they have the basic provisions of H.R. 4222 on which to build. Freed from the terrible financial burden of coping with the whole problem through public assistance, the States will be able to concentrate on supplementing the basic plan to take care of special needs where such are found to exist. While the AMA does not understand why State revenues are overburdened and why social security financing is practical, any of us who know of the practical limits to sources of State revenues understand the impossible choices faced by the States in allocating available funds which fall far short of meeting the total needs for education, mental hospitals, highways, assistance to the indigent aged, and now medical assistance to the medically indigent aged. . . . Obviously, the hard-pressed States will be able to meet the needs of the medically indigent aged only after the biggest part of the job is done through social insurance. Even the present cautious steps taken by some States will prove too much for a great many States, particularly the ones with lowest income, to take. In evaluating the potential of the medical-assistance-for-the-aged programs, it should also be borne in mind that future new tax money that may become available in the States for welfare programs will not necessarily be channeled into medical assistance for the aged. Other unmet welfare needs may often have higher priority. Even the long-established cash old-age assistance programs of a number of States do not cover what the States themselves have determined to be the recipients' needs. In a survey of 49 States conducted for the 1960

Advisory Council on Public Assistance, it was found that the old-age assistance payments made by 36 States failed to meet the State's own standards of needs for the aged on the rolls, and these standards are in many cases very low. The assistance payments made under the State's aid-to-dependent-children programs were reported to fall much shorter of need than those for the aged.

The AMA speaks of past improvements in medical assistance for the aged and predicts further improvements. . . . Yet it does not tell of the experience of West Virginia, which I have mentioned above, where the State was not able to sustain its original program because a program such as H.R. 4222 was not enacted. To assure that with their limited resources States will provide truly adequate medical assistance to the aged who need it, the primary role in financing basic health care for the aged must be assigned to social security.

Medical Care for the Aged Under MAA, 1960-63

HELEN E. MARTZ

There were 144,033 recipients of MAA in September 1963 in 32 active programs . . . . They represented 12 per 1,000 persons aged 65 and over in these States and 8 per 1,000 of all the aged in the United States.

During the first 2 years of the program, nearly one-fourth of the approved cases had been transferred from other assistance programs, primarily in States that had large numbers of old-age assistance recipients requiring costly nursing home care and long-term hospital care.[h] States in which the largest number of transfers occurred were California, Connecticut, Idaho, Massachusetts, Michigan, New York, and North Dakota.

Between October 1, 1960, the effective date of MAA, and September 30, 1963, a total of $596 million was expended under MAA. Of this, $306 million, or 51 percent, came from Federal funds, and $290 million from State and local funds . . . . Over 74 percent of the expenditures were made by three States (California, Massachusetts, and New York). About 85 percent of MAA expenditures were made either for persons transferred from OAA or other public assistance programs or for persons who would have been eligible for another assistance program insofar as income is concerned if no MAA was available.

From "Medical Care for the Aged Under MAA and OAA, 1960-63," *Welfare in Review*, February 1964, pp. 3-12. Dr. Martz is a social-welfare adviser in the Bureau of Family Services of the Department of Health, Education, and Welfare.

[h] Prior to the enactment of the MAA program, the average monthly old-age-assistance payment in some states exceeded the maximum amount that would be matched by the federal government. Many of these old-age-assistance recipients were receiving medical care. By transferring them from the OAA rolls to the MAA program, the states could remove the ceiling on federal matching (remember—there is no dollar ceiling on federal participation in MAA), and thus get the federal government to pay a larger share of the cost of supporting these persons. This means that, insofar as the transferred recipients are concerned, the MAA program was not helping additional people, but rather serving as a vehicle for increasing the federal share of their support.

See also HEW SSA Division of Program Research, *The Health Care of the Aged* (Washington, 1962), pp. 92-96, and the *Congressional Quarterly* article, "32 States Reduce Own Spending Under Kerr-Mills Bill."

There is considerable range among the participating jurisdictions in the number of elderly persons receiving medical care under MAA and in the average payment per recipient. For example, in September 1963 the number aided ranged from 73 in Florida (which had recently initiated its program) to 30,000 in New York. The District of Columbia and Wyoming had programs in operation but made no payments for medical care in September. Over half of the recipients were in three States (California, Massachusetts, and New York). Average MAA payments ranged from $4 in Guam, $7 in the Virgin Islands, and $28 in Kentucky to $419 in Illinois. The average payment per recipient for all jurisdictions was $196. . . .

Most jurisdictions began their MAA programs conservatively. By September 1963 only 4 States (Hawaii, Massachusetts, New York, and North Dakota) provided for "comprehensive" programs, that is, programs based on care in each of the five major areas of medical services: physicians' services, dental care, hospitalization, nursing home care, and prescribed drugs. Seven additional jurisdictions gave some care in each of the major areas but with significant limitations on the condition for which care would be provided or the extent of such care, and 14 others provided three or four major services (10 included hospitalization, nursing home care, and practitioners' services) with some limitations on one or more of these. Seven jurisdictions provided only the two minimal institutional and noninstitutional services required by law. All 32 jurisdictions included inpatient hospital care; 30, physicians' services; 22, nursing home care; 15, dental care; and 17, drugs.

About 47 percent of the expenditures made in MAA during fiscal 1963 were for hospitalization—a service provided in all jurisdictions with programs. While only two-thirds of the jurisdictions included nursing home care under their MAA programs, expenditures for nursing home care were higher than for hospital care. Hospital care and nursing home care costs combined accounted for 94 percent of total MAA expenditures; about 2 percent of expenditures were for physicians' services, 2 percent for prescribed drugs, and 1 percent for all other services.

Basis of Financial Eligibility for MAA

In more than half the 32 jurisdictions, persons eligible for MAA who have health insurance or other potential resources covering services provided by MAA must use the resources before payment is made under MAA. Five jurisdictions include a deductible feature—

an amount which must have been obligated by an individual in a year for medical care before he can be eligible for MAA.

In determining financial eligibility for MAA, the consideration given to income and other resources also varies among States. For example:

1. Most jurisdictions use a specified level of income in determining financial eligibility. In 10 jurisdictions, the income figure represents the amount considered as needed for living expenses, and income or available assets beyond that amount are evaluated against the cost of medical care received by the individual. The most liberal annual income level used by a State is $2,400 for a single person, although one State goes up to $3,000 in relation to hospital costs only; the most common income level is $1,500.

2. Twenty-nine of the 32 jurisdictions exclude life insurance from consideration as an asset under specified conditions, such as, in 14 jurisdictions, within a dollar maximum ranging from $500 to $3,000 with $1,000 the usual limit, and in 12 jurisdictions, within the dollar maximum for all personal property. Three jurisdictions consider as a resource the full loan value available from insurance.

3. All 32 jurisdictions take into account the availability of other personal property to meet medical care costs. In 29, there are dollar limits on the amount that may be held without affecting eligibility. These range from $50 to $2,800, with most between $1,000 and $2,500.

4. All jurisdictions exempt real property used as a home, but six require that equity in the home not exceed a stated amount. One jurisdiction does not allow holding other real property, one permits it only if encumbered, and seven require it to be income-producing or developed into a resource that can be applied toward medical care costs. Of the other 23 jurisdictions, some require the value of other real property in excess of certain limits to be applied to medical costs, and others specify limits on the value of such property which may be held.

SELECTED BIBLIOGRAPHY

American Medical Association. Council on Medical Service. "Financing Medical Care for the Aged," *Federal Medical Services Newsletter,* December 1960.

Axelrod, S. J. "The Evaluation of Old Age Assistance Medical Care Programs," *American Journal of Public Health,* LI (January 1961), 1-10.

Braestrup, Peter. "Health Care for Aged Dividing West Virginians," *The New York Times,* April 15, 1962.

Edstrom, Eve. "Ailing Aged Aren't Sold on AMA Bill," *Washington Post,* June 25, 1961. Reprinted in *Congressional Record,* June 29, 1961, p. A4997 (daily ed.).

Financing Health Care of the Aged: A Study of the Dimensions of the Problem. Chicago: Blue Cross Association and American Hospital Association, 1962.

Govan, E. S. L. "Indigent Medical Care: The Needs of the Recipient," *Canadian Journal of Public Health,* XLVI (February 1955), 80-86.

"Health Insurance for Older Folks: A Checklist of What's Available After 65," *Changing Times,* April 1962, pp. 41-47.

Lear, Walter J. "Medical Care in the United States," in Karl Evang, D. Stark Murray, and Walter J. Lear, *Medical Care and Family Security* (Englewood Cliffs, N.J.: Prentice-Hall, Inc., 1963).

Martz, Helen E. "Medical Assistance for the Aged Under Public Assistance," *HEW Indicators,* March 1963, pp. 5-16.

Notkin, Herbert. "Medical Care in Public Assistance—The American Scene," *Medical Care,* III (July-September 1965), 146-151.

"Record of Kerr-Mills Program Crucial to Medicare Debate," *Congressional Quarterly Weekly Report,* November 22, 1963, pp. 2039-2043.

Report on Guaranteed Lifetime Health Insurance. New York: Health Insurance Institute, 1961.

Rutstein, David D. "The Medical Care Pork Barrel," *Atlantic Monthly,* CCVII (June 1961), 61-64.

Simpson, Roger A. "Insuring the Elderly: Private Health Policies Face Steep Cost Rise, Scrutiny by Congress," *The Wall Street Journal,* April 6, 1964.

"32 States Reduce Own Spending Under Kerr-Mills Bill," *Congressional Quarterly Weekly Report,* July 21, 1961, pp. 1275-1279.

U.S. Cong. HR W&M. *Medical Care for the Aged: Summary of Provisions in Social Security Amendments of 1960 (Public Law 86-778) Relating to Federal-State Grant-in-Aid Medical Assistance Programs for the Aged.* Committee print. 86th Congress, 2nd Session, 1960.

U.S. Cong. Sen. Fin. *Social Security Amendments of 1960: Report.* Senate Report #1856. 86th Congress, 2nd Session, 1960.

U.S. Cong. Sen. Aging. *State Action to Implement Medical Programs for the Aged.* Committee print. 87th Congress, 1st Session, June 8, 1961.

———. Subcommittee on Health of the Elderly. *Blue Cross and Other Private Health Insurance for the Elderly: Hearings.* 88th Congress, 2nd Session, 1964.

———. *Blue Cross and Private Health Insurance Coverage of Older Americans: Report.* 88th Congress, 2nd Session, 1964.

———. *Medical Assistance for the Aged: The Kerr-Mills Program, 1960-1963.* Committee print. 88th Congress, 1st Session, October 1963.

U.S. Cong. Sen. Aging. *Performance of the States: Eighteen Months of Experience with the Medical Assistance for the Aged (Kerr-Mills) Program: Staff Report.* 87th Congress, 2nd Session, June 15, 1962.

U.S. HEW. *Medical Resources Available to Meet the Needs of Public Assistance Recipients: Report to the Committee on Ways and Means.* House Report 1799, 86th Congress.

———. *Report on "Medical Care Under Public Assistance" (October 1960-October 1961) to the Committee on Ways and Means, U.S. House of Representatives.* Committee print. 87th Congress, March 15, 1962.

———. SSA. Division of Program Research. *Blue Cross Provisions for Persons Aged 65 and Over, Late 1958.* By Agnes W. Brewster and Ruth Bloodgood. Research and Statistics Note #5, 1959.

U.S. HEW SSA. Division of Research and Statistics. *Blue Cross–Blue Shield NonGroup Coverage for Older People.* By Louis S. Reed. Research Report #4, 1963.

White, Gladys O. "Determining Financial Eligibility for Medical Assistance for the Aged," *Welfare in Review,* June 1964, pp. 8-15.

Williams, Harrison A., Jr. "Blue Cross Is Playing Politics With Health Care for the Elderly," *Congressional Record,* CVIII (October 11, 1962), 21927-21932 (daily ed.).

V | Financing Medical Care

Before the enactment of H.R. 6675, the employee's social-security tax was assessed at the rate of 3.625 per cent of the first $4,800 of annual wages. The employer matched the employee's contribution. Self-employed persons paid 5.4 per cent of the first $4,800 of their earnings. H.R. 6675, in addition to enacting the medicare program, also broadened old-age, survivors, and disability benefits. To pay for this increase, the social-security tax rate for employees and employers was raised to 3.85 per cent each, and the rate for the self-employed to 5.8 per cent. These rates will increase in several steps, reaching 4.85 per cent and 7.0 per cent respectively in 1973, and remaining at that level thereafter. The earnings base on which the tax is assessed has also been increased, from $4,800 to $6,600.

Medicare benefits for most of the aged will be financed by an additional social-security contribution. To pay for the basic medicare plan, H.R. 6675 levied this additional tax, at the same rate for employees, employers, and self-employed. The rate is 0.35 per cent in 1966, increasing gradually to 0.8 per cent in 1987. The cost of providing basic medicare benefits for persons who are not eligible for social-security benefits is to be met from general revenues. Persons who enroll in the voluntary supplemental plan pay an additional premium of $3 monthly, to be matched by a government contribution from general funds.

Cost of Medicare

As the exact content of the medicare program changed from year to year, so did the size of the tax increase that was proposed to pay for it. Throughout, however, the Social Security Administration asserted that the level of taxation called for by each bill was adequate to pay the costs of the benefits provided by that bill. Opponents of medicare challenged this assertion, citing cost estimates that were as much as several times the estimates of the Social Security Administration.[a]

This disagreement continued in 1965, but in a somewhat muted form. In 1965, the SSA's chief actuary and representatives of the insurance industry for the first time confronted each other before the Ways and Means Committee and were simultaneously questioned about their differences. Questions of cost thus became somewhat less a matter of political slogans and more a matter for serious analysis by the committee.[b]

Whose cost estimates were correct? It is very difficult to estimate the costs of medical benefits of the kind provided by H.R. 6675. Future costs will be affected by changes in the age and sex com-

---

[a] For a detailed presentation of the Social Security Administration's estimates, see *Hospitalization Insurance for OASDI Beneficiaries: Report Submitted to the Committee on Ways and Means by the Secretary of Health, Education and Welfare* (86th Congress, 1st Session, April 3, 1959), pp. 76-89, 101-103; *Actuarial Cost Estimates for Health Insurance Benefits Bill*, by Robert J. Myers, Actuarial Study #52 of the Division of the Actuary of the Social Security Administration (July 1961); and the Finance Committee's hearings on *Social Security; Medical Care for the Aged Amendments* (88th Congress, 2nd Session, August 1964), pp. 141-146. For the estimates of the insurance industry, see the statement by E. J. Faulkner at the Ways and Means Committee's hearings on *Hospital, Nursing Home, and Surgical Benefits for OASI Beneficiaries* (86th Congress, 1st Session, July 1959), pp. 449-458, and those by H. Lewis Rietz at the Ways and Means Committee's hearings on *Health Services for the Aged under the Social Security Insurance System* (87th Congress, 1st Session, July and August 1961), pp. 801-807, and at the same committee's hearings on *Medical Care for the Aged* (88th Congress, 1st Session, November 1963), pp. 1134-1147. All of these estimates are for legislation similar, but not identical, to the 1965 legislation. Accordingly, the specific figures are not applicable to the 1965 bills, but the general discussions preceding the figures provide useful background.

[b] Discussions of cost of the 1965 bills appear in *Actuarial Cost Estimates for Hospital Insurance Act of 1965 and Social Security Amendments of 1965*, by Robert J. Myers, Actuarial Study #59 of the Division of the Actuary of the Social Security Administration (January 1965); in the Ways and Means Committee's hearings on *Medical Care for the Aged* (89th Congress, 1st Session, January and February 1965), pp. 192-196, 397-424, 436-441, 453-460, 890-898; and in the Finance Committee's hearings on *Social Security* (89th Congress, 1st Session, April and May 1965), pp. 186-198, 412-418. See also the Ways and Means Committee report, *Social Security Amendments of 1965* (House Report #213, 89th Congress), pp. 49-62, and the Finance Committee report of the same title (Senate Report #404, 89th Congress), pp. 57-70.

position of the aged population and by changes in the unit costs of the various benefits. These changes can be estimated with varying degrees of certainty. More difficult to estimate are the effects of changes in medical practice, either as a result of the bill itself or as a result of medical research. Any estimator must therefore make certain assumptions on which to base his estimates. It is these assumptions on which the SSA and its critics have differed.

The major disagreement in 1965 was over the extent to which the elderly would utilize hospital benefits. In effect, both the SSA and the insurance industry admitted that the data underlying their estimates were inadequate in some ways and made adjustments accordingly—adjustments which the other side said were not large enough. The SSA estimates were based on a 1957 survey of OASI beneficiaries, adjusted upward to allow for the hospitalization of persons who died during the year and were therefore not included in the survey. These estimates were adjusted further upward on the assumption that formerly uninsured persons would increase their hospital utilization once they were insured. No provision was made for possible future increases or decreases in utilization rates due to changes in medical-care practices or in the supply of hospital beds. The insurance industry's estimates were based on a composite of its past experience, adjusted downward to reflect the high utilization rates among the elderly signed up under mass enrollment plans. The industry argued that the OASI survey was a poor basis for estimating utilization, pointing out that other studies had shown underreporting of from 14 to 18 per cent in such surveys. The SSA countered that the insurance companies' experience was an inappropriate basis because those who are ill are more likely to sign up and because the insured elderly are older, on the average, than those who are eligible for medicare. In view of the insurance industry's criticism, Congress (or, more accurately, the Ways and Means and Finance Committees) set the tax level on the basis of a utilization estimate higher than that of the SSA.

Another important disagreement between the SSA and the insurance industry was over the average daily cost of hospitalization. The industry started with the actual average cost, as reported by the American Hospital Association. The SSA reduced this average by 13 per cent, arguing that the AHA figures include some costs not attributable to in-patient care (for example, the operation of outpatient clinics and gift shops) and that the average daily cost of elderly patients was less than that for younger patients. The insurance industry argued that, if this reduction of 13 per cent were made, hospitals would have to increase their rates for younger users in order to remain solvent. The Ways and Means and Finance Committees in this case accepted the SSA estimate.

Other disagreements between the SSA and the insurance industry were over the extent to which the provision of nursing-home benefits and home health-service benefits would decrease hospital utilization; the rate at which hospital costs would increase; the rate of use and the daily cost of nursing-home and other secondary benefits; and the size of administrative expenses.

Use of the Social-Security Mechanism

In addition to the disagreement over the cost of medicare, there has also been disagreement over the use of the social-security mechanism as a means of financing hospital insurance for the elderly. There are two related controversies in this issue: the desirability of social insurance in general, and the use of social insurance to finance medical care.

In the selections that follow, John J. Carroll presents some of the reasons for the use of social insurance in general, and Robert M. Clark discusses the differences and similarities between social insurance and private insurance. Ray M. Peterson raises doubts about the social-security system, and Wilbur J. Cohen responds.

The second selection by Wilbur J. Cohen and the one by Dr. Osler Peterson present, from different points of view, the advantages they see in the use of social insurance as a mechanism for financing medical care. Those who oppose medicare have, for the most part, not taken issue with these points individually. Rather, they consider them irrelevant or less significant in view of the fact that use of the social-security mechanism would provide hospitalization benefits to many social-security recipients who are not in financial need. This and other disadvantages they see to the use of the social-security mechanism are outlined by Dr. Wallwork in the concluding selection.

The Government as Insurer

JOHN J. CARROLL

The objectives of the government as insurer are, of course, different from the objectives of private insurers. The government might go into the insurance business, just as it might go into any other private enterprise, and proceed to operate it much as though it were a privately owned concern bent upon covering its expenses and a return upon the capital invested. Such a venture might be instituted if the government discovered that private concerns were unwilling to cover certain risks which were, in fact, insurable; or that coverage was being rationed in a manner unacceptable from a public policy standpoint.

Our major social insurance ventures provide protection which would not be written by private agencies. Future costs of the unemployment insurance and OASDI programs cannot be estimated with sufficient degree of accuracy to encourage private underwriting, and the redistribution inherent in the benefit formulae of the programs would make them impossible to sell on a voluntary basis.

It is within the power of the government to write "insurance" which could not be written by private insurers primarily because the government's plan is compulsory. The government is neither obliged to sell the insurance to willing purchasers nor to establish a cost-to-benefit relationship in its charges for the protection. OASDI provides compulsory protection of this type to 75 million persons. It could not be denied that a large share of these persons have the means to save for their old age and/or to purchase insurance to protect their survivors in the event of death during their productive years. However, even if the government offered such protection on a heavily subsidized voluntary basis, some (those with the lowest incomes) could not purchase it and others would not.

The strongest argument for compulsory social insurance does not

From *Alternative Methods of Financing Old-Age, Survivors, and Disability Insurance* (Ann Arbor: University of Michigan Institute of Public Administration, 1960), pp. 2-3. Reprinted by permission of the Institute of Public Administration.

rest upon the assumption that private provision is impossible. Rather, it is the fact that, in the absence of compulsory social insurance, those who make private provision for themselves are forced to carry *in addition* the expense of those who choose to make no provision. Society is unwilling to allow the dire consequences which logically follow failure to provide on a voluntary basis.

Compulsory social insurance has another important advantage. It offers a method of guaranteeing minimum social standards without one of the most serious disadvantages of the public assistance program. It eliminates the needs test. Each person attains coverage and potential benefits as a matter of legal right.

Social Insurance and Private Insurance

ROBERT M. CLARK

Points Of Similarity Between Social And Private Insurance

A. *Private insurance and annuity business, like social insurance, is essentially based on the pooling of definable risks over a large statistical population.* Just who in Canada will die in 1960 cannot be ascertained. On the basis of carefully kept records for many thousands of people it is possible, however, to estimate with a high degree of accuracy what proportion of the Canadian population will die in that or other years—always assuming that the world's growing supply of nuclear bombs is kept safely under lock and key.

Such actuarial prediction is based on the regularity of behaviour of a very large number of items in a statistical population. It is the basis not only for life insurance and annuities, but also for fire, burglary, automobile, crop, marine, health insurance and other insurable risks, whether these be provided by competing private firms or by a department or agency of government.

B. *While the nature of the relationship between premiums and benefits usually differs for social and private insurance, both share the common characteristic of requiring the payment of premiums or contributions. . . .*

C. *For persons with insured status the payment of predetermined benefits under private or social insurance does not depend upon the demonstration of individual need.* Instead it depends upon the occurrence of specified contingencies, such as the attainment of a certain age, or sickness, which may be regarded as evidences of presumptive need.

D. *The provision of benefits under both private and social insurance is advantageous not only to the insured individual who receives cash benefits, but also to the insured person who does not, and, indeed, to society as a whole.* An individual covered by unemployment insurance

From *Economic Security for the Aged in the United States and Canada: A Report Prepared for the Government of Canada* (Ottawa: The Queen's Printer, 1959), pp. 26-50.

219

may carelessly say that he has received no benefit from it because he has never been unemployed. But the knowledge that he has some protection against such a contingency contributes to his sense of financial security in a way that is no less valuable because it cannot be measured. The same argument is valid regarding fire, burglary, marine, crop, life or health insurance.

E. *Both social and private insurance are undermined by inflation* . . . .

Points Of Contrast Between Social And Private Insurance

. . . A. *The different objectives under private and social insurance have usually resulted in the former being voluntary and the latter compulsory.* . . .

Private insurance exists for those who feel the need for protection against certain contingencies sufficiently to join voluntarily with others exposed to a similar risk, in maintaining a fund from which will be paid the risks that occur within the group.

Because of its voluntary nature, . . . private insurance must be built on principles which assure the greatest practicable degree of equity between the various classes insured.

It would be regarded as obviously unfair in principle if one homogeneous group of privately insured persons were required to pay part of the costs of providing insurance for another group for which the risk was very much greater. . . . Moreover, if it were known that an insurance company were charging the same rates for individuals or groups with widely differing risks, those with the lower risks, once aware of the discrimination against them, would demand to be treated as a separate group, and charged rates appropriate to the degree of risk for their group. If this demand were not met by one company, they would try to get more equitable treatment from competing firms. Under private insurance, then, the emphasis is very properly placed on equity as between various categories of risks. . . .

Social insurance is compulsory in the sense that individuals in occupational groups covered by it generally have no choice as to membership, amount of benefits, or the contributions to be paid by or for them. Legislators resort to such compulsion largely because they are concerned to ensure for the sake of society as a whole, as well as for the individuals directly covered, that each of the latter is assured, insofar as is feasible economically and politically, of some minimum income.

Opinions differ, of course, as to the size of this minimum. . . .

B. *The different objectives under private and social insurance have usually led to a difference in the relation between premiums or contributions and benefits under these two categories of insurance.*

Under private insurance, in conformity with the principle of equity as among persons covered, as described above, premiums are adjusted to the risk for various groups of insured persons or objects. Within any group a given premium will buy the same amount of protection.

In social insurance, as already indicated, the objective of securing adequacy of benefits takes precedence over the idea that each individual should receive benefits in direct proportion to his contributions. Consequently there usually is some element of subsidy in a social insurance system, either from outside the system, or within it, or both. . . .

The Old-Age Insurance Program in the United States . . . is an illustration of a social insurance system under which there is no simple direct relation between contributions made by an employee plus his employer on his behalf, and the benefits for which he is eligible. Under this system there is no provision for any direct contribution from Federal Government revenues, even for administrative expenses. From the outset, however, the benefit formula has favoured the lowest income groups. There are several other internal subsidies within this Program, some temporary and others of longer duration. Some of these subsidies have been larger in amount for those with incomes near or above the maximum earnings taxable under the Program than for those with very low incomes. Probably the most striking example of this occurred when by amendments in 1950, 1954 and 1956 coverage was extended to most categories of the self-employed and to certain new categories of employees, such as farm workers, and employees of non-profit organizations, and of state and local governments. Persons in these categories were allowed to receive full rate benefits after contributions had been made for a minimum of six quarters as compared with the more than 40 quarters of contributions that had been collected from those originally covered under the Act and retiring currently. This is a temporary subsidy, however, and will disappear gradually within four decades.

Two further examples of internal subsidies under the Program are as follows. In 1939 the Social Security Act was amended to favour the married man over the single man without dependents. Both pay the same contribution on the same income. The wife of a contributor, however, receives a pension on attaining a given age, and under certain circumstances is entitled to survivor benefits. The second example relates to the covered self-employed as a group. They have been and are taxed at only 75 percent of the combined rate on employees plus employers, although they are entitled to the same benefits as employees. . . .

C. *Both private and social insurance involve a redistribution of income or assets. In one important respect the objective is the same. It differs in other respects.*

. . . On any given day some insured people are healthy, employed, and in possession of property untouched by fire or theft. Other insured persons have suffered losses or reduction of income through illness, unemployment, fire or burglary. The essence of insurance is to redistribute funds between those who have not suffered losses and those who have. In this respect social and private insurance do not differ.

From the examples already given, however, it is clear that there are several other types of redistribution of income involved in social insurance that usually are not found in private insurance. In general, these types of redistribution favour women as compared with men, families as compared with single individuals, and lower income groups as compared with higher ones. It is chiefly because of their concern for adequacy of benefits for the family that legislators have favoured subsidies under social insurance programs for the lowest income groups and for persons with dependents. . . .

D. *Under most forms of individual private insurance the insured pays the entire cost of the premium. It is customary in social insurance for the employer to contribute at least as much as his employees. . . .*

F. *Costs are usually more predictable for the most common types of private insurance than for social insurance.*

Future costs are uncertain in all types of insurance, but in general are much more uncertain in government social insurance programs. Several reasons for this are as follows.

(i) Private insurance is much older, and well-established companies have accumulated vast amounts of experience in predicting such hazards as the occurrence of fire, theft, and death. Most forms of social insurance, on the other hand, are relatively new. . . .

(ii) Much more important is the fact that the major forms of private insurance deal with risks which are capable of being calculated within closer limits than in social insurance, at least under peacetime conditions. In the computation of premiums for life insurance, actuaries do not have to take into consideration such a widely fluctuating variable as the proportion of the labour force that is unemployed. This factor has a significant bearing for a social old age insurance program, such as the American system, affecting both revenues and expenditures of the system.

(iii) Private insurance companies, with rare exceptions, are careful to limit their liabilities in terms of fixed dollar amounts. . . .

Under the American Government's Program of Old-Age Insurance, the amount of benefit to which an insured individual is entitled could not be predicted precisely even if it could be assumed that future benefit payments were not changed by amendments to the Social Security Act. Aside from survivor benefits to which his estate may be entitled, the amount of an insured person's pension depends upon when he chooses to retire, his family status, and the amount of his earnings in a stipulated period before retirement. . . .

G. *Private insurance is based on legally binding contracts between an insurance company and the purchasers of annuities or insurance policies. Social insurance is based upon statutory legislation which promises certain benefits to insured income earners or to the latter and their dependents. These promised benefits are not the subject of contractual guarantees in most types of social insurance programs, but are open to legislative modification. . . .*

The Social Security Act explicitly reserves to the Congress the right to alter, amend, or repeal any of its provisions. Amendments to the Act have for the most part enlarged benefits greatly. There have been, however, a few amendments which definitely reduced benefits for certain categories of insured persons. For example, when survivor benefits were added to the Social Security Act in 1939, the provision was repealed which in essence guaranteed that each insured person or his estate would at least get back his own contributions with interest. Since 1939 there is no benefit payment except a limited death benefit for a single person with no dependents who is covered under the Act and who dies before receiving the old-age benefit. . . .

H. *The objectives of private insurance and the methods of achieving them are the subject of the widest agreement, with the possible exception of the problem of coping with inflation. The objectives of social insurance and the best methods of attaining them are subject to widespread differences of opinion.*

In the private insurance field, the basis for charging premiums in accordance with concepts of individual equity is invariably accepted. Both the premiums charged and the benefits paid have become stabilized to a substantial degree, because accumulated experience has provided sound actuarial bases upon which to establish both benefit structures and premium rates. From time to time new hazards arise which are susceptible to appraisal by insurance companies. The degree of risk changes in regard to older hazards, or knowledge of the degree of risk improves. For example, the risks of death from motor vehicle accidents and from lung cancer have increased in the last three decades, while the risks of death from tuberculosis and pneumonia have declined. Usually such changes occur gradually, and cause no major difficulty in adjusting rates.

Changes in social insurance programs, on the other hand, are very frequent, and sometimes drastic, especially in the early development of the program. . . .

The American Social Security Act provides . . . striking illustrations. Not only has the coverage been broadened, and the amount of benefits and contribution rates increased, but the Program has moved away from the recommendations of the Committee on Economic Security in some major respects. Survivor and disability benefits have been added. The original Act placed more emphasis on individual equity than the present Act. . . .

In 1950, 1954 and 1956, as mentioned earlier, coverage was extended on extremely favourable terms to virtually all categories of the self-employed and to a large proportion of employees who had not been previously covered. However desirable the extension of coverage to these groups was, the discrimination between those newly admitted and those covered from the inception of the Act was a gross injustice from the viewpoint of equity among individual contributors. From the viewpoint of adequacy of benefits, however, which is the more important concept in social insurance, this discrimination was not objectionable, and could even be defended as desirable. . . .

I. *The financial implications of private and social insurance are very different.* . . .

Private insurance must operate on a basis that is financially self-sustaining. The general acceptance of this principle partly explains the fact that life insurance companies are probably the most closely regulated of all types of business—private or government owned—in Canada and the United States. . . . An insurance company must operate its affairs in such a way that if it suddenly or gradually stopped receiving premiums, it could discharge in full all its liabilities to policyholders.

As a consequence of this obligation, it is of paramount importance for insurance companies to be able to forecast on a reasonably cautious basis the premiums and reserves necessary to meet the guaranteed commitments; and to be able to manage company investments successfully. If mistakes in judgment cause losses, an insurance company cannot look to government subsidies or other outside aid to bail it out of its financial predicament.

A social insurance system differs in several essential respects.

(i) It is invariably set up on the assumption that its operations will be permanent. Since coverage is compulsory for broad segments of the population, the administrators of the system do not have to contend with the possibility faced by all insurance companies that insured persons or prospective purchasers may become dissatisfied and take their business to a rival firm.

(ii) If revenues of a compulsory social insurance system are inadequate, it is always possible, within political and economic limits, to require employers and employees to increase their rate of contribution. Alternatively it is possible, although not necessarily in the public interest, for the government itself to make a direct contribution to the system.

A highly significant difference between social insurance and private insurance results from these distinctions. A private insurance company must operate on the basis of reserves large enough to produce revenues that in conjunction with premiums to be received will fully provide, even though no more new policyholders are acquired, for discharging liabilities to policyholders, for meeting administrative expenses, and for leaving a small margin of surplus. A compulsory government social insurance system does not need to build up a trust fund of anything like this magnitude. . . .

K. *While both private and social insurance benefits are undermined by inflation, there are two respects in which private insurance policies and annuities are likely to be more adversely affected than social insurance.* . . .

(i) The private insurance and annuity business is operated on the basis of building up large reserves to meet future commitments which the companies have guaranteed to meet. . . . No matter how skillfully insurance companies manage these investments to maximize the rate of return in a manner consistent with reasonable prudence, inflation undermines the real value of their fixed dollar investments as well as the income from them. . . .

(ii) If retirement benefits paid by a life insurance company . . . are inadequate because of inflation, . . . the company [cannot] be expected to put up any additional money to compensate for the decline in value of the retirement income.

Under a social insurance program, however, a parliament or congress can impose additional taxes to add to the benefits of those already retired. . . .

While recognizing the degree of variation of opinion as to what constitutes actuarial soundness for a private pension plan, Mr. Bronson offers the following definition.

An actuarially sound plan is one where the employer . . . arranges for meeting . . . costs through a trust fund or insured contract on a scientific, orderly program of funding under which, should the plan terminate at any time, the then pensioners would be secure in their pensions and the then active employees would find an equity in the fund assets commensurate with their accrued pensions for service from the plan's inception up to the date of termination of plan.

. . .

Mr. Bronson makes it clear that he does not consider that it would be appropriate to apply such a definition to a social insurance program that is national in scope, such as the American system of Old-Age Insurance.

A much less stringent definition of actuarial soundness is appropriate for such a program. There are four basic reasons for this.

(i) In setting up a government program of old age insurance, it is assumed that it will operate in perpetuity. There is, therefore, no need so to arrange the finances of the system that it could discharge in any given period, such as a year, all the accrued liabilities of the system.

(ii) Because the system is compulsory, employers and employees under the system cannot refuse to pay their contributions and put them instead into private pension plans.

(iii) Because a congress or parliament has the power to raise the rates of taxes used in the system, or to subsidize it from general revenues, there is no need to rely on invested funds to nearly the same extent as under a private pension program.

(iv) The combination of the assumption of perpetual operation, the power to compel entry into the system and the power to tax, means that future entrants may be taken into consideration on a basis where the value of their contributions exceeds the value of their benefits. The subsidy to current members resulting from such an excess value may be regarded, from their point of view, as equivalent to a subsidy from general taxation, and the system, therefore, is not independent and self-sustaining in regard to the current membership. This assumption of net revenue from future entrants is a most important difference between private and social insurance pension programs. It explains why a social insurance pension program may be regarded as actuarially sound even though it is operated with a very limited trust fund. It also explains how a social insurance pension program may at any one time be in the position where all, or virtually all, of its current members both active and retired are subsidized in the sense that the value of benefits exceeds the value of contributions. In addition, the assumption of net revenue from future entrants is in effect the instrument which enables a social insurance pension program to be fully adjusted from time to time to take into account rising rates of wages and of consumer spending which reflect inflation and rising standards of living.

Mr. Robert J. Myers, the Chief Actuary for the American Old-Age Insurance Program, has defined actuarial soundness for that system as follows:

... it may be said that the ... system is actuarially sound if it is in actuarial balance—that is, if future contribution income plus future interest receipts will support the outgo for benefits and administrative expenses over the long-run.

This definition of actuarial soundness for a government old age insurance program has been accepted by many experts in this field. Others would insist that this definition should be amended to include specific provision for a trust fund at least large enough to constitute a contingency fund for years of depression.

The Coming Din of Inequity

RAY M. PETERSON

A great national debate is now in progress as to the issue of providing medical care and hospital benefits under the social security system. That debate can be pursued intelligently and wisely only if we understand the true nature and implications of the social security financing mechanism. Advocates of the social security approach assert that it is best because the social security financing mechanism is "time-tested" and "tried and proved." In my opinion this is not so. The social security financing mechanism has not yet met the test of time; its crucial tests still lie ahead. To argue otherwise either reveals an inaccurate or incomplete conception of the true nature of the social security financing mechanism or suggests a willful attempt to distort and misrepresent.

. . . The public is being given the false impression that our social security program has many of the unique attributes of voluntary private insurance—attributes which the American people have come to value highly. When the American people ultimately come to know that the nature of our social security program is distinctly different, a rude awakening may well occur, one which could have important political and economic consequences. Will the youngsters of the future protest what the oldsters of this generation have voted for themselves? During the decade ahead, will we oldsters, as we seek to enjoy our social security benefits, hear a rising clamor of unfairness—a din of inequity? . . .

Background Information

. . . In financing a national old-age pension program, there are possible two approaches as extremes—"pay-as-you-go" and full reserve —and an infinite number of combinations of the two.

From the article of the same name, *Journal of the American Medical Association*, CLXXVI (April 8, 1961), 118-124. An abridged version was published in *The Wall Street Journal* June 29, 1961, and was reprinted in the *Congressional Record*, CVII (July 14, 1961), 11720-11721 (daily ed.). Reprinted by permission of the publisher and the author. Ray M. Peterson is vice-president and associate actuary of the Equitable Life Assurance Society of the United States.

"Pay-as-you-go" financing, as the term is used in the field of social insurance, means that the Government raises currently through taxes just enough funds to pay the cost of benefits currently due. No reserve is accumulated; no element of *prepayment* is involved; money is raised as and after payees become eligible to receive benefits. . . .

Full reserve financing, on the other hand, is a *prepaid system* of financing. All benefits are fully paid for or financed during the years *prior* to the time they are entered upon. Under full reserve financing, the dollar sum of all payments into the fund, together with the interest income earned from its investment, is sufficient to pay off all liabilities for guaranteed or promised benefits. No benefits are promised beyond what can be provided for—at any given point in time—by payments into the fund, plus interest earned.

Full reserve financing in the field of private insurance is the test of *actuarial* soundness, and it is the only concept of actuarial soundness with which the American people are generally familiar. The actuarial soundness of private insurance is assured by the use of *insurance principles;* any *fiscal* soundness (not actuarial) possessed by social insurance depends mainly on the *taxing power* of the Government. To call a social insurance program actuarially sound just because income balances outgo is to misuse the term.

Two other important points need to be made. One is that under voluntary private insurance the principle of *individual equity* is preserved; i.e., there is a direct relationship between contributions and benefits; one receives as insurance or annuity coverage precisely what one pays for. This is rarely the case under a social insurance program. There a new concept, called *social adequacy,* prevails. . . . "Social adequacy" usually makes it impractical to have "individual equity" for the insured in the sense of a mathematical *quid pro quo* return on account of the contributions made by or on behalf of the individual. A socially adequate benefit provides an income sufficient as basic protection against want and destitution, and, consequently, may be much more, or even much less, than an "equity" benefit.

True Nature of Social Security Financing

Now, let us establish the true nature of our social security financing mechanism. Evolving through a political process, there has been, beginning with the 1939 Amendments, a continuing shift away from substantial individual equity toward social adequacy, and the financing method has become a mixture of full reserve financing and "pay-as-you-go," with the latter far outweighing the former. . . .

For the years 1956 through 1965, tax collections for Old Age, Survivors, and Disability Insurance (OASDI) will total $115.1 billion and OASDI benefits and expenses will total $114.5 billion. These figures clearly show that we are now almost *completely* on a "pay-as-you-go" or *"hope as you pay"* basis.

A Permanent and Growing Debt

. . . For the vast majority of *present* members of the OASDI system, benefits will be much greater than an "equity" benefit. An income that meets social needs includes a large element of unearned benefit or unearned increment for most of the *present* members. *But the pendulum swings the other way for the youngest members and for all new entrants.* Social adequacy for some means individual inequity for others.

The decided swing away from substantial individual equity toward social adequacy which began with the 1939 Amendments has been accelerated since 1939. This has been the result of *deferring* scheduled tax increases, *extending* coverage to new groups, and *increasing* benefits for both retired and nonretired groups without increasing the taxes with respect to them by an amount sufficient to cover the cost of their increased benefits.

One need not be an actuary to realize that if large classes of persons receive benefits of greater value than the taxes paid with respect to them, then somebody else must pick up the tab. The unearned benefits are in one sense a subsidy which the older generation has voted for itself, and in another sense a debt representing the present worth of the subsidy which that same generation has assigned to younger generations for service or payment. In view of Section 1104 of the Social Security Act giving Congress "the right to alter, amend, or repeal any provision" of the Act, this debt does not have the same legal character as the national debt represented by Government bond promises to pay, but if social security promises are to be honored, the debt is *just as real* as the national debt. The younger generations can either pay off the debt or they can settle for just paying the interest on it. Under the present system of self-support through payroll taxes, these are the only two choices seemingly open to them, short of congressional repeal.

But, is it that simple? Are there really two choices? The great emphasis on social adequacy has some very disturbing implications.

The first is the dawning realization that we have but one choice, and that choice is to pay the interest on the debt *forever,* since the debt is permanent! The only way the debt can be reduced is to have a given generation of workers build up a huge reserve fund (over and above present payments) solely for that purpose. To expect this to happen is to be politically and economically unrealistic. With no reserve fund in sight to reduce the debt, the burden being passed on to future generations is permanent. It is not something that will somehow work itself out, or go away; it is not an actuarial fantasy.

Second, not only is the debt permanent, but the burden being passed on to future generations is a *growing one.* Under the 1956 Act, the debt arising out of the unearned increments was estimated to be $269 billion. This is the difference between (*a*) the present worth, $486 billion, of all future benefits and expenses for all persons *then* OASI members and (*b*) the sum of the present worth, $194 billion, of all future taxes with respect to such members and the trust fund, $23 billion. The corresponding present worth of unearned increments at the end of 1958 was $289 billion. Estimates of the writer, based on available data, show the debt growing from about $150 billion under the 1952 Act to $200 billion under the 1954 Act, and on to about $300 billion under the 1958 Act. The 1960 Act will produce some further increase.

Third—and most serious of all—because of this debt, employee and employer taxes with respect to the average new entrant will always exceed the value of the benefits such a new member will receive. The constant combined employer-employee tax rate estimated as sufficient to pay for all future benefits was 7.00% of taxable payrolls under the 1954 Act. Of this, 4.60% was needed to support benefits for the average new entrant, and 2.40% was interest on a debt of about $200 billion. Under the 1958 Act, such tax rate requirement was about 8.75%, of which 5.25% was needed for a new entrant and 3.50% for interest on a debt of about $300 billion. Under the 1954 Act, the value of total new entrant taxes was 152% of the value of the benefits (7.00 divided by 4.60); under the 1958 Act this became 166⅔% (8.75 divided by 5.25). There is no intrinsic reason why this percentage cannot exceed 200%. At this point, the average new employee, alone, more than pays his own way. Today, the average *new* self-employed person is paying 20% more than the value of his benefits. The taxes payable by and in respect of the new entrant must *forever* be greater in value than the value of the benefits that the new member will receive. *The price of social adequacy is perpetual individual inequity.*

When the magnitude of this individual inequity becomes more fully understood, will a "din of inequity" arise? Will there be a demand for support from general revenues? Will there be a refusal to pay increased social security taxes? Will there be a demand for reduction of benefits? Will an employer ask a private insurance company whether he can obtain larger benefits for new employees with the same joint employer-employee contributions? If he should ask me, this is what I would have to say. "About 80% of joint employee-employer taxes involving your new employees is for old-age benefits for the employee, his wife or widow. The remaining 20% is for survivor and disability benefits before retirement. Depending upon the marital status and the sex of your *new* employees and the rate of earnings, this 80% of taxes would buy under an Equitable group annuity contract, at our present rates, *40% to 60% more* in old-age benefits than are provided under the OASI system."

The foregoing situation would be further aggravated if more is added to this unearned-increment debt by deferral of scheduled tax increases and by benefit increases without fully compensating tax increases with respect to those receiving the benefits. This is to be expected because the 1958 Advisory Council on Social Security Financing questioned whether the 1969 tax increase should go into effect, and benefits are almost certain to be increased by Congress.

Trust Fund vs. Value of Current Benefits

The shift in principle from individual equity to social adequacy and from "full reserve" emphasis to "pay-as-you-go" financing is vividly reflected by the change in the relationship between the amount of the Old Age and Survivors Insurance (OASI) Trust Fund and the value of the benefits for persons currently on the benefit rolls (Disability Benefits and Trust Fund excluded). . . . For example, . . . if taxes had ceased in 1950, the trust fund would have covered 113% of the benefits promised for the future for those then in receipt of payments; but if taxes should cease in 1965, it is estimated that *only 20%* of the benefits for those then on the rolls would be covered, *with no provision for those not on the rolls.*

[Table omitted.]

In the 20th Annual Report of the Trustees of the OASDI funds, an estimate is made of the progress of the OASI Trust Fund "in the unlikely event of a sharp reduction in the level of economic activity during calendar years 1960-1964, with a relatively high rate of unemployment during the entire period." Based on these estimates, the OASI Trust Fund would drop to only 10% of the value of benefits current in 1964!

Expansion Beyond Social Adequacy

We have observed the growth of unearned increments and the departure from individual equity in the name of social adequacy. For a social insurance system established to provide only a minimum basic coverage as protection against want and destitution, this is fully justified. It is in harmony with the 1937 Supreme Court decision which declared the system constitutional as a welfare measure. The advocates of great expansion of social programs, however, have now dropped the adjective "social" and speak only of adequacy. Here are proposals for departure from social adequacy to higher orders of "adequacy."

Professor Wilbur Cohen of the University of Michigan (now Assistant Secretary of Health, Education, and Welfare) recently said we must develop a concept of "greater adequacy." Speaking of the 50-50 payroll tax financing, he said that there was no reason why it could not be 40-60, or have the government make a substantial contribution.

Nelson H. Cruikshank, Director of the AFL-CIO Department of Social Security, recently wrote:

> The proportion of present earnings that is represented by benefits on retirement must be materially increased for workers in the middle and upper income brackets. A worker with average wages in industry today receives only about 30 percent of his present earnings. In order to keep pace with the rising levels of living and to maintain confidence of the system on the part of those in the middle and upper wage ranges, he should receive 25 years from now, or sooner, at least 60 percent of his earnings on retirement.

(Based on a current average wage of $4600, the primary amount is about 32% for an employee, and the total benefit for a married couple is 48%.)

These proposals go far beyond the concept of social adequacy. Their enactment could increase the permanent social security debt to more than ONE-HALF TRILLION DOLLARS.

True Nature of Social Security Rights

The true nature of social security rights has been well stated by the Solicitor-General of the United States and by the Supreme Court of the United States.

Solicitor-General.[1]— . . . social security must be viewed as a welfare instrument to which legal concepts of "insurance," "property," "vested rights," "annuities," etc., can be applied only at the risk of a serious distortion of

---

[1] *Flemming v. Nestor*, 363 U.S. 603, *Appellant's Brief*, p. 68.

language. We are dealing with a social instrument by which public action, involving compulsion, is invoked to deal with the social problem—the lack of basic economic security of large segments of our society. An understanding of the difficult and changing problems of public policy arising out of attempts to eliminate individual or family insecurity on a national scale will be obscured by Procrustean efforts to force the social security program into the mold of inappropriate analogies.

Supreme Court.[2]—The Social Security system may be accurately described as a form of social insurance, enacted pursuant to Congress' power to "spend money in aid of the 'general welfare' . . . It is apparent that the non-contractual interest of an employee covered by the Act cannot be soundly analogized to that of the holder of an annuity whose right to benefits are bottomed on his contractual premium payments."

Inaccurate Private Insurance Parallels

. . . It must be clear to all discerning readers that, in the light of our initial analysis, there is no foundation for these inaccurate parallels. Indeed, there is desperate need to dispel these self-mesmerizing, foggy concepts.

Social Security Financing of Medical Care

What happens when the social security financing mechanism is used for medical care benefits? Let us first recall that the proponents of the contributory old-age and survivors insurance system, led by Arthur Altmeyer, have always been anxious to preserve the contributory principle; i.e., no one receives cash benefits under that system unless he contributes for a minimum period of time. Even though contributions have been only token payments for hundreds of thousands of members, Congress has adhered to this principle. Now, with an entirely new type of proposed benefits, i.e., medical care, for which the present persons on the old-age payment rolls would pay nothing, this principle is thrown overboard; all present social security payees would be blanketed-in. Also, millions of active workers and their employers would pay in taxes only a fraction of the cost of the benefits.

With no necessary application of the principle of social adequacy, another segment of unearned increment would be granted which would add to the permanent social security debt on which future generations and their employers would need to pay interest forever. . . . This would be only the start. The admitted political technique is a fragmentary approach: separate pieces of benefits are added from time

---

[2] *Flemming v. Nestor*, 363 U.S., pp. 609-610 (1960).

to time. . . . Furthermore, most students, pro and con, believe that it will be virtually impossible to limit benefits to the aged. Such benefits will inevitably be extended to all ages. In this steady procession of developments, the principle of social adequacy—the idea of basic protection against want and destitution—*is lost, with no replacing anchor of control* to restrain expansion of so-called social insurance.

Conclusions and Recommendations

What to do? The objective of the social insurance system should be clearly enunciated. It is imperative that the objective be to serve only the limited purpose of social adequacy, the recognition of society's obligation to provide basic minimum protection against want and destitution. The objective should be unequivocally declared by the Congress. *As our society becomes more affluent, the relative role of social programs should diminish.* The following measures are necessary to meet that objective:

(1) *No further increases* in OASDI benefits should be enacted except those required to recognize changes in living costs for the aged. . . .

(2) Congress should enact legislation that will provide *tax incentives* for all persons to save for their own old age needs, including, in particular, funds dedicated to pay premiums for medical care insurance.

(3) *The self-supporting principle must be retained* so that we do not lose its values of cost control and cost-consciousness. If benefits are restricted to the social-adequacy level, pressure for support from general revenues can probably be successfully resisted.

(4) To promote better public understanding of the nature of the financing method and of social security rights, a separate agency, similar in function to the Federal Trade Commission and state insurance departments, should be responsible for checking all statements and publications of the Social Security Administration for the purpose of disclosing to the public inaccurate and incomplete statements.

(5) To promote better understanding of costs, congressional committees and other responsible persons not in Government should know, with respect to each proposed social security amendment under consideration, in addition to a single constant tax rate requirement: (*a*) the tax-rate requirement for the average new entrant; (*b*) the present worth of the unearned increments for present members; and (*c*) the tax-rate requirement for the interest on the additional debt represented by such increments.

The adoption of these measures may be expected to have the following salutary effects:

(1) As real wages increase, *lower rates* of social security taxes than those now in the law will suffice to support the present level of benefits, workers will have greater margins to save for their own old-age needs, and the wage-related feature of OASDI benefits will become less of a feature as more persons in the course of time will have the same flat benefit represented by the present maximum.

(2) As the American people gain a better understanding of the nature of the social security system with the social objectives limited as herein stated, and of the differences between private and social insurance, chances of *public acceptance of a certain measure of individual inequity* for coming generations would be much improved.

(3) As the following factors become effective it should become increasingly clear that provision of medical care benefits under the social security mechanism is unnecessary and unwise: (*a*) tax incentives to save for cash- and medical-care needs in old age; (*b*) the increasing capacity of present workers to save, as compared with the former capacity of the present aged; (*c*) the vigorous development of the Federal-State Medical Aid for Aged Program; and (*d*) the further evolution of voluntary private insurance.

Our social security system can be preserved only if we keep benefits within the limits of carefully defined social objectives. Abraham Epstein, a pioneer in the development of old age income programs, is reported to have said that social insurance is like a drug: a limited quantity can serve a vital need; an excessive quantity can be fatal.

If the recommended measures are not substantially adopted, but, instead, we attempt to finance cash benefits of "greater adequacy" and also full medical care benefits through the social security system on the self-supporting principle, and the system continues to be likened to private insurance, then surely a great Din of Inequity will be heard. The towering social security structure which we will have piously erected in the name of taking the burden of the old from the shoulders of the young will fall flat on our posterity!

The Din of the Equitable

WILBUR J. COHEN

Mr. Peterson's article itself, the fact that it was published in . . . the Journal of the American Medical Association, and the widespread distribution it has been given—including free and wide distribution of reprints by the Equitable Life Assurance Society—make it plain that Mr. Peterson, backed by the facilities of his company, is engaged in an effort with the American Medical Association to try to discredit the old-age, survivors, and disability insurance program and to shake the people's confidence in it. . . .

Social Insurance Is Insurance

Mr. Peterson implies that old-age and survivors insurance is not at all like private insurance, and may even not be insurance at all. Actually, while the social security program differs from voluntary private insurance in many ways, the two types of insurance have many attributes in common. . . . As the article on "Insurance" in the Encyclopaedia Britannica says, "The modern institution of insurance is divided into the two broad categories of voluntary or commercial insurance and compulsory or social insurance, both relying on the same basic principles but differing in many details of philosophy and organization." . . .

The two branches of insurance of course differ in some respects. One way in which they differ is the nature of the right to the payment. The terms of the legal right to social insurance are spelled out in a statute, which can be amended as any law can be amended; the rights under private insurance are spelled out in a contract, which for the duration of the period of the contract can be changed only by agreement of both parties to the contract.

The fact that the right to social insurance is not a contractual right is made much of by those who seek to discredit social insurance, yet

From the article of the same name, *Congressional Record*, CVII (July 12, 1961), 12342-12345 (annual ed.) or 11471-11474 (daily ed.). An abridged version was also published in *The Wall Street Journal*, July 26, 1961. Wilbur J. Cohen is Under Secretary of the Department of Health, Education, and Welfare.

actually the fact that Congress can change the law is an advantage in social insurance. The contractual nature of private commercial insurance gives it an inflexibility in comparison with social insurance, since the latter can be changed from time to time to keep pace with changing conditions. . . . To illustrate this point: the social insurance program has been amended several times in recent years to raise the benefits in order to compensate for rising prices and to allow the beneficiaries to participate to an extent in the increase in the general level of living enjoyed by the country as a whole. Most private insurance at the present time does not provide for this type of adjustment although variable annuities now being sold by some private insurance carriers have as their objective to adjust benefits to changing economic conditions.

In this respect it is quite unrealistic for those who contend that the program is not insurance to assert that the right of Congress to amend the law may be used to deliberalize the program rather than to improve it. Those who are trying to make people feel that the right to amend the law constitutes an element of insecurity in the program are, in my judgment, very shortsighted in trying to stir up an uneasiness about contributory social insurance. Moreover, I am sure they do not really believe that the Congress will take away the benefits of millions of people who have contributed toward the cost of those benefits from their earnings.

Incidentally, the Supreme Court, in the . . . decision [Mr. Peterson] referred to, very positively indicated that the right to benefits under the social insurance program is protected by the due process clause in the fifth amendment to the Constitution against denial and diminution by arbitrary governmental action. . . .

Under private insurance, of course, the only possible basis for the arrangement between the insurer and the insured is a contractual one. And there are advantages in private insurance to a long-term contractual arrangement; such an arrangement eliminates the kind of insecurity that can occur when a policy is written to cover a relatively short period of time—1 year, for example—and can be continued in the following year only on conditions that suit the company. The deficiencies of health insurance policies that are cancelable when the insured has proven to be a bad risk are well known. Increasingly, health insurance policies are being made uncancelable and guaranteed renewable. Yet, because the contract is written to protect the insurer as well as the insured, only too often these guarantees are not as meaningful as they seem. Primarily, this is because there is no guarantee that the premiums will not be increased and often they have risen sharply. In other instances the protection afforded to the aged has been reduced below that available to persons insured as members of employment groups. These underwriting practices are proper in private insurance to prevent the insurer from being wiped out by increasing costs that he cannot meet; but they result in a very insecure situation for the people involved.

Another point at which social insurance differs from many branches of private insurance is in the nature of the reserves. Because compulsory social insurance is assured of new entrants into the program, it does not have to build up the kind of reserves that are necessary at all times in an institution that might have no new customers and might be forced out of business. Private insurance is required to maintain the type of reserves that will meet the threat of dissolution. Social insurance, on the other hand, is actuarially sound as long as it operates under a plan of financing which is designed to provide income sufficient to meet all benefit costs as they fall due.

It is because there are differences between private and social insurance that we need both branches of insurance. The characteristics the two branches have in common are what give them claim to the common term "insurance," and the differences are what define the two branches. Yet these differences are cited by those who wish to discredit social insurance and discourage improvements in it in support of their contention that social insurance is not insurance. They seem to reason as follows: "The American people have accepted the idea of insurance; they think insurance is a good thing. If we can convince them that social security is not insurance, that it is unsound, that the benefits can be taken away at any time, and even that this is likely to happen, they will be afraid to press for improvement of the program."

Much of the current propaganda on this subject is based on statements in a brief filed by the Solicitor General under the last administration in the case of *Flemming* v. *Nestor*. This brief was unfortunate in its general slant and emphasis; several of the statements in it are quite misleading. And although the Supreme Court arrived at the same conclusion as the Government brief, it did not endorse the arguments in the brief, nor base its conclusions on those arguments. The Supreme Court specifically stated, "The social security system may be accurately described as a form of social insurance, enacted pursuant to Congress' power to 'spend money in aid of the "general welfare" '." . . .

Younger Workers Are Treated Equitably

The main contention of Mr. Peterson's article is that future generations of workers are going to consider themselves inequitably treated under the social security program because a part of the employer contributions paid with respect to the earnings of those future workers will be used to meet part of the cost of the benefits paid to people who retire in the early years of the program and who were not under the program long enough so that their contributions, together with those of their employers, could have an actuarial value equal to that of their benefits.

Underlying Mr. Peterson's contention is an assumption that the employer contributions paid with respect to the wages of a given worker are paid for the use of that worker, and that he has a right to get protection equal to what the sum of his own social security contributions and his employer's contributions with respect to his wages will provide. . . .

[I] look upon the employer contribution as pooled . . . and used where needed to make the system adequate without a Government subsidy.

It is of course perfectly reasonable to consider that the employer contribution is pooled and used where needed to make the program effective in meeting its objectives. This is the philosophy Congress has embodied in the present program. Among the objectives of the program is the payment of full-rate insurance benefits to people already near retirement at the start of the program; another is the payment of insurance benefits that are kept in line with current wages and prices. The man who is covered under social security from age 21 to age 65 has 44 years of earnings out of which to pay toward the cost of his benefits; it is entirely reasonable to expect him to pay a greater proportion of that cost than the worker who, because the program became effective when he was already along in years, has only, say, 10 years of earnings out of which to contribute toward the cost of his benefits. It is, then, reasonable to say that a relatively large proportion of the employer contribution goes to meet the cost of paying full insurance benefits to workers who were old when the program started and that a smaller proportion is used to help pay for the insurance benefits of future generations.

Actually, there is no reason why younger workers should feel that they are being treated inequitably because in the future they will not get the full advantage of the payroll contributions made by employers.

Moreover, those who understand the protection they are getting in return for the contributions they pay will certainly not feel that way. What the younger worker is getting under social security is insurance protection that can, and in all likelihood will, be increased by the Congress as wages go up without a corresponding increase in the contribution rates. Congressional action adjusting benefits upward in 1950, 1952, 1954, 1958, and 1960 make it very clear that the younger worker's protection will be related not to current wages and prices but to those prevailing during the period of his retirement. If wages go up, as of course there is every reason to expect they will, the program is over-financed at the contribution rates now scheduled, and insurance benefits can be increased to some extent without contribution rate increases.

The Program Is Actuarially Sound

Mr. Peterson contends that old-age, survivors, and disability insurance is not and cannot be actuarially sound because it does not maintain the same kind of reserves that private insurance must maintain. The philosophy which the Congress has embodied in the present law is that because compulsory social insurance is assured of continuing income (since new workers must come into the program), it does not have to build up the kind of reserves that are necessary in an institution that might have no new customers and might be forced out of business. Private insurance is required to maintain the type of reserves that will meet the threat of dissolution. Social insurance is financially sound, on the other hand, as long as the legislation on which it is based provides for a plan of financing which yields income sufficient to meet all benefit costs as they fall due. And the social security law does so provide.

Mr. Peterson contends that while social insurance may be fiscally sound, the concept of actuarial soundness cannot be applied. This contention is based on a definition of terms that is not universally used by actuaries. . . . In any case, there is very little point in this sort of argument about words; the important thing is that Congress has provided the mechanism to assure there will be money to pay the benefits when they are due both in the short range and in the long range.

Mr. Peterson mentions that for the years 1956 through 1965 contribution collections under the social security program and benefits and expenses under that program will be nearly equal, and then concludes that the program is "now almost completely on a 'pay as you go' or 'hope-as-you-pay' basis." The figures given by Mr. Peterson are correct but his conclusion is incorrect. Indeed it is hard to believe that he did not select the decade he mentions for the purpose of coming to this conclusion, since over the coming decade—from 1961 to 1970—the combined assets of the trust funds, now amounting to about $22 billion, are expected to about double. . . .

Mr. Peterson brings out that a private insurance company taking on the responsibility of providing benefits for only those employees entering the system at the younger ages could provide protection for them at premium rates that are lower than the taxes required to be levied under the social security program to provide the same benefits for both these younger people and people who are already old. This of course is true. In the same way, if insurance company A had a group annuity plan and a rival insurance company offered to take over from the plan the new entrants, the latter could quote a much lower premium rate than the rate under the exising plan. This would not reflect upon the operations of insurance company A. It would be the expected result of the contracting out of the long-service group. The fact that insurance protection for new entrants at younger ages can be provided with lower premium or contribution rates than those required for a group including also people first covered at older ages is just simple mathematics, applicable to both private insurance and social insurance, and not at all a reflection upon the operation, the nature or equity of the social insurance program.

Social Adequacy

Mr. Peterson criticizes various proposals made to improve the adequacy of social security benefits. This is in line with what appears to be his overall objective to prevent social security from meeting the social needs of the American people. He points out that "social adequacy for some means individual inequity for others." This is a play on words. The program can be improved to meet social as well as individual needs without in any way losing its fundamental insurance characteristic or, on the other hand, becoming a dole. As I have already pointed out, as wages and earnings increase, some improvements can be made in the program without increasing the contribution rate.

Mr. Peterson implies that I have stated that there is no reason why the 50-50 sharing of contributions could not be changed to a 40-60 sharing and that I have stated that the Government should make a substantial contribution to the insurance system. I did discuss these

alternatives in a speech. But I have not made any such recommendations. Mr. Peterson makes such implications in an attempt to attribute
to people views which they do not hold. It is illustrative of his approach to only refer to part of the facts in making his analysis thus
leaving an inaccurate conclusion in the mind of the reader.

Social Security Financing of Medical Care

Mr. Peterson has only two brief paragraphs on the issue of financing
medical care under social security. However, it is apparent from the
article that the entire din of his views is to set up certain straw men
which he then demolishes in order to attempt to prove why health insurance for the aged should not be made a part of the social security
system.

For instance, Mr. Peterson states that "most students, pro and con,
believe that it will be virtually impossible to limit benefits to the
aged" if health insurance for the aged is enacted. He states: "Such
benefits will eventually be extended to all ages." Mr. Peterson is certainly entitled to utilization of his crystal ball to predict what the Congress in the future will do. However, if private insurance satisfactorily
meets the problem of financing the health costs of the American people
then there should be no fear that Congress will extend any such program to cover younger people. If, however, private insurance fails to
make socially adequate protection available to the American people
then Mr. Peterson may be correct. I should think therefore that instead
of spending his time and energy attacking the social security system he
would want to direct his efforts toward so improving private health
insurance that the contingency that he fears would be certain not to
come to pass.

His Conclusions and Recommendations

Before stating his specific recommendations, Mr. Peterson indicates
the following—in fact he italicizes it—as his guiding principle: "As our
society becomes more affluent, the relative role of social programs
should diminish." I disagree with Mr. Peterson. Private and public
insurance in my opinion are social programs. Does Mr. Peterson believe private insurance should decline relative to economic development? I would hope that as our society becomes more affluent it will
recognize that it can afford to do more for its disadvantaged members
—the aged, the widows and orphans, the disabled—than it does now,
through private and public insurance and other social programs.

Along the same line, Mr. Peterson recommends that no further increases in old-age, survivors, and disability insurance benefits should be enacted except those required to recognize changes in living costs for the aged. If this recommendation were followed the result would be that the aged, and the other groups looking to old-age, survivors, and disability insurance benefits as their major or only source of support, would be effectively excluded from getting their fair share of the increasing productivity and affluence of our society. I would not like to see that happen, and I don't think it will. Mr. Peterson is fighting a rear-guard delaying action. I am confident that the people of this country and the Congress not only will continue to support the old-age, survivors, and disability insurance program but will want it improved as was done in the recent social security legislation enacted by the Congress in June 1961.

Mr. Peterson attempts, in his article, to give the reader the erroneous impression that the old-age, survivors, and disability insurance program is inequitable and financially unsound. He completely ignores the fact that Congress has exercised both wisdom and responsibility in devising a system which meets social need in a financially sound manner. He ignores the further fact that in revising the program the Congress has shown great concern for financial soundness and for maintaining a balance between income on the one hand and the costs of benefit changes on the other, not only in the short run but in the long run.

Social Insurance Versus Voluntary Plans

WILBUR J. COHEN

There are several important financial differences between voluntary hospital insurance and the hospital insurance financed by the For-and bill.

1. *Contributions under the bill are collected as part of the social security system.* As a result a large number of employed persons would contribute. This tends to reduce the cost per person and assures a strong financial base to the whole program. There is no need for salesman or acquisition costs, thus reducing administrative costs as compared with a voluntary plan.

2. *Contributions are payable under the bill only while the individual is employed....* In voluntary plans, contributions must be paid whether the insured person is earning or not.

3. *Contributions under the bill are levied in some measure with ability to pay.* In voluntary plans, contributions customarily are on a flat basis in relation to the number of dependents. . . .

4. *Contributions in the bill are levied over the individual's working lifetime and are not paid during the period when he is not earning and is retired.* Under most voluntary plans, the individuals must continue to pay their premiums after they retire and until they die. When employers contribute toward the cost of voluntary protection before retirement, such contributions usually stop with the end of employment. This is burdensome to many older people whose incomes are sharply reduced when they retire. The result is that, as people grow older, they may drop their voluntary insurance in order to conserve their limited funds. If they retain their voluntary insurance, the flat rate premium takes a very high proportion of a small income. . . .

5. *Contributions in the bill are not related to the number of de-*

From "Health Insurance Under Social Security," *American Journal of Nursing*, LX (April 1960), 505-506. Reprinted, with permission, from the *American Journal of Nursing*, April 1960. At the time this article was published, Wilbur J. Cohen was Professor of Public Welfare at the University of Michigan. He is now Under Secretary of the Department of Health, Education, and Welfare.

pendents. In voluntary plans, the contributions usually increase with the number of dependents. . . . The result is that the individual with the family has to pay a higher proportion of income for his protection than the individual without a family. . . . The individual with the family has the cost of maintaining and educating his family and, since his health costs rise in relation to the size of his family but not in relation to his earnings, he is doubly penalized. . . .

6. *The employer is required by the bill to pay one half of the cost.* Under many voluntary plans, the employer pays part of the cost, and in some voluntary plans the employer pays all of the cost. However, this trend is spotty. In many plans, the employer makes no contribution. Under the bill, the employer would have to pay one half of the cost. The law permits employers to pay a larger proportion—or all of the cost—if the employer wishes, or if this is agreed to by the employer and employee by contract or collective bargaining.

7. *Benefits are not cancelable under the bill.* In many private plans benefits are cancelable at the option of the insurance carrier or the employer. . . . They can be terminated by action of the insured when sufficient income is not available to pay the premiums. Whatever may be the reasons for these actions, they inevitably result in public agencies' having to bear the cost of the care of those persons who cannot finance their medical care. . . .

8. *Benefits under the bill in many cases are more adequate than under private plans.* In some voluntary plans, hospital insurance benefits for the aged are limited to 30 to 50 days, have a fixed dollar limit on payments per day of hospital care, or have other important limitations. This completely undermines the security provided in the plan. Under the bill, no lifetime limit is provided or necessary. Thus, the social security approach is much superior to the private plan.

9. *The cost of administering a single nationwide plan would be less than the administrative costs under many competing private insurance plans.*

Financing a Medical-Care Program Through Social Security

OSLER L. PETERSON

The national debate on government aid to help old people meet their medical bills has shifted ground since Congressman Forand first raised the issue several years ago. The support now given the Kerr-Mills legislation apparently is recognition that old people have special problems in paying for medical care that require government action. The debate is now concentrated on the question of an amplified welfare program or the use of social security to meet this financial problem. . . .

Many of the arguments that are directed at the use of social security are based upon fears that the freedoms of medical practice and the patient's choice of physician will be lost to a large and inefficient bureaucracy. The very broadness of these arguments makes it impossible to give them adequate consideration here. However, the values held in a democratic society are the ultimate protection of such freedoms. The general acceptance by our society of freedom and choices in medical care makes it unlikely that these will be abridged if we understand the issues clearly and act wisely. . . .

The medical profession has been right in describing the social-security approach as an entering wedge for government medicine. A welfare program is no less of a wedge. . . .

The Kerr-Mills Act has, of course, provided for a federal-state welfare program, though with a less comprehensive means test than has been thought necessary in the past. Disease and poverty have been linked through all of history—disease produces poverty and poverty produces disease. A welfare program fails to deal with this association. Even though funds for medical care may be given generously, they are not given until some measure of destitution has been reached. The aged have a reduced potential for rehabilitation, physically and

From the article of the same name, *New England Journal of Medicine*, CCLXV (September 14, 1961), 526-528. Reprinted by courtesy of the *New England Journal of Medicine*. At the time this article was published, Osler L. Peterson was a visiting lecturer in the Department of Preventive Medicine, Harvard Medical School.

economically, so destitution once reached may be irreversible. Very probably the fundamental problem of the impoverishing effect of illness will be left untouched by any welfare program. It is also hard to believe that a means test will be widely acceptable, and it must be anticipated that its application will cause some people to delay or not obtain care when needed.

The strength of the social-security approach rests in the fact that the individual will, by making his payments while he is working, ascertain his ability to meet medical-care bills when he is old, when needs for medical care are greatest. The intimate relation of illness and poverty will be lessened, although not abolished. Since the number of people included in social security has increased progressively since its founding, virtually the whole population will ultimately be covered.

The possible long-term consequences of both these approaches to medical care are related to the fact that any popular government program will be subject to expansion—and any program that provides greater security against the cost of illness is likely to be popular. . . .

Much of the medical profession has chosen to support the welfare program provided by the Kerr-Mills Act as the alternative least likely to lend itself to extension. This may be true, though only for the short run. Examples taken from some state programs will explain why this is so. Massachusetts restricts welfare to single aged persons with incomes up to $150 and to aged couples with incomes up to $225 per month. In New York State the income limits vary at about the same level. From information available about the income distribution of the aged, it appears that three quarters or more of the people over age sixty-five are eligible for medical assistance in these two states. The value of a means test is depreciated in proportion to the liberality with which funds are given. Since the administration of a means test costs something, a point can be reached where logic dictates that it be discarded—particularly where the test will affect only a minority of the group. There are, of course, other states that are less generous, but the normal tendency will be for all state programs to equate. This will be encouraged by the annual infusion of federal funds. The existence of competing legislative proposals will tend to encourage extension of plans based upon the present Kerr-Mills Act.

The welfare approach is based on the use of general government revenue and hence will be subject to annual partisan debate on the size of Congressional appropriations. The kinds and amounts of service purchased are not likely to escape attention at these times. If this becomes the pattern, the Congressional debate will be repeated in 50 legislatures where feelings will be no less strong. This approach will put medical care directly into the political arena.

The use of the social-security approach to finance medical-care payments will result in a premium or tax designated specifically for medical care. Although Congress authorizes expenditures of such funds each year, the fact that the money comes from an earmarked revolving fund would somewhat insulate such a program from political controversy. The relatively peaceful operations of the social-security fund can be contrasted with the Farm Program or other programs that evoke strong diverse opinions and require annual appropriations.

. . . Doctors have a right to care about the preservation of their organizational prerogatives and their professional freedoms. There are unfortunately many precedents within welfare administrations for investigations and regulations with consequent arbitrariness. . . . If the welfare approach is expanded, the numbers of people covered will require that some of these restrictions be dropped. Some of the obnoxious precedents may survive.

The extension of social security to cover medical-care costs, since it involves a specifically designated tax, is likely to occasion less concern with the annual Congressional authorization for expenditure. Furthermore, such medical care would be given as a right. By itself, this is not a point likely to engender enthusiasm among doctors, but it would probably reduce the necessary administrative action both for the doctor and the patient. As part of the attempt to sell this bill, every effort is being made to design a system that will disturb the practice of medicine as little as possible. In addition, members of the Administration are making promises with respect to freedom of the doctor-patient relation and to practice that should not be dismissed lightly. It has become very clear during the past year that it is no longer possible to keep the Government out of medical care. In these days when there is so much thought about negotiation and what is and is not negotiable, it may be well for the medical profession to consider whether it has clearly made this distinction.

The possible effects of these two contending programs on voluntary health insurance have received surprisingly little attention. Obviously, doctors want to preserve voluntary health insurance. The ability of health insurance to cover a population is one of the most basic measures of its success. Equally obvious is the fact that health insurance has not been as successful in covering the aged as the rest of the population. The lower incomes and the extensive hospital use characteristic of the aged make this a most unfavorable group for Blue Cross or commercial insurance to underwrite. A welfare program will not solve this problem. The use of social security, particularly as the more completely insured age groups advance to retirement, could take the problem of insuring the elderly off the backs of Blue Cross–Blue Shield and other voluntary health insurance agencies. This would leave voluntary health insurance with a population that it has already demonstrated it can serve well.

Doctors might consider whether it might not be more prudent to back the use of social insurance for the aged in the hope of preserving voluntary health insurance for the rest. It is a calculated risk. . . .

The welfare approach involves a different risk. It may delay further government programs for a somewhat longer time. The risk in espousing this approach is that we will back into the very form of medical service we want least.

Which Pocket, Whose Pocket, and How Much?

DAVID W. WALLWORK

For the last twenty years the cost of medical care has been rising steadily, and this phenomenon has become the cause of serious professional and public concern. In the latter half of the same period, the impact of this rising cost on the financial resources of the aged has been highlighted and dramatized until finally it is the subject of lively and somewhat bitter political debate. However, we must remember that during all this period medical care has been available to the aged, the aged have been cared for, and the cost has been met in one way or another. The problem has recently been recrystallized in the form of the King-Anderson Bill (H.R. 4222), and the question in the present debate can be stated quite simply: "Does the Health Insurance Benefits Act of 1961 (H.R. 4222) provide a necessary or desirable method of financing the medical care of the aged?" Since H.R. 4222 is a *legislative* proposal, and its enactment is a *political objective,* one would indeed be naïve if, having determined one's stand on the basic question, one did not then ask also, "Is provision of a method of financing the care of the aged all that this bill does or is designed to do?" The apparent answer to this question makes organized medicine fear that an acrid and bitter medication has been offered it in a deceptively palatable vehicle. However, the second question will not concern us here.

It is estimated that there are 16,600,000 persons over sixty-five years of age in the United States and that 2,328,800 are on the Old Age Assistance rolls. One of every 7 of the "aged" is demonstrably and admittedly in need. In Massachusetts, at least, about a third of the cost of maintenance of these needy is devoted to their medical care. Actually this cost should be somewhat higher because medical and surgical services during hospitalization always have been provided without charge to Old Age Assistance cases in the great majority of

From the article of the same name, *New England Journal of Medicine,* CCLXV (September 14, 1961), 528-530. Reprinted by courtesy of the *New England Journal of Medicine.* At the time this article was published, David W. Wallwork was President of the Massachusetts Medical Society.

Massachusetts communities. Let us assume, then, that half the cost of maintenance of one seventh of the aged is attributable to medical care. It seems fair to assume that this represents the actual basic demonstrable "need." . . . Certainly the demonstrated actual need does not lend credence to the oft repeated statement that the "majority" of those over sixty-five need help in financing their medical expenses, and P.L. 86-778 (Kerr-Mills Act) already provides a mechanism for financing the medical care of *all* those who *demonstrate need.* Of the entire 16,600,000 of the "aged," between 3,000,000 and 4,000,000 would not be eligible for health benefits under social security. Of the 2,328,800 persons presently receiving Old Age Assistance, only 600,000 would receive medical benefits under the social-security approach, and, in some cases, these benefits would be less extensive than those currently available under federal-state programs. For those eligible for social benefits, H.R. 4222 provides that *all* shall receive such benefits whether or not need is present. Regardless of pension plans, veterans' benefits, voluntary health-insurance coverage, investment income and estate size, the benefits shall be available. The medical profession asks simply, "Why?"

Consider in this regard, too, the fact that the number of persons over sixty-five receiving Old Age Assistance (22 per cent in 1950) dropped to 15 per cent in 1959. By 1970 it is expected that this percentage will be 11. This improvement in the economic status of the aged is a manifestation of the better financial standing especially of the recent entrants into this age group, improvements due to better and more widespread corporate pension plans, increasing efforts to encourage continued employment of those sixty-five years of age or older, and increasing numbers eligible for social-security benefits, increasing coverage by voluntary prepayment health-insurance plans. About 8,000,000 of those over sixty-five years of age have some form of health insurance. Why commit the federal Government to a program of disputable value for a segment of the population in which need is apparently lessening? In other words, H.R. 4222 would furnish medical care to many *who do not need it,* would furnish, to those eligible, *care that often is inadequate* for their needs and would *fail to furnish any care at all* to many with demonstrable need. If one grants the Kerr-Mills Act nothing more, one must admit at least that it pulled the teeth of urgency from a problem that may well be diminishing in magnitude.

Since we are stressing need as a criterion for extending aid, it is appropriate to note that the method of determination of this need, the "means test," is repeatedly described as demeaning and degrading. This would seem to be a bit less than valid when advanced by proponents who, by providing services instead of cash benefits, would imply that the aged are either too imprudent or too stupid to use additional cash benefits for health care. . . . One is not especially convincing if one denounces a means test as demeaning or degrading and at the same time offers all those sixty-five years of age or older at the time of enactment of the proposed legislation a dole of free hospital, nursing-home and, in some instances, home care for the remainder of their lives. None of these recipients will have contributed one cent to the funds with which their medical care will be financed. There are two sides to the coin of human dignity! Furthermore, a taxpayer certainly is entitled to some safeguards to ensure proper prudent expenditure of public funds. If the means test is degrading in determining need for medical care, it can be no less so in determining who shall have the benefit of federal-state programs for public housing, yet no outcry against its use in these programs is heard. In fact the outcry in the present debate is heard not from the aged themselves but from their self-elected spokesmen.

The social-security approach, besides being unnecessary and ill fitting, will become more expensive as the number of the aged increases, even though the population of needy aged apparently will decrease. It is estimated that there will be 20,000,000 people over sixty-five in 1970, 90 per cent of whom will be covered by social security. The absolute number of needy may increase, too, despite the fact that the percentage of those over sixty-five in need may fall. The cost under P.L. 86-778 may increase, but it will be a reflection of actual need and not a reflection of the cost of a dole on top of actual needs.

A program that places the cost burden of medical care for the aged primarily on low-income workers by means of payments based on gross income, without the exemptions granted in the case of income taxes, is basically unfair and unjust. The tax increase not only will take money from these workers but also will cause an equivalent increase in the cost of the goods the taxpayer must purchase and the aged must purchase. As has frequently been pointed out, the aged are hit relatively harder by inflation than any other group, and this is one of the basic reasons for frequent inability to meet their own financial needs. In the case of income taxes, exemptions are recognition of the fact that the middle-age group, too, with the responsibility of rearing and educating children, has very realistic problems or "needs." A tax on gross income denies recognition of this need. Senator Kerr has estimated that 40 per cent of taxable income in the United States is not subject to the social-security tax. If medical care for the aged is a national problem, it should be financed from general revenues as provided by P.L. 86-778.

The King-Anderson Bill's approach to medical care for the aged is oriented toward institutional care—it provides hospital care and care in nursing homes and at home after hospitalization—and would lead to significant overcrowding of existing facilities owing to excessive utilization. . . . H.R. 4222 authorizes neither usual physician services nor out-of-hospital drugs. P.L. 86-778 authorizes financing of complete medical care without limitation, and this without orientation toward institutional care.

The Health Insurance Benefits Act of 1961 calls for new federal administration machinery, more federal employees, more bureaucracy. Bureaucracy has a very expensive habit of self-perpetuation and self-aggrandizement and is to be avoided when other modalities are available. P.L. 86-778 simply utilizes the already existing state public-assistance mechanisms. . . .

One frequently hears that enactment of this legislation will remove from the voluntary plans the burden of providing for the elderly and thus make it possible for these plans to offer smaller premiums or more services for the same premiums. This certainly seems to be a creditable accomplishment, but, just to be sure, take a second look. What is happening? The cost of the care of the aged is removed from the voluntary plans, but not from those who are employed and paying premiums. The cost is simply to be taken from another pocket, the tax pocket. The same people are going to pay the bill, all of it if from the tax pocket if this legislation is enacted, less than all of it if the cost is distributed among all those paying health-insurance premiums—employed, unemployed, wealthy, poor, social-security participants, nonparticipants in social security, aged, middle-aged and young—under the voluntary plan. What difference does it make, then, from which pocket it comes? Just this—any governmental plan inevitably will be more costly than a voluntary plan with similar benefits. It behooves us, then, to give the voluntary method more time to solve the problem, to give P.L. 86-778 more time to prove whether its provisions can adequately care for the medically indigent and truly indigent aged.

In this new modification of the social-security program, a new precedent is established,—that is, the provision of benefits rather than cash payments. These services presently are those of hospitals, nursing homes and home nursing organizations. With the precedent established, the services of all physicians seem almost certain to be the next objective, and the provision of services of dentists, chiropodists, morticians and lawyers, to mention only a few, might well follow if the program is modified every election year as has happened to the social-security program since its inception.

In brief, organized medicine opposes enactment of the King-Anderson Bill: first of all because it is a compulsory tax on one segment of the population for transfer to another chiefly in the form) of institutional medical care, providing often inadequate coverage to the actual needy and unnecessary financial outlays to others simply because of age; secondly, because it is designed to benefit those whose economic status appears to be steadily improving; thirdly, because P.L. 86-778 already provides a mechanism for complete medical care of the needy aged but has not yet been given time to prove its worth; fourthly, because the bill does less well and at greater costs something that voluntary-health-insurance plans bid fair to do; fifthly, because excessive utilization and unpredictable costs have proved to be the bane of similar programs elsewhere; sixthly, because the bill involves more bureaucracy with its inevitable self-perpetuation and self-aggrandizement; seventhly, because the bill provides a precedent for provision of other services by the social-security mechanism; and finally, because organized medicine fears, whether justifiably or not, that this bill is actually the crack in democracy's fortress through which socialized medicine, even socialism itself, may eventually engulf us.

SELECTED BIBLIOGRAPHY

Altmeyer, Arthur J. "The Development of Social Security in the United States of America," *Bulletin of the International Social Security Association,* VII (December 1954), 447-462.

Burns, Eveline M. *The American Social Security System.* Boston: Houghton Mifflin Company, 1949.

———. *Social Security and Public Policy.* New York: McGraw-Hill, Inc., 1956.

Carlson, Valdemar. *Economic Security in the United States.* New York: McGraw-Hill, Inc., 1962.

Dickinson, Frank G. "Reappraisal of Social Security," *Journal of the American Medical Association,* CLVII (March 5, 1955), 849-852.

Folsom, Marion B. "How to Pay the Hospital," *Atlantic Monthly,* CCXI (June 1963), 79-82.

Harris, Seymour E. *Economics of Social Security.* New York: McGraw-Hill, Inc., 1941.

Kelly, Matthew A., and Hazel C. Benjamin. *Social Security: Selected List of References.* Princeton: Industrial Relations Section, Princeton University, 1947.

Meriam, Lewis, and Karl Schlotterbeck. *The Cost and Financing of Social Security.* Washington, D.C.: The Brookings Institution, 1950.

"Social Security in the United States," *Bulletin of the International Social Security Association,* XIV (Ocober 1961), 541-609.

Somers, Herman M. and Anne R. "Trends and Current Issues in Social Insurance," *Proceedings of the Ninth Annual Meeting of the Industrial Relations Research Association,* pp. 1-25. Reprinted as Reprint #97 of the University of California Institute of Industrial Relations, 1957.

U.S. Cong. HR W&M. Subcommittee on Social Security. *Analysis of the Social Security System: Hearings.* 83rd Congress, 1st Session, 1954.

———. *Social Security After 18 Years: A Staff Report.* 83rd Congress, 2nd Session, 1954.

———. *Social Security After 18 Years: Statement of the Democratic Members of the Subcommittee.* 83rd Congress, 2nd Session, 1955.

U.S. Cong. Sen. Committee on Labor and Public Welfare. Subcommittee on Problems of the Aged and Aging. *Action for the Aged and Aging: A Report.* Senate Report #128. 87th Congress, 1st Session, March 28, 1961.

U.S. HEW SSA. *Basic Readings in Social Security.* 1956. An annotated bibliography.

———. *Social Security in the United States.* 1959.

U.S. Federal Security Agency. Social Security Board. Bureau of Research and Statistics. *Social Insurance Financing in Relation to Consumer Income and Expenditures.* By S. J. Mushkin, Anne Scitovszky, and Leila N. Small. Bureau Memorandum #63, June 1946.

U.S. Library of Congress, Legislative Reference Service. *Financing Social Security.* By Raymond E. Manning. Public Affairs Bulletin #46, 1946.

VI | The Role of Government

The preceding chapters have discussed some of the more important issues in the Kennedy-Johnson Administration's proposals for financing health care for the aged. Some of the less significant issues raised by the proposals have not been discussed. One of these is the extent to which the deductible provisions present a hardship for those who could not afford to pay the deductible amount. Although these provisions certainly do present some hardship, they were not the basis of the opposition to medicare. For the most part, the people who raise this argument against the King-Anderson and Mills bills also opposed the Forand bill, which had no deductible provision. Similarly, one argument frequently made against the Forand bill was that it did not include those elderly who were not eligible for social security. The King-Anderson and Mills bills cover all aged, whether or not eligible for social security, but this change has not won medicare many new supporters from the ranks of those who were opposed to the Forand bill because of its more limited coverage.

Rather, there is an underlying issue which determines for most people whether or not they favor medicare; arguments such as those cited above and to some extent the arguments discussed earlier are merely debaters' points. The underlying issue is one's attitude toward the role of government in society, and, in particular, toward its role in the provision of medical services.

The Argument against Government

One view holds that "that government is best which governs least"—government activities restrict individual freedom, and society must limit government activities to assure the full flowering of that freedom. A minimum-wage law, for example, is to be opposed because it prevents the individual from working for any wage he sees fit to accept.

Government activities limit the individual's freedom indirectly as well as directly. This statement is true because government activities are usually financed by taxes, which are compulsory. Taxation thus diminishes the individual's freedom to decide for himself how he wishes to spend his earnings.

Not only should each person be free to spend his income as he thinks best; he should also be responsible for his own needs. If he cannot meet his own needs, he should turn to his family for assistance. Individual and familial responsibility are good things in and of themselves. To undermine them with government assistance is to deprive individuals of their self-respect.

Linked to this moral argument is an economic argument. Prosperity is best assured by the free play of the market: each individual, pursuing his own self-interest, will in the end promote the over-all good of the entire society. If government protects people from economic hardship, they will not have any incentive to help themselves, and the economy will be deprived of their productive efforts. The taxation necessary to support government activity will also reduce incentive—why work when one is working for the government a large proportion of the time, rather than for oneself? Moreover, high taxation also prevents the accumulation of capital necessary for investment.

Those who adhere to this point of view regard all governments with suspicion; if an individual cannot help himself, and his family cannot be of help, he should then turn to private charity, rather than to the government, for assistance. If government activity must be undertaken, it should be done at the state or local level to prevent, first and foremost, the accumulation of power in the hands of a centralized national government. It was to prevent the growth of a powerful central government that the framers of the Constitution established a federal system, reserving to the states and to the people all powers not delegated in the Constitution to the federal government. This is the second reason for undertaking such government programs as may be necessary at the state or local level—the Constitution prohibits the federal government from undertaking them. Third, state and local governments are closer to the people and have better insight into local needs; thus, they can structure programs to meet these needs, whereas a federal program cannot permit local variation. Fourth, state and local taxes are more regressive than federal taxes; they would therefore be less of a burden on higher-income groups, thus providing them with the incentive to invest and the capital necessary to do so.

The Argument for Government

The opposing point of view looks on government as a means for accomplishing social purposes. Government activities need not limit the individual's freedom, but may enlarge it. A minimum-wage law enlarges freedom because it prevents the exploitation of the individual by his employer. Those who adhere to this point of view frequently point to the technological and urban nature of modern society as a reason for more extensive government activity now than in the past. In such a complex society, power is held by many large private institutions which can restrict the individual's freedom. The individual is unable to protect himself against these institutions, and it is necessary for the government to play a more extensive role in protecting him than in the past.

Taxes, rather than being a limitation on freedom, are an expression of freedom. They are not imposed by a foreign power, but rather levied by elected representatives of the people. They are an expression of the individual's choice, through his representatives, to spend part of his income for social purposes.

As for individual and familial responsibility, they are certainly desirable. However, the urban family is not as self-reliant as the farm family, which has the ability to provide itself at least with essentials even in times of adversity. Nor has private charity been able to meet the demands of economic adversity in our cities; it is inadequate in amount and overlooks many who are in need. Moreover, our concern with self-respect should extend to the self-respect of the poor. Such self-respect is more likely to be maintained by a system which provides certain essential needs to all than by one which requires them to expose their poverty in order to get assistance.

Those who hold to this point of view do not see the free market as a moral imperative, rather citing the lesson of history that there are certain social needs which the market is unable to satisfy. From an economic point of view, they say, free competition is often unable to sustain itself without government intervention. People maintain their incentive to work and to invest in a system with a high degree of government activity—the experience of the Scandinavian states is an illustration of this. As for the accumulation of capital, there has been no decline in the level of savings in the United States in proportion to the national income in recent years, a period in which there has been a higher level of taxation and government activity than previously.

Those who adhere to this point of view prefer that government activity be undertaken at the federal level. They find the Constitution more permissive than do their opponents, and are less concerned about the growth of power in the federal government. Indeed, they suggest that it is really the federal government which is closer to the people, who are likely to know more about their Congressman than their state legislator, and the President than their mayor. The federal government generally attracts a higher caliber of person, in elective and appointive offices and in the bureaucracy, than do state and local governments. The federal government is under closer scrutiny from the press and from opposition political parties than are state and local governments and is therefore less likely to trample on individual rights.

Moreover, adherents to this point of view look on the United States as a single national community, and they are concerned with assuring national standards. Undertaking a program at the federal level permits all areas, regardless of their economic condition, to participate. Nationwide participation is particularly important in an era of high mobility, when an individual who is poorly educated because his state cannot afford high expenditures for education may very well spend the bulk of his life in another state. Where necessary, federal programs can permit local variation to suit local needs, while at the same time providing a minimum floor. Adherents to this point of view are also concerned with the financing of government activity, and prefer federal activity because the federal tax structure is generally more progressive than the state and local tax structures,[a] thus putting less of a burden on lower-income groups, who are less able to pay taxes.

Government and Medical Care

The statements of these two positions that have just been given are, of course, brief summaries of much more extensive ideologies. There are also positions that stand between these two, and there are individuals who adhere to one ideology in word and thought, but to the other in practice. Ideology may also, of course, serve the function of masking self-interest, even from the individual who espouses the ideology himself.

The ideological conflict over government activity in general has a specific application to the field of medical care. Those who oppose medicare fear that it will lower the quality of medical care for the aged in three ways. First, it will encourage utilization of medical services by those who do not really need them, thereby overcrowding existing facilities and resulting in poorer care for those who really need medical care. Second, if the government pays for medical-care benefits, then the government will have to exercise some controls over the services provided. Third, medicare will lower the physician's incentive to serve his patients. For all three reasons, the doctor-patient relationship will be disturbed. Medicare opponents point to foreign medical-care systems, especially the British National Health Service, as examples of the inferior medical care resulting from government intervention. And, they fear, medicare will soon be expanded to include all medical expenses for the entire population.

Those who favor medicare deny that it will lower the quality of medical care, emphasizing the safeguards written into the bill. They also disagree with the unfavorable evaluation of the British

---

[a] This is one of the ironies of the controversy over medicare. Medicare opponents, who would normally be considered in the first group described above, are supporting the Kerr-Mills program, which is primarily financed through general federal taxation. Medicare supporters, who are in the second group, find themselves supporting a program based on social-security taxes, which are more regressive than general federal taxation.

National Health Service made by their opponents,[b] and assert that medicare need not lead to a similar, or more extensive, medical-care program for the entire population.

In the following selections, Herman and Anne Somers discuss the traditional and the modern doctor-patient relationship. "King-Anderson and the Quality of Medical Care" presents the point of view of the American Medical Association, and Congressman King, Nelson Cruikshank, and Wilbur J. Cohen present opposing points of view.

---

[b] The virtues and deficiencies of the National Health Service have been argued at length. The interested reader should consult some of the sources cited in the bibliography at the end of this chapter.

The Changing Doctor-Patient Relationship

HERMAN M. SOMERS AND ANNE R. SOMERS

The origin of the "traditional" doctor-patient relationship reaches deep into the past. From the beginning of medical history, the practicing physician has been part priest, part technician, part personal or family counselor. In early days, when medicine had very little in the way of scientific knowledge to rely on, it was inevitable that the subjective priestly element should be dominant. In the words of the pioneer anthropologist, Malinowski, "Magical beliefs and practices tend to cluster about situations where there is an important uncertainty factor and where there are strong emotional interests in the success of action." Historically and universally, illness and medical care have provided classic examples of the combination of "uncertainty" and "strong emotional interests" and hence have always involved, to a greater or lesser degree, an appeal to supernatural or occult powers.

In modern times medicine has become more scientific. But the traditional reliance on mystical forces and a highly authoritarian doctor-patient relationship persists to a degree unknown in other contemporary human relations with the exception of priest-parishioner in certain religious groups. . . . There is no general acknowledgment or acceptance of the significant change that has, in fact, been taking place in the doctor-patient relationship. Of the manifold and complex reasons, only a few of the more important can be noted here.

First and basic is the persistence—in spite of scientific progress—of large elements of uncertainty and fear regarding illness and medical care which are conducive to continued reliance on hope, faith, confidence and other subjective factors on the part of both doctor and patient. . . .

As the boundaries of medical ignorance and uncertainty are pushed

From *Doctors, Patients, and Health Insurance* (Washington, D.C.: The Brookings Institution, 1961), pp. 458-475. Copyright 1961 by the Brookings Institution. Reprinted by permission. At the time this article was written, Herman Somers was chairman of the Department of Political Science at Haverford College; Anne Somers was Research Associate at Haverford College. Herman Somers is now Professor of Politics at Princeton University.

back, one would expect this resort to supra-scientific factors to decline, and, indeed, it has in the case of bacterial and other diseases where the cause and cure are clearly established. But the reduced role of subjective factors in the treatment of specific cases has been more than offset by an increasing interest in the role of the emotions in illness. A widespread increase in psychotherapy and psychosomatic medicine has renewed the emphasis on a personal doctor and a personal doctor-patient relationship of a type that permits knowledge of the "whole man." . . . Moreover it is now widely believed that illness, *per se*, tends to create—even in the most intellectual of patients—an attitude of dependence, of "regression" to helplessness, and perhaps to childlike behavior. . . . In this state, confidence in the authority and benevolence of the doctor, as well as in his scientific knowledge and technical skill—the now-familiar "father-image"—is generally desired and often desirable.

Finally, there is the impenetrable mystery of death. The physician's relation to this event—however helpless he in fact may be—has endowed him, in the eyes of centuries of patients, with an aura of the mystery. To the extent that the physician identifies himself with this priestly role and takes on himself the burden associated therewith, or at least appears to do so through the gravity of his personal demeanor and behavior, his supra-scientific role continues to be respected and perpetuated, reinforcing in the eyes of individual patients and society at large his status as a dispenser of increasingly scientific medicine. . . .

. . . It was not until the twentieth century that any but a tiny fraction of mankind—even in the most advanced civilizations of the past—had access to a personal doctor. The very concept of a personal doctor-patient relationship was inconceivable for most people. In part this was due to the almost universal poverty and ignorance; in part to the low state of medical science. But these were not the only reasons.

Historically, medicine has been a scientific discipline and a means of livelihood as well as a humanitarian vocation. Sometimes the periods associated with the most dramatic scientific advances have also been noted for callous disregard of individual suffering. Greek medicine—even in the days of the idealistic Hippocrates—was largely a privilege of the leisure class. The first result of the eighteenth century development of teaching hospitals and clinical research was to close the hospitals to cases that did not appear scientifically "interesting." . . .

The barriers to a good relationship, especially the economic ones, are less extreme today than they used to be. Nevertheless, they still exist. Rapidly changing conditions have brought conspicuous maladjustments and anomalies in their wake. The scientific development of medicine was not an isolated phenomenon but part of a general advance in science, technology, income, and education. As the doctor grew more capable, his patients also became more knowledgeable—less dependent on his devotion, and more demanding of the specialized skills of his profession.

Consider, first, the typical American patient around 1960. He is likely to be older than in [the nineteenth century]. He is better educated and has a higher income. He usually sees the doctor not when he is flat on his back but in the doctor's office or clinic. One out of four visits are made when he is not sick at all but for preventive purposes. The extent of his medical knowledge is still very limited, but it has increased rather dramatically. His own attitudes are more scientific. In many, if not the majority of, cases he knows enough to recognize ignorance or gross incompetence on the part of a doctor. On average, death is further removed and fear hangs less pervasively over the atmosphere.

He expects to pay for services rendered—directly or through a third party—and does not feel that he owes the doctor any special gratitude after the bill has been paid. His health insurance probably does not cover the doctor's visit, but the knowledge that he has hospital and surgical insurance reassures him in case serious illness and high costs develop. While the role of uncertainty, fear of suffering and death, and the emotional regression of sick people have certainly not disappeared, it is evident that the average American patient is now far less dependent, better informed, and less frightened than he was . . . .

On the doctor's part, he is now rarely confronted with penniless patients. His collection ratio is running 90 per cent or better. There is clearly neither the need nor the opportunity there used to be for philanthropy or "noblesse oblige" on his part. Little outright charity is expected or bestowed. He knows that most people can and are willing to pay for medical care. If they cannot, a public or private agency is likely to do so. The practice of medicine has become highly profitable, and the medical doctor is now the best paid professional in the country. He is not only making money but is becoming a successful businessman—in terms of managerial techniques and even temperament.

There is little time for friendly conversation with the patient or family counseling. The next patient is always waiting. The brisk impersonal atmosphere of office and hospital combined with the typical five- to ten-minute consultation are effective inhibitors of social intercourse or of tales of woe—financial or emotional.

Related to this situation is the distaste of the average practitioner for patients whose problems are mainly emotional or where the organic disease is complicated by emotional involvement. The attitude starts in medical school where the young doctor acquires a strong bias against "neurotics," "hypochondriacs" and other "crocks." . . .

The concept of the "uncooperative patient" has become deeply imbedded in medical mores. A recent study in the outpatient clinic of a teaching hospital, for example, found that students, faculty, and other medical personnel readily agreed on the definition: a patient is "uncooperative" "when he is stubborn," "when he won't recognize that help is being given to him," "when he refuses to accept his condition," or "when he fails to appreciate the effort that has been expended on his behalf."

Unfortunately for the doctor's peace of mind, however, the desirability of a completely passive patient is now widely challenged, not only by many patients but by leaders of the profession. It is increasingly recognized that the patient's active cooperation is frequently essential to effective therapy, whereas too great dependence on the doctor—emotionally, financially, or otherwise—can be disastrous. Large reliance on placebos—intellectual as well as physical—is frowned upon. . . . "We still are not sufficiently aware," says Dr. Flanders Dunbar, "that the physician himself is often pathogenic . . . ." He is so, according to this school of thought, when he permits the patient's craving for dependence and his own craving for admiration to dominate the diagnosis and the choice of therapy. By refusing to help or even force the patient to assume some responsibility for his own cure, he may, it is alleged, be contributing to a prolongation or "fixation" of the physiological symptoms and thus injure him physically as well as emotionally.

The risk of fixation is increased whenever treatment becomes very intensive, very elaborate, or very impersonal, and today, when ever-growing facilities are available for mechanistic diagnosis and therapy, there is a danger . . . of inducing "fixation invalidism" on a scale hitherto unknown.

This is a very serious indictment and it is, of course, deeply resented . . . .

If today's critics are correct, it can only be concluded that the image of the "traditional" doctor-patient relationship is not only inaccurate, but that it has lost most of its beneficent value and may now have become injurious to doctor and patient alike. . . . Benevolent authoritarianism was [once] appropriate . . . , but is out of harmony with the realities of 1960. The image appears to have degenerated into a public relations stereotype, potentially harmful to patient and doctor—therapeutically, ethically, and financially. These developments are not due to financial and organizational mechanisms that improve access to modern medicine. They are more likely related to futile attempts to perpetuate the past—a past which, for the great majority of sick people, never existed.

King-Anderson and the Quality of Medical Care

AMERICAN MEDICAL ASSOCIATION

The opening section of the bill suggests that none of its provisions will result in Federal control of medical practice. Under the heading "Prohibition Against Interference," Title XVI states, in part, that no Federal officer or any Federal employee shall exercise any control over the practice of medicine or the administration of hospitals, facilities or agencies.

The very next section declares that the patient may freely choose those who will provide the services covered.

Taken at face value, this is most reassuring. But while the first provision of the new title contains a prohibition against interference in the practice of medicine, it also contains the following language, describing the power of the Secretary of Health, Education and Welfare, and I quote:

". . . Or, *except as otherwise specifically provided,* to exercise any supervision or control over the administration or operation of any such hospital, facility or agency" (emphasis added).

Mr. Chairman, those five little words—"except as otherwise specifically provided"—are a blanket authorization for the Federal government to control the providers of services. Put this language into its proper perspective, and it means that the Secretary of HEW *can* exercise control over the administration or operation of a hospital, facility, physician, or agency.

For the bill also states that the Secretary would be empowered to set "such other conditions of participation . . . as the Secretary may find necessary in the interest of health and safety of individuals who are furnished services by or in such institution." Here the measure is referring to requirements for participation by a hospital.

Now before the Secretary can establish "such other conditions of participation," he would be required to consult with a Federal

From testimony at hearings on *Health Services for the Aged under the Social Security Insurance System,* held by the Committee on Ways and Means of the U.S. House of Representatives, August 2, 1961, pp. 1317-1326, 1344-1350.

advisory board which would be appointed by him, appropriate state agencies, and recognized listing or accrediting bodies. Surely this would be a safeguard, the bill's supporters say. But would it? H.R. 4222 says that the Secretary need only *consult* with the advisory board. Nowhere does the bill state that the Board's recommendations to him would be binding.

The permissive language of this proposal thus provides the means by which Federal officials can regiment and control all providers of the services covered. I say Federal officials *can* regiment and control. Would they?

I submit that the answer is an unqualified "yes." It is axiomatic that the Federal government tends to control what it subsidizes. Indeed, the government must, for it is duty-bound to see that the taxpayer's money is spent properly and with efficiency. The problem arises as a result of the fact that the providers of services and the government may not see eye-to-eye on the subject of what constitutes "efficiency." For as I shall discuss later, government must concern itself primarily with the financial aspects of these programs; and the health professions must, if they are to provide quality medical care, concern themselves with quality medical care above all else.

H.R. 4222 disclaims its intention of meddling with the free practice of medicine, Mr. Chairman, as is customary in all bills which seek to utilize the compulsory Social Security mechanism as a device for financing health care for the aged. But if a single government agency were empowered to buy from ten to twenty per cent of all care in the nation's general hospitals, it takes no ouija board to predict that this agency would wield the power it had been given to influence the operation and management of such hospitals.

Under this type of arrangement, it would be well nigh impossible to avoid a situation in which government employees would be telling doctors what drugs and treatment they could provide; telling hospital administrators how to run their hospitals; and telling the nursing homes what they could and could not do.

The proponents of this legislation make much of the fact that hospitals will not be forced to participate in this program and that its beneficiaries will have freedom of choice.

What kind of freedom of choice would a patient have if the hospital where his physician had hospital privileges chose not to participate or was considered ineligible? Or what kind of freedom of choice would a patient have if the only hospital in his area chose not to participate or was considered ineligible?

This brings us to the point of considering to what degree physicians' services are covered under H.R. 4222. According to Section 1603, under the heading of "inpatient hospital services," beneficiaries would be entitled to services supplied by pathologists, radiologists, physiatrists, anesthesiologists, and all interns and residents in training under an approved teaching program.

The providers of these services are physicians, Mr. Chairman. And when spokesmen for Health, Education and Welfare state publicly—as they often do—that only a handful of physicians would be affected by the bill, they are either deliberately misstating the facts or demonstrating that they have failed to comprehend the full implications of the proposal. . . .

As of September 1, 1959, there were 37,843 interns in the United States. To this number must be added 3,100 to 5,000 anesthesiologists; 3,500 pathologists; 3,500 to 4,000 radiologists; and 250 to 400 physiatrists. Taking the smallest numbers involved in these ranges, we emerge with a figure of 48,193 physicians; and taking the upward figure in the range I have given, we have 50,743.

Further, we must add to these figures the numbers of other staff physicians in hospitals with approved training programs who are responsible for the services provided by physicians in training under approved teaching programs.

Let me also point out that the bill authorizes the financing of outpatient hospital diagnostic services. This provision would, in effect, establish an outpatient hospital diagnostic program designed, not for the indigent, but for all aged persons entitled to Social Security benefits. Persons who would normally go to their own private physicians could go to a hospital outpatient clinic where they would receive services performed by a resident or intern, presumably under the direction of a teaching physician. . . .

There is also the matter of hospital and nursing home utilization committees, Mr. Chairman. H.R. 4222 provides that hospitals and skilled nursing facilities should have such committees to be eligible for participation in the program.

To begin with, few hospitals—and fewer nursing homes—have such committees. But presuming this condition of eligibility were met by participating facilities throughout the country, would the overall effect be good or bad in terms of the authority which it would potentially place in the hands of the Federal government?

The basis for all good medical care is in the intimate relationship between a doctor and his patient. One of its essential ingredients is the physician's particular knowledge of his patient's medical needs. It is on the basis of this intimate knowledge that a physician selects a course of treatment based on his patient's individual need.

Thus, the physician is best qualified to judge how ill his patient is, what treatment should be prescribed, whether or not he should be admitted to a hospital, when he is well enough to go home. Is it wise to subject his judgment to the critical review of a group which is, first of all, far removed from the individual doctor-patient relationship; and which is, second of all, subject to the influence of such regulations as the Secretary of Health, Education and Welfare may promulgate?

We doubt that this is wise. For the moment, it is sufficient to say that if this legislation were adopted, HEW is faced with only two choices:

On the one hand, HEW can hold this program within the financial limits imposed by tax receipts, tightening the reins on services as costs rise. Here, government keeps an eye on the budget instead of on the patient, with consequent lowering of the quality of medical care.

On the other hand, HEW can give the program free rein and wind up by confronting Congress every year or two with a request for more money.

It is not hard to predict how HEW will resolve its dilemma, Mr. Chairman. It will use its power to regulate—and use it to the fullest. Parenthetically, we are convinced this program would be so drastically underfinanced that even the power to regulate would not keep it fiscally sound without further tax increases.

But HEW would at least try to hold costs down through its power to impose regulations. In the process, it could seek to restrict admission to hospitals and nursing homes; cut down on the patient's length of stay within these facilities; impose limits on prescription of drugs, tests or treatment: in sum, HEW could apply the brakes in any of a hundred ways.

The utilization committees would simply become one of the means through which HEW would seek—however vainly—to balance its books.

The powers entrusted to the Secretary under H.R. 4222 are broad indeed, Mr. Chairman. Under Section 1609, these words appear:

"The amount paid to any provider of services with respect to services for which payment may be made under this title shall be the reasonable cost of such services, as determined in accordance with regulations establishing the method or methods to be used in determining such costs for various types or classes of institutions, services and agencies."

There's that word "regulations" again. And with it goes the requirement that payment be made on the basis of the "reasonable cost" of services.

Costs will be reasonable for any product, Mr. Chairman, only when the buyer and the seller agree that they are reasonable. If agreement cannot be reached, any party to the negotiations is usually at liberty to withdraw and seek a satisfactory understanding elsewhere.

A different situation prevails when the Federal government sits down to the bargaining table to negotiate agreements with the providers of medical care. In this case, HEW is in the position of buying perhaps ten to twenty per cent of all the hospital care in the country, plus a substantial percentage of the skilled nursing home care. The providers of service, in the final analysis, are given the option of selling at the customer's price, or not selling at all.

"Reasonable cost" thus winds up by meaning reasonable from HEW's viewpoint. Anyone not satisfied with the HEW interpretation of the word is given the sole option of staying out of the program— to the disservice of older patients.

Physicians are not recognized under the bill as eligible providers of services, of course, although the services of more than 50,000 of them are involved. They would therefore not be represented in negotiations between government and the hospitals for the fees to be paid for their services. . . .

H.R. 4222, in the process of giving the whip hand to the Secretary of Health, Education and Welfare, requires that the eligibility of hospitals to participate in the program be based on three conditions. These are: (a) adequate medical records; (b) bylaws in effect with respect to staff and physicians; and (c) such other conditions as the Secretary may find necessary, in the interest of the health and safety of the individuals receiving the services provided.

Here again H.R. 4222 provides a device for Federal control of hospitals and the medical services they furnish.

We do not argue that hospitals, like other institutions or businesses, should not maintain "adequate records." But who is to say what records are adequate and what records are not? The bill is clear on this point. The arbiter of adequacy is to be the Secretary of HEW. If he so wished, the Secretary could require records so "adequate" that compiling and maintaining them would require a doubling or tripling of hospital administrative staffs.

The Secretary is further empowered to determine such other conditions of participation as he may find necessary in the interest of health and safety. What the Secretary and his successors might find necessary, Mr. Chairman, I cannot venture to guess. I can only point out that this section of the bill gives him enough authority to become the nation's czar of hospital care.

Very properly we fear unrestrained power in this country. It is all very well to say that our public officials are men of good will and that we can count upon that alone as a safeguard of the regulatory power. But the unrestrained power to regulate can become the power to destroy, whether it be a free nation or a free system of medical care. Even if we could be guaranteed the good intentions of the Secretary and all of his successors, could we be guaranteed that all would be knowledgeable and wise in their exercise of this great authority?

I suggest that we could not. Standards set by an appointed official, and regulations promulgated by him, may be responsive to the wishes of an Administration. But it is unlikely that the political expert will be equally expert in his control of a health system. Delegate these powers to the Federal government, Mr. Chairman, and our free system of medical care—the world's best—would be placed in extreme jeopardy. . . .

Now let us take a look at the availability of the promised benefits. The bill sets up a number of requirements which must be met by the providers of services before they can participate in the program. I have referred to several of these.

One of the eligibility requirements for nursing homes is that they have a 24-hour-a-day nursing service.

According to a statement made by Representative Adam Clayton Powell (D-N.Y.) during the debate on a bill to extend the Practical Nurse Training Act, of the 23,000 nursing homes in the United States, only 9,000 had the services of either a professional or a practical nurse. Obviously, then, nursing home services—limited under the bill to conditions for which the patient was treated in the hospital—will be unavailable in many nursing homes and in many parts of the country.

Similarly, there is reason to question the availability of home health services, for there are only 900 such organizations in the 3,067 counties of this country.

There is even some question as to whether all our hospitals, especially those in the rural areas, will be qualified. . . .

Finally, Mr. Chairman, I should like to point out that this is an institution-oriented measure. It places its emphasis on putting the older patient in a hospital or nursing home.

Medically, this is unsound. Physicians do everything within their power to keep the older patient *out* of the nursing home or hospital. Recovery is faster, health is better when the older person is at home, among familiar surroundings and when he remains within the mainstream of community living. . . .

As the members of this Committee are well aware, the controversy over national compulsory health plans has gone on for many years in this country. It has waxed and waned, but never entirely abated. Those who would like to see a socialized system of medicine set up for the United States are grimly determined, tireless, and disciplined.

Undiscouraged by repeated defeats, they return to the attack.

Invariably, they fix upon the Social Security Act as the vehicle best suited to their purpose. . . .

Why have all these measures chosen Title II of the Social Security Act as the vehicle through which our present system of medical care can be taken over by the Federal Government? I think there are several reasons.

First, the sponsors of such legislation hope to gain public approval of their proposals through the use of a system generally accepted by the American people.

Second, there is the lesson they have learned from abroad—that social insurance plans are evolutionary, not revolutionary, in character. They move gradually from lump sum benefits to retirement payments, to survivorship payments, to cash disability benefits, to temporary cash sick benefits, to national compulsory health schemes.

Third, those who like the idea of placing our system of freely practiced medicine under the thumb of the Federal Government know that decent, humane people try to help their neighbors. Thus they have sought to create a broad-gauged problem—the inability of the aged to finance health care costs—where no problem, or a small problem exists. After dramatizing the alleged "need" of an entire group, after picturing sixteen and a half million people as poverty stricken and debilitated, the proponents of socialized medicine then say: "This isn't socialized medicine. We're only talking about the aged. We're not covering physicians. We're simply asking that our retired people be protected as a matter of right, through the Social Security system."

The argument, on its face, sounds harmless enough. But it is riddled, through and through, with illogic, lack of candor, and disregard for the facts.

Now the entire push to make our present system of medical care a federally controlled and operated activity is simply a single battle in a continuing war. Our nation is divided into two camps. At issue is the vital question of the proper role the Federal Government should play in our society.

On one side are those who demand—vigorously and through every means of persuasion—an ever-enlarging role for the Federal Government. On the other side are those, like ourselves, who oppose the efforts now being made to increase the government's direction and control over our way of life.

That the Federal Government functions in areas which do not concern it is an unarguable statement. Members of the Committee have read, I feel sure, the Hoover Commission reports and the reports of the Commission on Intergovernmental Relations. Even the most casual study of these documents discloses example after example of Federal trespass into areas formerly reserved to private effort, or into areas more properly the purview of state and local governments.

This, then, is one of the major problems of our time. The nation's physicians are among those who believe that increasing Federal direction, regulation, and control threaten the existence of individual freedom. To be candid, Mr. Chairman, we feel that the Federal Government is once more seeking to broaden the scope of its encroachment.

The steady drift of the Federal Government into areas of activity in which it does not belong has been accelerated by political expediency, in many cases. We are now confronted with such a case:

H.R. 4222—the campaign issue, the platform pledge, the political promise.

Mr. Chairman, we are convinced that campaign issues, pledges and promises are not the basis on which to deal with health care. As doctors, we are concerned with the prolonging of lives, the control of disease, the provision of health care.

We have done our job. If we had not, the life expectancy of the average American would not have increased as it has. We have succeeded, not failed, in prolonging life for millions of people under a system of freely practiced medicine. Are we to be penalized for our success because of campaign issues, platform pledges, and political promises? Are we to remain passive and silent while others seek to destroy the world's finest system of medical care in the name of political expediency?

We proudly acknowledge, Mr. Chairman, that the health professions have, in prolonging life, helped create a vast sociological problem. And we submit that only a free medical profession can cope with that portion of the total problem involving the health care of the elderly.

The Federal Government is not being asked to move into a vacuum of unmet need. It is being asked, under H.R. 4222, to pre-empt an area of successful accomplishment in the name of political expediency.

From the beginning of the Social Security system, the Congress has adhered to certain basic principles in drafting legislation affecting the system. Among these principles have been those providing that benefits should bear some relation to the individual's earnings, and that benefits should be paid in cash, not in services.

It has once more been proposed that we abandon these principles. Instead of allowing the beneficiary to use cash benefits in any way he pleases, it is now suggested that he be required to accept health services for himself regardless of whether he likes the idea or not, or whether he needs these services or not.

This is a hazardous deviation from the original purpose of the Social Security Act. And it demonstrates a dangerous brand of thinking, not new to the world, but comparatively new to the United States.

It is the thinking of "Government knows best."

This legislation proposes that we distrust the brains and capacities of today's Americans. It suggests that the aged—as an entire group—are not capable of looking after their own affairs and providing for their own needs.

In my opinion, this is patronizing and paternalistic. . . .

H.R. 4222 sees the Federal Government as "parent and guardian" for the health care of sixteen and a half million older people, presumably because the aged are "unable to look after their own interests."

Subscribe to this premise, and government—authoritarian and wise—could brush aside any or all of our individual freedoms. Under the slogan "it's all for your own good," the Federal Government could regiment doctors, nurses, patients, hospitals, nursing homes and any other element of our health care system that stood in its way.

All of H.R. 4222's disclaimers of control of the practice of medicine and of the administration of medical facilities and programs do not alter the fact that what the Government subsidizes, it also controls.

. . . This country's system of medical care is unlike that of any other. It is unique, in that it operates freely. Although government performs a number of essential functions within this system at the local, state and Federal levels, it thus far has sought to supplement, not supplant, the efforts of the health professions. In the United States, the health professions have therefore been free to pursue their constant search for better methods of treatment, more effective drugs, more efficient techniques.

By way of contrast, other countries have developed systems under which government exercises, to a greater or lesser degree, controls on the provision and financing of health care. Further, these controls are not confined to programs of indigent care but cover the entire population regardless of need.

Which approach is the more effective? And which is better for the United States?

In seeking to answer these questions, it is relevant to point out that America has become, in recent years, the medical Mecca of the world. When I began medical practice, students who could afford it flocked to the medical centers of Europe for their basic and post-graduate education. Today, medical students from all over the world come to the United States.

The quality of medical education in American schools is unsurpassed anywhere. The qualifications of the American physician are unmatched anywhere. We research, we experiment, we improvise and we treat freely because we are free to do so; and the results speak for themselves.

Ours is a *dynamic* system of health care—and it works. The very fact that we now have sixteen and one-half million Americans 65 years of age or older proves that it works.

Yet, this same system of medical care is now under attack. At a moment when American medicine is pre-eminent throughout the world, it is proposed that we adopt the very systems under which one European nation after another has lost its former leadership in medical science. . . .

The staggering costs of such plans, the administrative problems they create—let these considerations be secondary. The important thing is . . . the disruption of the doctor-patient relationship; the delays in admission to hospitals; the time wasted in the over-crowded offices of doctors; the regimentation of medical practice; the effect of the program on medical research; the availability of medical facilities and personnel—in other words, medicine in action on a government-run, assembly-line basis. . . .

It is important not to minimize the patient's role in the private medical care system. It is the patient who demands the best of facilities, equipment, drugs, laboratories, operating rooms, hospitals. He demands these necessary resources for himself as an individual; and he also acts to assure that they will be available to his entire community, either through private or local governmental agencies.

It is the patient, and his ability to choose freely, that exact the utmost from the doctor-patient relationship. The physician who does not possess the confidence of his patient is handicapped in his effort to cope with disease. But so long as the patient is free to seek professional treatment without restraint, he can quickly find the physician in whom he does have confidence.

Given that confidence, a doctor's skill can sometimes surmount shortcomings in the facilities and resources available to him.

There are only two ways in which government can function in any medical care system. One way is helpful, the other is destructive.

Government can *supplement* the effort of the individual patient. It can do this by helping finance the deficit between the total cost of care and what the patient can pay. This assistance in financing can be accomplished either through welfare programs or through the community's subsidizing of resources. Again, government can properly and helpfully act to *supplement*.

Government can also *supplant* the patient in his relationship with professional personnel and available resources. When it does so, it undertakes to decide *for* the patient what services should be provided and by whom. Having reached that decision, government then assumes the function of paying for those services.

H.R. 4222 falls in the latter category. In doing so, it overlooks the bedrock premise on which any high quality medical care system must be based:

Quality care can be obtained only when the needs of the individual patient are placed first, and financing is placed second.

Our own free system of medical care is aimed, first and foremost, at *treatment of the illness.*

Contrast this with a system under which government pays for care directly, rather than supplementing the private individual purchase of care, and the difference becomes obvious. Here the stress has been shifted from quality to cost.

It is axiomatic that first-rate medical care must be appropriate to the needs of the patient—medically, socially, economically and psychologically.

Under such a system, it is possible to control quality; for the patient helps control quality through his role as the person who selects and pays for his care; and the professions help control it through the use of their professional skills.

Government programs, and voluntary programs, must be supports only—supports to the patient when costs exceed his means.

If the government supplants the individual as payer, though not as patient, government becomes the intruder—the third party striving vainly to reconcile the demands of the patient for high quality care and the demands of the taxpayer for an efficient use of tax funds.

These conflicting demands can be resolved by government in only one way: the deciding factor in providing the care soon becomes not the need of the patient, but the money available to pay for the program.

When we seek to help the aged, we are seeking to cope with a human problem—in fact, with an entire spectrum of human needs and problems. Behind the statistics, with which the Committee has been bombarded, are individual men and women, as distinctly different from one another as their fingerprints. It seems to me that this important fact has been overlooked by those who support H.R. 4222. They ask us to assume that the only question in the minds of our aged population, their families, and the physicians who will care for them, is how to find the money to pay for the costs of health care.

Nothing could be further from the truth. Our aged patients want, and expect, what the rest of our patients want:

An interested, dedicated physician; the most competent care obtainable; and treatment with dignity as respected individuals—not as casually handled units on an impersonal, medical assembly-line.

Yet the accent is placed on financing, not quality, under H.R. 4222 —the dollar approach instead of the medical care approach is stressed. This preoccupation of H.R. 4222 with finances rather than quality is illustrated by the fact that the bill would limit the services to be provided. In terms of dollars, this makes sense. It is infinitely more controllable to pick a group of services, set specific standards and rates of payment for them, and confine government financing to those services alone. But control of the use of tax funds is not the way to produce top grade medical care.

Incomplete medical resources result in limited medical care.

Suppose the patient needs services not covered under the bill? Presumably he is required to obtain them on his own, at his own expense.

He is, in effect, being asked to inhabit a medical world that is half public, half private.

This state of affairs would not continue for long, for a double-entry system of this sort has predictable consequences.

First of all, H.R. 4222 as planned, defined and publicized, is intended to be a primary resource of medical care for the majority of our aged population. It is not intended to supplement private initiative in cases of emergency, as the Kerr-Mills Law does. Thus, the measure pits the overwhelming weight of governmental pressure against all other alternative plans—private or public. Ultimately, as expanded, there is no doubt it would drive these plans out of existence.

Second, the very limitations of H.R. 4222 would lead to irresistible pressures to extend benefits until the program became a complete, across-the-board medical program for the aged.

Third, there is an immediate psychological by-product of this legislation. It is being sold as the Administration's answer to the medico-economic problems of the aged. To the degree that Administration salesmanship is successful, the aged will come to expect that the services provided under the program will cover all their major medical needs. Thus, they and their children will be unwilling to accept, or undertake, any major course of therapy which does not fall for the most part under the coverage of the government plan.

Pressure will be exerted by the patient and his family upon the doctor, in the effort to force him to fit the treatment, willy-nilly, into the services provided by the program.

And too often the patient will postpone treatment until such time as it *can* be covered under the program—this on the assumption that the program takes care of all so-called "serious" conditions.

Here we come to the doctor's dilemma.

Let us say that a patient needs treatment of a sort not covered by the program and therefore not reimbursable under it.

The physician is confronted with two unsatisfactory courses of action, neither of which contributes to the provision of quality medical care.

On the one hand, he may follow his best professional judgment and refuse to recommend a course of treatment covered under the program. For example, he may decide the patient is better treated at the physician's office and that hospitalization is not required. In such a case, it is not unlikely that the patient will go to another physician, hoping for a different professional judgment; or that he will postpone the treatment he needs.

Alternatively, the physician may accept the patient's plea that he can finance the cost of care only through the mechanism of H.R. 4222, and then choose the lesser of two evils—treatment in an improper facility simply because it is covered by the program; or no treatment at all because the patient refuses to undergo treatment except at government expense. In this case, the physician's medical decision has been influenced by non-professional considerations. Further, if the doctor accedes to the patient's request, however unwillingly, he risks censure by the "hospitalization utilization committee" and the possible rejection of his claim by HEW.

I do not claim, Mr. Chairman, that some individual patients might not receive perfectly adequate treatment under the program. Many undoubtedly would, for the needs of their cases would fall within the bill's imposed limitations. Others may receive quality medical care because the skill of individual practitioners can sometimes surmount the limitations placed upon it by the requirements of a particular program.

But many of the aged will receive a lower quality of medical care simply because the services covered do not represent the full range of facilities required by the physician for optimal treatment. You cannot reduce the physician's armamentarium of treatment facilities without reducing the effect of his skill in the process.

I have pointed out that the physician's alternatives would be the unsatisfactory courses of choosing poorer treatment rather than no treatment at all. Let me also mention that H.R. 4222 provides for payment only on certification by the attending physician that the services provided were "required" for the patient's treatment. That word "required" is in the language of the bill.

Now if a doctor decides it is better to put a patient in a hospital, although this may not be the best method of treatment, rather than see the patient postpone a needed course of therapy, can he—or should he—attest that treatment was "required"? Is the sometime need to choose reimbursable courses of treatment for the patient's financial sake sufficient ethical justification to warrant an untrue attestation?

Implicit in the measure, Mr. Chairman, is the physician's responsibility to keep the cost of the program under control. This would be a difficult, if not impossible burden to bear, unless the physician is willing to shift the emphasis, along with the government, from quality to dollars in his approach to the provision of health care.

Any governmental effort to control the cost and use of health services through fiscal means alone is almost certain to fail. It is rather like trying to control highway accidents by manipulating insurance premiums. Safe driving is influenced by many factors—good roads, stop lights, traffic policemen, driver training, licensing practices, law enforcement, and many other things.

The same applies to the cost and use of health services.

In the very effort to control this program, government inevitably would thrust its way deeper and deeper into the field of medical services. It could not avoid this. And before long, the government would be preoccupied with efforts to regulate quality, regulate distribution, regulate the providers of the health care which it purchased.

This is not an area in which government should operate—or can operate—without disastrous effects.

Let me remind the Committee that the practice of medicine involves the constant exercise of professional judgment. The physician must constantly choose between action and inaction, surgery or medical treatment, hospital or outpatient care, one drug or another. The decisions involved are momentous, for they involve health or illness, and sometimes life or death.

Must these decisions be further complicated by the current condition of the HEW budget? Would the physician's power to decide a health problem on its own merits be influenced for better or worse by government pressures, say, to restrict hospital admissions in the interests of economy?

I think the answers to these questions are clear, Mr. Chairman.

We know what our patients want from us. And we know under what conditions physicians must practice if they are to continue to deliver high quality medical care.

Doctors want to be responsible for their patients to the limit of their competence. They want freedom to give their best effort in their offices, operating rooms, and other areas of practice. They want privacy in their dealings with their patients, not the intruding presence of government.

Physicians oppose any course of action that will erode the wholly voluntary relationship now existing between doctor and patient. Members of Congress and the public should not make the mistake of taking America's high quality of medical care for granted. Because it is high under our present system does not guarantee that it will remain high in the hands of non-professional government administrators.

To the contrary: the quality of medical care under our present system is high because of the very nature of that system—free, thus far, of government regimentation.

If H.R. 4222 became law, those most immediately affected by a deteriorating quality of health care would be, of course, those of the aged who are covered.

But they wouldn't be the only ones. Patients of all ages would also experience this loss of quality. For the whole is equal to the sum of its parts; and if we lower the quality of care provided to one segment of our population, we lower the quality for the entire population of which that segment is a part.

H.R. 4222 would introduce into our system of freely practiced medicine elements of compulsion, regulation, and control; and the result would be severe damage to the entire mechanism. But let us pretend this wouldn't be so. Let us pretend that some of this measure's proponents are correct when they state that it would affect the aged, and the aged only; that no further expansion is either necessary or contemplated; that we are only talking about a handful of doctors, not all doctors, and only about providing a medical program for the aged, not the entire population.

Is it possible for a system of medical care to exist for long with part of it government-controlled and the balance free? I submit that it is not, Mr. Chairman.

Those who maintain that there will be no expansion of H.R. 4222 are blind to the lessons of history and deaf to the voices of the bill's most ardent supporters. For those supporters are ardent *only* because they know the measure is certain to expand.

Why, otherwise, would avowed proponents of national compulsory health insurance support H.R. 4222? It would be naive, Mr. Chairman, if we attributed this new position to a change of heart. I believe they consider the benefits of the bill *too* limited, and its coverage *too* restricted. On the other hand, they believe that a tax increase can be sold on the "nickel-a-day" basis and that the inclusion of deductibles provides an aura of fiscal respectability. They further believe that if the measure is passed now it can be changed later, for the precedent will have been solidly established. . . .

I submit, Mr. Chairman, that considerations of the Congress regarding this proposal cannot be limited to the merits or demerits of H.R. 4222 in its present form; they must include the question of what H.R. 4222 would become. President Kennedy himself has characterized this measure as "just a beginning." Many others have been equally candid.

The question that must be answered overrides the matter of whether use of the Social Security mechanism is a good or a bad way to go about helping the aged in the financing of their health care. The multi-billion dollar question is this:

Do the people of the United States want to purchase, through an increased compulsory payroll tax, socialized medicine for the elderly, and ultimately for every man, woman and child in the country?

The medical profession is convinced the people do not. Socialized medicine, when presented to the Congress without subterfuge, in the Wagner-Murray-Dingell proposal, was overwhelmingly defeated. Similarly, any forthright proposal to socialize medicine for Americans would, we believe, encounter the same fate.

Because we believe this to be true, and because our faith in the people of this nation has never weakened, the medical profession has bent its every effort to strip the disguise from measures like H.R. 4222 and reveal them for what they are: plans to socialize medicine for one segment of our population. . . .

Many of my colleagues have studied the British system at first hand. All have said the same thing about their experience: socialized medicine is not for the United States because it would decrease the quality of our medical care.

They have told me of limitations imposed upon physicians in prescribing the best drugs for a patient; of desperate searches for a hospital bed in which to place a critically ill patient; of overutilized services; of staggering patient loads; of forms to be filled and certificates to be made out and endless correspondence with the government. They have told me of waiting lists for admission to hospitals so long that routine elective surgery sometimes required delays of a year or more. . . .

These and similar complaints are the by-product of any medical system in which finance is considered more important than quality. And as I have discussed at greater length elsewhere, this inevitably happens when government enters the health care field. The conflict between government's effort to hold costs down and the effort of the health professions to supply quality care is always resolved in government's favor.

Needless to say, the patient is the ultimate sufferer.

To sum up, Mr. Chairman, H.R. 4222 would provide socialized medicine for the aged. It would become socialized medicine, in time, for everyone.

My Bill Will Not Damage the Quality of Medical Care

CECIL R. KING

, . . The American Medical Association alleges that the bill provides "blanket authorization for the Federal Government to control the providers of services." . . . The "proof" of the allegation is that the Secretary would be permitted to do what is "specifically provided" in the law. This exercise in logic—in which a statutory limitation to do only what is "specifically provided" becomes a "blanket authorization" to exercise power without limit—illustrates clearly the AMA's approach to the problem: the approach of a calculated attempt to distort the meaning of the bill. In an effort to support this distortion, reference is made to the provision in H.R. 4222 which states that the Secretary of Health, Education, and Welfare would be empowered to set "such other conditions of participation—as the Secretary may find necessary in the interest of health and safety of individuals who are furnished services by or in such institution." . . . This provision, the AMA says, "provides the means by which Federal officials can regiment and control all providers of the services covered." . . .

How strange this argument. I cannot believe that the individual doctors this association claims to represent have the same feelings about the conditions in the bill—the conditions that preclude participation by institutions that are firetraps or present other serious hazards to the safety or health of their patients. I cannot believe that the witnesses who testified here representing the American Medical Association are unfamiliar with the valuable and fully accepted activities of the Government in regard to the Food and Drug Act, water pollution safeguards, and the many other areas in which the health of our citizens is safeguarded. These witnesses do not cite a single instance of regimentation, or even an attempt at regimentation, of the health professions, in all of the Government's protection of the public health. What reason is there to assume that the Government would now quite suddenly adopt arbitrary methods?

From "Comments on Testimony of American Medical Association," *Congressional Record,* CVIII (March 5, 1962), 3106-3108, 3110-3111 (daily ed.).

. . . The conditions of eligibility really constitute . . . a description of those components of institutional and home health care which are essential to the safety and well-being of our older people. These conditions have not only been thoroughly reviewed and approved by distinguished representatives of the American Hospital Association, but the association stands squarely behind the inclusion of these eligibility conditions in any legislation that may be enacted. The hospitals, which, unlike the doctors, are major providers of service under the bill, would hardly encourage the retention of these standards if, in fact, the standards could be used—as the AMA charges—as the means by which Federal officials can regiment and control all providers of the services covered.

Let me say where these conditions came from and why they are so easily accepted by the American Hospital Association. Every condition save two is part of the requirements an institution must meet even to be considered a hospital by the American Hospital Association. The remaining two are: First, the health and safety requirement, which must be met for accreditation according to standards set jointly by representatives of the American Hospital Association, American Medical Association, American College of Surgeons, and the American College of Physicians; and second, the utilization committee requirement, which the American Hospital Association has proposed for inclusion as part of these accreditation requirements.

The AMA asserts that, "it is axiomatic that the Federal Government tends to control what it subsidizes." . . . It subsidizes the building of hospitals and nursing homes under the Hill-Burton program. Does it already control hospitals and nursing homes? . . .

The AMA also bases its allegations that the program would result in regimentation and Federal control on the fact that payment for services would be on the basis of reasonable costs. . . . Yet, this is the basis which the American Hospital Association, in its "Principles of Reimbursement for Hospital Care," proposes and which has proved successful in application by Blue Cross and a multitude of State and Federal Government programs. Provision for reimbursement by Government on the basis of reasonable cost has never had any such effects as the AMA says it would have in this instance.

The AMA also attaches implications of Government control to the requirements that hospitals maintain "adequate medical records" and establish bylaws for their medical staff. . . . The AMA implies that the Secretary might misuse authority by requiring medical records to be too "adequate." The AMA knows that medical records are required for accreditation because a medical history is essential for proper treatment of the patient. The AMA also knows that clearcut guides have been developed for purposes of accreditation as to what constitute adequate medical records. The AMA knows that the Secretary would have authority under the bill to accept accreditation of an institution as evidence that the requirements are met and that Secretary Ribicoff has said, in his testimony before this committee, that he would do so. Instead of recognizing these facts, the AMA analogizes medical records to business records. . . .

The existence of bylaws for the medical staff is a requirement the American Hospital Association uses to determine whether an institution is a hospital—it must have a medical staff which is organized under bylaws so that there is some expectation that the medical staff will participate in running the hospital. . . .

The AMA further suggests that it is wrong to require nursing homes to provide 24-hour nursing service because some nursing homes would be excluded from participation under the bill. . . . But this can hardly be regarded as a reasonable suggestion. After all, the point of the bill is protection against health costs and it is the provision of nursing services that distinguished nursing homes from domiciliary care. . . . The intention is to cover only health care costs when the care is provided by facilities able to render health care services. In some places such institutions are in short supply, but paying boarding home bills instead will not remedy the scarcity. Other administration proposals . . . will help to remedy this scarcity as will the payments under H.R. 4222 towards the operating costs of the needed facilities. The AMA by its very description of the scarcity of proper health facilities rebuts its own allegations that without this bill the aged are getting the care they need.

All this talk of arbitrary control by Government is just scare technique. The Government needs the willing agreement and cooperation of the hospitals in the plan. The Government is prepared to deal responsibly and fairly with them. It is nonsense to think that the Government could deal arbitrarily with the providers of services, ignore their just demands, and ignore the advice of the statutory advisory council provided in the bill.

. . . The AMA statement also criticizes the assertion that only a relatively few physicians would be affected by the bill. To support their contention that this assertion is not correct, the AMA says that the bill "involves the services, and the provision of services of at least 50,000 physicians." . . .

This figure is grossly misleading. The AMA statement itself recognizes that the vast majority—almost 38,000—of the 50,000 "physicians" referred to are interns, few of whom are licensed as physicians, and residents-in-training. Interns are salaried employees of hospitals completing a necessary part of their professional education without which they are not fully prepared to assume the responsibilities of a physician. Residents-in-training are also salaried employees who are training for the practice of specialties and subspecialties, including general practice.

The practice that would be followed under the administration bill would be to pay the hospital, in which the intern is finishing his education, the reasonable cost of the services which the hospital undertakes to provide, including the services of the intern. This is fully in accord with the "Principles of Payment for Hospital Care," developed and approved by the American Hospital Association as a guide to hospitals and to agencies which contract to purchase hospital care. . . .

The AMA claims to be apprehensive about the consequences that might ensue if hospitals are paid on a "reasonable cost" basis. . . . Is it not strange, however, that the AMA is more worried than the organization representing those whose pocketbooks are affected by the method of payment? It is true that the American Hospital Association has expressed mild reservations about the shades of interpretation which might be placed on the word "reasonable." Unlike the AMA, however, in the course of testimony before this committee, they said they believe that this is something which can be worked out without difficulty to the mutual satisfaction of hospitals and Government.

. . . If the AMA expects an increase in unnecessary hospital utilization it must subscribe to the view that physicians are either collaborating with their patients in unethical practices or are unable to make proper medical judgments. The AMA cannot gainsay the fact that hospital admissions are controlled by physicians. Indeed, the AMA insists that the right to admit patients remains the prerogative of the physician. If, however, the AMA rejects the thesis that physicians are responsible for unnecessary utilization, on the grounds that physicians are subjected to pressure from their patients, it cannot reasonably object to a professional and impartial group of physicians established by the hospital, reviewing cases in order to determine whether patients are—for whatever reason—overutilizing services.

The AMA's criticism of hospital utilization committees—which, incidentally, have been recommended by two State medical associations and are operating without appearance of difficulty in many hospitals—appears at this time after we have been informed by the American Hospital Association that it has recommended the Joint Commission on Accreditation of Hospitals require a hospital to have a utilization committee in order to be accredited. . . . The AMA objects to the requirement of a utilization committee because it does not consider it wise to subject a doctor's judgment on use of services to the review of his peers; this, despite the fact that many services are already subject to review. The AMA seems to forget for the moment that it has long subscribed to the view that it is desirable for hospitals to have committees, such as medical records committees and tissue committees, to review the medical practices of physicians. In fact, as a member organization of the Joint Commission of Accreditation, the AMA supports the requirements for accreditation, one of which is that hospitals carry on, through medical staff committees, "constant analysis and review of the clinical work done in hospitals." . . .

The AMA seems very fond of the false dilemma. On the one hand you have this, on the other hand, that, and both are bad. Since they do not talk of other alternatives, the listener is supposed to feel that all paths lead to ruin. . . . [An] example is their statement that the Government has two choices: First, it will either be so budget conscious it will lower the quality of care; or second, the program will be faced with runaway costs. . . . They wish to avoid consideration of the possibility that the program will operate well—with an eye for assuring that high quality of care is encouraged and at the same time that money is not wasted. Utilization committees and payment made on a cost basis, as H.R. 4222 provides, will mean that costs are in keeping with the necessary services provided. Apparently the AMA can imagine no instance in which people—nonphysicians, that is, merely do what is reasonable; everything must be extreme. . . . With reference to the AMA charge . . . that the Federal Government is seeking, through H.R. 4222, to encroach on individual freedom, let me make clear that this bill preserves individual freedom not only for physicians but also for hospital administrators, for nursing home proprietors and managers, for the aged who would benefit from this bill, and for the individual members of what we call the public. Moreover, my bill would make individual freedom a reality for many who, because they don't have the means to meet the cost of needed health care, cannot now enjoy their freedom in old age.

There is nothing in the bill that would in any way interfere with the established practices of providing health care. Health care would remain—as it is now—a matter determined by the patient, his physician, and the hospital or other provider of services. The Government would provide no care and offer no services; it would establish only the means of paying for the health care of the aged.

The medical profession would continue to be responsible for the quality of the care available to the people of the United States; the providers of service would still be responsible for determining what services they would make available. The process by which they would be paid for the services furnished would be much the same as that now used by Blue Cross and other large insurers of health service costs. The program would follow practices already well established and accepted by the hospitals in their relationships with Blue Cross, the States, and other Federal programs.

I gladly give credit to the medical profession for its great contribution to improvements in medicine and health care that today help us to live longer and more comfortable lives than ever before. Even though I believe that other groups should be mentioned for their significant contributions to this process. I would take no credit from the physicians of this country; they have my highest respect and my deepest gratitude. It is preposterous, however, to suggest that provisions that would enable our people to prepay, through the accepted social security system, some of the costs of the health care that they will need in old age might impede, or in some way interfere with, the efficiency of the medical profession. The physician in this country is a well-trained, highly skilled, humane expert in medical care. He does not, I believe, profess to be an expert in economics or insurance, though the AMA representatives pose as such experts. He does not look upon himself as a Solomon whose business is to advise people how they should go about paying their medical bills, though the AMA does. He does not always share the views of the AMA; however, because he may fear AMA sanctions he sometimes is constrained to ask, when writing to his Representative in the Congress, that his position favoring H.R. 4222 not be made public. This bill, let me repeat, has nothing to do with the practice of medicine; it simply affords a means for helping people to pay for the cost of certain medical services in old age.

Furthermore, this bill is, contrary to the AMA's charges, ... in keeping with the purpose of the social security system and with the basic principles of this system. While the insurance provided by social security has been in the form of monthly cash benefits there is nothing in the nature of this system or in its history that would make the payments provided under my bill inconsistent or incompatible with the objectives, the principles, and the philosophy of social security in this country. H.R. 4222 would provide for payments to be made to hospitals and certain other medical facilities—but not to physicians—for specified and limited medical services received by social security beneficiaries. The bill would authorize neither the Federal Government nor any other level of government to furnish health services to anybody. No one would be required to accept health services by reason of this bill—and the AMA persists in spreading the contrary impression. The charge that this bill is contrary to the principles of the social security system is not only false but also strange coming from the AMA—strange because available evidence indicates that the AMA knows little about the principles of the social insurance system and cares less.

The charge is also made that my bill is paternalistic—that it implements a "Government knows best" kind of thinking. . . . Nonsense. I am convinced that the people are capable of deciding how to spend their money and know how to do it without AMA advice. That is why they are for this bill. I am confident that the people know that my bill would give them valuable protection, and the correspondence that I have received indicates that they know better than the AMA what is good for them.

If the AMA seeks to substantiate its charges of impending Federal encroachment it should in all fairness approach this task, however impossible, by dealing with the provisions of my bill rather than talking about what could happen under some other plan that has not been proposed, and talking about that other imaginary plan as if it were that proposed in my bill. Under H.R. 4222 the Federal Government could not "regiment doctors, nurses, patients, hospitals, nursing homes, and any other element of our health care system" and the AMA knows the Government could not, even though the AMA statement deftly leads one to infer the opposite.

. . . The AMA has said repeatedly that a Federal health insurance program "would lower the quality of medical care available to older people." According to the AMA, the program would do this by substituting a concern with costs for a concern with quality. The Government, in its search for methods to reconcile the need for care with the need for cost controls, would "decide for the patient what services should be provided and by whom." . . . As a result, the AMA says, the Federal insurance program would produce a series of catastrophes: "The disruption of the doctor-patient relationship, delays in admissions to hospitals, time wasted in the overcrowded offices of doctors, the regimentation of medical practice," and impairment of medical research. . . .

In vain do we look for any concrete evidence, beyond bald unsupported statements about medical care in other countries, to corroborate the AMA's assertions, or for any consistent logic which demonstrates that a Government plan must have results which its counterparts outside of Government—Blue Cross for example—have not produced.

The facts of the case are quite different, and when carefully examined they demonstrate that the charges of "regimentation" and "deterioration of quality" are baseless. Under this bill, there is no compulsion imposed on any provider of service to participate in the program. The conditions of participation which are provided in the bill are based upon requirements formulated and recommended by professional bodies concerned with the quality of care. Freedom of choice of physician and hospital by patients is guaranteed. There are provisions designed to assist the physician in resisting pressures which may be exercised to secure unnecessary care; for example, the utilization committee. And the bill provides, through the Advisory Council, for the effective expression of all shades of opinion on the administration and future development of the program. . . .

The AMA asserts . . . that a high quality of care can be obtained only when the needs of the patient are placed first, "and financing is placed second." . . . This truism is followed by the statement that at present medical care is aimed at "treatment of the illness." We are then exhorted to contrast this with a system under which "Government pays for care directly," because under this system emphasis is "shifted from quality to cost." . . . This extraordinary set of assertions is supposed to prove something. Yet, all that has actually been said is that quality care can be furnished only if we treat the patient and he pays for it. But if the cost is paid for through insurance we presumably stop "treatment of the illness."

We are treated elsewhere in this document to similarly empty statements; "under H.R. 4222—the dollar approach instead of the medical care approach is stressed." . . . Is not an insurance program supposed to deal with the financial aspects of care? Moreover, is it not possible to couple concern for costs with a concern for standards, as in fact H.R. 4222 does? But the AMA is not really interested in looking at the merits of the case, nor in being logically consistent, for it later predicts with horror that "Government would be preoccupied with efforts to regulate quality."

Won't This Program Result in All the Problems and Abuses Found in the British System?

NELSON CRUIKSHANK

There is no relationship between President Kennedy's proposed Hospital Insurance for the Aged through Social Security, and the British National Health Service.

In evaluating the Anderson-King bill, there is nothing that an assessment of experience under the British system can contribute. There is no similarity between the two programs.

In Britain, the government provides medical and hospital care to the entire population.

In the U.S., under the Kennedy proposal, the government would provide basic hospital insurance to a limited group with special needs.

The charge of the opposition that the Anderson-King bill should not be enacted because the British have had bad experience and are dissatisfied with their National Health Service is false and misleading both because the British, including all 3 political parties and the British Medical Association, support the Service, and because the British experience is not relevant to the Anderson-King bill.

From Nelson Cruikshank, *Facts and Figures on Hospital Insurance for the Aged Through Social Security* (Washington: AFL-CIO, 1963). Nelson Cruikshank is Director of the Department of Social Security of the American Federation of Labor–Congress of Industrial Organizations.

Health Insurance and the Government

WILBUR J. COHEN

Much fear of this proposed governmental program arises out of the idea that this program would be but a first step to something else, that it would be soon broadened to provide other medical services to the aged and then may be extended to the rest of the population. At the same time it is also said that the program would hurt doctor-patient relationships and lower the quality of care. I would like to point out that both of these things can hardly be true. If this program is enacted or extended it will be because voluntary insurance has not adequately handled the need. Moreover, in my opinion the public will not urge and Congress will not act to extend a program which has been found to lower the quality of health care. I would also like to point out that this program by removing the burden of the aged from private insurance, and thereby lowering the cost of health insurance to the rest of the population will aid the insurance industry in meeting the needs of the rest of the population more effectively. President Kennedy has stressed that this health insurance program is not a program of socialized medicine. Every person will choose his own doctor, his own hospital. The proposed insurance program would simply be a means of paying for health services, not a means of providing them. Moreover, in my opinion, it will help preserve the voluntary system of hospitals in this country.

From an address of the same title delivered at the annual meeting of the American Risk and Insurance Association, December 29, 1961. Reprinted by permission of the author. Wilbur J. Cohen is Under Secretary of the Department of Health, Education, and Welfare.

SELECTED BIBLIOGRAPHY

Abel-Smith, Brian, and Richard M. Titmuss. *The Cost of the National Health Service.* London: Cambridge University Press, 1956.

"The American Medical Association: Power, Purpose, and Politics in Organized Medicine," *Yale Law Journal,* LXIII (1954), 937-1022.

Anderson, Odin W. *Administration of Medical Care: Problems and Issues.* Ann Arbor: University of Michigan School of Public Health, 1947.

———. "Health Services Systems in the United States and Other Countries—Critical Comparisons," *New England Journal of Medicine,* CCLXIX (October 17 and 24, 1963), 839-843, 896-900.

Arnold, Thurman. *Folklore of Capitalism.* New Haven, Conn.: Yale University Press, 1937.

"Benefits and Contributions Under National Compulsory Health Insurance Programs," *Social Security Bulletin,* XIV (January 1951), 17-20.

Burns, Eveline, *et al. Social Security in the United States: Four Lectures Presented at the University of California.* Berkeley: University of California Institute of Industrial Relations, 1961.

Carr, Edward H. *The New Society.* Boston: Beacon Press, 1957.

de Huszar, George B., ed. *Fundamentals of Voluntary Health Care.* Caldwell, Idaho: Caxton Printers, 1962.

Dingell, John D. "The AMA and the Health of the American People," *Congressional Record,* CVII (April 10, 1961), A2357-A2358 (daily ed.).

Eckstein, Harry. *The English Health Service: Its Origins, Structure and Achievements.* Cambridge, Mass.: Harvard University Press, 1958.

Falk, I. S. "Medical Care Insurance: Lessons from Voluntary and Compulsory Plans," *American Journal of Public Health,* XLI (May 1951), 553-559.

Farndale, James, ed. *Trends in the National Health Service.* New York: The Macmillan Company, 1964.

Finer, Herman. "Government Services and Individual Freedom," in Wilma Donahue and Clark Tibbitts, eds., *The Politics of Age.* Ann Arbor: University of Michigan Division of Gerontology, 1962.

Follmann, J. F., Jr. *Medical Care and Health Insurance: A Study in Social Progress.* Homewood, Ill.: Richard D. Irwin, Inc., 1963.

Gemmill, Paul F. *Britain's Search for Health: The First Decade of the National Health Service.* Philadelphia: University of Pennsylvania Press, 1960.

———. "The British Health Service Today," *New England Journal of Medicine,* CCLIX (July 3, 1958), 19 ff.

Gerig, Daniel S., and Carl H. Farman. "Medical Benefits for Old-Age Pensioners Under Foreign Social Security Programs," *Social Security Bulletin,* XXVI (January 1963), 21-26.

Glaser, William A. *The Compensation of Physicians.* New York: Bureau of Applied Social Research, 1963.

————. *Social Contexts and Health Institutions*. New York: Bureau of Applied Social Research, 1963.

Goldmann, Franz. "Foreign Programs of Medical Care and Their Lessons," *New England Journal of Medicine* (January 31, 1946), 155 ff.

"Government and Medicine Abroad," *Current History*, XLIV (June 1963), entire issue.

"Government and Medicine in Britain," *Current History*, XLIV (July 1963), entire issue.

Hall, Durward G. "In Defense of the AMA," *Congressional Record*, CVIII (June 5, 1962), A4299-A4300 (daily ed.).

Harris, Seymour E. "The British Health Experiment: The First Two Years of the National Health Service," *American Economic Review*, XLI (May 1951), 652-666.

Harrison, Gladys A. *Government Controls and the Voluntary Nonprofit Hospital: An Exploratory Study*. Chicago: American Hospital Association, 1961.

Hayek, F. A. *The Constitution of Liberty*. Chicago: University of Chicago Press, 1960.

Here We Go Again . . . King-Anderson (1963) . . . Administration's New Fedicare Scheme. Chicago: American Medical Association, 1963.

Hogarth, James. *The Payment of the General Practitioner*. New York: Pergamon Press, Inc., 1963.

Jewkes, John and Sylvia. *The Genesis of the British National Health Service*. Oxford: Basil Blackwell, 1961.

Kulp, Clarence A. "Voluntary and Compulsory Medical Care Insurance," *American Economic Review*, XLI (May 1951), 667-675.

Lees, D. S. *Health Through Choice: An Economic Study of the British National Health Service*. London: Institute of Economic Affairs, 1961.

Lindsey, Almont. *Socialized Medicine in England and Wales*. Chapel Hill: University of North Carolina Press, 1962.

Peterson, Osler L. "How Good Is Government Medical Care?" *Atlantic Monthly*, CCVI (September 1960), 29-33.

Roemer, Milton I. "Government's Role in American Medicine: A Brief Historical Survey," *Bulletin of the History of Medicine*, XVIII (July 1945), 146-168.

Rothenberg, Jerome. "Welfare Implications of Alternative Methods of Financing Medical Care," *American Economic Review*, XLI (May, 1951), 676-687.

Titmuss, Richard M. "What British Doctors Really Think About Socialized Medicine," *Harper's Magazine*, CCVI (February 1963), 18 ff. Reprinted in *Congressional Record*, CIX (February 5, 1963), A541-A543 (daily ed.), and CIX (February 7, 1963), A600-A602 (daily ed.).

Tollen, William B. "Financing Medical Care for the Aged," *Social Work*, VI (April 1961), 3-11.

U.S. Library of Congress. Legislative Reference Service. *Compulsory Health Insurance—Background, Issues, Proposals.* By Carl E. Ortmeyer. November 9, 1956.

———. *Controls Used in Other Countries to Hold Government-Financed Medical-Care Programs Within Financial Limitations.* By I. M. Labovitz. February 20, 1961.

———. *National Health Insurance.* By Helen E. Livingston. Public Affairs Bulletin #85, June 1950.

———. Education and Public Welfare Division. *Selected Excerpts and Bibliography on the 1960-61 Intercollegiate Debate Proposition—Resolved: That the United States Should Adopt a Program of Compulsory Health Insurance for All Citizens.* September 27, 1960.

Weinerman, E. Richard. "The Quality of Medical Care," *The Annals,* CCLXXIII (January 1951), 185-191.

Epilogue

As the preceding chapter has shown, the major source of concern about government participation in the financing of medical care is the fear of governmental controls and their effects. Focusing attention on government, however, tends to distract from the fact that the conflict is not between the medical practitioner and government, but rather between the practitioner and social organizations, whether governmental or private, lay or professional. The relationship between the practitioner and the patient is moving from a private one to one that interests insurance companies, medical societies, labor unions, and other third parties. These third parties have become concerned with the problem of controlling the rising costs of medical care.

Concern has also been mounting about the quality of medical services received by a public which is generally unable to judge this quality.[a] As a result of this concern, the medical-care professions have developed institutions such as hospital-utilization committees and tissue committees in an attempt to control quality and costs. But supervision by the professions themselves has not stilled the rising demand for greater lay voice in, or even control of, the nonscientific aspects of medical care.

All this concern has come about because of the impact of modern technology on medical care—an impact that has transformed an art into a science, raising problems of organization and cost as it did so. Recognition of these problems has transformed sickness

---

[a] See, for example, "Does the U.S. Really Have the World's Finest Medical Care?" *Consumer Reports,* XXX (March 1965), 146-150.

and its cost from personal problems into social problems. This new status has led to a steadily increasing role for government and other social institutions in preventive health measures and in the provision and financing of medical care. Decisions about the extent and manner of government participation have been made and continue to be made through the policy process described in Chapter III. Are our political forms and procedures adequate to the needs of a modern industrial society?

APPENDIX
A

A Selected General Bibliography

[Each chapter is followed by a bibliography of material specifically pertaining to the subject of that chapter.]

Anderson, Odin W. "Medical Care—an Historical Perspective," in National Conference on Social Welfare, *Community Organization.* New York: Columbia University Press, 1959.

Association of Teachers of Preventive Medicine. Committee on Medical Care Teaching, ed. *Readings in Medical Care.* Chapel Hill: University of North Carolina Press, 1958.

Brewster, Agnes W. "Meeting the Health Needs of the Aged," *The Annals,* CCCXXXVII (September 1961), 114-125.

Epstein, Lenore A., and James C. Callison. "Financing Health Care for the Aged," *Law and Contemporary Problems,* XXVII (Winter 1962), 102-132.

Follmann, J. F., Jr. *Medical Care and Health Insurance: A Study in Social Progress.* Homewood, Ill: Richard D. Irwin, Inc., 1963.

"Government and Medicine in the United States," *Current History,* XLV (August 1963), entire issue.

Klarman, Herbert E. *The Economics of Health.* New York: Columbia University Press, 1965.

Meyers, Harold B. " 'Medicare,' the Cure That Could Cause a Setback," *Fortune,* LXVII (May 1963), 131 ff.

Miller, Helen Hill, ed. "Health: Are We the People Getting Our Money's Worth?" *New Republic,* CXLIX (November 9, 1963), entire issue.

Parsons, Talcott. "Social Change and Medical Organization in the United States: A Sociological Perspective," *The Annals,* CCCXLVI (March 1963), 21-33.

Sanders, Marion K., ed. *The Crisis in American Medicine.* New York: Harper and Brothers, 1961.

Somers, Herman M. and Anne R. *Doctors, Patients, and Health Insurance: The Organization and Financing of Medical Care.* Washington, D.C.: The Brookings Institution, 1961.

Tucker, R. W. *The Case for Socialized Medicine.* New York: The Call Association, 1961.

University of Michigan. School of Public Health. Bureau of Public Health Economics. *Public Health Economics.* A monthly journal digesting a wide variety of materials.

U.S. Cong. HR W&M. *Hospital, Nursing Home, and Surgical Benefits for OASI Beneficiaries: Hearings.* 86th Congress, 1st Session, July 1959.

———. *Medical Care for the Aged: Executive Hearings.* 89th Congress, 1st Session, January and February 1965.

———. *Medical Care for the Aged: Hearings.* 88th Congress, 1st and 2nd Sessions, November 1963 and January 1964.

———. *Services for the Aged Under the Social Security System: Hearings.* 87th Congress, 1st Session, July and August 1961.

U.S. Cong. Sen. Fin. *Social Security Amendments of 1960: Hearings.* 86th Congress, 2nd Session, June 1960.

———. *Social Security: Hearings.* 89th Congress, 1st Session, April and May 1965.

———. *Social Security; Medical Care for the Aged Amendments: Hearings.* 88th Congress, 2nd Session, August 1964.

U.S. Cong. Sen. Committee on Labor and Public Welfare. Subcommittee on Problems of the Aged and Aging. *The Aged and Aging in the United States: A National Problem: A Report Together with Minority Views.* Senate Report #1121. 86th Congress, 2nd Session, 1960.

———. *Health Needs of the Aged and Aging: Hearings.* 86th Congress, 2nd Session, April 1960.

U.S. HEW PHS. *Medical Care in Transition.* 1964. A two-volume collection of articles reprinted from the *American Journal of Public Health,* 1958-1962.

———. Division of Community Health Services. Health Economics Branch. *Medical Care Financing and Utilization: Source Book of Data Through 1961.* Public Health Service Publication #947, 1962.

U.S. HEW SSA. Division of Program Research. *The Health Care of the Aged: Background Facts Relating to the Financing Problem.* 1962.

U.S. Library of Congress. Legislative Reference Service. *The Federal Government's Role in Providing Medical Care to Citizens of the United States: Selected Excerpts Prepared for the National High School Debate Subject, 1963-1964.* 1963.

U.S. President's Commission on the Health Needs of the Nation. *Building America's Health.* 5 volumes, 1952-1953.

van Dyke, Frank. "Medicare: The Major Defects," *Nation,* CC (June 28, 1965), 697-700.

Summary of Medical-Care Portions of Social Security Amendments of 1965

The law establishes two related health-insurance programs for persons aged 65 and over: (1) a basic plan providing protection against the costs of hospital and related care; and (2) a voluntary supplementary plan covering payments for physicians' services and other medical and health services not covered by the basic plan.

The basic plan will be financed through a separate earnings tax and separate trust fund. Benefits for persons currently over 65 who are not insured under the social security and railroad retirement systems will be financed out of federal general revenues.

Enrollment in the supplementary plan is to be voluntary and will be financed by a small monthly premium ($6 per month initially—$3 to be paid by enrollees and an equal amount to be supplied by the federal government out of general revenues). The premiums for social-security, railroad-retirement beneficiaries and Civil Service Retirement annuitants who enroll will be deducted from their monthly benefits. Uninsured persons desiring the supplemental plan will make the periodic premium payments to the government. State welfare programs could arrange for uninsured assistance recipients to be covered.

A. Basic Plan—Hospital Insurance

1. *General description*

Basic protection, financed through an earnings tax, will be provided against the costs of inpatient hospital services, post-hospital extended care, post-hospital home health services, and outpatient hospital diagnostic services for social-security and railroad-retirement beneficiaries

---

Adapted from Social Security Administration, *Commissioner's Bulletin* #29, July 21, 1965. A summary of the other provisions of the law may be found in Wilbur J. Cohen and Robert M. Ball, "Social Security Amendments of 1965: Summary and Legislative History," *Social Security Bulletin*, XXVIII (September 1965), 3-21.

when they attain age 65. The same protection, financed from general revenues, will be provided under a special transitional provision for essentially all people who are now aged 65, or who will reach age 65 before 1968, but who are not eligible for social-security or railroad-retirement benefits. Together, these two groups comprise virtually the entire aged population. The persons not protected would be federal employees who are covered, or who were covered on February 15, 1965, or who, if they retired after February 15, 1965, could have been covered, under the provisions of the Federal Employees Health Benefits Act of 1959. Others excluded would be aliens who have not been residents of the United States for 5 years, aliens who have not been admitted for permanent residence, and persons convicted of violating certain laws dealing with espionage, censorship, sabotage, treason, sedition, and subversive activities.

Benefits will be first effective on July 1, 1966, except for services in extended-care facilities which will be effective on January 1, 1967.

2. *Benefits*

The services for which payment will be made under the basic plan include:

a. Inpatient hospital services for up to 90 days in each spell of illness. The patient will pay a deductible amount of $40 for the first 60 days plus a coinsurance payment of $10 a day for each day in excess of 60 during each spell of illness; hospital services include all those ordinarily furnished by a hospital to its inpatients; however, payment will not be made for private duty nursing or for the hospital services of physicians except services provided by interns or residents in training under approved teaching programs. Inpatient psychiatric hospital service will be included, but a lifetime limitation of 190 days will be imposed. Inpatient services in Christian Science sanatoriums will also be covered.

b. Post-hospital extended care (in a facility having an arrangement with a hospital for the timely transfer of patients and for furnishing medical information about patients) after the patient is transferred from a hospital (after at least a 3-day stay) for up to 100 days in each spell of illness, but after the first 20 days of care patients will pay $5 a day for the remaining 80 days of extended care in a spell of illness. Under a special provision, extended care in Christian Science sanatoriums will be covered for up to 30 days, with the patient paying $5 a day.

c. Outpatient hospital diagnostic services with the patient paying a $20 deductible amount and a 20 per cent coinsurance for each diagnostic study (that is, for diagnostic services furnished to him by the same hospital during a 20-day period).

d. Post-hospital home health services for up to 100 visits, after discharge from a hospital (after at least a 3-day stay) or extended-care facility and before the beginning of a new spell of illness. Such a person must be in the care of a physician and under a plan established by a physician within 14 days of discharge calling for such services. These services will include intermittent nursing care, therapy, and the part-time services of a home health aide. The patient must be homebound, except that payment could be made for services furnished at a hospital or extended-care facility or rehabilitation center which require the use of equipment that cannot ordinarily be taken to the patient's home.

No service will be covered as post-hospital extended care or as outpatient diagnostic or post-hospital home health services if it is of a kind that could not be covered if it were furnished to a patient in a hospital.

A spell of illness will be considered to begin when the individual enters a hospital and to end when he has been out of the hospital or extended-care facility for 60 consecutive days.

The deductible amounts for inpatient hospital and outpatient hospital diagnostic services will be increased if necessary to keep pace with increases in hospital costs, but no such increase will be made before 1969. For reasons of administrative simplicity, increases in the hospital deductible will be made only when a $4 change is called for and the outpatient deductible will change in $2 steps.

3. *Basis of reimbursement*

Payment of bills under the basic plan will be made to the providers of service on the basis of the "reasonable cost" incurred in providing care for beneficiaries.

4. *Administration*

Basic responsibility for administration will rest with the Secretary of Health, Education, and Welfare. The Secretary will use appropriate state agencies and private organizations (nominated by providers of services) to assist in the administration of the program. Provision is made for the establishment of an Advisory Council which will advise the Secretary on policy matters in connection with administration.

5. *Financing*

Taxes to finance the basic plan, paid by employers, employees, and self-employed persons, will be placed in a separate hospital insurance trust fund established in the Treasury. The same contribution rate will apply equally to employers, employees, and self-employed persons and will be as follows:

	Per Cent
1966	0.35
1967-1972	.50
1973-1975	.55
1976-1979	.60
1980-1986	.70
1987 and thereafter	.80

The taxable earnings base will be $6,600 a year.

The schedule of contribution rates is based on estimates of cost which assume that the earnings base will not be increased above $6,600. If Congress, in later years, should increase the base above $6,600, the tax rates established can be reduced under the cost assumptions underlying the bill.

The cost of providing basic hospital and related benefits to people who are not social-security or railroad-retirement beneficiaries will be paid from general funds of the Treasury.

B. Voluntary Supplementary Insurance Plan

1. *General description*

A package of benefits supplementing those provided under the basic plan will be offered to all persons 65 and over. Individuals who enroll initially will pay $3 a month (deducted, where possible, from social-security, railroad-retirement, or civil-service-retirement benefits). The government would match this amount with $3 paid from general funds. Since the minimum increase in cash social-security benefits for workers who are 65 or over when the benefit increase is effective for them will be $4 a month ($6 a month for man and wife receiving benefits based on the same earnings record), the benefit increase will fully cover the amount of monthly premiums.

2. *Enrollment*

Persons aged 65 before January 1, 1966, will have an opportunity to enroll in an enrollment period which begins on the first day of the second month after the month of enactment and ends March 31, 1966.

Persons attaining age 65 subsequent to December 31, 1965, will have enrollment periods of 7 months beginning 3 months before attaining 65.

In the future, general enrollment periods will be from October to December 31, in each odd year. The first such period will be October 1 to December 31, 1967.

No person may enroll more than 3 years after the close of the first enrollment period in which he could have enrolled.

There will be only one chance to reenroll for persons who are in the plan but drop out, and reenrollment must occur within 3 years of termination of previous enrollment.

Coverage may be terminated (1) by the individual filing notice during a general enrollment period, or (2) by the government, for nonpayment of premiums.

A state will be able to provide the supplementary insurance benefits to its public-assistance recipients who are receiving cash assistance if it chooses to do so.

Benefits will be effective beginning July 1, 1966.

3. Benefits

There will be an annual deductible of $50. Then the plan will cover 80 per cent of the patient's bill (above the deductible) of the following services:

a. Physicians' and surgeons' services, whether furnished in a hospital, clinic, office, in the home, or elsewhere.

b. Home health services (with no requirement of prior hospitalization) for up to 100 visits during each calendar year.

c. Diagnostic X-ray and laboratory tests, and other diagnostic tests.

d. X-ray, radium, and radioactive isotope therapy.

e. Ambulance services.

f. Surgical dressings and splints, casts, and other devices for reduction of fractures and dislocations; rental of durable medical equipment such as iron lungs, oxygen tents, hospital beds, and wheelchairs used in the patient's home; prosthetic devices (other than dental) which replace all or part of an internal body organ; braces and artificial legs, arms, eyes, etc.

There will be a special limitation on outside-the-hospital treatment of mental, psychoneurotic, and personality disorders. Payment for such treatment during any calendar year will be limited, in effect, to $250 or 50 per cent of the expenses, whichever is smaller.

4. *Administration by carriers: Basis for reimbursement*

The Secretary of Health, Education, and Welfare will be required, to the extent possible, to contract with carriers to carry out the major administrative functions of the voluntary, supplementary plan such as determining rates of payments under the program, holding and disbursing funds for benefit payments, and determining compliance and assisting in utilization review. No contract is to be entered into by the Secretary unless he finds that the carrier will perform its obligations under the contract efficiently and effectively and will meet such requirements as to financial responsibility, legal authority, and other matters as he finds pertinent. The contract must provide that the carrier take necessary action to see that where payments are on a cost basis (to institutional providers of services), the cost is reasonable cost. Correspondingly, where payments are on a charge basis (to physicians or others furnishing noninstitutional services), the carrier must see that such charge will be reasonable and not higher than the charge applicable, for a comparable service and under comparable circumstances, to the other policyholders and subscribers of the carrier. Payment by the carrier for physicians' services will be made on the basis of a receipted bill, or on the basis of an assignment under the terms of which the reasonable charge will be the full charge for the service. In determining reasonable charges, the carriers will consider the customary charges for similar services generally made by the physician or other person or organization furnishing the covered services, and also the prevailing charges in the locality for similar services.

5. *Financing*

Aged persons who enroll in the supplementary plan will pay monthly premiums of $3. Where the individual is currently receiving monthly social-security, railroad-retirement or civil-service-retirement benefits, the premiums will be deducted from his benefits.

The government will help finance the supplementary plan through a payment from general revenues of $3 a month per enrollee. To provide an operating fund at the beginning of the supplementary plan, and to establish a contingency reserve, a government appropriation will be available (on a repayable basis) equal to $18 per aged person estimated to be eligible in July 1966, when the supplementary plan goes into effect.

The individual and government contributions will be placed in a separate trust fund for the supplementary plan. All benefit and administrative expenses under the supplementary plan will be paid from this fund.

The provision in the income-tax law which limits medical-expense deductions to amounts in excess of 3 per cent of adjusted gross income for persons under 65 will be reinstituted for persons 65 and over. Thus, provision is made for partial or full recovery of the government contribution from enrolled persons with incomes high enough to require them to pay income taxes. A special deduction (for taxpayers who itemize deductions) of one-half of premiums for medical-care insurance will be added, however. This special deduction, which will be applicable to taxpayers of all ages, cannot exceed $150 per year.

Premium rates for enrolled persons (and the matching government contribution) will be increased from time to time in the event that costs rise, but not more often than once every 2 years. The premium rate for a person who enrolls after the first period when enrollment was open to him will be increased by 10 per cent for each full year he stayed out of the program.

C. Cost of the Basic and Supplementary Plan

Benefits under both plans will become payable for services furnished in July 1966, except for services in extended-care facilities, for which benefits will become payable in January 1967. Benefits and administrative expenses under the basic plan will be about $2.2 billion for the first year of operations. The costs for the uninsured under the basic plan (paid from general revenues) will be about $290 million per year for early years with a substantial offset for public-assistance savings. Costs of the supplementary plan will be about $1.2 billion in the first year of operations.

Index

Ability to pay, 3, 4
"Adequate medical records," 272, 286
AFL, 94
AFL-CIO, 101, 104, 113
"Aged," definition of, xiii
Aged:
in agricultural society, 24
AMA on medical profession's aid to, 160-164
AMA on private aid to, 158-160
AMA on private insurance for, 173-179
assets, 36, 38-41, 52, 54-56, 58-59, 75
attitudes of society toward, 28-30
changed status, 24-25
concern for involvement with society, 28
debts, 52
demands on financial resources, 64-81
efforts of insurance industry to cover, 170-172
financial needs, 35-84
financial resources, 35-63, 81-84
gifts from others, 69-70, 76, 78-79
greater age of, 24, 25
income, dynamic nature of needs, 62-63
income data, 35-44, 49, 52-58, 60-63, 68-76, 81-84
income related to budget require-
ments, 67-68, 71-72
in industrial society, 24-25, 29
and inflation, 41
insurance coverage, 52, 58, 170-183
insurance coverage, charge of inflated data, 171
King on medical profession's aid to, 166
King on private aid to, 157, 165
King on private insurance for, 180-183
living costs, 64-68
living with others, 69, 73-76, 81
medical debts, 49, 51, 78
medical expenditures, 26
medical needs, 25, 26-27, 31-32, 33
methods of paying for medical care, 77-81
nonmedical needs, 29-30
nonmedical sources of health complaints, 27, 28-34
number, 24
pensions, 57-58, 60-61
proportion of population, 24
retirement plans, 57-58, 60-61
sociological problems of, 28, 33
tax advantages, 52-53, 155
use of medical care, 25-26
Aging:
AMA policy on, 162-164
White House Conference on, 36n, 48, 49, 57, 58, 114, 161

311

proportion of population with, 15, 58

proposals for government, 85-156

public desire for increased coverage, 17

service benefits, 9, 14, 18

special policies for aged, 59, 170, 176

state legislation, 93-94, 97-98

"voluntary," xii

work status and 170

Interdepartmental Committee to Coordinate Health and Welfare Activities, 92

Ives, Irving, 97

Javits, Jacob, 97, 107, 113, 121, 129, 134, 140

Javits amendment (1960), 113

Javits bill (1960), 103, 107

Jennings, W. Pat, 127

Johnson, Lyndon B., 100, 104, 108, 109, 111, 112, 137, 147, 148

Johnson Administration and medicare, 130-148

Joint Council to Improve the Health Care of the Aged, 162

Keane, Robert, 114

Keating, Kenneth, 121

Kennedy, John F., 104, 112-115, 120, 130

Kennedy Administration:
and medicare, 114-130
legislative strategy, 115-116
willingness to compromise, 115-116

Kerr, Robert, 111, 112, 113, 124, 127, 129

Kerr-Mills Act, 53, 104, 119, 129, 137, 140, 184-212, 247-250, 252
attitude of Kennedy toward, 113
attitude of Nixon toward, 113
attitude of Rockefeller toward, 113
broadening, 120, 131
enactment, 110-113

extent of participation, 186, 202-206, 208-210

King, Cecil R., 116, 136
effectiveness of MAA, 204-207
medical profession's aid to aged, 166
preferability of social insurance to private, 193-195
private aid to aged, 157, 165
private insurance for aged, 180-183

King-Anderson bills, 85, 85n, 97
1961, compared to Forand bill, 115-116
1961, summary, 115
1963, compared to Anderson-Javits amendment, 125
1963, summary, 125
1965, summary, 139

Kuchel, Thomas, 121

Lambert, Alexander, 87-88

Landrum, Phil, 127, 140

Larson, Arthur, 114

Larson, Leonard, 120

Lausche, Frank, 134

Lindsay, John, 119

Long, Russell, 112, 133, 145, 147

McCarthy, Eugene, 45

McNamara, Pat, 24, 45, 106, 110, 129

Means test, 185, 189-190, 195-200, 253

Meany, George, 113

Medical Assistance to the Aged (MAA), 184-212
AMA on desirability, 190-192
desirability of, 185, 190-192, 201-202
effectiveness of, 185-186, 201-207
eligibility for, 186, 209-210
expenditures, 208-209
extent of participation, 186, 202-206, 208-210

Medical care:
and economic status, 1-4
change in style and locale, 5

THE

LANGUAGE OF
LANDSCAPE

The Granite Garden: Urban Nature and Human Design

THE

LANGUAGE OF
LANDSCAPE

Anne Whiston Spirn

Photographs by
Anne Whiston Spirn

Yale University Press
New Haven and London

Designed by Mary M. Mayer
Set in Minion type by Amy Storm

Printed in the United States of America by Thomson-Shore, Inc.

Library of Congress Cataloguing-in-Publication Data
Spirn, Anne Whiston, 1947-
       The language of landscape / Anne Whiston Spirn.
            p.   cm.
       Includes bibliographical references and index.
       ISBN 978-0-300-07745-2 (cloth) — ISBN 978-0-300-08294-4 (pbk)
       1. Landscape architecture. 2. Landscape. 3. Landscape assessment.
4. Human ecology. I. Title.
SB472.S685 1998
                                                          98-7487
712—dc21
                                                          CIP

A catalogue record for this book is available from the British Library.

The paper in this book meets the guidelines for permanence and durability of
the Committee on Production Guidelines for Book Longevity of the Council on
Library Resources.

10 9 8 7

For
My Mother and Father
and My Danish Parents

Contents

The Language of Landscape

Why the language of *landscape?* The language you describe
is about so much more than landscape, it includes buildings
and cities.

   —*An architect*

Why not the language of *environment,* or *place*? Landscape
is so ambiguous.

   —*An environmental historian*

Landscape can't be *language!* You mean landscape is
representation.

   —*A scholar of literature*

Landscape. (Alex S. MacLean/Landslides)

Introduction

"But where's the art?" I was startled by this reaction, of some readers, to my first book, *The Granite Garden: Urban Nature and Human Design*. If the book was about sustaining health, safety, and welfare, was it, therefore, not about aesthetics? Their impulse to see the pragmatic and poetic as separate, or even contradictory, troubled me greatly, for it was my motivation to connect the two that had inspired and driven me to write the book. I was also surprised to learn how deep-seated was the resistance of some readers to considering cities part of the natural world; they were not persuaded that natural processes of air, earth, water, and life shape cities. I had failed to take account of how ideas of nature and what is "natural" stem from strongly held feelings and beliefs, how highly personal and varied these views are, and how persuasion is not simply a matter of marshaling compelling verbal arguments, but of reaching both mind and heart.

In response, I was determined to write an entire book about the *poetics* of city and nature, one that would fuse function, feeling, and meaning. I planned to derive this theory from places that exemplified it, and I hoped the new book would inspire the creation of many more, similarly successful places where people could feel, as well as reflect on, connections, and find them useful. But why propose a theory if argument alone fails to persuade many readers? Because the places I know about are so few and far apart and, further, are seldom perceived as linked. And because theory gives fresh meaning to old places, connects the seemingly unrelated, and guides action. Few people, even if they have seen both Glenn Murcutt's design for the house in Bingie, Australia, and my proposals for West Philadelphia, would regard the two as analogues, but they are, even though one is built, the home of a single family, the other a plan that may never be built, for a neighborhood of thousands of families. The design for Bingie and the plan for West Philadelphia are connected by the designers' kindred way of thinking and working.

But, in the process of looking, thinking, and writing the book on poetics, I came to realize that the poetics applies to all landscapes, not urban landscapes alone, and to buildings, too, and that defining such an aesthetic theory demanded, first, the description and codification of a *language* of landscape. But, just as some readers earlier objected to the idea that city and nature are of a piece and that art and function are related, so now I encountered considerable resistance to the concept of landscape as language. Arguments put to me forced me to confront many difficult questions, to reconsider certain proposals, and to respond. This book has, in consequence, taken far longer to write than I ever imagined.

3

The language of landscape is the principal language in which I think and act; my conviction that there is such a language arises first from that fact. It is also the language used skillfully by designers whose work I most admire. My own work has been a laboratory, theirs a library for me, in exploring and defining the language of landscape. Visual thinking—photography and drawing—my primary mode of thought, was extended through response to other senses, then recorded in my journals. Writing, for me, requires a translation of images and experiences into words and phrases, then a converting of weblike (landscapelike) writing into prose in which sentences follow sentences, constructing a line of reasoning that others can follow. Personally, I find digital web-authoring, with its linked, embedded structure and display of color images a more natural medium of expression than any other. My lectures are always composed of two parallel essays: one spoken, one seen, with the visual essay structuring the verbal.

Landscape architecture has been my sphere of action and service, just as photography is my touchstone and way of knowing. The landscapes I help shape are collective projects most successful when others assume ownership. The landscape architect's experience helps me see significance; the photographer's disciplined, feeling way of seeing leads me to deeper insights. I try to see things fresh by ranging broadly, then gradually zeroing in, often drawn to a detail without knowing yet what the whole is, then coming to understand the whole through many significant details. Photographs prompt and push my thinking: I let them speak, work on my feelings and mind, and sort them as images first, seeking connections. *The Language of Landscape* began this way.

Places are my primary data, and photographs and travel journals with written and drawn notes of sights, sounds, smells, and reflections are primary source material. For this reason I write primarily about places where I have been. Once, in the space of seven weeks, I traveled from a Philadelphia summer to an Australian winter, then back, in August, to San Francisco, Philadelphia, and Cape Cod, and then to Amelia Island, off the coast of Georgia, in September. The transect across climates heightened my sense of air's weight, wetness, light, and earth's texture, from Sydney's hard, dry ground to Philadelphia's soaked, soft, spongy soil to the grainy give of sandy beaches in Truro and Amelia. I appreciated why explorers like Lewis and Clark recorded their impressions of an unfamiliar world in vividly sensual terms, slogging through deep mud, the crunch of prickly cactus underfoot.

In an unfamiliar place, senses sharpen, a survival instinct; in familiar territory, senses dull, and it takes an effort to refresh them. Trying to read a foreign landscape is, for me, like reading Dutch, with English as my native language, Danish my fluent second, German limited: I may not understand everything, but I get the gist. Still, missing the meaning of a single key word or landscape feature can mislead. The language of landscape makes significant details stand out and helps me frame questions, but reading landscape deeply requires local knowledge. On foreign ground, one needs an interpreter.

I believe that we are imprinted with the landscape of our early childhood. I am a creature of the Eastern Deciduous Forest. Except for brief excursions into desert, prairie, and dry woodland, I have spent my life in the temperate forest of North America and Western Europe. I feel a sense of coming home every time I return to northwestern Connecticut, though my family moved away when I was two years old, first to Massachusetts, then to Ohio. Memories of my first place are layered: brief visits separated by long absence. I remember a landscape of steeply rolling hills and valleys, big rocks, swiftly flowing streams, thickly growing second-growth woods, houses and barns of weathered wood, stone walls, and white churches where my father and grandfather were ministers. The summer when I was eight and we drove from Cincinnati to stay for a month in Connecticut, I studied drawing with a local painter, sketching outdoors, in a nearby town, on a farm. A few years later, I was photographing river, rocks, and woods there. The light in those photographs is the low, weak light of November, and it is this light that I associate with the place, for in college and after Connecticut became, for my family, the landscape of Thanksgiving.

When I was six, we moved from Massachusetts to a suburb of Cincinnati, where we lived for the next twelve years. There my landscape broadened, progressively, from yard and street to neighborhood, town, city, and region. What I now know makes sense of what were mysteries then. There was a large vacant lot down the street with a meadow, a grove of trees, and a little stream—The Wilderness. I once dug a big hole there; as I dug, the dirt changed from dry, dark brown, to dense, yellowish brown, to sticky bluish-grey. One year, I drew charts of clouds. A bike ride away there was a forest with a creek whose bed was filled with tiny stone twigs and shells—fossils. Downtown Cincinnati was a twenty-minute bus ride away. There, green hills framed the Ohio, a broad, brown river that flooded the sloping stone landing where the *Delta Queen*, a steamboat like the one Twain piloted, was moored.

This book's philosophical foundations, like its landscape roots, were imprinted in childhood. Dialogues—with people, places, and self, between thinking and doing—were how I learned to learn. I was raised by the Socratic method, led by questions through response to insight, taught to frame questions, in turn, and listen to the answers. When I read John Dewey's *Art as Experience* in college and William James many years later, it was with a start of recognition, for I had absorbed the ideas, unattributed, as part of my family's atmosphere. My relationship to Emerson and the Transcendentalists is also cultural rather than scholarly; the texts I read in Unitarian Sunday school, and the hymns we sang, were steeped in their ideas.

At seventeen, I lived for a year with a family on a small farm in Denmark and attended school, a gymnasium, in a nearby town. There I learned landscape as livelihood, following my Danish father around, helping to feed and talk to the pigs, milk the cows, hoe sugar beets, polish eggs. I watched sows giving birth, made them roll over when they lay on their babies, loaded grown pigs onto the truck from the slaughterhouse, pulled a calf out of its mother's womb when its time came. The only hot water was in the barn where it was needed to sterilize milk cans. There was none in the house, except in winter in a room off the kitchen. Mornings began with a cold shower; a hot bath meant hauling in water from the barn. I learned the difference between standard of living and quality of life, between nature as poetic idea and natural phenomena as complex, unreliable reality.

I went to college expecting to major in art only to find that in Harvard's Fine Arts Department one studied the history of art not its making. In sophomore tutorial, I learned to *see*, to read works of art—drawings, prints, paintings, sculptures, buildings (but not landscapes!)—without the aid of written texts. Original drawings, prints, and paintings hung in pairs on the wall, confronted me each time I walked into the classroom in the Fogg Art Museum: landscapes by Rembrandt and Van Gogh, portraits by Rubens and Ingres, others by Picasso, Klee, as well as by their students and forgers. I had ten minutes to examine one pair of works, five to present my findings and reasoning: What artist, time, and place? Both by the same artist, or not: study and finished work? master's work and student's copy? or forgery? The culmination of the year was a thirty-page essay on a single work of art: mine was on El Greco's portrait of Fray Hortensio Felix Paravicino y Arteaga in Boston's Museum of Fine Arts. Many short papers led to that final product: on materials and techniques, formal analysis, style, subject, iconography, relation to other works, provenance, significance. I found a book of Paravicino's poetry in Widener Library, published in Spanish in 1650, and held my breath as the librarian checked it out to me; as I remember, the last borrower had been in the 1800s. I fell in love with scholarship that year and often wandered among the stacks of Widener, surrounded by books in so many different languages, feeling the condensed knowledge contained there, taking books off the shelves and paging through them. I feel the same way, now, in landscapes layered with deep, varied history. There is no Widener, no British Library of landscape literature, though; the texts are dispersed in places, in landscapes, around the world.

Ian McHarg's book *Design with Nature* introduced me to landscape architecture. His manifesto in the catalogue of the University of Pennsylvania, where he was chairman of the department of landscape architecture, promised a career of action bridging the arts and sciences. It stirred, then lured me. In graduate school at Penn there were no textbooks or reading lists for most courses, but rather field trips within the physiographic regions of the Delaware River Basin— from Coastal Plain to Piedmont, Ridge and Valley, to Appalachian Plateau— where we dug soil pits, collected rocks and leaves, interviewed people, and learned to read landscape. It was a surprisingly small step from discerning differences of style and quality in the lines of Old Master drawings to reading line, shape, and structure in trees, rivers, and gardens, and then a longer leap to using this knowledge to design new landscapes. Understanding relationships between process and material, form, and space was the key. I knew little landscape when I started graduate school and found it difficult, at first, to understand professors who taught with images more than with words. I learned to think and speak in drawings, diagrams, maps, and photographs.

McHarg was both professor at Penn and partner at Wallace, McHarg, Roberts, and Todd (WMRT), an office of landscape architects, architects, urban designers, and city planners. I worked in this office for five years on projects ranging from a study of an entire metropolitan region to portions of cities, from plans for new communities to park designs. On every project, he challenged us to reframe problems, take risks, break new ground, even as we drew from past experience, adapting that knowledge to new situations. Lessons learned in practice prompted refinements in the university curriculum. In the 1960s and 1970s, successive dialogues between theory developed at Penn and its application in practice advanced the field of landscape architecture: Penn's curriculum was a model imitated by universities around the world; one after another of McHarg's professional projects were, and still are, landmarks. Long before I read Donald Schon's description of professional thinking as reflection-in-action, I learned its power firsthand.

From private practice I moved to Harvard to teach, then to Penn, but the years in practice still influence the kinds of questions I ask, the methods I use, and what I write. Even in a successful, reflective practice like McHarg's there are avenues one has neither time nor funds to pursue. So I created a "research practice" in which grants and a university salary enable me to set my own agenda and support action-research projects for some clients, like community gardeners and children, who cannot afford a designer, and others who do not know they need one, like community development corporations, city agencies, and public schools. What began, in 1984, as a study of how vacant urban land could be exploited as a resource to restore the city's natural environment and rebuild inner-city neighborhoods, grew into an investigation of how to combine a comprehensive, "top-down" approach with an incremental, "bottom-up" approach to urban design and community development. Starting in inner-city neighborhoods of Boston's Roxbury and Dorchester and continuing in West Philadelphia, students and I met with community residents and politicians, planners, and engineers. We designed and built community gardens, playgrounds, and small parks on vacant lots and proposed strategic improvements to the urban infrastructure of streets, sewers, and open space as a framework for renewal that would stimulate investment and improve air and water quality. We surveyed vacant lots, plotted old floodplains, gathered census data, searched archives for historic maps, photographs, and newspaper articles, mapped land use and other features, and created a digital database with which to compare and overlay this information. The dedicated adults and bright, earnest children I met led me to reevaluate and reinterpret the dismal picture painted by statistics alone; we found rich resources and models of success in even the poorest communities. Contrary to professional wisdom and my own expectations, I discovered that many community gardeners are astute critics who recognize and value design that serves their needs and expresses their dreams. Furthermore, they are often quicker to grasp the devastating impact and potential value of natural features like buried streams than are the professionals responsible for planning the city. If community gardens are indeed communities, could the gardeners not apply their understanding of successful design and respect for natural processes to help plan the larger neighborhood and region? Watching, listening, talking, photographing, drawing, writing, I searched for a common language with which to shape and share visions for the future.

All my work—photography, writing, teaching, design, and planning—is devoted to helping people recognize the good and beautiful that exist in the world, to bolster and build from them, and to recognize the ugly and the dangerous, to avoid them. I want to demonstrate the commonalities among landscapes of natural beauty, those designed by trained designers and artists and those crafted by ordinary people, and to inspire the making of new places with extraordinary qualities and significance. And I want to trace the legacy of others who have built and written in this tradition.

This book is written out of my life as author and reader, performer and critic, artist and scholar of landscape, out of fieldwork and archival research. I use practice to develop and test theory, and theory to critique practice, alternating between engagement and detachment, passion and dispassion.[1] Making things happen is a messy process full of unforeseen obstacles and opportunities, disappointments and joys. Unexpected events challenge theory, demand revision; refined, theory holds. As actor and author, I have both a pragmatic and a poetic sensibility. When I look at a designed landscape, I calculate the difficulty of the task, judge the intentions implicit in others' deeds, applaud or condemn the risks they take, and admire the grace with which multiple demands are fulfilled.[2] As an artist, I respond to light, detail, and presence with the empathy for living and nonliving things that landscape photography demands.[3] As a scholar, I document the tradition within which I think and act, compare what other authors do to what they say, study the context of their actions and writings.[4] Art and action push me at times to take poetic license or to venture beyond the point where the scholar might stop.

My conviction that landscape is language has startled some people and outraged others, but it seems natural to many landscape architects, for landscape is a language derived from the core activity of landscape architecture: artful shaping, from garden to region, to fulfill function and express meaning. The roots of this theory are strong, deep, and varied, grounded in many fields—anthropology, geography, geology, ecology, history, art history, literature, linguistics, and landscape architecture, among others. It is a radical theory: in the sense of being rooted in the basic elements of nature and human nature; in the sense of offering a fundamentally different perspective than from any one individual root; and in demanding and enabling radical change in how we choose to think and act.

Landscape architecture is a profession I discovered by chance soon after college. Most of my students come to it much later in life, often after other careers. Despite its scope and the significance of the discipline, it is, in many respects, an invisible profession compared to the related fields of architecture and engineering, and this reflects the greater problems described in this book. If this book inspires others to enter and contribute to this wonderful, crucial profession, I will be happy.

Prologue: The Yellowwood and the Forgotten Creek

Once a yellowwood stood by an old library, leafing, flowering, fruiting, setting seed; roots grabbed hold, sucked air and water from beneath a plaza of brick. Its skin-smooth silver trunk bore knobby limbs. Floppy leaves clung to long stems, catching wind, moving green shadows across red bricks. Students sat each spring under the yellowwood, listening to names named, glad for green shade, walked under it to the library, breathed musky June flowers, kicked yellow leaves of October across red bricks.

For many years the yellowwood grew; red stone blackened, the building decayed. Then men came one day to fix the library, piled stacks of tools, tiles, and sacks around the tree, sealing soil under bricks. Two years later, the library reopened, leaded glass gleaming, blackened stone brightened, furnace fixed. How elegant, people said. That fall the tree lost its leaves in September.

Next May, the yellowwood flowered early and profusely. Thousands of fragrant white blooms hung in long clusters; petals covered bricks, blew across grass. How beautiful, people said. How sad, though. Several years' bud scars bunched up against each twig's growing tip. Abundant flowers signaled a dying, and seeds found no purchase in the plaza. People admired the tree and walked on; they had lost the language that gives tongue to its tale. Once a yellowwood stood. No more. And few knew why.

One day a street caved in. Sidewalks collapsed into a block-long chasm. People looked down, shocked to see a strong, brown, rushing river. A truck fell into a hole like that years back, someone said. A whole block of homes collapsed into a hole one night a long time ago, said someone else. They weren't sure where. Six months later, the hole was filled, street patched, sidewalks rebuilt. Years went by, new folks moved in, water seeped, streets dipped, walls cracked.

Once a creek flowed—long before there was anyone to give it a name—coursing down, carving, plunging, pooling, thousands of years before dams harnessed its power, before people buried it in a sewer and built houses on top. Now, swollen with rain and sewage, the buried creek bursts pipes, soaks soil, floods basements, undermines buildings. During storms, brown water gushes from inlets and manholes into streets and, downstream, overwhelms the sewage treatment plant, overflowing into the river from which the city draws its water.

Vacant lots overgrown by meadows and shrubby thickets near boarded-up homes and community gardens filled with flowers and vegetables follow a meandering line no one seems to see. In a school that stands on this unseen line, the gym floods every time it rains. Once a year, teachers take students on buses to a place outside the city to see and study "nature."

On a once vacant lot, brand new houses—red brick, yellow siding, green sliver of lawn out front, gates open—rise in contrast to nearby older, shattered houses and land laid waste: "First Time Buyers, own this home for less than you pay in rent," a sign urges. The houses have been built by churches from coins and foundation funds, the land a gift from the city. How beautiful, people say. No one wonders why the land was free, why water puddles there, why the name of the place is Mill Creek.

Signs of hope, signs of warning are all around, unseen, unheard, undetected. Most people can no longer read the signs: whether they live in a floodplain, whether they are rebuilding an urban neighborhood or planting the seeds of its destruction, whether they are protecting or polluting the water they drink, caring for or killing a tree. Most have forgotten the language and cannot read the stories the wildflowers and saplings on vacant lots tell of life's regenerative power; many do not understand the beauty of a community garden's messy order. They cannot hear or see the language of landscape.

Architects' drawings show no roots, no growing, just green lollipops and buildings floating on a page, as if ground were flat and blank, the tree an object not a life. Planners' maps show no buried rivers, no flowing, just streets, lines of ownership, and proposals for future use, as if past were not present, as if the city were merely a human construct not a living, changing landscape. Children's textbooks, from science to history, show no nearby scenes, suggest or demand no firsthand knowing, just formulas and far-off people and places, as if numbers and language had no local meaning, as if their present had no past, no future, the student a vessel not an actor.

The yellowwood was the first yellowwood I ever saw, its perfumed flowers an amazing surprise my first year as a graduate student, the same year the hole and the river emerged near my apartment. The yellowwood, gone, is still on my daily path; the forgotten creek is now the heart of my work. Back then I knew nothing of dying trees or buried rivers. Now I have learned to read what sloping valleys and sinking streets tell, what bud scars say. Landscapes are rich with complex language, spoken and written in land, air, and water. Humans are storytelling animals, thinking in metaphors steeped in landscape: putting down roots means commitment, uprooting a traumatic event. Like a living tree rooted in place, language is rooted in landscape.

The meanings landscapes hold are not just metaphorical and metaphysical, but real, their messages practical; understanding may spell survival or extinction. Losing, or failing to hear and read, the language of landscape threatens body and spirit, for the pragmatic and the imaginative aspects of landscape language have always coexisted. Relearning the language that holds life in place is an urgent task. This book is dedicated to its recovery and renewal.

One

"Nature's Infinite Book": The Language of Landscape

The face of the water, in time, became a wonderful book—a book that was a dead language to the uneducated passenger, but which told its mind to me without reserve, delivering its most cherished secrets as clearly as if it uttered them with a voice. And it was not a book to be read once and thrown aside, for it had a new story to tell every day.

—Mark Twain, *Life on the Mississippi*

In nature's infinite book of secrecy
A little I can read.

—Shakespeare, *Antony and Cleopatra*

Landscape as text: The Ridgeway. Avebury, England.

1
Dwelling and Tongue:
The Language of Landscape

LANDSCAPE IS LANGUAGE

The language of landscape is our native language. Landscape was the original dwelling; humans evolved among plants and animals, under the sky, upon the earth, near water. Everyone carries that legacy in body and mind. Humans touched, saw, heard, smelled, tasted, lived in, and shaped landscapes before the species had words to describe what it did. Landscapes were the first human texts, read before the invention of other signs and symbols. Clouds, wind, and sun were clues to weather, ripples and eddies signs of rocks and life under water, caves and ledges promise of shelter, leaves guides to food; birdcalls warnings of predators. Early writing resembled landscape; other languages—verbal, mathematical, graphic—derive from the language of landscape.[1]

The language of landscape can be spoken, written, read, and imagined. Speaking and reading landscape are by-products of living—of moving, mating, eating—and strategies of survival—creating refuge, providing prospect, growing food. To read and write landscape is to learn and teach: to know the world, to express ideas and to influence others. Landscape, as language, makes thought tangible and imagination possible. Through it humans share experience with future generations, just as ancestors inscribed their values and beliefs in the landscapes they left as a legacy, "a treasure deposited by the practice of speech," a rich lode of literature: natural and cultural histories, landscapes of purpose, poetry, power, and prayer.[2]

Landscape has all the features of language. It contains the equivalent of words and parts of speech—patterns of shape, structure, material, formation, and function. All landscapes are combinations of these. Like the meanings of words, the meanings of landscape elements (water, for example) are only potential until context shapes them. Rules of grammar govern and guide how landscapes are formed, some specific to places and their local dialects, others universal. Landscape is pragmatic, poetic, rhetorical, polemical. Landscape is scene of life, cultivated construction, carrier of meaning. It is language.

Verbal language reflects landscape. Up and down, in and out—the most basic metaphors of verbal language—stem from experience of landscape, like bodily movement through landscape.[3] Verbs, nouns, adverbs, adjectives, and their contexts—parts of speech and the structure of verbal language—mirror landscape processes, products, and their modifiers, material, formal, and spatial. Just as a river combines water, flowing, and eroded banks, sentences combine actions and actors, objects and modifiers. The context of a word or sentence, like that of hill or

Landscape legacy: avenue of stones. Avebury, England.

valley, defines it. Verbal texts and landscapes are nested: word within sentence within paragraph within chapter, leaf within branch within tree within forest. Words reflect observation and experience; dialects are rich in terms specific to landscape of place, like "estuary English," described so vividly by John Stilgoe.[4] Shakespeare, Mark Twain, T. S. Eliot, Anthony Hecht, and Adrienne Rich, like verbal poets of every literature, mine landscape for structure, rhythm, and fresh metaphors of human experience; so do poets of landscape itself, "Capability" Brown, Frederick Law Olmsted, Frank Lloyd Wright, Lawrence Halprin, Martha Schwartz.[5]

Landscape is the material home, the language of landscape is a habitat of mind. Heidegger called language the house of being, but the language of landscape truly is the *house* of being; we dwell within it. To dwell—to make and care for a place—is self-expression. Heidegger traced that verb in High German and Old English; in both, the root for "to dwell" means "to build." In German, the roots for building and dwelling and "I am" are the same. I am because I dwell; I dwell because I build. *Bauen*—building, dwelling, and being—means "to build," "to construct," but also to "cherish and protect, to preserve and care for, specifically to till the soil, to cultivate the mind."[6]

Landscape associates people and place. Danish *landskab*, German *landschaft*, Dutch *landschap*, and Old English *landscipe* combine two roots. "Land" means both a place and the people living there. *Skabe* and *schaffen* mean "to shape"; suffixes *-skab* and *-schaft* as in the English "-ship," also mean association, partnership.[7] Though no longer used in ordinary speech, the Dutch *schappen* conveys a magisterial sense of shaping, as in the biblical Creation. Still strong in Scandinavian and German languages, these original meanings have all but disappeared from English. *Webster's Dictionary* defines *landscape* as static, "a picture representing a section of natural, inland scenery, as of prairie, woodland, mountains . . . an expanse of natural scenery seen by the eye in one view"; the *Oxford English Dictionary* traces the word to a Dutch painting term (*landskip*).[8] But landscape is not a mere visible surface, static composition, or passive backdrop to human theater; therefore dictionaries must be revised, and the older meanings revived. The words *environment* and *place*, commonly used to replace *landscape* in twentieth-century English, are inadequate substitutes, for they refer to locale or surroundings and omit people. In midcentury, the declining use of *landscape* was in part a reaction to the Nazis' adoption of "blood and soil," a linking of native landscape and racial identity. *Environment* and *place* seem more neutral, but they are abstract, disembodied, sacrificing meaning, concealing tensions and conflicts, ignoring the assumptions *landscape* reveals. *Landscape* connotes a sense of the purposefully shaped, the sensual and aesthetic, the embeddedness in culture. The language of landscape recovers the dynamic connection between place and those who dwell there.

Landscape is loud with dialogues, with story lines that connect a place and its dwellers. The shape and structure of a tree record an evolutionary dialogue between species and environment: eucalypt leaves that turn their edge to bright sun, deciduous leaves that fall off during seasonal heat or cold. And they record dialogues between a tree and its habitat. Tree rings thick and thin tell the water and food of each growing season of the tree's life. Size, shape, and structure—low-branched or high, densely branched or spare—reflect dialogues between a tree and a group of trees in open field or dense forest. Each species has a characteristic form from which individuals deviate, as true of human body shape—muscled or fat, short or tall—as of trees. A coherence of human vernacular landscapes emerges from dialogues between builders and place, fine-tuned over time. They tell of a congruence between snowfall and roof pitch, between seasonal sun angles and roof overhang, wind direction and alignment of hedgerows, cultivation practices and dimensions of fields, family structure and patterns of settlement. Dialogues make up the context of individual, group, and place. The context of life is a woven fabric of dialogues, enduring and ephemeral.

Humans are not the sole authors of landscape. Volcanoes spew lava, remaking land; rain falls, carving valleys. Mountains, gardens, and cities are shaped by volcanoes and rain, plants and animals, human hands and minds. Trees shade ground and shed leaves, produce a more hospitable place for life with similar needs. Beavers cut trees and dam streams to make ponds: a dwelling place. People mold landscape with hands, tools, and machines, through law, public policy, and actions undertaken hundreds, even thousands, of miles away. All living things share the same space, all make landscape, and all landscapes, wild or domesticated, have coauthors, all are phenomena of nature and culture. Others share the language, but only humans (as far as we yet know) reflect, worship, make art, and design landscapes like the gardens of the Villa d'Este that "set the formal strictures" within a natural context "where the tension lectures us on our mortal state."[9]

Landscape Is Meaningful and Expressive

Landscape has meaning. Rivers reflect, clouds portend. Wilderness, for many now a sacred symbol of undefiled nature, was once a terrifying symbol of chaos. Some meanings are human inventions, and yet significance does not depend on human perception or imagination alone. Significance is there to be discovered, inherent and ascribed, shaped by what senses perceive, what instinct and experience read as significant, what minds know. Any organism with senses has the potential to read and understand landscape. To a deaf man, a rustling bush cannot signal an approaching animal, but moving leaves or vibrating ground may. To a canoer a river is a path, waves and eddy lines are signs to steer by. To a fish a river is a watery world of light and shadow, surface movement is sign of prey. Fly fishermen try to read rivers as fish do in order to trick them, picking then flicking the fly at line's end, mimicking real flies abroad on the stream to convince the fish the fly is real. Norman Maclean describes a master fly-tier who lay under a glass tank filled with water to study the insect he planned to imitate.[10] The best fly fishermen think like fish, become the fish, in an intimate bonding of hunter and hunted.

Landscapes are as small as a garden, as large as a planet. To a person the garden is a landscape, to a people the nation is, to the human species, a planet. A pond is a landscape to a beaver, a tree to a bird, a forest to a tree. Ice floes on a river, lake, or arctic sea, inhabited by birds and seals, are a landscape. Ice crystals on a winter window look like ice floes seen from the air, are uninhabited, yet to a poet a landscape of the imagination. Landscape may be inhabited in imagination alone.

There are landscapes within landscapes within landscapes. Every landscape feature is both a whole and part of one or more larger wholes: leaf and twig, twig and tree, tree and forest; garden and house, house and street, street and town, town and region. Every phenomenon, thing, event, and feeling has a context. A valley is not a valley if it has no ridge or plateau, no up and down. Motion is imperceptible without rest, sound without stillness. Without sense of past and future, there can be no present, without threat no refuge. The same material, form, or action may have different meanings in different settings—water in a desert, water in a sea.

Anomalies are clues to what the wider context is. A "wolf" tree is a tree within a woods, its size and form, large trunk and horizontal branches, anomalous to the environs of slim-trunked trees with upright branches. It is a clue to the open field in which it once grew alone, branches reaching laterally to the light and up. With that field unmowed, unplowed, or ungrazed, younger woodland trees grew thickly

In wolf tree, see the former field. Amherst, Massachusetts.

together around the older tree, their branches finding light by reaching up. The older tree, engulfed by a dense woodland of younger trees, no longer able to find light horizontally, sends new branches upward. Landscape is dynamic, present context includes the past; the story of the wolf tree is part of the human story.

When valley and river, path and user fail to correspond—when, for example, a valley is vast but a river small, a path broad and well-worn, but those who pass that way infrequent—valley and path may have been shaped by context not now visible or no longer relevant: valley by a great flood, path by an earlier surging crowd. Also, context may be actual or latent—every landscape has both real and potential form—what is, what has been, what will, what might be.

Metaphors grounded in landscape guide how humans think and act. George Lakoff and Mark Johnson demonstrate what Emerson observed: that humans understand and experience one kind of thing in terms of another, projecting bodies and minds onto the surrounding world: trees and clouds seen as bounded, a river seen as having a mouth, a mountain as having a foot, front, back, and side.[11] One might just as easily see things as continuous and undifferentiated; viewing them as separate is more a function of individual consciousness than an inherent quality of landscape. Many metaphors are grounded in fundamental relationships with landscape—moving, making, eating, wasting. The most common refer to space and direction: in and out, up and down. In American culture, high and in are good, down and out are bad; central is important, marginal is not. Landscape imagery conveys feelings and ideas: emotions churning like a stormy sea, rivers of time, clouds where gods live, sacred mountains, Father Sky impregnating Mother Earth with rain as the seed, Zeus and Thor hurling thunderbolts in anger, Siva flashing lightning from his Third Eye, a flare of cosmic intelligence, the god of Jews and Christians dispatching plagues of locusts and disease to punish the wicked. Personification, the attribution of human feelings like intention, anger, love to natural forms and phenomena, is the foundation of myth and religion.

Landscapes are the world itself and may also be metaphors of the world. A tree can be both a tree and The Tree, a path both a path and The Path. A tree in the Garden of Eden represents the Tree of Life, the Tree of Knowledge. It becomes the archetype of Tree. When a path represents the Path of Enlightenment of Buddhism or the Stations of the Cross of Christianity it is no longer a mere path, but The Path. The yellow brick road in *The Wizard of Oz* is both path and Path. The similar is the stuff of metaphor, simile, and personification; contrasts are the stuff of paradox and oxymoron. Landscape actors, objects, and modifiers may enhance meaning without rhetoric: rivers reflect and run, but they do not pun.

Built landscapes may be rhetorical. Landscape features, like hill and street, may be emphasized or embellished for effect, slope steepened to make climb difficult, street broadened and lined with trees to impress the viewer. Gardens of allusion reflect oral and written literature: Shakespeare gardens allude to the bard's plays and poetry, their herbs and blooms references to his works; eighteenth-century English gardens, with their buildings in classical style and pastoral landscape, refer to classical literature. When Mussolini built a monument in 1938 to those who died in a battle of the First World War in Redipuglia, near Italy's northwestern boundary, he used the language of rhetoric. More than one hundred thousand soldiers are buried there in twenty-two terraces of tombs, arranged from bottom to top in alphabetical order, sixty thousand buried at the top of the hill in a common grave surmounted by three crosses, like Calvary. Words engraved in the pavement tell how these soldiers died for the glory of Italy, immortal in memory. Facing the hill of tombs is the grave of their general, as if addressing his entombed soldiers. Their inscriptions answer, *"Presente."* "I am here."

The language of landscape can be spoken and read even though never codified, without recourse to rules. People follow paths and make them, plant gardens, are awed by the scale of mountains and cathedrals; great designers use landscape

Landscape of power and rhetoric: World War One cemetery. Redipuglia, Italy.

fluently, all without dictionaries or grammars. Thomas Jefferson linked landscape and learning at the University of Virginia where he designed and sited the original buildings. Sigurd Lewerentz and Gunnar Asplund comforted the bereaved in the Hill of Remembrance and Woodland Chapel at Forest Cemetery in Stockholm. Glenn Murcutt associated people, sun, wind, and water in a house at Bingie on the coast of Australia. Even those who exploit landscape cynically may do so masterfully, as Mussolini did when, at Redipuglia, he fostered feelings of heroic nationalism to promote fascism, or as Disney has exploited it, for profit, at Disneyland and Disney World.

Landscapes are a vast library of literature. The myths of Japan's Fuji and Australia's Uluru, the folksy tales of trolls and pink flamingos on American lawns, the classical works of earth, water, and wind at Yosemite and the Grand Canyon, the high art of the Alhambra and Manhattan's Central Park, and countless other places, ordinary and extraordinary, record the language of landscape. The library ranges from wild and vernacular landscape, tales shaped by everyday phenomena, to classic landscapes of artful expression, like the relationship of ordinary spoken language to great works of literature. Worship, memory, play, movement, meeting, exchange, power, production, home, and community are pervasive landscape genre. To be fully felt and known landscape literature must be experienced in situ; words, drawings, paintings, or photographs cannot replace the experience of the place itself, though they may enhance and intensify it.

Landscape literature is a resource to be treasured. Several decades ago, archeologists in Israel discovered ancient water-gathering systems in the Negev Desert that employed simple channels, check dams, and broad depressions. These techniques, lost for many centuries, have inspired the landscape architect Shlomo Aronson and others to reshape whole landscapes to gather water; they planted groves and grassy meadows in the desert, all sustained by dewfall and rain. The water engineer Ken Wright is working with archeologists to study the water systems of the Incas in Peru, not just to understand, but to use their knowledge. I have studied dozens of community gardens in Philadelphia as landscape expressions. The literature of landscape contains a vast repertoire of similar examples, adaptations to a wide range of circumstances, not just in the diversity of genes and behavior, but in ideas and cultures. Some are cherished and cared for, others are being rediscovered, but entire volumes of landscape literature are being lost and forgotten, whole libraries destroyed.

LANDSCAPE HAS CONSEQUENCES

The language of landscape is a powerful tool. A person literate in landscape sees significance where an illiterate person notes nothing. Past and future fires, floods, landslides, welcome or warning are visible to those who can read them in tree and slope, boundary and gate. Knowing how to tell what one wants to express—pragmatics—makes landscape authors more adept; making landscapes appeal to emotion and reason depends on understanding rhetoric. To know landscape poetics is to see, smell, taste, hear, and feel landscape as a symphony of complex harmonies. Natural processes establish the base rhythm that is expressed in the initial form of the land, to which culture, in turn, responds with new and changing themes that weave an intricate pattern, punctuated here and there by high points of nature and art. Landscape symphonies evolve continually in time, in predictable and unpredictable ways, responding to process and to human purpose, and, in landscape symphonies, all dwellers are composers and players.

The language of landscape humans have always known but now use piecemeal, with much forgotten. People still read paths and create them, identify boundaries and define territory, delight in a flowering tree comparing it to a lover, but most people read landscape shallowly or narrowly and tell it stupidly or inadequately. Oblivious to dialogue and story line, they misread or miss meaning entirely, blind to connections among intimately related phenomena, oblivious to poetry, then fail to act or act wrongly. Absent, false, or partial readings lead to inarticulate expression: landscape silence, gibberish, incoherent rambling, dysfunctional, fragmented dialogues, broken story lines. The consequences are comical, dumb, dire, tragic. Those who admired the yellowwood's excessive, early flowering on the campus in Philadelphia were blind to what the bud scars told, failed to read the flowers' poignant message, were unable to imagine the tree's connection to soil, plaza, and contractor. When I tried to convince the dean, himself an architect, to find another site for the contractors' trailer and tools, he refused, unconvinced or not caring that the yellowwood would die as a consequence. Those who first built houses over the buried creek in West Philadelphia and those who rebuilt in the same place were illiterate in the language of landscape and so could not read the creek's presence. I tried and failed, at first, to convince planners at the City Planning Commission and engineers at the Philadelphia Water Department that the buried creek was a resource to be exploited and a force to be reckoned with. The yellowwood is dead, but it is not too late to restore Mill Creek—the water, the people, the place.

Ironically, the professionals who specialize, reading certain parts of landscape more deeply than other parts and shaping them more powerfully, often fail to understand landscape as a continuous whole. Once those who transformed landscapes were generalists: naturalist, humanist, artist, engineer, even priest, all combined. Now pieces of landscape are shaped by those whose narrowness of knowledge, experience, values, and concerns leads them to read and tell only fragments of the story. To an ecologist, landscape is habitat, but not construction or metaphor. To a lawyer, landscape may be property to regulate, to a developer, a commodity to exploit, to an architect, a site to build on, to a planner, a zone for recreation or residence or commerce or transportation, or "nature preservation." As in the story of the blind men who each touch a different part of the elephant— trunk or tusk or tail alone—then arrive at a false description of the whole animal, so each discipline and each interest group reads and tells landscape through its own tunnel vision of perception, value, tool, and action. And as each shouts its own fragment, landscapes of cities, suburbs, and regions are severed, become impoverished, dysfunctional. It is even fashionable now to design buildings, gardens, and cities deliberately as dislocated and unconnected fragments to emphasize the erosion of common ground, a misanthropic view of cultural differences.

Loss of fluency in the language of landscape, in turn, impoverishes verbal language. Words like *bore* and *guzzle* refer to features and processes many no longer perceive—and which can injure or even kill. To know the meaning (and location) of bore and guzzle is to be safe, to survive: a bore is the "noisy rush of the tides against the current in a narrow channel"; a guzzle, the low place in the dunes where water drains and the sea comes crashing through in a "century storm."[12] To know bore is to avoid it at high tide; to know guzzle is to decide not to build and settle there. Such nuances, preserved in specialized, professional language, are now lost to common verbal language. Aboriginal peoples become more "civilized" and less attuned to landscape; young Papua-New Guineans, for example, no longer learn to sing with waterfalls and birds. A loss of language and loss of knowledge limits the celebration of landscape as a partnership between people, place, and other life and further reduces the capacity to understand and imagine possible human relationships with nonhuman nature.

We shape landscape and language; they shape us. To know landscape is to read in Boston's Fens and Riverway artful reconstructions of places laid waste by human occupation. Not to know is to fail to discern what merely grew and what was planted, and thus, for example, to mistake the Fens and Riverway as "preserved" wetland and floodplain forest; they were, rather, the product of human purpose mindful of natural processes of regeneration. Failure to recognize the Fens and Riverway as being *designed* and *built*, not happenstance, blinds us to the possibility of designing and building similar transformations elsewhere.

Landscape metaphors modify perceptions, prompt ideas and actions, molding landscape, in turn. To see wilderness as chaos provokes fear and prompts flight, perhaps even the urge to destroy; to believe it sacred fosters appeal, reverence, and the desire to cherish. To know nature as a set of ideas not a place, and landscape as the expression of actions and ideas in place not as an abstraction or as mere scenery promotes an understanding of landscape as a continuum of meaning.[13] Not to know, and to confuse landscape and nature, is to equate landscape with mountain, meadow, farm, and country road, but not highway or town. Yet a designed urban park is no less a landscape than a planted cornfield, the island of Manhattan no less a landscape than its Central Park. Notions of landscape as countryside, but not city, falsely fragment intimate connections and produce such ironies as inner-city schoolchildren bused out of town to study old-field meadows, ignoring the same plants growing on vacant lots next door.[14] To see landscape as mere scenery gives precedence to appearance at the expense of habitability and risks trivializing landscape as decoration—landscaping—concealing the significance of senses other than sight and of parts hidden from view, the deep context underlying the surface. To call some landscapes natural and others artificial or cultural misses the truth that landscapes are never wholly one or the other.

Once most of life was lived outdoors, in constant dialogue with wind, water, soil, plants, and animals; now most livelihoods no longer depend upon literacy in landscape. Or so we imagine. Our most intimate relationships with nature (finding food and water, disposing of waste) are now negotiated by large, distant institutions. Schools and popular media train children to experience the world many steps removed, through textbooks, calculations, and secondhand images and sounds in film, video, and computer. People work in offices with windows that do not open, or with no windows at all. Meanwhile naturalists, gardeners, and fly fishermen, like modern shamans, preserve and pass on bits of the language—knowledge of bird and insect, soil and seed, water and fish—and write books to reflect on and communicate the meanings of human life and relations with nonhuman nature, inheritors of Thoreau's *Walden* like Annie Dillard's *Pilgrim at Tinker Creek*, Michael Pollan's *Second Nature*, and Norman Maclean's *A River Runs Through It*.

Even farming and fishing are now high-tech, capital-intensive industries whose owners may never touch soil or sea. In 1990, for the first time in American history, the category "farmer" was eliminated from the U.S. Census. "Agricultural laborer" took its place. Laborers, those in most intimate contact with earth and plants, water and fish, now perform work dictated in distant offices by people who may never see the consequences of their policies and plans. At Disney's EPCOT (Experimental Prototypical Community of Tomorrow), an elaborate exhibit called "The Land," sponsored by Kraft Foods, shows a soil-less, factorylike future for American agriculture: plants hang from wires, move as products in an assembly line, roots exposed, sprayed by aerosols of water and fertilizers, divorced from dirt. This is a perilous vision because the sense of control it conveys is false, an illusion. The plants are fragile, dependent upon the sprayers' continued function; lives hang, literally, by a thread. If the sprayers fail plants shrivel rapidly, for their roots are not held in soil's reservoir of moisture and nutrients.

The power to read, tell, and design landscape is one of the greatest human talents; it enabled our ancestors to spread from warm savannas to cool, shady forests and even to cold, open tundra. But, now, the ability to transform landscape beyond the capacity to comprehend it threatens human existence. Having altered virtually every spot on the planet, humans have triggered perturbations that threaten to change it irrevocably and dangerously. Many, as a consequence, feel control slipping, exposed for the illusion it always was. Our lives are like the plants hanging from wires at EPCOT, roots exposed, dependent upon technologies which, should they fail, will spell disaster. Some speak of the end of nature, but it is nature as *we* know it that is threatened, not the planet itself, not the universe.

To recover and renew the language of landscape is to discover and imagine new metaphors, to tell new stories, and to create new landscapes. John Berger describes, and the photographer Jean Mohr illustrates, a language of lived experience with which to interpret the common and the particular across the gulf of different cultures.[15] Gregory Bateson says that humans must learn to speak the language "in terms of which living things are organized," in order to read the world not as discrete things, but as dynamic relations, and to practice the art of managing complex, living systems.[16] Aldo Leopold writes of the need for humans to "think like a mountain," to escape the short-sightedness that threatens the larger habitats of which humans are part.[17] Berger, Bateson, Leopold, and others have envisioned or implied the need for such a language; none have elaborated or codified it. The language of landscape is such a language: in terms of it the world is organized and living things behave, humans can think like a mountain, can shape landscapes that sustain human lives and the lives of other creatures as well, can foster identity and celebrate diversity.

The language of landscape prompts us to perceive and shape the landscape *whole*. Reading and speaking it fluently is a way to recognize the dialogues ongoing in a place, to appreciate other speakers' stories, to distinguish enduring dialogues from ephemeral ones, and to join the conversation. The language of landscape reminds us that nothing stays the same, that catastrophic shifts and cumulative changes shape the present. It permits us to perceive pasts we cannot otherwise experience, to anticipate the possible, to envision, choose, and shape the future. We can see what is not immediate, a forest in a meadow, the yellowwood dying of starved and suffocated roots, and seeing, we can choose to save or snuff it. Or we can see water underground in the tree along a dry creek bed, in the cracks of a building's foundation, the slumps in pavement in a city; or see the connections between buried, sewered stream, vacant land, and polluted river, and imagine rebuilding communities while purifying water. And we can imagine poetry.

Humans' survival as a species depends upon adapting ourselves and our landscapes—settlements, buildings, rivers, fields, forests—in new, life-sustaining ways, shaping contexts that acknowledge connections to air, earth, water, life, and to each other, and that help us feel and understand these connections, landscapes that are functional, sustainable, meaningful, and artful. Not everyone will be farmers or fishermen for whom landscape is livelihood, but all can learn to read landscape, to understand those readings, and to speak new wisdom into life in city, suburb, and countryside, to cultivate the power of landscape expression as if our life depends upon it. For it does.

2

Survival and Imagination: Reading and Telling the Meanings of Landscape

The surface of the Mississippi River, Mark Twain wrote, is "a wonderful book" that "told its mind . . . without reserve, delivering its most cherished secrets as clearly as if it uttered them with a voice."[1] Riverboat pilots read the river to steer safely around snags and sandbars, following the deep main channel. A pilot taught Twain to read the river's depth and shape from patterns on the water's surface: "Now look out—look out! Don't you crowd that slick, greasy-looking place; there ain't nine feet there." The "long slanting line on the face of the water" revealed a bluff reef below that would "knock the boat's brains out"; how at the head of the reef "where the line fringes out at the upper end and begins to fade away," it was safe to cross. Beneath "fine lines . . . that branch out like the ribs of a fan" lay smaller reefs: "miss the ends of them, but run them pretty close." The Mississippi tested even the experienced pilots, for it changes day by day, season by season, year by year: "It was not a book to be read once and thrown aside, for it had a new story to tell every day." From one year to the next, the river, altered, became an unfamiliar text, landmarks gone, submerged, displaced. The river had moved across the land.

Reading landscape reveals the past and foretells the future: history can be deciphered in shape of valley and hill, field and fence; tomorrow's weather can be told from evening sun and clouds. Verbal and mathematical languages, the word and the formula, merely describe and interpret the world for they are not the things they describe, but always one or more steps removed. In landscape, representation and reality fuse when a tree, path, or gate is invested with larger significance. In a sacred landscape, a path is seldom only a path, but the Path, where pilgrims climb to reach a hilltop shrine and, within a church, traverse the path between portal and altar, tracing a metaphorical and an actual journey. Ambiguity—layers of landscape meanings—and the metaphors and paradoxes it engenders are a source of rich material for reading and telling.

LANDSCAPE CONTESTED, CELEBRATED, RECLAIMED: SLESVIG AND THE DANISH HEATH

A tall stone column rises from Skamlingsbanke, the highest point in southern Jutland, Denmark's western peninsula. Up close, it looks like a stack of broken blocks, corners chipped. Its significance can be read even without understanding the Danish words cut into stone: "Raised 1863. Blown up by the Prussians March 21, 1864. Raised again May 1, 1866. Memorial to the Champions of the Danish

Cause in Slesvig." There is no broad river or high ridge between Denmark and Germany, and Danevirk, the ancient Viking earthwork, proved a puny obstacle to Prussian armies. The provinces of Slesvig-Holstein were a broad zone of contested terrain for more than seventy years from 1848 to 1920.[2] After a devastating defeat by Germany in 1864, Denmark was reduced to its smallest land area ever. From 1864 to 1920, the border between Denmark and Germany was just south of Skamlings-banke, and the Danish-speaking population of Slesvig-Holstein were forbidden to speak their own language. Between 1865 and 1905, some 55,000 Danes emigrated from Slesvig to the United States. When, in 1920, Slesvig became Danish once again by popular vote mandated by the Treaty of Versailles, there were only 165,000 people left.[3] On April 9, 1940, German troops marched across Slesvig once again to begin a new occupation, and, in 1945, more than 80,000 people gathered at Skamlingsbanke after liberation for a *folkfest* sponsored by the Danish Resistance.

Skamlingsbanke is both prospect and refuge. The hilltop, a landmark visible from afar, affords a distant view over farm fields to the south and west and over the water to the east. From the base of the monument, a narrow dale slopes steeply down to form a natural amphitheater. In 1843, some farmers bought the hill as a place to celebrate Danish culture. Skamlingsbanke soon became a spiritual Danevirk where Danish leaders spoke to large crowds in the amphitheater; here is where N. F. S. Grundtvig, founder of the Danish folk high schools, announced his plans. Memorial stones set up over the years link land, language, and motherhood.

In the eighteenth century, western Jutland was a remote part of Denmark, poor neighbor to more fertile lands in eastern and southern Jutland. Mostly heath, it was sparsely inhabited by people who eked out a meager living from graz-ing sheep and cutting sod for fuel. After the loss of Slesvig in 1864, reclaiming the heath became a patriotic cause. "What is lost without, must be won within," was the motto of the Heath Society, founded in 1866 to promote the process.[4] The transformation from heath to farm was achieved with great difficulty, for heather produces a tough, water-resistant hardpan in the dry, sandy soil of the outwash plain. Today only remnants of heath remain, the low, leathery heather replaced by hard-won wheat fields and conifer plantations.

Roaring in the windbreaks, bending trees so they lean permanently eastward, pruning them into arcs, the west wind blows from the North Sea across the open farmland and heath of western Jutland. Dense hedges enclose each farmstead like a snug collar, hemming in a compact cluster of house, barn, garden, and grove of fruit and shade trees. Out on the heath, there is nothing to stop the wind. It pushes against your body, sometimes so hard that standing upright is a struggle. One is grateful for the occasional dales and the refuge they offer.

Kongenshus Memorial Park is a large heath preserve, so large one can look out over the heather and imagine the landscape of western Jutland as it once was, as Danish authors and artists described the heath in the nineteenth century. At the heart of the park is a dale, its hillsides covered with purplish, greenish-brown

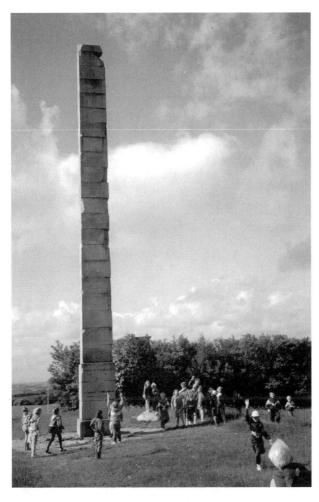

Landscape of instruction. Skamlingsbanke. Denmark.

heather, stiff, moving in clusters; for there is a breeze, even down in the vale. Tall, upright stones, like menhirs, line a long path leading down, their faces inscribed with text and symbols. Standing before one stone, reading the letters cut into the rock, I recognized the words of Hans Christian Andersen's "Jutland Between Two Seas" and recalled the weight of the thick, blue Folk High School Songbook with its thin pages and the melody, sung so often during morning song, the period which marked the beginning of every Danish school day.[5] The poem, written in 1859, urges Danes to go see the heath before it becomes wheat fields. Two circular graphs cut into the stone compare the extent of cultivated fields, forest, and heath in the district in 1850 (57 percent, 3 percent, 40 percent) and 1950 (80 percent, 13 percent, 7 percent). Each large, upright stone bears a text, each recording a different proportional change from heath to field and forest. The tall stones, thirty-nine in all, represent districts; smaller stones, lying prone, like headstones in Danish

Paradoxical memorial: the heath reclaimed, restored. Kongenshus Memorial Park. Denmark.

Recording the conquest: district stone. Kongenshus Memorial Park. Denmark.

churchyards, accompany each tall stone, one for every parish, bearing the names of farmers who tilled the heath. At the end of the path, at the bottom of the dale, is a circle of more than seventy stones, each inscribed with the name of a man whose words celebrate the heath or whose deeds reclaimed it. Past the circle, the dale opens out, the ridges framing a distant view of green pasture, wheat fields, and forest plantations. At the bottom of the little valley, heath, farm, and forest are juxtaposed in a single view. The park at Kongenshus is paradoxical—a memorial to the heath and a monument to the people who struggled to conquer it.

But the paradox is deeper still. The heath, reclaimed with such effort, must now be maintained, for without burning and grazing, trees will replace heather. Western Jutland was not always an open landscape; hundreds of years ago, it was covered with oak forest, as place-names like Agerskov (fieldforest), Egebjerg (oakhill), and Skovhus (foresthouse) testify.[6] Iron Age farmers burned and cut the forest, cultivated the soil, then grazed the land so intensively that they exhausted its fertility. Forced to abandon farming, many men from western Jutland joined the Germanic invasion of England in the fifth century, and heather invaded the fields and pastures they left behind. Like other Danish landscapes, this one has been worked over through the centuries since the last Ice Age; the heath is a human artifact, a by-product of agriculture—or so many scholars think. There is some debate among those who read oak pollen in bogs and dig under Bronze Age barrows to find heather buried there.[7] How one chooses to tell the story depends, at least in part, on whether one wishes to see the heath as the product of human abuse or as ancient, wild, Danish nature. Probably it is both.

There is also deep irony at Kongenshus, for the heath there was first reclaimed in the mid-eighteenth century by immigrants from the German Rhineland lured by the Danish king with promises of being given their own land. This was one hundred years before the conquest recorded in the stones, before the impetus to reclaim the heath after Denmark's defeat by Prussian armies in 1864. Many people in this area spoke German even in the late nineteenth century.

Kongenshus Memorial Park is a political monument, with a subtext as strongly ideological as the patched column on Skamlingsbanke. The land for the park was purchased in 1942 during the Nazi Occupation, and plans were delayed until 1945, the year of Germany's defeat; the park was dedicated by the king and queen of Denmark in 1953. Fifty years later, it is nature that seems endangered, not culture; the heath has taken on new meaning, and the Heath Society is villain, not hero. Kongenshus is a polemical landscape layered with complex, paradoxical meanings. "So very Danish," my Danish friends and family tell me.

These details are Danish, but the stories told are old and common: there is always a tension in landscape between the human impulse to wonder at the wild and the compulsion to use, manage, and control. And every nation has its "native" nature, worked by physical and mental labor into landscapes, with which its people identify. To authors from Cicero to Marx, "first nature" represents a nature unaltered by the human labor that yields "second nature." The Latin words *natura*, *naturans* refer to the given—naturally occurring materials, forms, and phenomena —*natura / naturata* to those reworked by human hands. Cicero wrote, "We sow corn, we plant trees, we fertilize the soil by irrigation, we confine the rivers and straighten or divert their courses. In short, by means of our hands we try to create . . . a second nature within the natural world."[8] To John Dixon Hunt and the sixteenth-century humanists whom he cites, gardens are yet a "third nature," a self-conscious re-presentation of first and second natures, an artful interpretation "of a specific place . . . for specific people."[9] As are other kinds of *designed* landscapes.

Meanings: Inherent, Invented, Ambiguous

Rivers reflect, clouds conceal. Water and fire purify and destroy. Circles have centers, paths have direction. These meanings are inherent in the qualities of landscape elements; they are grasped by humans and other life-forms as bodies and minds permit. Meanings of a landscape feature—a tree, for example—depend upon what it is in itself, its seed, its root, its growth and decaying, its networks of relationships, its setting, whether standing alone on a heath or surrounded by forest. They depend also on what it has come to mean in a human culture—a person, refuge from a storm, or the Tree of Knowledge. Trees, in some cultures, stand for humans, as long-lived individuals that grow from roots, stand upright, bear fruit, and die. Or a tree represents a family descended from a single ancestral pair, each branch a new pair or generation. A Tree of Knowledge may derive from trees' long life span and the association of age with wisdom.

Inherent qualities of landscape features and phenomena account for similar meanings across time and place: flowing rivers and growing trees, wet water and solid earth, round circles and angular squares, solid walls and open gates. Humans interpret landscape signs and elaborate upon them, reading meanings in to tell stories. The closer invented meanings are to significant, inherent qualities the more they draw from embodied knowledge rather than disembodied, abstract ideas, and the more likely those meanings are to be shared broadly; the further removed the less likely that meanings will be shared. Meanings and associations experienced directly are universal among human cultures or nearly so: water and purity, path and journey. Meanings not experienced bodily, as a sensation, even when strongly suggested by inherent qualities are not universal; not all cultures regard rivers as signifying time, air and light as intangible spirit, a circle as a cycle. Invented meanings remote from experience depend entirely on the mind's imagining: a circle as heaven, a square as earth.

Clouds and birds convey information and become ancestors: to the Hopi, clouds are signs of rain in a dry land; to the Kaluli tribe of New Guinea, birds surround their descendants with chatter and comment. Willows, with their weeping shape and ability to regenerate, are signs of resurrection; even cut branches of a willow planted as fence posts will sprout, and many nineteenth-century Christian cemeteries are planted with willows. Garden and paradise have strong associations in Christian and Islamic cultures, a connection renewed through centuries of dialogue between literature and architecture. Cloistered gardens with a central fountain (representing the Virgin Mary) have been set in monasteries and convents since medieval times and before. Light animates the world; many cultures link light to life, to knowledge, and to the sacred. Such meanings build upon inherent qualities—of clouds, birds, willows, gardens, water, springs, light—arising from landscape and cycling back through myth.

Some landscapes are sacred, some are homelands, others are cherished or abhorred for what once happened there. Plymouth Rock is particularly significant to descendants of Pilgrims who came from England on the *Mayflower*. A vacant lot at Prinz-Albrecht-Strasse 8 in Berlin is a place of horror to most who know it once was the site of Gestapo headquarters. As links to personal and collective pasts, such landscapes may inspire pilgrimage.

New ideas, new events bring fresh meanings. The ha-ha, widely invoked by landscape designers in eighteenth-century England, is a sunken fence or ditch to confine grazing sheep to pasture, so the larger landscape can be seen, unbounded, from the owner's garden. During the Iran hostage-taking crisis of 1979–81 and the 1991 war in the Persian Gulf, Americans tied yellow ribbons to doors, cars, and trees to express their support of American hostages and troops. Red poppies sold on Armistice Day (now Veterans' Day) recall the dead of Flanders fields in the First World War, and there was surely once a time when Englishmen could not see a field of flowering poppies without hearing, "In Flanders fields the poppies blow / Between the crosses row on row."[10] To Christians the cross is a symbol of the sacrifice of Jesus. Some meanings, like the yellow ribbons, are fleeting; others become embedded and endure.

If sky is associated with deity, then clouds and mountains are divine domains. If a square is earth and a circle heaven, square within circle is earth within heaven. In sacred landscapes, movement, path, and portal often overlap, with spiritual transformation at the threshold where they meet. Put two or more elements together and potential meanings and associations grow. Elements may overlap, coincide, or be a mere analogue, their relation immediate or mental. Mazes and mountaintops become sacred landscapes, the maze a puzzle-path whose destination is hard to reach, the mountaintop shrine with steep steps a difficult journey of commitment.

Ambiguity: Meaning as Complex

Landscape meaning is complex, layered, ambiguous, never simple or linear. A river flows, provides, creates, destroys, simultaneously a path and a boundary, even a gateway. Fire consumes, transforms, and renews. A circle is hierarchical— it has a center, after all—yet nonhierarchical—all points along the circumference are equidistant from the center. Landscape elements have, as I. A. Richards said of words, "equally and simultaneously, vastly different" meanings that weave a rich fabric. Meanings of elements, like those of words, are not stable, and multiple meanings are a source of metaphor and other tropes, as well.[11] Metaphor and irony juxtapose meanings: harmonious, contrasting, or conflicting. Figures and tropes are rarely isolated in landscape; combined, overlapped, juxtaposed, they introduce correspondences, prompt reflection, invite investment of meaning.

To many Danes, the landscape of Lejre is the ideal Danish landscape. Its features—low rolling hills and valleys, small villages, farms, groves of beech and linden, and ancient barrows—echo the words of songs sung at morning song from the Folk High School Songbook by every Danish child for the past century. Parts of this landscape are protected by law: as scenery, history, resource, nature, and wildlife habitat. Landscape records stories of continuous human settlement over thousands of years; to a historian, Stone Age burial mounds and ancient roads, old cottages with thatched roofs, tiny medieval churches, and baroque manor surrounded by gardens reveal glimpses of past lives. To an art historian, rolling terrain, brooks, barrows, farms, and groves were models for paintings from Denmark's Golden Age in the first half of the nineteenth century; modern windmills of white metal now intrude there. To residents of the new crop of homes built on soil deemed marginally productive by planners, the farmhouses and open fields they overlook are native Danish scenery, the windmills a source of electric power and symbol of green politics. Lejre is now more bedroom community than farm village. To a planner, highways, railroad, and underground water pipes all point to Copenhagen, more than twenty miles to the east, where one-quarter of Denmark's population now lives. The pipes are invisible, but the waterworks that pump groundwater to Copenhagen are housed in monuments of neoclassical modernism. To a hydrologist, these pipes and pumps reveal what is not present: there is no water in the low-lying meadows. The five-kilometer allée of centuries-old lindens that leads to and from the baroque manor, runs past the waterworks, pointing toward Copenhagen, perhaps a deferential gesture from a loyal subject to his king.[12]

This landscape was my home more than thirty years ago when I was seventeen and lived for a year with a Danish family. How it was then, how it is now, are juxtaposed in my mind. From a distance, the house and barn, tucked behind a windbreak of trees, look just as they did. Then, close up, I see the hedges are gone from under the trees, opening up a view out to the fields, but exposing the house to wind. The barns, once filled with pigs, cows, and chickens, are empty. The farmer, my Danish father, now retired, lives in a new housing development on a hill above the farm, his armchair turned to face out the window over the fields. There is no farmer in the farmhouse; the doctor and businessman who live there work in the city. By law, the fields must be plowed, planted, and harvested by a farmer, so the retired farmer is now a "gardener" hired by the new owner to cultivate the fields.

Danish nature, Danish culture: Åvangsgården. Lejre, Denmark.

A few summers ago, the green fields were full of red poppies, like Monet's paintings of the fields near Giverny, crimson dots so bright they sear photographic film, from a distance, red patterns in the fields. People said they had never seen so many poppies. But the farmer pointed out how poppies were concentrated in fields where rape grew thin, indicating a poor crop. He had watched as every year rape was planted, though rape ought not to be planted more often than once a decade. As I walked through the fields, I saw his meaning; where the poppies grew most densely, the rape stalks were sparse, the dry dirt exposed. As in many other places, decisions about what to plant and how to cultivate are increasingly made by those who have never worked the soil themselves or even seen the places their policies shape. There is imbalance between local knowledge and expert's overview, between the passionate provincialism of local residents and the indifference or ignorance of distant owners or bureaucrats.[13]

Readers and Readings

I once found a grove of dogwoods on a hillside in eastern Pennsylvania: slender, corky trunks, lacey branches, clouds of delicate, white blossoms. I remarked on its beauty to the owner, a farmer, and was surprised that he did not see the grove at all, only the field he had been forced to leave fallow a decade before. My beautiful grove was the farmer's abandoned field.

"You have to find more beautiful examples of community gardens if you expect me to get excited about them," an architecture student once told me. Community gardens have a messy vitality that some find appealing; and, like an occasional flower growing in a rocky field, they exist against all odds, especially in inner-city neighborhoods, where they are expressions of collective vision, artful inventiveness, sustained effort, an investment of hard-won resources. They may not always be Art, but, in the eyes of their authors, they are beautiful.

Never do all people have the same response or read identical stories in the same landscape through the lens of the same metaphor, and few recognize the picture whole. To naturalists, forests may be habitats for animals that deserve preservation for their own sake; naturalists read in a forest the diversity of plant and animal life and the size of their populations. To foresters, woods are a crop to be managed for human consumption; they read how hard the wood is, how straight the timber, how long till the next harvest and the next replanting. To a hiker, the forest may be a refuge from urban life and labor, to the lumberman a living. To a bird, high branches are refuge from predators, bark a source of bugs; to a beaver, a tree is material for dam and dwelling. Whether landscape is habitat, nature, system, artifact, historical record, ideology, wealth, site, or scenery depends on one's perspective, as visitor, resident, actor, or student.[14]

In *Touching the Rock*, John Hull, who is blind, describes relying on his hearing for spatial perception and orientation. The sound of rain reveals the surrounding landscape: "Rain has a way of bringing out the contours of everything. . . . Here and there is a light cascade as it drips from step to step. . . . I can even make out the contours of the lawn, which rises to the right in a little hill. The sound of the rain is different and shapes out the curvature for me. . . . everywhere are little breaks in the patterns, obstructions, projections, where some slight interruption or difference of texture or of echo gives an additional detail or dimension to the scene."[15]

Blindness transcends the eyes. Culture can prevent eyes from seeing and ears from hearing. Those who see nature and city as opposites or deserts and forests as disordered are blind to the natural processes in cities and the order in wilderness. I was shocked when an Australian architect told me she had no desire to visit her country's Red Center because it was a desert "chaos"; to me it was one of the most clearly ordered landscapes I had ever seen, organized by extremes of light, heat, and water. Landscape as chaos or order depends largely upon expectation and knowledge. During a five-month stay in suburban southern California a few years ago, a place foreign to my customary urban, temperate-forest habitat, I was reminded of how essential knowledge is to reading landscape. I could read only the most obvious stories and not the subtleties. I did not know the plants that grew there, their seasonal patterns, their preferences for soil and water. I felt blinded and disoriented.

With knowledge, one sees what is invisible to the unaided eye. The Walbiri, desert dwellers of Australia, find underground water by signs on the surface. A geologist sees notches lining opposite hillsides as shoreline terraces cut by waves into the slopes and sees the glacial lake that once filled the valley. Mark Twain, after years' experience, learned to read the Mississippi. Microscopes and telescopes, microphones and amplifiers, cameras and satellites extend human ability to look and listen; they reveal landscape patterns and contexts we otherwise would not see or hear. But sophisticated tools do not bring understanding, necessarily. Without knowledge, a person notes nothing, like the passengers on Twain's steamboat who were oblivious to the river's text, like those who walked past the yellowwood with no eyes for its distress.

"The land offers us good reading, outdoors, from a lively, unfinished manuscript," writes May Theilgaard Watts. "Records, prophesies, mysteries are inscribed there, and changes—always changes. Even as we read from some selected page, whether mountaintop, forest, furrow, schoolyard, dune, bog, we see changes: in stirrings and silences, flavors and textures, spacing, tolerances, and confrontations and tensions at the edges."[16] Novice readers, moving from Watts's guidebooks to the landscapes of North America and Europe to the texts outside their doors, will find that the more they know, the more they can read. And the more they read the more they can tell.

Landscape Dialogues: Reading and Responding

We see, hear, smell, touch, and taste what our human eyes, ears, nose, skin, tongue, and tools permit and our cultures condition. The sense of up and down, forward and backward, left and right is determined by the form of the body that perceives them: by head and feet, face and back, by the distinction between one eye, one arm, one breast, one leg, and the other. Our human bodies predispose us to recognize symmetrical patterns. Had humans different bodies and minds we would sense different qualities and read and respond to different meanings.

Humans are not alone in reading and responding; animals read landscape, too, and they also are limited by their bodies and brains. Birds, baboons, and people hear a bird's alarm call as a signal of danger, cows follow the beaten track from barn to field and back again. Frogs' vision, quite different from birds' or primates', is geared to "detecting an accessible bug" by an object's size and how it moves, but "a frog will starve to death surrounded by food if it is not moving."[17] What is significant to a person is not relevant to a frog. Other life-forms participate in the language of landscape; to the extent that their senses, memories, or social behavior resemble ours they read and inscribe it similarly. Ethologists describe how bees, birds, beavers, and baboons interpret their landscapes, build, and even transform them; zoosemioticians codify signs by which animals communicate.[18] Plants, animals, rivers, and mountains create landscape, and some use the language, but in their own, nonhuman, terms.

Nineteenth-century artists and poets like Caspar David Friedrich and William Wordsworth believed there was a language of nature manifest in landscape that spoke directly to human emotions independent of culture. They sought to return to inherent "meanings" of landscape features as vehicles for expressing their own emotions as artists and to jettison meanings traditionally associated with such features.[19] John Ruskin objected to the tendency of some authors to personify nonhuman organisms, inanimate objects, and abstract ideas, to attribute human emotions and intentions to them, and coined the term *pathetic fallacy* to describe it.[20]

To say that landscape elements have inherent qualities to which humans (and others) attribute significance is not to insist, necessarily, that meaning, for humans, can exist outside of culture; to say that animals, plants, and other features of landscape participate in the language is not to personify them, necessarily. They participate on their own terms. Neither mountains nor bacteria *decide* to create form (though people of some cultures might say they do), but even the most primitive living organisms reproduce and may even make architectural shells to protect themselves. Initiation and intention mark the difference between the animate, inanimate, and inorganic, whether an entity reads and responds to its landscape involuntarily or deliberately, by instinct or learning, or is merely an unwitting respondent to forces of gravity and water flow. Many animals are social; they experience community, dominance, kinship, exchange, and mark and make territory for those activities, but apparently none reflect or imagine. Humans initiate, consider, remember, imagine; only human life, as far as we know, reflects on its past and invents possible futures. The ability to imagine and create what is not yet, *to design*, is human; so are art and worship. Landscape literature, though it may include the works of nonhuman nature, is a phenomenon of the human imagination.

Dialogues: Unconscious, Deliberate, Extroverted, Introverted

Landscapes are a cacophony until sorted into individual dialogues by focusing on a primary signal to which many elements respond, by tracing a single set of dialogues. The sun sends a pervasive signal. All landscape elements respond to its light and heat: sunflowers track the sun, turning faces east to west from morning to evening; earth dries out on west-facing hillsides so only drought- and heat-tolerant plants grow there; desert plants develop a thick skin to buffer temperature extremes from day to night; desert people build houses with thick walls. In summer, desert dwellers fall into a rhythm, rising early when the light is low and air is cool, sweating, seeking shade by late morning—even the narrow shadow cast by a palm trunk or saguaro cactus—staying inside during the afternoon, craving water to replace the moisture sucked out of body, drinking water, glass after glass, going out again in the evening after sunset. Animals do the same; there is no birdsong at midday, the desert landscape comes alive with the noises of evening. Sunflowers' tracking, soil's drying, plants' thick skin, people's sweating are unconscious dialogues with the sun; building thick walls is deliberate.

The common garden bean, *Phaseolus vulgaris*, in its thousands of varieties, is the product of dialogues between humans and beans over millennia. As we shaped the bean, it shaped us, notes William Cronon: "It will not sprout, it will not grow, it will not thrive or yield seed unless we treat it in the ways it demands."[21] In *Nature's Metropolis*, Cronon traced how Chicago's commodity markets shaped the American West: from fields to silos to pigs, to market, from cows to pastures to barns; from corn to fields to silos to grain elevators to railroads.[22]

Landslides are dialogues among rain, rock, soil, building, and living. John McPhee tells such stories in "Los Angeles Against the Mountains."[23] On landslide-prone slopes, falling rain soaks soil, weighs it down, and sends it slipping—an unconscious, involuntary dialogue. People cut into such slopes to make level ground, then build streets and houses, weighing down soil; rain falling and sprinklers spraying lawn soak soil, and send it slipping. Cutting, building, and watering are deliberate acts, but often not recognized as dialogues with slope and soil. Failure to recognize the resulting landslide as part of ongoing dialogues, misreading dialogues as fate or Mother Nature's revenge, leads to rebuilding in the same place and in the same way despite repeated disasters.

Some dialogues are extroverted and physical. People plant hedgerows to block strong winds, build steep roofs where snowfall is heavy; then wind blows up and over, snow slides off. Similar dialogues take place between cultivation practices and field dimensions, family structure and settlement patterns. The vernacular landscapes that emerge from such dialogues have a coherence, like that of the Illinois corn belt, which Robert Riley describes as governed by two laws: "square to the road, hogs to the east."[24] For more than thirty years, the Swedish landscape architect Sven-Ingvar Andersson has engaged in dialogues with his garden. He describes how four privet shrubs, left over after planting the hedges of his garden, were set in a serendipitous group, then a few years later "developed a sudden desire to become long-necked birds." "We helped them," he said, "with pruning and clipping."[25] His garden is full of such dialogues—a single rose stem "decides" to grow through the privet hedge and blooms alone against clipped green. The autonomy of nonhuman actors and the impulse to interpret their stories underlie garden design, inform the dialogue of clipped and unclipped, of control, serendipity, and response.

Some dialogues are introspective, like the dialogue between Claude Monet and his garden: between artist and landscape; practices of designing, gardening, and painting; the actual and the virtual. Monet started by observing and representing landscape through painting, then created a garden that was planted, painted, and altered repeatedly from 1883 until his death in 1926. Like Monet at Giverny, the Zen monks at the Japanese Buddhist monasteries Saihoji and Shisendo, Pliny in his country villa, and many others used their gardens to reflect on nature. So too, not only poetry and painting, but scientific experiments and the forms of human settlements record such introspective dialogues. In *Fish Magic* (1925), Paul Klee painted flowers growing in a vaselike vessel, fish swimming, moon shining, a clock, and a person with two faces poised between realms of nature and culture.[26] "For the artist," observed Klee, "dialogue with nature remains

Garden dialogues. Marnas. Sweden.

a *conditio sine qua non.* The artist is a man, himself nature and part of nature in natural space."[27]

Joining the Conversation

Landscape is the sum of countless dialogues. It has no silence to be filled, no blank page; in landscape, dialogues have already begun before a new author enters the conversation. Some designers do not understand the ongoing dialogues and offer irrelevant responses, even rude interruptions. While one may welcome abrupt interruptions from genius, when every designer presumes genius the result is merely confusing and annoying.

Designers and planners of landscapes must try to read a place through their clients' eyes, as well as their own, to read and respond to the ongoing dialogues. The task is easiest for a single designer working with a single client. With many clients, in a political arena, the task is difficult, even with good intentions, especially since many professionals now commonly work outside their own regions and cultures; the best-known practitioners travel back and forth across oceans and continents to work in other countries. Sven-Ingvar Andersson, though Swedish, practices in Denmark and was chosen by the Dutch, after a year-long international search, to prepare a plan for the Museumplein, one of Amsterdam's most important public spaces. "It is difficult to work in foreign countries," he writes, reflecting on his seven years' work on another project, Vienna's Karlsplatz, not so much because of language or lack of a professional network, as because "one is outside one's professional and social tradition."[28] A sense of one's own place in time, space, and culture helps one navigate the shoals of foreign customs, but things can easily go awry. Misunderstandings and misreadings can also occur closer to home.

Many years ago I sat in a public meeting in Boston's Roxbury, listening first to a landscape architect present proposals for a new park design, then to the heated, hostile discussion that followed. The audience was primarily African American, many of them residents of the public housing project nearby; the designers were all Caucasian and lived elsewhere. The site of the park-to-be was at the heart of the community on vacant land; once filled with homes and businesses, it had been condemned and cleared for a highway. Some at the meeting were among those who had opposed and halted the roadway's construction; to them the site and its history had personal and political significance. Many objected to the proposed design because its bland lawns and groves reflected neither their own needs nor their interests; it told no stories they found meaningful. Others opposed the entire idea of a park; they wanted a supermarket, a laundromat, a bank, places to work. Furthermore, they were insulted by the designer's presentation. Following common practice, he had offered three schemes: one design that required minimal investment, a second unattractive for some other reason, and a third that the designer preferred. His presentation was intended to steer the choice to the third; the audience, like Goldilocks tasting the bears' porridge, was expected to find his own scheme to be "just right." His strategy failed; this audience saw through the sham, was outraged at the failure to offer genuine options, and rejected the designer's plan. He had failed to read the landscape through their eyes, failed to see, hear, and respond to their landscape dialogues.

A few years before that Roxbury meeting, I experienced a similar failure as a graduate student in landscape architecture at the University of Pennsylvania. The occasion was an experimental course meant to teach us students sensitivity to local dialogues; landscape architecture and anthropology students worked in teams to study and plan for a real place. My team's assignment was Alloway, a small town and farming community on the coastal plain of southern New Jersey. We conducted field surveys and interviews to elicit people's needs and desires, attended local events like the Volunteer Firemen's Pancake Supper, and developed plans and designs based on our readings of the landscape. Curious about our proposals, residents invited us to present our plans at a potluck supper at the Grange Hall in May. Midway through our presentation, I showed a slide of a vacant lot in the middle of town where we were proposing that new apartments be built. "That's no vacant lot, that's Elmer's potato patch!" shouted someone in the audience. The crowd laughed. So did I, though mortified; there had been no sign of potatoes, or Elmer, when we surveyed the town that winter.

Some dialogues continue for years before anyone knows whether they are successes or failures. My dialogue with Mill Creek in West Philadelphia is one such. It began in 1971 when I was a student, and the street caved in. The sight of the big, hidden, brown river was so startling, it changed forever how I look at depressions and valleys in urban landscapes, and it compelled me to seek to track the history not only of this, but of other, buried streams in other places. On my return to Philadelphia in 1986, after nine years' practicing and teaching in Boston, I resumed my dialogue with the forgotten creek, tracing its course in cracks and dips and vacant lots, plotting its restoration and the rebuilding of the neighborhood through which it flowed. I began more than a decade of conversations with community gardeners, city planners, engineers, teachers, and with schoolchildren and parents whose basements flooded after rains. Some of these dialogues have yielded tangible results: gardens in the creek's floodplain, a Mill Creek curriculum in the local middle school where the community itself has become the classroom. Other of my dialogues with the landscape are still dreams.

My dialogue with Mill Creek, like any other, must be read alongside others, large and small, plain and obscure, predictable and unforeseen, enduring and ephemeral, concluded and open-ended. Together, they form the context of Mill Creek, the place. Some of those other dialogues have extended over thousands of years: the erosion of mountains and building of plains, the growth and decline of forests, the rise and fall of cultures. Every place embodies enduring stories that are deeply embedded in the shape and structure of landscape.

Building public landscapes can be accomplished successfully only by close collaborators who care to define and agree on what ideas will guide the project, especially ideas about special qualities of the place, how the place will be used and experienced. The larger the project, especially if it is a public project, the more numerous and diverse the clients to get to know, the agencies to confer with, the colleagues in other disciplines to consult, the contractors in construction and maintenance to meet with. The essence of a project can easily be lost in a welter of confusing misunderstandings or competing interests, or be sacrificed to tight funding or bland common denominators. Andersson has evolved a simple strategy to draw all the actors involved in a project together. After initial meetings, he composes a brief, lyrical statement of the special qualities of the site, the clients' hopes, and the intent of the design, which blends the sensual and ecological, the poetic and pragmatic.[29] His text is integral to the act of design and forms an implicit compact between himself and his clients. The ideas in his texts are elemental, simple, stated with charm, but, unexpressed, they would readily be lost. These touchstone texts serve as a standard against which to measure results, a reminder that the material product must hold the dream.

Lawrence Halprin also frequently works on complex and often controversial public projects with diverse clients who are in actual or potential conflict, but he has a different strategy. He was hired by Orange County, California, for example, to propose alternative alignments for a new highway to cut through the Laguna

Canyon Wilderness Park. He was expected to engage many participants in the process: elected officials, public employees, developers, and interested citizens, including those altogether opposed to the highway. Halprin's method is to conduct workshops that bring the various actors into a public conversation; he employs techniques that he calls "RSVP cycles": "R" for the resources in a place; "S" for scores, the means by which activities are carried out; "V" for "valuaction," evaluation leading to decisions on actions to take; "P" for performance, the acting out of a score; cycles, to emphasize that the process is interactive and nonlinear.[30] Halprin uses this method in undertaking projects for highways and downtowns, in designs for new transit malls, main streets, and parks. It has succeeded in facilitating public dialogue and often results in a consensus that amounts to collective speech. In the Laguna Canyon Wilderness Park project, he "scored" a series of "awareness" tours designed to give all participants a common experience of the place, to stimulate their ideas, and to establish a common language. Their responses formed the basis for beginning to work together and they guided his work. Then he led several workshops in which small groups of participants sketched proposals, presented them to the larger group, and discussed and debated the issues they raised. Halprin's own proposals, presented at the very end of the process, after several workshops, incorporated many ideas that emanated from the workshops.

"Designing with the Bloody Invisible": Murcutt's Ball and Bingie

The architect Glenn Murcutt, who has invested a lifetime in reading and responding to local landscape, does not accept commissions outside Australia. "Did you see the structure on those buildings? It takes your breath away . . . how does he dare?" "He's designing with the bloody invisible!" Two experienced architects looking at Murcutt's work were referring to its spare structure and the way his buildings capture and play with breezes and winds. To Murcutt, these phenomena are not invisible, but rather felt, embodied knowledge. He grew up along Sydney Harbor, swimming the currents, sailing with winds "by the seat of his pants," literally, by feeling the shifts and bumps in air and water. He learned to use his body like a fine-tuned instrument, to rely upon observation and experience when a learning disability made reading difficult. He learned winds by building model airplanes, watching them glide, then by refining shape and set of wings, and he learned the flood of water by diving once into a river in flood, as Loren Eiseley had floated down the Platte River, letting himself go, feeling part of the flow.[31] Murcutt swam to the bottom, felt the speed of water flow change with depth, the increased friction near the bottom, the mass of water above, like boundary layer winds slower at earth's surface, in response to friction. His dialogues with wind, water, light, plants, and animals are deliberate and habitual. He is like Norman Maclean's brother, a master fly fisherman who tried to explain his own success: "All there is to thinking, is seeing something noticeable which makes you see something you

Embodied knowledge: wind, rain, sun, shelter. Bingie, Australia. (Glenn Murcutt)

weren't noticing which makes you see something that isn't even visible."[32]

Murcutt studies his clients' patterns of living as closely as he studies the processes of sun shining, plants growing, water flowing, and wind blowing, and he designs rooms and rooms' arrangement to correspond to the patterns of clients' lives. When the artist Sydney Ball requested a place of meditation, Murcutt designed an elevated verandah enclosed on three sides, on a wooded slope, facing downslope, with a view of blue, distant mountains. The elevation and the sloping ground beneath bring tree branches to eye-level, an unusual perspective that lifts one out of the everyday to a transcendent view.

Murcutt works alone; because he is in great demand, clients must wait two to three years for a design of their home, office, or museum. But the period is not fallow; Murcutt meets with them, from time to time, to talk about their lives, habits, likes, dislikes, hopes, and dreams, and, in turn, shares with them his ideas of an ecologically responsible approach to design. He addresses the dimensions of production, construction, and maintenance and relates how materials, site layout, and the design itself conserve environmental resources. He and his clients come to consensus about basic aims, or, if not, he suggests another architect. The product of these dialogues, like the house for Ball and a vacation home for the Magnie family at Bingie, along the Pacific coast in southeastern Australia, express the daily and seasonal rhythms of the place and the people who live, work, or come there. The Magnies camped out on the site in tents on weekends and holidays for years

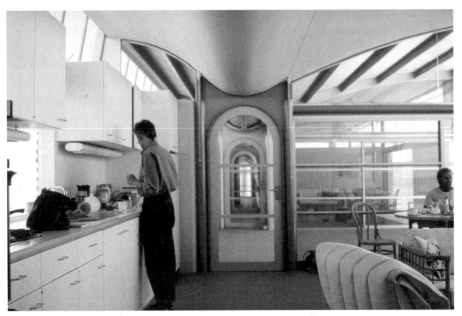

Empathetic imagination: water, light, and life, aligned. Bingie, Australia. (Glenn Murcutt)

before they built the house. Murcutt designed a building like a spacious, sunny tent, with two bedrooms and a verandah facing the water, with windows, doors, and vents that can be opened or closed, and with kitchen, bathroom, and corridor along the back. The roofline echoes the silhouette of a gull in flight, wings spread; the gutter is in the middle of the inward-sloping roof, instead of at the edge, and two downspouts are columns at either end. The shape of the ceiling inside the house and the corridor along which people move reflect the path along which the water flows. Rain drums on the roof, streams into the gutter, swirls down the cylindrical downspouts, visible through glass doors at either end of the hall, and falls into an underground tank—the only water supply for the house. Water is linked to its source in rain and sky and to a reservoir in the ground, necessary dialogues made poetic, everyday experience made aesthetic. Elegant spareness, a hallmark of Murcutt's work, expresses his environmental ethics.

Murcutt's skill in the language of landscape brings his clients in deliberate dialogue with processes that sustain their lives, and that are often taken for granted. People adjust windows and walls to admit, intensify, or block light and air flow, as one adjusts sails on a boat to catch or avoid the wind, and, in the process, they *learn*. For those who live in such houses, light changing, wind blowing, rain falling, and reservoir filling become visible, audible, and tangible. Imagine an entire neighborhood or town—buildings, streets, sewers, parks—as at Ball and Bingie, that engage residents in dialogues with natural processes.

Living in such places, one learns to read and tell landscape, to understand connections among seemingly unrelated phenomena, to phrase an appropriate response. Such dwelling invokes a sense of empathy, prompts reflection on the continuity of human lives with other living things and with the places we all inhabit. Empathy, the imaginative projection of one's own consciousness into another being, especially the sympathetic understanding of other than human beings—is surely one of the most important human abilities.[33] Fluency and literacy in landscape are aids not only to survival, but also to the empathetic imagination.

3
Artful Telling, Deep Reading:
The Literature of Landscape

The Poetry of Worship, Conquest, and Defense: Mont-Saint-Michel

Even before the silhouette of the Mount appears in the distance across the coastal plains of Normandy, the traveler anticipates the mythic isle shrouded in mist, shining in sun, surrounded by sea, by vast tidal flats. The real matches the image. The abbey's spire, wrapped by ramparts, looks like (and is) both cathedral and fort; it is dedicated to St. Michael, captain-general of the hosts of heaven, protector of the church militant. When "there was war in heaven" St. Michael took up the sword and cast Satan out.[1]

In the *Chanson de Roland,* at the climax of Roland's death, the Mount appears as "Saint Michael in Peril from the Sea." The Mount rises off the northern coast of France in a bay leading to the English Channel. The four main piers of the abbey were built in 1058, eight years before William of Normandy launched the Norman conquest of England. During the Hundred Years War when English armies occupied Normandy, the Mount remained French. The Bayeux Tapestry (ca. 1095) shows Harold of England pulling soldiers out of quicksand near the Mount.[2]

The bay has the strongest tides in Europe, with a swing between low and high tides of up to forty-five feet, and many unwary pilgrims (and numerous tourists) crossing at low tide on the nine miles of exposed sands have been sucked down or trapped and drowned on the sand flats by a rushing high tide. When the tide runs up narrow channels, it produces a bore, a wave up to three feet high. For pilgrims, the trip across the bay was once a risky allegorical journey, tides, currents, and sands like the menace of Satan, yet undertaken with the protection of the Archangel Michael. Once an island out in the middle of the bay, a mile from shore, accessible only by boat at high tide, by foot, horse, or carriage at low tide, the bay around the Mount has silted in and, since 1856, has been deliberately filled. A causeway was constructed in 1879; it is an island no more.[3] The modern pilgrim risks neither life nor limb to reach it.

From mean sea level to the original peak, which lies under the center where nave and transept cross between the original piers, the Mount rises 240 feet. The church, large western terrace, cloister garden, and refectory all perch on a huge platform in the sky, supported by crypts and other buildings rising from lower slopes in a sheer wall pierced by narrow windows. The Mount is hierarchical: secular town at the bottom, church and monastery at the top; vernacular buildings in the town, classic structures in the abbey and its church. The church is visible from miles away; close-up, from below, one first sees only the town and its street after entering the outer gate—the only breach in the ramparts—into a fortified courtyard, then under a portcullis through the King's Gate. Just beyond, the abbot's soldiers lived on the Grande-Rue, the only real street of the town. Narrow, lined with restaurants and shops catering to pilgrims and tourists for hundreds of years, the street ramps steeply up, curving around the hillside to several steep flights of steps, through a gate into the abbey's domain and up another long flight. At the top is a large terrace, facing west over bay and mainland. At low tide, the rivers' and bay's channels can be seen etched in sand, a huge brown sandpainting of braided, branching, meandering channels with pools of water trapped here and there, reflecting sky and clouds.

Inside the abbey is an interior landscape of darkened stairs and corridors, faintly lit by slitted windows, leading to room after room, one, a forest of great round pillars, its trunks lit softly on one side, in deep shadow on the other. Seen through the forest is a large, luminous room, its stone floor and walls awash in a blue-green light as if under the sea. Here and there, narrow rays of sunlight shine through the pale glass, moving patterns on the window's deeply recessed stone reveal. In all these rooms, the blue-green panes are translucent not transparent, telling a story of those who chose an inward focus over the panoramic view of the world beyond the walls.

Landscape Stories

When the stone marker inscribed with the words Taliesin West was set up near the entrance to his home in Arizona, Frank Lloyd Wright pointed to the name Taliesin molded into the wall of the parking area opposite: "That's the book," he said; then to the new marker, "And that's the chapter."[4] As with Taliesin North, in Wisconsin, he saw his homes as texts with the same plot. Taliesin North, rooted in the first half of Wright's career, was built as "a garden and a farm behind a workshop and a home," and Taliesin West was a new chapter in his work, both of them built versions of his utopian texts, *Disappearing City* and *The Living City*, his ideas of a world made better by design.[5] The Taliesins, as villas, belong to a landscape literature thousands of years old, rooted in the contrast between city and country, integrating the genres of home, production, and power.[6]

In landscape, each rock, each river, each tree has its individual history. A river's history, a tree's, is the sum of all its dialogues, nothing less but nothing more; they contain no emotion, no moral. Human cultures embellish these stories in gardens, buildings, and towns. Stories humans tell have a plot, often with beginning, middle, and end, a deliberate narrative: stories of survival, identity, power, success, and failure. Like myths and laws, landscape narratives organize reality, justify actions, instruct, persuade, even compel people to perform in certain ways. Landscapes are literature in the broadest sense, texts that can be read on many levels.

Landscape stories have common themes across cultures: struggle for survival; the character of human society (the relations of individuals to family, deities, state, or corporation); the nature of nature and the place of humans within it; where things came from, and how specific places came to be (stories of origins and creation—of mountains and rivers, of flowers and humans). How you read a scene, the patterns you see there and the context you see them in, influences the story you will tell. The opposite is also true. The story you want to tell influences how and what you read. Some narrators see the world as getting better, others as getting worse. William Cronon describes how two historians, Paul Bonnifield and Donald Worster, read the same scene, the Dust Bowl, in quite different ways, a reminder that story is at the heart of *history*.[7] To Bonnifield the Dust Bowl is a story of human triumph in the face of natural disaster; he concluded that the landscape of the Great Plains was ultimately improved as a result of the Dust Bowl. Worster saw the Dust Bowl as a story of human failure to adapt to nature and concluded that the landscape was getting worse. Stories have consequences. If cities are seen as treasures of civilization, they will be made treasures through cultivation. If cities are seen as degraded, they will be made so through neglect.

Bonnifield and Worster told their stories through words; landscape authors tell similar stories by shaping landscape directly: siting the paths along which others experience landscape, choosing what people will see (and what they will not see), and in what order, framing the view. Telling a story by designing a path and the elements along it is a common narrative technique, particularly in religious and political landscapes in which path represents "the way." Kongenshus Memorial Park, in Denmark, was deliberately, artfully composed as landscape literature. The Danish heath was shaped without conscious intent of self-expression, but its story can, and has been, read as literature. The Mississippi River and Yosemite Valley did not compose themselves as literature but become literature when we read our own stories into them. Vernacular landscapes may acquire the status of folklore, as they are retold, reproduced, and adapted over time. Extraordinary places crafted to express ideas and evoke feeling, ordinary places of everyday activities, all are connected to each other. Landscape literature is the product of life not a mere representation of it.

Folklore, Myth, Tragedy, Comedy, Epic, Poetry

Landscape literature, like all literatures, has multiple modes: prosaic homilies, folklore, myths, drama—tragic and comic, satires, parodies, epics, oratory, and poetry. Mont-Saint-Michel is mythic and poetic, part classical (gates, cathedral, cloister), part folk (the hodgepodge of shops and houses lining the single, rising street). Vernacular landscapes, such as memorials to persons killed in automobile accidents along the side of a highway, are expressed in everyday language, usually in the dialect or common mode of expression of a particular place. Built usually by amateurs who work unself-consciously with local materials and in a folk tradition, they tend to reflect their ethnic origins and religious traditions. Classical landscapes, which employ more formal language drawn from precedents or models from the past, are more likely to be designed by trained artists or professionals. The Vietnam Veterans Memorial is such a work, an elegy, a lamentation for the dead. It begins in a descent, arousing feelings of mourning, then, as one moves up to ground level again, it ends in a mood of calm and consolation.[8] Going down instead of up, using black stone instead of white, it goes against convention for monuments in Washington, D.C.

Memorials to the famous (Pantheon, Lincoln Memorial) or to horrific events (Dachau, Mont Valérien outside Paris and Ryvangen in Copenhagen where members of the French and Danish Resistance, respectively, were executed during the Second World War), and monuments of wars and battles (Verdun, Gettysburg) may also be forms of elegy. They are often composed with deliberate allusions to other literary works, written or built: Stowe, in England, with its sculptural monuments to "Ancient Virtue" and the "British Worthies," set within a pastoral landscape of lawn and groves, is a self-conscious landscape version of classical elegy.

Kongenshus Memorial Park and the St. Louis Arch (its official title, the Thomas Jefferson Memorial to Westward Expansion) are epics, landscapes designed to tell heroic tales about deeds and events of great cultural significance. Other landscapes are full of lighthearted comedy, like the jokes and tricks in Italian gardens—fountains that spray unexpectedly. The garden of stones at Ryoanji is poetry, its language condensed and figurative: metaphor—rocks as mountains, gravel raked in wavy lines as sea, the whole as Japan; paradox—dry stones as water. The rocks are placed with rhythmic precision, and though the garden is small, not all the elements can be seen at once. One has to read and reread.

To the architect Steen Eiler Rasmussen a garden is a slow play, an art of time, space, and story.[9] Landscape's evolving play is never finished; to design landscape is to come on stage during a performance already long under way and to engage and extend ongoing dialogues. Landscape is a play with many actors—flowers, people, trees, rocks—who come and go across the stage, some staying a day, a week, a season, others remaining for eighty or two hundred or a thousand years. Beatrix Ferrand designed the garden for Abby Rockefeller's summer home on Mount Desert Island in Maine so the actors—the flowers—would bloom in June when the owners were in residence. Landscape can also be the stage, with living figures acting a role. Marie Antoinette and her guests dressed up as shepherdess and shepherds to play at the Hameau, an ornamental farm at Versailles. Eighteenth-century English landowners created pastoral landscapes linked to classical tradition with replicas of classical buildings, incorporating whole villages, and they sometimes employed "hermits" and shepherds to inhabit the gardens. At Williamsburg in Virginia, Sturbridge Village in Massachusetts, and many other reconstructed places, people in period costume act and cook and shoe horses. "Hosts" at Disney's Magic Kingdom dress as Mickey Mouse, Donald Duck, Goofy, and at EPCOT's World Showcase, Germans, Norwegians, Mexicans, Japanese, and Frenchmen wear native costume to wait on customers in themed restaurants and shops. The inhabitants of France's Regional Cultural Parks act themselves for tourists by practicing their traditional lives and crafts. "All the world's a stage / And all the men and women merely players."[10]

Author's Voice: Provocative, Dignified, Disguised

Twenty buried automobiles push up out of the asphalt in the parking lot of Hamden Plaza, a shopping mall in Connecticut, some almost fully emerged, others only a bulge in the pavement the shape of a car roof. Plenty of spaces remain for customers' cars, some of them right next to cars covered with asphalt. It is Ghost Parking Lot (1978), a project by SITE (Sculpture in the Environment), an environmental design firm based in New York City. The work of SITE's designers makes one laugh first, then think, for their humor often depends on an inversion, in this case, of asphalt and cars, whimsical yet black, extending beyond a one-line joke to gentle social critique. In the ghost lot they bury the automobile, producing an artwork that, in contrast to more conventional public sculpture plopped down on a location, cannot be separated from its site. SITE is perhaps most famous, or infamous, for a series of shopping mall showrooms for the Best Company that poke fun at contemporary architectural theory. The facade peels off one building in Richmond, Virginia, and tilts (seemingly) precariously off a second in Towson, Maryland, while forest invades a third, also in Richmond. The authors' voice that imbues SITE's landscapes is simultaneously hilarious and dead serious. As James Wines, SITE's creative director, says of humor, "It's the last plateau between oneself and the apocalypse. One cannot possibly accept the serious world as being truly serious."[11]

Bryant Park, behind the New York Public Library on East 42nd Street, has a new authors' voice, heard in the recent revision of the park (1980s) that had been rebuilt once before (1935) in a Beaux Arts style in tune with the massive neoclassical library building (on the site of the city's old waterworks). The park has now been opened up to surrounding streets and sidewalks: iron fences removed, openings cut in stone balustrades, ramps and steps installed to provide access in and out, shrubs and trees removed and other trees planted.[12] Because the comprehensive rebuilding matches the tone of the building and the former park so well, many will mistake the new park for part of the original composition. Others may believe the same of the promenade along the Hudson River in Battery Park, also in Manhattan; the stone pavement, solid metal rail, and traditional lampposts and benches recall the best of the city's older public places. The voice of the landscape authors Robert Hanna and Laurie Olin, who designed Bryant Park and the Battery Park Promenade, is serious, dignified, elegant, formal, polite, like their urbane

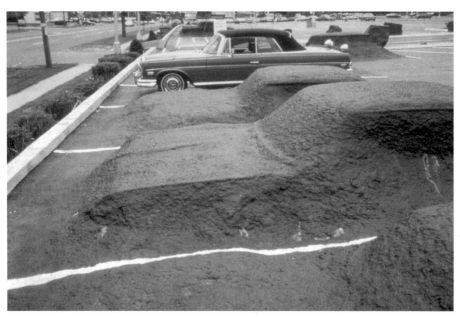

Provocative and irreverent: Ghost Parking Lot. Hamden, Connecticut (SITE)

public and their corporate clients. Literate in classical landscape literature, their works allude principally to English, French, Italian, and nineteenth-century American gardens and urban places. Their voice is distinctive, though subtle, their landscapes well crafted, with painstaking attention to details of material and form. They have been attacked by professional peers for not being more provocative at Battery Park City, for example, but their intention was "to produce an environment so quintessentially 'New York' that it would unconsciously become part of people's lives . . . that would not call attention to itself, but rather direct one's consideration elsewhere."[13]

Aldo Leopold struggled for twelve years (1935–48) to restore soil fertility and native plants and wildlife to an old farm along the Wisconsin River not far from the one where John Muir grew up a century before. Twenty years after Leopold died helping neighbors fight a grass fire, at least half of the 16,000 pines he and his family planted were thriving; more than sixty years after they began, the sandy, once depleted soil of a worked-out farm sustains prairie grasses, stands of pine, oak, and hickory.[14] Leopold's daughter Nina recalls how they "gathered seeds of native grasses, planted them among the old corn stubble, planted native hardwoods and forest wildflowers and shrubs, carried pails of water. We learned how to nurture, how to care."[15] There is little sign of design on the Leopold Memorial Reserve; plants seem to sow their own seed, blown on the wind, carried by birds, and so they do, helped then and now by the Leopold family, a nursery of native

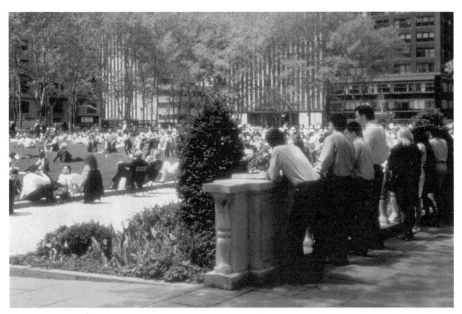

Urbane and polite: Bryant Park. New York City. (Hanna/Olin)

prairie plants the only overt clue to their role. The voice of its human authors is modest and disguised; the voice of its nonhuman authors is prominent. The reserve and also Leopold's book, *Sand County Almanac,* are classics of environmental literature; in the book, he describes the place and reflects on the ethical issues the process of its transformation prompted. The shack he built, in which he wrote the book, has become an icon, a place of pilgrimage for environmentalists. How ironic it is that the shack, the simple human shelter, is taken as the symbol and not the landscape itself, the focus of his efforts: the soil, water, plants, and animals.

This is an old paradox: the works of those human landscape authors who are most deferential to nonhuman landscape authors are often not appreciated at all as the literary constructions they are. Frederick Law Olmsted (1822–1903) left a legacy of wonderful places, from New York's Central Park to Boston's Emerald Necklace, from Niagara Falls to Yosemite, but few recognize these now as built landscapes.[16] Many people are startled to learn that Central Park was constructed, that even the Ramble is an "artful wilderness," and that Boston's Fens and Riverway were molded out of polluted mudflats and carefully planted to grow into tidal marsh and floodplain forest. Even those who do recognize Central Park and the Fens as constructions are surprised at how extensively the experiences of Niagara Falls and Yosemite are also shaped by design, for both have come to stand, incorrectly, as monuments of nature untouched by human artifice. Olmsted's contemporaries certainly recognized that landscapes like Central Park and the Fens were

Deferential and disguised: Leopold Memorial Reserve. Sand County, Wisconsin.

designed and built—after all, they were familiar with what those sites had looked like before and also, with the lengthy and ambitious process of transformation. However, this realization soon faded with time. Olmsted was so skilled at concealing his artifice that the projects he so brilliantly constructed as well as the profession he had worked so hard to establish—landscape architecture—became largely invisible. Today the works of the profession of landscape architecture are often not seen, even by contemporaries, not understood as having been designed and deliberately constructed, even when the landscape has been radically reshaped. Thus, many landmarks of landscape architecture are assumed to be either works of nature or felicitous, serendipitous products of culture. Their very success prevents appreciation of their triumphs as artful answers to knotty problems of conflicting environmental values or competing purposes.

LANDSCAPE GENRES

Landscape genres correspond to archetypal activities like movement, play, or worship that share patterns of function and form from culture to culture yet are adapted to a certain people, a certain place, a certain period.[17] Genres relate and often combine; so, Mont-Saint-Michel was (and to varying degrees still is) a locus of worship, conflict, defense, commerce, and community. Ancient trade routes were landscapes of movement and meeting, boulevards and main streets still are.

Danish farms were built as units of home and production, house and barn enclosing an interior courtyard. Villas, from ancient Rome and Renaissance Veneto to eighteenth-century England and nineteenth-century America, were landscapes of home, production, power, and play. In cities of Western Europe, home, movement, commerce, production, power, and play often occupy the same space, an integration of landscape genres. In North American metropolitan regions of the twentieth century, home and production tend to be in separate domains.

Wilderness—now enshrined in national parks and world biosphere reserves—is sacred ground to many, as it was to Muir, who invited Ralph Waldo Emerson to join him "in a month's worship with Nature in the high temples of the great Sierra Crown beyond our holy Yosemite."[18] But what is sacred to some is a place to play for others or even a place of production. Multiple genres often appear in one landscape, and there is tension when they conflict. To Gifford Pinchot, Yosemite's water and timber were resources to conserve and use; to his contemporary Muir, grazing the meadows and cutting the trees was sacrilege, a plunder of paradise. And millions of people come yearly to play in Yosemite.[19] Design can reconcile conflict, as Olmsted's did. He could speak of the sacred qualities of Yosemite, the "reverent mood" it evoked, yet condone cutting and planting trees and shaping the scene, envisioning future groves and glades still sublime.

Landscapes of Worship

The forest at Ise, ancestral shrine of the Japanese emperor and Shinto gods, is ancient, dark, and dense. Most of the broad, towering cypress and cryptomeria trees are hundreds, some more than a thousand years old. The trunks of the largest trees soar upward, veiled by layered foliage of smaller trees, saplings, seedlings. The trees germinate, grow, reproduce, and die, yet the forest endures. By ritual the huge forest of ordinary trees is transmuted into a sacred precinct, set off from the profane world by distinctive boundaries; only priests and those engaged in ritual may leave the path and walk within it. Uncut for thirteen hundred years, except for a few trees felled to construct the shrines, the forest embodies both the enduring and the ephemeral.

Naiku, the Inner Shrine of Ise, is a building complex within a sacred precinct in the forest atop a huge platform of stone and earth. The principal shrines, and also the bridges and gates within the huge forest domain, are taken down and rebuilt deliberately every twenty years; these artifacts, like the individual trees of the forest, do not endure, though the ritual of rebuilding has continued for more than a millennium.[20]

At Ise the crowds are subdued. Before I reached Naiku itself, I had entered a special domain, passed through torii (gates) and crossed a bridge over the river into the forest reserve. I had cleansed my mouth and hands in the river, then walked some distance through the forest on a broad, ceremonial path.

Here and there, huge trees rise from the path, their trunks embraced by protective armor of bamboo slats to prevent people from peeling off bits of bark as mementos of this sacred place. The branches of these trees, isolated from the forest by the gravel path at their base, join the canopy far above the ground. I approach Naiku obliquely. A wall of massive boulders, covered in lichens and moss, looms behind the trees—the foundation for the monumental platform. I walk up the worn stone steps and beneath the first gate through the outermost fence and encounter another gate, its opening covered by a white silk cloth through which only ghostly outlines of the buildings within are visible. Beyond the fence are two other wooden fences, each different, each delimiting a progressively more sacred precinct. I watch as people approach the white silk screen, throw coins into a broad box, bow deeply two times, clap twice, bow again, and back away. For the millions of pilgrims who journey to Ise each year, this is their destination. They may go no further.

But I did. As I wait to be led, by special permission, into the precinct beyond the second fence, I hear the background murmur of people talking softly, punctuated by the clink, pause, clap clap of each person's praying, like phrases overlaid but distinct, the interval between clink and clap marking the depth of each bow (and, thus, reverence). And encompassing it all is the roaring buzz of cicadas.

I follow the priest down the narrow alley between the two outer fences, walking on rough, grey river cobbles that clatter underfoot. The priest's large, black wooden shoes amplify the sound, emphasizing passage across the rocks, up the wooden steps of the gate and down again into a large, open area: clatter clatter, clomp clomp, clatter clatter. We cross the clearing, pass under three trees, step onto a broad path of white rocks, and stop. We face a torii, and through that a fence and gate, and beyond that another fence and gate—the two innermost precincts we would not penetrate. The noise of our walking underscores the stillness of our immobility. Now, no sound of people, only the cicadas.

Within three years all of these artifacts will vanish, to be replaced by new construction on the adjoining vacant plot. Twenty years later this site will be reoccupied in turn. Ise is a celebration of cultural continuity; ritual reconstruction of the shrines has endured for more than a thousand years. The bridge of raw wood at the entrance to Naiku's domain, recently reconstructed, presages the coming reconstruction and destruction of Naiku. I feel both the presence of these constructions and their absence. We bow twice, clap twice, bow again, and return.

Ise is also a political landscape, for the authority of the Japanese emperor is vested in his divine descent from Amaterasu, the sun goddess; Ise is her shrine, and only the emperor may enter the innermost precinct. But Ise also speaks to fundamental conditions of human existence within nature and community, the forest and its long-lived trees a contrast to the transience of a human life.

Sacred landscapes are shaped by ritual, usually progressing from secular to sacred: a series of nested enclosures at the Japanese shrine in Ise, the innermost the most sacred; a climb from low to high at Mont-Saint-Michel, from shops selling

Landscape of worship. Ise shrine. Japan.

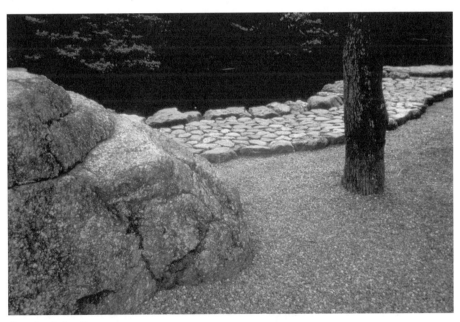

Carp. Ise shrine. Japan.

souvenirs below to the church at the top, from outside the town to inside the abbey. There are thresholds or gateways that mark progressive passage and, often, an inner domain that only initiates may enter, as at the sacred places of Australian Aborigines. The destination may require an arduous journey—a long pilgrimage, dangerous passage, or steep climb—a metaphor for the difficulty of reaching the desired goal, be it enlightenment, virtue, or strength. There is often a place of prayer or reflection.

In worship one transcends separate, individual consciousness and becomes a part of something beyond oneself. Movement, offering, reflection, transformation are part of religious rituals, prescribed and repetitive acts reenacting the creation of the world, inducing a sense of transport from the material world to a world of the spirit or an altered state of consciousness.[21]

The setting of worship at Gothic cathedrals like Chartres and Notre Dame of Paris contrasts with the settings of daily life: there are portals decorated with sculptures, stained-glass windows shining like jewels, soaring ceilings. The Ise shrines of Japan offer no such lavish display of precious metals or jewels or monumental structures, but are rather modest buildings of human scale, built from plain, unadorned, weathered wood, decorated with white rice paper and small branches from a particular tree, the *sakaki* (meaning, literally, plant-god).[22] The ground of the shrine's most sacred precincts is covered with white river cobbles, elevated from the ordinary to the extraordinary by the uniformity of their color and size. The gods honored at Ise are gods of everyday phenomena: the sun, the harvest, the wind. The most extraordinary places in Japan are often a simple, subtle transformation of the everyday.

Light is used significantly in most sacred landscapes, for emphasis or, figuratively, for divinity, enlightenment, or spirit. Light filters dimly through densely layered leaves of the forest at Ise, shines brightly in the clearings around important shrines. The cathedral of Notre Dame in Paris is like a sacred grove, its aisles dark, enclosed, arches forming a low canopy, but the brighter nave is lined with columns like tall trees; the cross's center, where nave, apse, and transepts meet, is brightest, like a forest clearing. Afternoon sun shines through a Rose Window— red, magenta, blue glass brilliant like backlit leaves at a clearing's edge seen against black, branching tracery. The light cast on the stone floor, filtered through all those colors, seems as green as forest light. At Mariebjerg Cemetery, north of Copenhagen, two parallel, long dark avenues, lined by four rows of elms, culminate, like a church's nave, in a bright clearing formed by a circle of trees.

Sacred landscapes are revered for qualities associated with the divine, found (as in mountaintops, springs, and forest clearings) or built (as in Mariebjerg and Notre Dame). Some remain sacred to successive cultures: springs and hilltops in England were used by Druids, later by Christians. Ordinary landscapes can become sacred for what happened there—real or mythic—as the farm fields and woods at Gettysburg had for Lincoln: "We cannot dedicate, we cannot consecrate, we cannot hallow this ground. The great men, living and dead, who struggled here, have consecrated it far above our poor power to add or detract." Many people are compelled to make a *place* in which to remember a death or traumatic event. Memorials and cemeteries become sacred ground.

Landscapes of Memory

Verdun is a sacred landscape to many French. Thousands of soldiers lost their lives in the siege of that city during the First World War. The sole lifeline by which Verdun was supplied—the Sacred Way, or Voie Sacrée—is lined with mileposts decorated with stars and laurel branch and topped with a soldier's helmet along its entire fifty-eight-kilometer length. Battles had raged across cropland, pasture, homes, and villages; whole villages outside Verdun were destroyed, pummeled into muddy, metaled craters by tons of mortar, their fertile soil rendered untillable. "Mort pour la France" reads a memorial stone to the town of Fleury, set up on its former site. Villages and forts are now overgrown within a great forest preserve and military reservation, but beneath the trees the ground is still hummocky, cratered. The streets of Fleury are laid out where they once were, marked by street signs in German, French, and English, sites of shops and homes identified by their former use (bakery) or by the owners' occupation (street worker). The only building is a tiny chapel, Our Lady of Europe. Up the road from Fleury is the huge cemetery for soldiers killed in the Battle of Verdun: 15,000 graves in rows of identical white stone crosses set in green grass, a red rose planted at the base of each—Frenchmen all. Above the long, sloping lawn stands a monumental stone ossiary, shaped like an upright missile, or a phallus, tomb for the remains of 130,000 unknown soldiers.

On Mont Valérien, a hill outside Paris, long straight rows of white marble crosses set in clipped green grass march under trees and up, down, and along the slopes at the cemetery for American soldiers who died in the First World War. Except for those who came from the same family (who may be buried next to one another), the dead are buried at random, without regard to rank or date of death. Crosses have name, rank, batallion, division, date of death, and the state each was from; the only variation, here and there, are posts with a Star of David. Further up Mont Valérien, on the Rue Calvare (Calvary), is a wall against which the Nazis executed 4,500 prisoners during the German Occupation in the Second World War. Were the Nazis aware that this had been a sacred site for hundreds of years, a place where pilgrims once climbed the hill on their knees?[23] The old wall, part of the fortifications of the Mount (the military still occupies the hilltop fort), pitted with bullet holes, is now the National French Resistance Memorial. The memorial, set against the wall-hill, is flanked by stepped terraces of asphalt and stone and faced by a large open plaza. It is a place made for a throng to come together, not for the solitary visitor.

A First World War cemetery at Redipuglia existed before Mussolini, in 1938, built the largest Italian war memorial to remember that war in a very different way; he had the bodies in the first cemetery disinterred and moved across the road to the new monument. The former one was on the Hill of St. Elia, where the graves in concentric circles around the hill bore simple markers with lines of poetry and the rows were marked by relics representing the roles of the dead as soldiers: infantry with weapons and helmets, signal corps with radio, and so on. At Mussolini's monument, the soldiers are buried in alphabetical order, in tombs set into gigantic terraces. IN GLORIA PATRIA say huge words cut into the stone. Crowds are visiting when I am there, small children with parents and grandparents. This is a landscape of instruction.

What comfort can the individual who grieves the loss of a friend or relative find in these places? In the American cemetery at Mont Valérien the loved one is one of a vast army of dead, the place, the marker undifferentiated; at the Resistance memorial, at Redipuglia, one is reminded that the cause—defense against an oppressive force, or for national honor and glory—was considered greater than the individual, and that one should salute the cause and not mourn the loss.

The Vietnam Veterans Memorial in Washington, D.C., in contrast, is about loss and grieving; it honors the memory of the soldiers not the war itself. The sponsors wanted the memorial to be "conciliatory," "reflective and contemplative in character," and stipulated that it must make no political statement about a war still a source of national rift. Although it is on the Mall, it was built with private, not public, funds. By March 31, 1981, the deadline, 1,421 entries were received, making this the largest design competition ever held in America or Europe. Maya Lin, then a student at Yale, won the competition with a design submitted as an assignment in a class on funerary architecture: two two-hundred-foot-long retaining walls of polished black granite. The walls form a right-angled V set into the ground facing a grassy slope. At the point of convergence, the walls are ten feet high, at their tips, flush with the ground. On each wall are seventy panels inscribed with the names of the more than fifty-seven thousand Americans killed in Vietnam and of the several thousands still missing.

The Vietnam Veterans Memorial is now the most-visited site in a city of memorials and monuments. Many who come are moved to tears, many touch or kiss a name or take a rubbing of it; many leave flowers, messages for the dead and missing named on the wall. Mementos are taped to the wall or laid at its base; photographs, boots, medals, letters from kids who never knew their dad. They personalize memory and promote empathy, as did the original cemetery at Redipuglia; Mussolini's monumental memorial made the dead a faceless mass. Psychotherapists who specialize in the treatment of Vietnam veterans have brought therapy groups to the memorial. Yet at the time of its construction, critics called the design "a shameful degrading ditch, a black gash of sorrow," and a group of congressmen sent a letter of protest to President Ronald Reagan: "The Black Hole of Calcutta needs no re-creation on the Washington Mall . . . this

Hill of Remembrance. Forest Cemetery. Stockholm.

design makes a political statement of shame and dishonor." They demanded that "the color be changed to white, the wall be raised above the ground, and the scheme include an American flag." In 1982, the sponsors agreed to erect a flagpole near the memorial and commissioned the sculptor Frederick Hart to design an eight-foot-high bronze sculpture, *Three Fighting Men*. People pause by that statue for a photograph, but it is the wall that draws and holds them.

The crosses, row on row, and destroyed towns around Verdun still evoke feeling. Will the Vietnam Veterans Memorial do so once the friends and families who experienced loss are themselves dead? When the names erode, what will the memorial mean in one hundred years, or five hundred? The war in Vietnam divided the American nation; like the Civil War it prompted violence within, set brother against brother, father against son. It was a national trauma with far-reaching consequences for American society, when many Americans felt betrayed by their government, lost faith in and gained a cynical distrust of those who professed to lead them. Will the sense of pathos evoked by the memorial endure?

In Stockholm's Forest Cemetery, another starkly simple landscape that focuses and amplifies emotion, the Hill of Remembrance was designed "to give form to a sorrow that cannot be told."[24] As I walk through the passage into the cemetery, enclosed between two stone retaining walls that start high overhead and end much lower, creating an effect of distance through "forced perspective," I see it in the distance: a rounded, grassy hill, rising out of undulating land, with a grove of

Enfolded ascent. Hill of Remembrance. Forest Cemetery. Stockholm.

elms at the top—the trees catch the wind and move—and under the trees, a low wall. To reach the top, I climb a path up stairs set within grassy berms, enfolded by the hill. The steps rise, then gradually level out, carrying me through an opening in the low stone wall. I come to rest in a little clearing under the trees, within the precinct of the walls. There is a progressive sense of threshold, gateway, refuge. The trees are small, a species selected for their dwarfed habit to make the hill seem bigger.[25] Enclosed by the low wall of stone, the hilltop provides a prospect over meadow, graves, a large cross, a chapel and crematorium, the city. The Hill of Remembrance is a classic place of reflection, where a sense of overview and refuge engenders a special kind of remembering in which past and present are compared and integrated.

Later, I sit on the bench just inside the cemetery entrance on an overcast summer evening. A man cycles by. A woman leaves. A huge hare lopes across the grass. The birds are in full song—many different songs. Then, black smoke rises from the crematorium chimney for a few, brief moments, and is gone, dissipating, floating off into the sky. A bird flies in and perches on the top of the cross. And then, at last, the light comes; a low, golden light bringing the landscape alive.

Landscapes affirm or negate the memory of a personal past, record a collective, cultural past, even a past beyond individual experience or human memory. They transmit memories from one generation to another, as adults teach children at Verdun, Redipuglia, and Washington, D.C., a prompting to remember a person or event in a particular way. "To know what we were confirms what we are," David

Lowenthal says in *The Past Is a Foreign Country.*[26] Memory is central to identity. When American cities like Boston and Dallas razed entire districts as part of urban renewal programs, substituting new office buildings, cultural enclaves, governmental and convention centers, they erased parts of their identity. Forgetting the past can be foolish, and attempts to reinvent it may even be dangerous: in Berlin, traces of the wall are being rapidly and systematically expunged, denying and forfeiting an opportunity to come to terms with a tragic past.

Landscapes of Play

Johan Huizinga calls humans *Homo ludens*, describing places of play as "temporary worlds within the ordinary world, dedicated to the performance of an act apart."[27] Sports fields are places apart, for recreation (from the Latin word for "restore" or "refresh") and entertainment (from the French word for "hold"): players engage in action, and are restored; spectators are entertained, held in thrall, but are passive bystanders who may neither participate, except by cheers or catcalls, nor invade the field. Many games, such as basketball, soccer, baseball, and tennis, require movement within a fixed frame of rules and landscape geometry; golf is a marked-off ground. Places designed for play alone have multiplied in the twentieth century, from the first urban playgrounds at the turn of the century to the sports fields and large recreation areas of midcentury, to the elaborate end-of-the-century theme parks like Disney World and Sea World. A broader spectrum of society than ever before has sought out seaside resorts and ski lodges, and new towns of second homes are booming.

Down the street from our house in Belmont, Massachusetts, when my son was two to five years old, was a playground with a small sandbox, swings, a stage coach of metal pipes painted red, yellow, and blue, ducks that bounced on metal springs, two concrete benches, and an open lawn. The assumption was that adults would stand and watch, not play. Parents tried to sit on the ducks or swings, and failed, then shifted uncomfortably on the hard, backless benches. No one stayed very long. Nor did any of the expensive play "equipment" hold children's attention for long; they ran from place to place, trying one thing then another; the sandbox was the exception. The playground made me angry, not just because it was so boring but because it demonstrated such ignorance of the importance of play. My own most vivid memories of play before the age of five are of climbing huge rocks in the woods and exploring a thicket of sumac. I don't remember playing in playgrounds except during school recess. At six, I hid under a huge rosebush so dense no one could see in and I built dams in a gutter in the street when it rained. I swung in a swing suspended on long ropes from a tree branch from the time I was six, through my teens. From seven to nine, the most magical places were vacant lots, construction sites, remnant woods, and storm sewers.

When I asked my graduate students in landscape architecture to design a playground, the designs they produced were unimaginative. They had forgotten what it was like to be a child, so I invited my son's day-care class of four-year-olds to visit as consultants. First they told the students what they liked to do best: "Dig for dinosaur bones!" "Trap wild animals!" We unrolled a long sheet of paper on the floor, and each child drew an ideal playground; one drew a "bottomless pit," another a "ladder to the sky." Digging or unearthing was central to many, the idea of discovery was in all. When it was time to leave, the four-year-olds lined up, and I led them out to the railing that looked out over three floors of open architectural studios, all under one roof, connected by a long series of stairs, filled with hundreds of students working at drawing tables.[28] The children looked down over the three floors below and realized instinctively the dramatic potential of the space: "Hello down there," yelled my son. Four hundred heads looked up from their desks to the small figures along the fourth-floor rail. The children waved, the students responded, waving and clapping, many climbed up on their drafting stools and stood there as the children paraded down four flights of open stairs and out the door. It was only the second time I had seen this space used theatrically in seven years. After the children left, my students were very quiet. "How did we lose that?" I could see them thinking. The results of such loss are everywhere.

Ever since that time, I have tried to help my students recapture their most vivid memories of childhood play. I have discovered that my own memories are not unique. Students remember exploring, hiding, and imagining; their special childhood places commonly include leftover bits of space between properties, on vacant land, often with some measure of danger, real or imagined, forts, hiding places, prospects or overviews. None mention playgrounds. Their remembered places were often destroyed by adults, and they report a sense of loss, and wonder why adults failed to appreciate what a special place it was. Kevin Lynch and Clare Cooper Marcus, who have studied children's play and adults' memories, have found many similar stories.[29] Lynch, writing in 1956, described one man's memory of Manhattan's Riverside Park along the Hudson River before and after it was "developed" with playgrounds: "I remember there being a lot more space to play in [before playgrounds were built]. [Afterwards] there simply wasn't enough space just to go and play in and do idiotic things in. You couldn't dig, for example."[30] Playgrounds, as Galen Cranz reminds us, are an artifact of the twentieth century.[31]

Tanner Fountain, just outside Harvard Yard in Cambridge, was not built as a playground yet it has become a place for play. Rocks form a field of circles, small jets in pavement emit steam in winter and intermittent, misty spray in summer, sparking rainbows. Many small children jump around the circles, from rock to rock, screech when water sprays, reach for rainbows. A fountain at Parc André Citroën in Paris is even more successful as a playground (whether or not it was meant to be one). Even when the water is not running, the fountain is still a place: a large, sloping plane of stone. When it is running, more than a hundred jets of water erupt from the pavement, transforming the space, their height changing at random intervals, their patterns unpredictable and seemingly never the same. One

Landscape of play: Parc Citroën. Paris.

moment all 120 jets are bubbling up a few inches above the surface, the next they are shooting twelve feet up then disappearing, rising again to one foot, or three, or six, or ten, then back down again. From the top of the slope to the bottom there are fifteen rows of spouts, each row eight spouts across; in each row, water spurts up to the same height, though height may vary from row to row. Sometimes the tops of the jets form a plane of water, level or tilted, high or low. When the jets are shooting high, over eight feet, the fountain is like a forest, the columns of water like trees; children dash up and down and across the spaces between them. Some people bring beach balls to balance on top of the spouting water. Children, singly and in groups, invent games, variations on water play, like playing in the shifting water's edge of a beach. When the water disappears, momentarily, a child sits on a nozzle, waiting for the water to blast up from below. On a hot Saturday afternoon in July, the place—like a beach itself—is filled with people: young, old, some playing in the water (in swimsuits, clothes, underwear, bare), others watching, some with children, some not.

Carl Theodore Sørensen watched children playing on construction sites with sand, bricks, and tree stumps, and proposed, in 1931, a new kind of playground—*skrammelejeplads*, or "junk playground"—of old cars, packing crates, and timber so children could build their own places.[32] He saw "nicely designed" play equipment and hopscotch lines painted on asphalt as evidence of adults' profound misunderstanding of children's play.[33] The first adventure playground, built in 1943 in

Landscape of play: West Philadelphia. (West Philadelphia Landscape Project)

Emdrup, just north of Copenhagen, was a flat, open area of dirt sunk below the level of the surrounding land and bounded by berms covered with dense, thorny shrubs; entry was through a small wooden building in one corner.[34] The whole created a frame for activity and for messy constructions. The dense boundary provided privacy and shielded the children's work from view. Photographs from the 1940s show an open space with piles of bricks, old boards, pipes, barrels, water, and other construction materials and children, in groups and alone, laying bricks and hammering nails, fixing a flagpole atop a shack. Photographs from the early 1960s depict neat rows of little houses. Adult play leaders had taken over as supervisors and regulators; Sørensen was very disappointed. Emdrup Adventure Playground, as it originally was, captured the imagination of many in other countries. Arvid Bengtsson was inspired to build adventure playgrounds in Sweden. Lady Allen of Hurtwood came from England to see it in 1945 just after the war was over: "Some caves are dug twelve feet down into the earth, look-out towers are built, and finally an artesian well to irrigate the cement channels which guide the water to the paddling pool built by the older children for their younger brothers and sisters."[35] From Denmark to Sweden and England, the idea spread farther to Switzerland, Israel, and the United States.

Sven-Ingvar Andersson regards adventure playgrounds as important for grown-ups as for children, a place to express themselves, to do something silly that does not count. Marnas, his own garden in Sweden, is a fantasy world, a personal playground of past projects and ongoing experiments: a man made of boards, a sculpture of branches, a pear growing in a brandy bottle.

Landscapes of Movement and Meeting

Lawrence Halprin calls freeways, with "their graceful, sinuous, patterns . . . like great free-flowing paintings," among the most beautiful and typical structures of the age. To him, they speak "in the language of a new scale," of the high-speed motion and the changes of everyday experience.[36] He considers freeways "a form of action calligraphy where the laws of motion generate a geometry which is part engineering, part painting, part sculpture, but mostly an exercise in choreography in the landscape."[37] In the early 1960s, he urged that freeways, so destructive to cities, be reconceived as works of art and as social opportunities; he invented choreographic techniques, called scoring, to understand and design motion and change in landscape, and applied them to designs for freeways and freeway parks, plazas, malls, gardens, and communities. At their best, his works are something to experience, not merely to look at, places where the whole is understood only through the process of movement, an overlapping of many viewpoints.

The destruction wreaked by highway building in many cities since the 1950s stems from the single-minded pursuit of efficient movement of cars and trucks. Two years after Halprin's book *Freeways* was published in 1966, the city of Seattle asked him to help them solve a problem: a freeway was a chasm between downtown and a nearby neighborhood, isolating two districts once closely related. Halprin proposed to bridge the freeway with an elevated park: "The trick," he explained, "is to perceive the old freeway as part of the city-scape and tame it, rather than complain about it."[38] Cars, trucks, and buses now whiz by on a highway through the heart of Seattle, then disappear beneath the hanging vines, trees, plazas, and gardens of Freeway Park, and reemerge moments later. From the park itself, the traffic is sometimes visible between branches of trees, but mostly it is hidden, the noise of its passing disguised by rushing water in the park's many waterfalls. Halprin's integration of the freeway into other aspects of urban life, such as walking, playing, and meeting, is part of a larger tradition of parkways and boulevards. Boston's Riverway, built in the 1890s, had walking and bridle paths, a stream for boating, a broad roadway for through traffic; it was a precursor to Freeway Park, as was New York's Bronx River Parkway, built in the 1920s. The Blue Ridge Parkway of Virginia and North Carolina celebrates the delights of movement; its designers, landscape architects, chose the route, shaped the scene, and directed the gaze. The Blue Ridge Parkway is a national park, a destination in itself, as Seattle's Freeway Park has become.

From trade routes to main streets to commercial strips, principal routes are not only thoroughfares but also places to meet and exchange goods and information. When Walt Disney made Main Street the primary route of Disneyland and a principal place of exchange, he was tapping a fundamental association. His Main

Street is the way in and out; behind its decorated facades are places to store belongings, to purchase film, cameras, and souvenirs, to learn about Disney.

The subways crisscrossing Japanese cities like Tokyo and Osaka are places of movement, meeting, and exchange. Subways stations are filled with people all day and late into the evening. In downtown Osaka and Tokyo, the principal subway stations are large, subterranean neighborhoods with restaurants and grocery stores, often connected to the interior of tall buildings by elevators that open out not only to offices, but also to stores and restaurant districts high in the sky. One hurtles along in a subway car, steps off and walks through subterranean corridors, then rises up in an elevator, each floor a different world.

I travel for half an hour through the subway to Osaka Center on a weekday evening, through a maze of corridors, filled with people traveling in groups. I board an elevator and ascend, reminded of a science fiction fantasy in which, by stepping through a portal, one is transported to a distant and exotic place. The elevator rises toward a restaurant district on floors 29 through 34; each floor is a neighborhood of restaurants of a similar cuisine from Oriental to Western. I step off on the thirty-fourth floor onto a street of small restaurants offering Japanese-style food, tempura, noodle shops, tearooms. Each has a different decor, its menu displayed as plastic models of food in cases along the corridor. It is my first day in Japan. As I go from point to point within the enclosed capsules of subway car and elevator, I become disoriented and long to go outside to get my bearings. Some days later, I would become accustomed to these interior worlds.

Landscapes of Production and Waste

Middleton Place, in South Carolina, the oldest landscape garden in the United States, was once a rice plantation, its ornamental ponds an integral part of a productive landscape, a system powered by water flow and slave labor. Gardens, house, and fields are oriented to the Ashley, a tidal river and the main route to Charleston, twenty miles downstream. The river was more easily traveled than the inland road, which was often impassable well into the early twentieth century. Tidewater rice cultivation, once prevalent in South Carolina and now defunct there, required an understanding of hydraulic engineering, for rice needs periodic flooding at specific times and cannot tolerate saltwater. Planters used slaves to carve out rice fields from tidewater swamps, to build dikes, ditches, and tidal gates along the river, and to clear and dam upland swamps for reservoirs, to dig canals leading to rice fields. Such extensive water systems buffered the fields at Middleton Place from effects of drought and flood. Upland reservoirs were a source of freshwater in drought and when coastal storms drove saltwater upriver; they protected fields from flooding by freshets—floods from inland. Tidal gates controlled drainage and permitted the river's upper layer of freshwater to enter at high water, blocking saltwater; dikes prevented flooding from the river. Water flow from a dammed millpond powered a mill that hulled the rice to be sent downriver to Charleston.[39]

Henry Middleton (1717–84) had laid out the garden in 1741 with a series of water canals and ponds on terraces that step down from high ground to rice fields and tidal river. The house on a bluff overlooks gardens, fields, and river, aligned on an axis with the river's course. Middleton plotted the gardens precisely within the structure of a 90 degree triangle. One side bisected the main house (now destroyed), principal terraces, and Butterfly Ponds, and points down the river; the other side still bisects a long reservoir that doubles as a reflection pool. It took one hundred slaves nearly ten years to build the gardens and pools.[40] In 1774, when Middleton was elected president of the Continental Congress, he was one of the largest landholders in Carolina, owning more than fifty thousand acres and about eight hundred slaves.[41] Sherman's army burned the main house in 1865 at the end of the Civil War; its shell was toppled by the earthquake of 1885. The gardens fell into ruin, overgrown and neglected until 1916, when their restoration began. Middleton is no longer a rice plantation, but grassy terraces still step down to the river, overlooking the ponds and sky mirrored in their surface, and the skeleton of the water system is still clear, a landscape shaped by power and production.

Like Middleton Place, the English patchwork landscape of small fields and hedgerows and of mill towns like Manchester is a landscape of production. Though the rural fields and industrial townscapes are different in form, they belong to the same landscape, linked by the process of growing sheep for wool and weaving cloth, a process no longer economically viable here. Fields and hedgerows, valued highly by the English for their scenic beauty and traditional associations, are still maintained despite their outmoded form; urban mills, not so valued, were left to ruin. Abandoned mills and factories, clear-cut forests, slag heaps, and derelict land have become wastelands, by-products of improvidence or outmoded production. Landscapes of production are shaped by demands of materials—rice and its cultivation, sheep grazing and shearing—and processes of their transformation into products—harvesting and milling, spinning and weaving—and they change with shifts in fashion, technology, capital, and labor.

Wastelands and wilderness, once synonymous, are now often seen as opposites. In contemporary North America, a wasteland generally refers to lands laid waste by humans: mined-out regions, clear-cut forests, garbage dumps, and abandoned factories and neighborhoods, no fit abode for man or beast. Wilderness, originally the space beyond the pale—the common boundary fence—a place where wild beasts roamed, a lawless region, a fearful place with no value to anyone but hermits and prophets, has been promoted to sacred place and city has been demoted to wasteland, revealing a belief that humans degrade what they touch, leading to failure to link landscapes of production, waste, and renewal. One kind of ignorance has replaced another, both examples of cultural blindness and environmental illiteracy.

The transformation of Boston's Fens and Riverway from urban wasteland into urban "wilderness" (in the modern sense of the terms) was the first attempt anywhere, so far as I know, to *construct* a wetland. It was built over nearly two decades, the 1880s and the 1890s, the Fens dredged out of the muddy flats of a former millpond, the Riverway shaped from floodplains fouled by sewage and industrial effluent. Both were designed to purify water and to protect adjacent land from flooding, to reclaim and reoccupy "lands laid waste by human improvidence or malice . . . [by becoming] a co-worker with nature in the reconstruction of the damaged fabric."[42] The marshes, meadows, and floodplain forests Olmsted conceived were built of materials both given and worked: earth, rock, water, and plants of the place; dredged mud, quarried stone, channeled water, and bred plants. His landscapes were constructed by human imagination and human labor, then by processes of nonhuman nature. His drawn plans and on-site adjustments guided the work of others—dredging, grading, planting, pruning, tending—to carry out his visions of how trees, shrubs, grasses, and flowers would grow, beget, and nurture other plants, live, and die, and how water, flowing through the channels he molded, would modify further the shorelines he shaped.

Everyone at the time was aware of the transformation of a filthy, stinking, muddy mess into the Fens and Riverway. Their awareness became part of the social meaning and aesthetic power of the Fens and Riverway. But today these works are widely, and falsely, assumed to be preserved bits of nature in the city, not the designed and built places they really are, daring experiments of engineering, ecology, landscape design, and city planning. The function and the appearance of the Fens and Riverway were also revolutionary; earlier, most urban parks were designed in formal or pastoral styles.[43] Olmsted introduced a "wild" landscape to bring the appearance of "natural scenery" of places like Yosemite to "those who cannot travel" to see them.[44]

Like the Fens, Werribee Farm in Melbourne, Australia, is a landscape of waste and renewal. Its canals, lagoons, marshes, and grasslands cover twenty-seven thousand acres and treat 60 percent of the sewage from a region of nearly three million people. Engineers and wildlife ecologists have designed lagoons for sewage treatment and wetland habitat. The farm is open to birdwatchers, who have sighted more than two hundred species: ground birds, arboreal birds, birds of prey, wetland and sea birds. Werribee Farm is also a landscape of production, one of the largest farms in southern Australia. Sewage irrigates and fertilizes pastures grazed by a herd of fifteen hundred cattle and a sheep flock of comparable size. The cattle and sheep are slaughtered and sold for meat, producing income that reduces the cost of sewage treatment. The landscape of Werribee Farm displays connections between wastes and resources, processes of production and renewal.

Landscapes of Home and Community

A garden was, in the biblical story, the first home. Garden is a potent and complex symbol; it embodies pleasure, fertility, sustenance, and renewal. Gardening is a life-embracing act, an act of faith and hope, an expression of commitment to the

Landscape of waste and renewal: Werribee Farm. Melbourne, Australia.

future; it can even be a political act. Community gardens are a place for planting, growing, and harvesting food, but they are also the locus for many other life processes: for sharing and trading, for meeting and play, for making and building, for dreaming and worship. They are the scene of both cooperation and conflict.

"This garden is a town, we have everything but a penal colony," says Hayward Ford, president of Aspen Farms, a community garden in Mill Creek, the inner-city neighborhood of West Philadelphia named after the forgotten creek buried beneath the surface. Aspen Farms looks like a miniature farm, but it is more like a town, with individual plots and common ground. The plots are laid out in a grid, divided by straight paths, much like Philadelphia's streets. Each plot is related to the community garden as a whole, just as each individual private property is to its surrounding neighborhood. Just as urban real estate changes hands, so owners of the gardens change, but the boundaries remain the same year to year. There are meeting places and shared resources, like the greenhouse, the compost pile, the water supply and irrigation system. Originally colonized in 1976 with parallel plots divided by small paths and one large, central path, the garden has continued to change, with individual initiatives, negotiations, and group decisions. The gardeners set the rules and elect officers, including a chaplain.

Aspen Farms' gardeners range in age from 12 years old to 103; most are over 60, all are African American. One or more of the fifty gardeners seem always to be there, digging, planting, cleaning, weeding, harvesting, building, talking, resting,

"This garden is a town": Aspen Farms, 1988. (West Philadelphia Landscape Project)

watching. "If you can't improve each year, why be here?" So Ford sums up the gardeners' philosophy. In 1975, the site was like much of the land nearby: vacant, weedy, full of trash; by 1980, gardeners had taken over half of the large vacant lot. The garden brought people together to improve their neighborhood. The houses in blocks around Aspen Farms are well maintained with small front gardens; none is vacant. Every year the gardeners take on new projects, host neighborhood parties, and give away much of their harvest. They tend flowers outside the garden's gate and have lured the pink hollyhocks growing along the interior of the fence to creep through and embellish the sidewalk.

I first met Ford and the other gardeners in 1988, when they asked my landscape architecture students at the University of Pennsylvania to design a new meeting place for the garden. It was a complex design problem. Not only were there fifty gardeners, but the garden community had already been in existence for twelve years. Carving out a place for meeting meant taking away space from one or more garden plots. The students began by getting to know their clients and the neighborhood; each stayed for a weekend with one of the gardeners. The students' designs turned out to be both similar to and different from each other. Most proposed a circular or square place for meeting, but some sited it in the middle of the garden, some at the corner nearest the street, some at the entrance. All offered good reasons for their decisions, based on what they had heard the gardeners say. One student, responding to a group who wanted a new fence, designed a fence in-

Main street: Aspen Farms, 1990.

stead, but because of a fixed budget, spending money on a fence would mean no meeting place. Two days before the presentation to the gardeners, one student, John Widrick, decided to revisit Aspen Farms and ask for comments on his design for a circular meeting place in a central location. He was unprepared for the reaction of polite horror. What we had idealized as one big community was actually several smaller groups, each with its singular territory and leaders. Widrick's original scheme not only displaced several garden plots, it disposed of most of one group's entire territory. He returned to class, distressed, threw out his drawings, and, with one day to go, began again by thinking how to use what he now knew about the garden's politics and turfs.

Widrick had been my research assistant for two years on the West Philadelphia Landscape Project, my laboratory for developing and testing ideas about the language of landscape. He reflected on that work and discarded the assumption that a meeting place had to be a broadly shaped space; a path is a meeting place, he realized. His new plan proposed that the central path become the common meeting place so each group's territory would border it and the space given up to create the common area could be evenly shared. When the students presented their designs to the gardeners at the Mill Creek Community Center the next day, the gardeners chose to build his.

Two gates lead into the wide meeting place–path that forms the main street of Aspen Farms. The path now resembles a small street with benches for people to sit, rest, watch, and talk. The benches and raised flower beds are boundaries between the public path and the adjacent, more private, garden plots. Small openings between benches and planters are gateways leading to the garden plots beyond. Groups of plots form small neighborhoods within the larger garden that compete with each other for the best flower beds along the main path outside the gate to their plots. The design for Aspen Farms' main street turned conflict and competition into common benefit.

Unlike a garden where plots of similar size and regular pattern are laid out prior to planting (like Aspen Farms), Powelton/Summer-Winter Community Garden, in another West Philadelphia neighborhood, has no regularity. Individual plots are carved out of a weedy meadow of grasses and wildflowers still thriving at the edges of the garden, on untended plots, and over the fence and sidewalks to form a border of spontaneous growth for the garden as a whole. Each plot merges into the next garden, with barely discernable borders. Plots of varying shapes and sizes are distinguished primarily through the types of plants each gardener grows and how they are cultivated, whether, for example, they are laid out in rows or mixed together. The seeming chaos reflects an anarchist political structure, in which gardeners act as free agents, governed not by set rules but by common values.

Form conveys meaning. Both the pattern of Aspen Farms with its regular boundaries and the seemingly amorphous plots and sprawling edges of the Powelton/Summer-Winter garden are eloquent expressions of different governance and different values. The Spruce Hill Garden, in yet another part of West Philadelphia, with lawn and flower beds that flow into one another to form a single, larger whole, marks one mind at work, and Aspen Farms, with its many, clearly divided plots, many minds and hands.

Nærum Garden Colony north of Copenhagen has dozens of separate gardens, each enclosed by an elliptical hedge, each with a tiny house and its own address; a numbered map is posted at the main gate. Most everyone has an apple tree, a small lawn, flowers near the house, a vegetable garden. The hedges are laid out in the same elliptical form, but of several different species, privet, hawthorn, and beech. And yet, each garden reflects its owner's taste. Each maintains an oval hedge, but at quite different heights. Some are only waist high, their owners being outgoing gardeners who want to see who walks by and want everyone to see in, perhaps to stop and talk. Some hedges are dense and over six feet high, their owners gaining more privacy. But the grassy common land between the hedges is uniformly clipped; each owner is responsible for maintaining the lawn outside their own hedge. Freestanding hedges were the designer C. Th. Sørensen's solution to the most common disputes between neighboring gardeners when hedge boundaries are shared: how high to clip the hedge. They leave odd-shaped, curving spaces between the gardens that echo and emphasize the curve of the hilly ground plane.

Nærum Garden Colony is like a little *landsby*, that is, a Danish country village. The fields have shrunk to a lawn between the house/gardens snug behind their boundary hedges, clipped short, revealing the roll of the land just as cropfields do in the rural landscape. On a fine day, the Danish flag flies over many of the gardens, for each has its own flagpole. How very Danish the place is, with its rolling landform, its cultivated landscape, its protected private life, its well-ordered public life, and its flags.

Living in Village Homes, in Davis, California, is something like living in a community garden such as Nærum year round. Here, much of the landscape is edible: pomegranate hedges and dwarf grapefruit, orange, and lemon trees line public walkways within; double rows of almond trees border the roadway outside. There are vegetable plots of various sizes on common land; surplus produce may be sold at the Davis Farmers' Market. In Village Homes, there are at least three levels of property ownership, each with fuzzy, often invisible boundaries: a private lot, a space common to small clusters of houses, and the larger public space shared by the entire community. Houses are small and close to one another, private gardens tiny. Decks and porches are the principal private outdoor space behind the houses; the private lot is almost entirely occupied by the house itself and extends only a few feet from the building line. It is difficult, even impossible, to tell where one person's private walk ends and where common land begins. Space owned in common by clusters of houses is maintained by the people who live there, in many places by extending their own garden into the common space. Community public space—drainage ways, roadways, greens, vegetable plots, vineyard, nut orchard, day care, swimming pool—is maintained by gardeners employed by the community association. The developer of Village Homes lives in the community himself. By not building underground storm drains, he saved enough money to pay for the landscaping of all the common property and to give new residents money to plant what they wanted. In one cluster, some residents built a dam in the stormwater channel to create a tiny pond stocked with mosquito fish. Village Homes has a village feel, largely because of the personalization of the landscape. The small, cluster-maintained common spaces keep the larger public space from seeming uniform and bland. This is different from other developments that try to establish a sense of village or community largely through architectural features constructed before anyone moves in.

When those of one culture mistake their own conventions for human universals, problems arise. Recent architectural history is full of such examples: in Australia, the government built new houses for Aborigines, but they chose not to live in them; instead they locked up their valuables in the house and continued to eat, meet, and sleep outdoors. Compared to those of many other cultures, American houses are extroverted. Windows and doors usually open out onto the street; front yards are rarely bounded by an opaque wall or fence, but are open to view of passersby. Americans' home landscapes emphasize identity over privacy. Japanese houses tend to be introverted, though sited directly upon the street; most have shuttered doors and windows. The garden, if there is one, is walled, a private precinct, part of the interior world, and there is seldom any hint of these gardens from the street. But within a traditional Japanese house is an open, fluid space with no locked doors, only sliding paper screens, or shoji; in an American house, rooms are divided by thick walls and doors. The nature of privacy is distinctly different: from the outside view in Japan; from the inside view in the United States. But the outward orientation of the American home seems to be changing, in response to fear of crime and perhaps to discomfort with diversity: new suburban homes are increasingly built within guarded enclaves; random shootings and street crime in inner-city neighborhoods are driving people indoors, older folks off their porches, children off the sidewalks.

Superficially, Tokyo, Osaka, and Kyoto appear much like their North American counterparts; streets provide access to blocks of single or multiple properties, doors or gates to buildings generally face the street, and each property has an identifying number. These similarities obscure a profound difference. Finding an address in a Japanese city can be a bewildering experience for a westerner. It is not just a matter of trying to decipher the Japanese characters, for often there are no street signs. American addresses are defined by their location along public property—the street; Japanese addresses refer to their position or chronology on privately owned property—the block. In American cities, an address denotes location along a street with numbers progressing consecutively, usually odd numbers on one side of the street, even numbers on the other. The numbers continue from one block of properties to another, marking and spanning the street's linear path across the city. A block is a group of properties facing each other across a street, and it receives its name from the segment of the larger street; thus, Americans refer to the 4400 block of Walnut Street, for example. In Japan, only major streets have names. Numbers on buildings refer to their location on the block itself; the numbers of houses facing each other across a street are unrelated. An address in a Japanese city is a nested series of locations: the position on the block (sometimes related to the order in which buildings were built rather than geographic location); the block itself; a named cluster of blocks; a city district; and the city. Thus, the address 3-1-1 Kasumigaseki, Chiyodaku, Tokyo, identifies building number one on block number one in ward three of the Kasumigaseki neighborhood of the Chiyoda district in Tokyo.

In an American city, the streets are figure and the blocks are ground. Streets form the spine of each block, and each block is a segment of a network linking all parts of the city. In the Japanese city, the blocks are figure and the street is ground; each block is self-contained. The American emphasis on the street, a segment of a line, underscores the importance of movement, the Japanese emphasis on the block underscores place, which implies repose. So, also, the contrast between the games of chess and go. In chess, you capture your opponent through direct, linear movement; in go, you capture your opponent through enclosure.

Western urban design traditionally has been concerned with public space, with avenues, plazas, and the relationship of buildings, particularly their facades, to these public places. Commonly axial, Western design is based on the street and the vista. Traditional Japanese urban design has an interior orientation, nested enclosures recurring in both everyday and sacred precincts, marking the progression from the public to the private, from the profane to the sacred.[45] Japanese subways are well suited to the high density and this nested, place-oriented urban space. Everywhere in Japan, I was aware of stepping across boundaries from one domain into another; gates are prominent features, so are bridges, channels, walls, and fences.

Artful Telling, Deep Reading

Landscape, like Twain's Mississippi, "is not a book to be read once and thrown aside," for not only does it have a new story to tell every day, but it has many stories. Rudolph Arnheim describes art as combining high order and high complexity, a work capable of inspiring and sustaining multiple readings versus a decorative "one-liner" that has no lasting effect. Artful authors craft many-layered landscapes with multiple meanings, overlapping functions and contexts. Deep readers decode these layers, view each element within the context of landscape features, each feature within place and region, the author's other work and life, country, period. Artful telling and deep reading demand knowledge of the vocabulary and of the grammar that governs their relationships, not for the purpose of following routine by rote rules, but to recognize when and why to break them.

Allusion: Origins, Authority, Sentiment

An allusion is a reference, usually indirect, to an event, person, place, or work. The Vietnam Veterans Memorial in Washington, D.C., alludes to the war, the deaths of individual soldiers, and other walls of mourning and memory. The heather at Kongenshus Memorial Park alludes to the heath, the tall stones lining the path to ancient menhirs (one of Sørensen's early sketches showed a dolmen instead). But landscape features like mountains and trees also allude to the processes and materials that shape them, when people read them as such. The wolf tree and the wind-pruned tree are allusions to past events, interpreted by humans in stories of science and myth. To geologists, the small holes in the flank of Uluru (Ayre's Rock) in Australia allude to erosion; to Aborigines who live nearby the marks are scars alluding to a mythic battle. Allusions may be taken for granted or go unperceived, like the bean which does not call attention to itself as something created or the flowers planted to bloom in June which the owners do not see as a deliberate allusion to their arrival and departure.

An allusion communicates shared understanding and relies upon common knowledge. Like Mussolini's monument at Redipuglia, it can remind one of collective identity, traditions, values, or heritage, establish authority or instruct, evoke mood or create a setting. An allusion can tap powerful personal and cultural memories and elicit strong emotions. A flower transplanted from a dead relative's garden and planted in one's own is an allusion with great personal significance.[46] The three crosses above the hill of crypts at Redipuglia evoke Calvary, thus portraying the Italian soldiers buried there as martyrs to a Christian cause.

By placing the glistening, golden fountain of Apollo and his horse-drawn chariot on axis with his bedroom at Versailles, Louis XIV, the Sun King, asserted his authority as kin of the god of the sun. Landscape architects may seek to establish the authority of their gardens and clients by using classical motifs or by echoing forms used in the gardens of French kings and Italian princes; architects do the same for houses. Chains of allusion connect American corporate headquarters, estates of American industrialists, eighteenth-century English landscape gardens, ancient Roman villas. Frank Lloyd Wright, Jens Jensen, and other members of the Prairie School eliminated or disguised allusions to European traditions in an effort to establish an American style. Wilhelm Miller spoke for them: "Let us not copy Europe and the East, but have something they can never have! The way for every new country to come into its own is to apply universal principles of design to the native materials."[47]

Parks and gardens often allude to or imitate other garden traditions. The perennial borders so popular now in American gardens imitate English borders developed by Gertrude Jekyll and others at the turn of the twentieth century, which referred in turn to the informal mix of plants in the traditional English cottage garden, a contrast to the fashionable, formal "carpet beds" of the Victorian era. Such choices may or may not be highly significant. In southern California developers of new housing establish an identity for their projects through a mixture of fashionable allusions: courtyard gardens with tile-lined fountains refer to Spanish gardens, irrigated lawns with groves of trees to English pastoral parks. But, when the English landscape garden displaced the formal garden in France after the French Revolution, not fashion alone but ideology had influenced both change and choice.

Disneyland's Main Street alludes, with deliberate intent and unmistakable message, to the American small town of the turn of the century. The rides in Fantasyland are designed as stories, with allusions to fairy tales and children's books as told in Disney feature cartoons like *Snow White, Peter Pan, The Wind in the Willows;* other areas, like Tom Sawyer's Island in Adventureland, embody similar allusions. Disneyland belongs to a long tradition of dialogues among the literatures of landscapes, words, and art. Classical Chinese gardens contain complex allusions to poetry, with clues inscribed on rocks, above or beside gateways and windows. According to Sun Xiaoxiang, Chinese scholars banished from the Imperial Court built gardens with subtle poetic references that were treasonous political statements concealed by the seeming innocence of the garden.[48] English landscape gardens, like Stowe and Stourhead, represented Arcadian landscapes described by Virgil and emulated paintings of classical motifs by Claude Lorrain; they also in-

Allusion. Aspen Farms. (Bilge Friedlander, West Philadelphia Landscape Project)

spired the novels of Jane Austen and the poetry of Alexander Pope. Ian Hamilton Finlay, a twentieth-century landscape designer and poet, continues this tradition. His garden Little Spartica in Scotland is full of words and scenes from poetry and art, like a stone inscribed with the words "See POUSSIN Hear LORRAIN," a reference to the seventeenth-century artists Nicholas Poussin and Claude Lorrain and their influence on landscape perception and design. Another scene, "The Great Piece of Turf," a stone carved with Albrecht Dürer's initials beneath a clump of grasses, is a garden version of a Dürer drawing. The density of allusions to classical literature in gardens like Stourhead and Little Spartica can be cloying, even euphuistic— affected, ornate, striving to be elegant and erudite.[49]

A landscape can even come to be, for some, an allusion to the story rather than the reverse: the English Lake District as an allusion to the poetry of Wordsworth, the "downs" to the novels of Thomas Hardy, the Danish heath to the poetry and prose of Steen Steensen Blicher and Jeppe Aakjær.[50] Many have read Aldo Leopold's book, *Sand County Almanac*, but few have read the restored landscape of the old farm to which much of the text alludes; most visitors undoubtedly perceive the place as an allusion to the book.

Inner-city community gardens in African-American neighborhoods frequently allude to the Bible. Gethsemane, a healing garden in West Philadelphia, is named for the place where Jesus prayed before being forsaken and betrayed by his disciples. The name of another Philadelphia community garden—The Garden of

Eatin'—is a punning allusion to the Bible's first garden. At Aspen Farms, the phrase "Deut. 24:19," hand-painted on a wooden sign, is an allusion to the values shared by those who garden here and live by these words: "When you reap your harvest in your field, and have forgotten a sheaf in the field, you shall not go back to get it; it shall be for the stranger, the fatherless, and the widow, that the Lord your God may bless you in all the work of your hands."

A Literature of Lived Life

The power of landscape literature lies in its potential not only to symbolize, represent, or project feelings and ideas, but also to be the very site where life and death take place. The Hill of Remembrance at Stockholm's Forest Cemetery gives "form to a sorrow that cannot be told"; it *is* also the cemetery where loved ones are buried or ashes scattered, where trees and flowers are fed by bodily decay, planted and tended by grieving friends and family. By the authors' design, visitors are made to feel close to earth and sky: earth enfolds those who climb the steps of the hill; sky is framed by trees at the summit. Suzanne Langer calls art "the creation of forms symbolic of human feeling," and works of art "congruent with the dynamic forms of our direct, sensuous, mental, and emotional life," projections of "felt life," as Henry James puts it, "into spatial, temporal, and poetic structures."[51] Forest Cemetery is art, a work that belongs to great landscape literature.

Literature endows common experience with significance. In the small provincial Danish town of Åbenrå, a walk to school or into town becomes a sacred passage through a secular cathedral. C. Th. Sørensen made this place at the edge of town by planting a long allée—four rows of poplars planted close together, now fifty feet tall—a sheltered path from countryside to town, a transition from pasture and meadow to house, school, and street. A meandering brook enters one end of the allée and is transformed into a straight canal. From a distance, the tall line of trees stands as a landmark on the flat plain. A rushing noise, like the sound of running water in a stream, grows louder as you approach, but the wind on the sports fields, broken by the trees, grows calmer. A surprise, the stream is a placid canal, the noise is from millions of poplar leaves catching the wind, loudest as you walk down the path between the trees, softer beyond it. Within the allée, leaves flutter, making a magical, flickering light. The dark green canal reflects a white strip of light—the sky—its surface rippling with moving water, sparkling with leaf/shadow dancing. The air itself seems to shimmer. So simple, so ordinary, so extraordinary.

Overlapping functions, feelings, and meanings enrich the experience and reading of a place when expressed in material form. At the Hill of Remembrance, the fusion of walking, rising, enfolded by hill and trees, mourning, thinking, of associations with other hills, like Calvary, brings multiple feelings and meanings into play simultaneously. So does the allée at Åbenrå, as one walks through its cathedral-like space, to and from town, sheltered from wind. Feeling and meaning also merge in the experience of the St. Louis Arch, but the arch does not arch over anything; it is a freestanding monument, *only* a representation. Meaning, but not related feeling or function, is present in Philadelphia's Welcome Park, a plaza whose paving represents the original plan of the city, as drawn by Thomas Holmes in 1682: streets are bands of white marble, dark brown clay tiles are the blocks within. Meaning is expressed primarily through words rather than landscape: texts are inscribed in pavement, on walls, a decorated surface of words.[52] On a hot, sunny, summer day, reflected glare and radiated heat do not welcome but repel.

One can barely feel the wind's force through words and images, or appreciate its lull down in a dale, hear birds' song or silence, feel the contrast between hot, sunny plaza and cool, shady patio; far better to be there. Verbal texts can be printed and experienced by a reader directly; landscapes are like musical or choreographic scores that must be performed to be fully experienced. Every landscape has a distinctive set of sounds, smells, and textures: the Danish heath is windy, the soil dry and sandy; the air in Japan is humid, the light green; the desert soil of Arizona is hard, its plants prickly. Words, drawings, paintings, photographs, or video cannot replace the experience of the place itself, though they may enhance and intensify that experience and may even inspire construction of actual landscapes. No matter how many photographs I have seen of the Vietnam Veterans Memorial, I am unprepared, when I am there, for the ways in which it evokes feeling, even beyond the names on the wall, mementos left there, other people's actions, and what they mean. It is easy to control my feelings at the start when the wall is low, hard when scale changes and the wall is over my head; feelings well up and do not lighten again until your head is above ground again on the other side. The air is loud with chatter at the entry to the memorial; hushed down at the bottom where the wall is highest. Like many great works of tragedy, it arouses feelings of pity or grief then provides catharsis.

Landscape, as a literature of lived life, must be experienced in place to be fully felt and known. And skill in the language of landscape amplifies the experience. Those fully literate recognize stories, themes, and genres shared across cultures; they read regional landscapes as inscriptions of environmental and cultural history, values, and visions. The barely literate may read some significance in landscape, especially in their own region, but miss allusions and multiple layers of function, feeling, and meaning. They fail to recognize the ethical and aesthetic intentions in landscapes like those by Olmsted and Leopold, mistaking them for accidents. The illiterate compose crude, dysfunctional landscapes, full of gibberish. With literacy and fluency comes an appreciation of figurative and rhetorical landscapes and an awareness of how such landscapes evoke feeling and instill meaning; with them comes the ability to shape landscapes more knowledgeably and expressively. To be fluent is to master landscape composition—the elements of landscape language and the context and grammar that govern their meaning—and to grasp pragmatics, poetics, and polemics.

Two

"WITHOUT FORM AND VOID" TO "HEAVEN AND EARTH": LANDSCAPE COMPOSITION

In the beginning God created the heaven and the earth. And the earth was without form, and void; and darkness was upon the face of the deep. And the spirit of God moved upon the face of the waters. And God said, Let there be light: and there was light. And God called the light Day, and the darkness he called Night. And the evening and the morning were the first day.

—Genesis 1:1–5

Anatomy must contain an analogue of grammar because all anatomy is a transform of message material, which must be contextually shaped. And finally, contextual shaping is only another term for grammar.

—Gregory Bateson, *Mind and Nature*

Two paths, sea. Denmark.

4

Is a Leaf Like a Noun, Flowing Like a Verb?
Elements of Landscape and Language

Elements of landscape language are like parts of speech, each with separate functions and associations. Flowing, like a verb, is a pattern of events expressed in both water and path. Water and path, like nouns, are action's agents and objects; like adjectives or adverbs, their qualities of wetness or breadth extend meaning. Elements do not exist in isolation, but rather combine in significant ways, like words in a phrase, clause, or sentence, to make a tree, fountain, street, or a larger, more complex landscape story—garden, town, or forest. Every landscape feature, such as a mountain, embodies at least one complete expression—its own formation. Describing the elements is like looking at landscape—scanning the scene, then successively zooming in and out on significant details, letting the context blur but keeping it always in view.

The Vietnam wall of war, memory, and mourning conjures up boundary, blocked passage, executions against a wall, the Wailing Wall. The meaning of the memorial would be different were it white instead of black, or composed of rough, unpolished stone instead of polished granite, or of many small stones set in thick mortar, rather than large sheets set flush, almost seamless. Materials modified by form give landscapes presence and space. Processes—polishing of stone—like verbs, provide action and time. The meanings of the Vietnam Memorial come not just from the inherent qualities and traditional meanings of individual elements—stone, grass, wall, polished surface, path rising and falling—but from the ways they modify and amplify each other. The meaning would be different if the wall were freestanding rather than embedded in earth, if one could walk behind it, if it were a single straight line, rather than broken and angled. And the meaning would be different if no one left mementos there or traced the names of loved ones on the face of the stone. Process is perceived through the act of polishing in the surface of the granite, the act of remembering in the names cut into its surface, as well as the offerings people leave. Material influences shape and structure: the hard stone holds a smooth, sharp outline, can be cut into thick blocks to make an upright wall. Form affects material properties: the flat surface enhances the dark stone's ability to reflect. Process molds form, and form shapes process: the narrow path hugs the base of the wall, keeping the visitor close to the names that are listed in order of death, and all the messages left by mourners. As you leave, it rises, directing the gaze to the Washington Monument and the Lincoln Memorial.

The elements are so intimately linked—why, then, try to separate them? To read landscapes more deeply, as signifying wholes, and to tell other landscapes more artfully. To be literate and fluent, one must first have a vocabulary. Although some learn the language of landscape intuitively, through living and making, without studying vocabulary or grammar, many miss significance and connections and fail to see and make the landscape whole. Many designers compose formal arrangements, quoting the plan of a historic garden, borrowing a phrase here and there from a contemporary work. Many choose materials belatedly and consider processes rarely, if at all. This is like trying to compose a sentence entirely of nouns and adjectives, without verbs. In landscape, context supplies elements the author neglects or forgets. Incomplete utterances lead to unforeseen consequences: to buildings, parks, and playgrounds which fail to function or are unsustainable, destroyed by those who use them or by wildfires, floods, and landslides.

Process: Actions and Patterns of Events

Burning, Blowing, Raining, Slipping, Growing, Building: Orange County

October 1993, Irvine. Wildfires burn out of control along the California coast south of Los Angeles. Spicy, smoky smells of burning eucalypts and sage fill the air miles away. Flames flash and flicker on television screens, while reporters, in apocalyptic language, invoke images of heaven and hell, paradise and expulsion from paradise, Mother Nature's revenge. Scientists explain cause and effect: hot, high, Santa Ana winds; canyons shaped like chimneys; fire suppression; piled-up fuel; flammable plants and houses; lightning; arson; a homeless man, mentally ill, building a small fire to keep warm. Burned-out residents stand stunned, staring, speak of insurance, wonder if they will rebuild, tell reporters they do not recall other fires of several years before or never imagined it would happen here.

February 1994, Laguna Canyon. Four months later, the earth is still bare and brown, green gone. Coarse black skeletons—burned shrubs—stand out against a clear blue sky. The size of remaining branches tells how hot the fire burned: very hot, for the charred branches are thick as a finger, ending in stubby stumps, twigs vaporized.[1] Prickly pears—prostrate masses of blackened flesh, like deflated balloons—are the most grotesque of all, perhaps because their shriveled flesh is still visible. A prickly pear, just one, has sent forth tiny shoots of reddish new growth, and minute leaves are sprouting from the base of a few blackened skeletons. Down in the canyon all that remains of the houses are concrete slabs, fireplaces, and chimneys—the hearth; furniture, walls, roofs are gone. A few isolated homes are left, untouched by fire. Up on the ridge what look like black tree trunks stand against the sky: chimneys. The low afternoon sun rakes across the hillsides, lights up short, green shoots of new plants on the opposite and moister slope; another slope, hydro-seeded after the fire, looks like a greyish-white moonscape. The mulch has formed a crust that seeds cannot penetrate: the human urge to do something has been counterproductive. Winter rains cut deep gullies in soil stripped of plant cover, especially along the road. Heavy storms are forecast for the coming week; sandbags line the street. We speak in hushed voices. The scene is almost beyond imagining, so much life gone, no movement, no sound.

FEBRUARY 1994, IRVINE. Thick, brown mud, flowing, slides down slopes, through doorways, out windows, carries houses down, flows onto Route 1—on the television screen. Reporters warn of roads closed and slides to come on burned slopes. Scientists speak of cause and effect: roads cut and houses built on unstable hillsides; watered gardens, leaky swimming pools; barren slopes stripped of plants by fire; heavy winter rains.

MAY 1994, LAGUNA CANYON. Flaming orange poppies and yellow goldfields bloom brightly along paths leading to concrete pads. Long, green grasses cover burned-over slopes. New street signs stand on each corner. A few houses are under construction.

MAY 1996, LAGUNA CANYON. The air is full of buzzing insects, birdsong, hammers, and workmen's distant voices: the process of regeneration. A huge prickly pear, once blackened and deflated, is overgrown by luxuriant new growth of other shrubs; the pear is gone except for a few branches with new sprouts. Up on Skyline Drive, two years' difference is dramatic and disorienting, the streets nearly unrecognizable. Most houses are rebuilt, though many lots remain empty, For Sale signs on some. The street down in the canyon is full of movement, cars and trucks coming and going, people bustling. Public money has been spent: a new bridge, road, and culvert. Most of the rebuilt homes are fancier than the houses that survived: insurance money? new owners? or residents had more money than their old, rather modest houses led one to think? Only a few concrete pads remain. On a house under construction a sign above the door, hand-lettered in white paint: "And the birds will sing again." Ready for the next fire, for it will surely come.

MARCH 9, 1998, PHILADELPHIA. "Dream houses are toppled," says the headline over a large color photograph on the front page of the morning newspaper; shattered debris, unrecognizable as a home, cascades down a steep slope: "Home gives way on a hillside in Laguna Beach." The story describes the many houses destroyed and the homeowners' astonished response: "It's a million cubic feet of mud that came down on my house. Who ever imagines that something like that's going to happen?"[2]

Transforming Events, Repeating: Order, Rhythm, Change

Burning is a process; flame and ashes, burning and burned substances that can be seen and touched. Wind is sensed through fanned flames, moving trees and clouds, rustling leaves, whipped waves, blown sand dunes, air pressed against body, evaporation through dry skin, chapped lips, and thirst. Falling rain and flowing, seeping water weather, color, crack, and crumble rock, cause it to slide. The idea of process shows landscape features as dynamic, as related markers of change, not discrete, not fixed objects. Mountains are thrusting up or eroding, not static; trees are growing, or not, evidence of invisible events.

Water flowing, like sun shining, shapes and structures landscape. The trail up Palm Canyon in the Anza Berega Desert of southern California starts out level, crosses a wide rubble-strewn wash fanning out onto the desert, winds among rocks brought down by water; the trail climbs up the alluvial fan in a narrow streambed cut between two mountain ridges. Higher up, the trail bends around boulders and crosses a small stream; the sound of water rare and soothing, brilliant green plants along the stream bank are shocking against the dusty desert plants below. As the trail rises, the cleft between knife-sharp, rocky ridges narrows, the boulders become huge—a claustrophobic space. One can sense the rushing torrent that has torn these boulders off the hillsides and tumbled them into the valley. It would be unimaginable but for the rocks and broad, sandy washes. At the head of the trail is an oasis of palms, fed by a spring.

Water flowing off the broad, red sandstone flanks of Uluru (Ayre's Rock) in Australia structures the desert landscape for a mile from its base. As one walks across the red sand, Uluru still miles away, the red rock rises in the distance. A thousand feet from the rock, plants are greener, mulga trees grow in slight hollows. Closer still, black marks appear, streaking down from notches in the orange-red rock, traces of water, streaming rarely, over thousands of years. At the bottom of each black streak is a pool and a grove of trees filled with brilliant birds, the air cooler, moister, filled with their song. The Aborigines' sacred places are not on Uluru's summit, but at its base.

Thousands of years ago, Persian engineers built *qanats*, underground tunnels to bring water from aquifers under mountain slopes to arid plateaus. Many are still used. Water flowing—tapped to irrigate crops, to drink, to carry wastes— orders human settlement. The drier the climate, the more elaborate the water system, the more pervasive and enduring the system's influence on the form and meaning of landscape. In Persian settlements, houses of the wealthy are uphill of fields and poorer districts; they receive water before others do; as water flows downhill it is used and reused. When the City of Los Angeles obtained the rights to water in the Owen River and transported it more than two hundred miles to the San Fernando Valley, Los Angeles bloomed and grew, the Owens Valley withered and declined. Water, the material, and the process by which it was bought, then brought, transformed these places.

When a single process or a single set of processes dominates—water flowing, wheat growing, wind blowing—or when contexts are relatively homogeneous, as in sandy seashores, arid deserts, and grassy prairies, then landscapes reveal process most clearly. Beaches and deserts are good landscape primers. Sandy beaches and silty tidal flats reveal patterns of water flow; sand dunes and wheat fields reveal wind. But landscapes are seldom the product of a single process or even a small set of dominant processes. As in Laguna Canyon, the processes they reflect are simultaneous and successive, congruent and conflicting, layers upon layers, overlain and overlapping, continuous and interrupted, contingent and independent, once acting or still acting.

Fires spread rapidly in Laguna, through canyons and up hillsides, turning vast areas to ashes within hours; muddy slopes after heavy rains brought down rocks, streets, homes also within hours. But fires and mudslides do not happen every year. Fire's fuel, houses and plants, accumulates over years of fire suppression; slopes may have slipped in the same place, from time to time for thousands of years. Tempos, durations, and rhythms differ, hence events recur, and parts of a landscape evolve, at divergent rates. Processes have speed (fast or slow), duration (long periods or brief spurts, seconds, days, years), and rhythm (character of repetition, constant or intermittent). Landscape composition must take speed, duration, and rhythm into account; it must acknowledge or adapt to change over time.

The rhythm of repeating events—order in time—is even or uneven, regular or irregular: periodic fires and mudslides, daily fluctuations of tides and the commute of cows and people, seasonal migration of nomads, snowbirds, and summer people, irregular occurrence of earthquakes. The pulse and periodicity of the sun coordinate and synchronize melting snow to rushing streams to rising sap, to plowing of fields, to budding plants, or the Rockefellers' visit to their blooming June Garden in Maine. Time is relative to the process that shapes it, the organism that experiences it. A sense of time depends upon perceptible change, patterns of recurring events, and culture. Rhythms differ from place to place. Aborigines in Australia's tropical northeastern Arnhem Land name at least six seasons, each associated with patterns of temperature, rain, wind, thunder, plant growth, and animal behavior: Dhuludur, the pre-wet season (October-November), Barramirri, the growth season (December-January), Mayaltha, the flowering season (February-March), Midawarr, the fruiting season (March-April), Dharratharramirri, the early dry season (May-July), Rarrandharr, the principal dry season (August-October).[3] The traditional four seasons of temperate climates seem gross in contrast. And, within them, there are nuances. Bostonians call March slush season, a month when ankle-deep, icy water fills street gutters, drains blocked by piles of snow. In Denmark, patterns of light change radically from summer to winter; there are traditions associated with each. In Danish mid-December, when dawn comes late and twilight early, one goes to school or work and back in the dark; in mid-June, when sun sets in late evening and rises a few hours later, night is never truly dark. Both winter and summer have a long twilight, "darkening" in the winter, "summerlight" in the summer. Candles, "living lights," flicker in windows, as beacons on winter afternoons; in the summer, twilight lingers for hours, dim, glowing.

Time controls much behavior, a process recognized in landscape itself. Certain landscapes are devoted to marking time: sundials convert sun's changing shadows into time of day; Stonehenge, some think, charted the position of sun and moon, permitting prediction and celebration of the equinox and solstice,

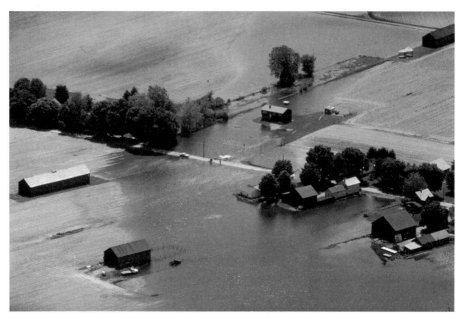

Water flowing: farm in floodplain. (Alex S. MacLean/Landslides)

when the rising sun shone directly through the pillars of the avenue leading to the inner circle of stones.[4] Most landscapes are designed to be sensed through movement, at a particular tempo, for a specific duration, in a rhythm. The vast scale of seventeenth-century French gardens, like Versailles, Vaux-le-Vicomte, and Chantilly, was calculated to impress at a walking pace. Nineteenth- and early twentieth-century American parkways, like Boston's Riverway and New York's Bronx River Parkway, were meant to be seen at the speed of a horse-drawn carriage, then by automobile. "New vistas unfold because of elevated freeways," writes Lawrence Halprin. "Vast panoramic views are disclosed which were never seen before. The great vivid skylines of the city can be seen, all of a sudden, not as a static picture, but as a series of constantly changing impressions which move by like the frames in a motion picture."[5] The landscape of the San Jose freeway was designed to be experienced at an even, high speed. The series of framed views of Rousham, an eighteenth-century English garden largely by William Kent, are seen from a path at a rhythm of long, leisurely movements in a single direction, punctuated by occasional stops. In Bowood, also in southwestern England, a garden of the same period by "Capability" Brown, with no single principal path, the rolling terrain, the rounded groves of trees with trunks silhouetted up to the height of browsing sheep, and the architectural monuments propel walkers through the landscape to the destinations. Bowood, cinematic, not photographic, is experienced through continuous movement, not static views.

Water flowing: buildings and vacant land in floodplain. Dudley Street neighborhood. Boston. (Alex S. MacLean/Landslides)

Processes Connect: Making Sense of Events and Experience

When I first saw the Dudley Street neighborhood of Boston in November 1984, I was dismayed. I knew the statistics—twice the unemployment rate of Boston as a whole, 30 percent of the land abandoned—but they simply did not prepare me for the place itself: entire square blocks of vacant land, some heaped with big chunks of concrete, piles of tires, and trash; playgrounds with broken equipment, cracked pavement, and smashed glass; wooden houses with peeling paint, sagging porches, roofs with holes, both triple-decker apartments and large, single-family homes with fine architectural details. The waste was overwhelming. With me that day was Hans Kiemstedt, a German friend; he said he had not seen such destruction since Germany after the war; how could Americans permit such conditions in peacetime? Our guide, Charlotte Kahn, director of Boston Urban Gardeners, pointed to what was neither waste nor destruction, the many community gardens, not as visible in late fall as they would have been in summer, and also houses under repair, 40 percent of them owned by those who lived in them.

As I lay awake that night, sure I had missed something, I replayed what I had seen. The fifteen hundred vacant lots were not scattered evenly, but concentrated. Few were on hilltops and hillsides; houses there were substantial, most in good condition, some had sweeping views over the city. I got out of bed and pulled out the U.S. Geological Survey maps of Boston. With colored pencils of light to dark brown, I filled in the spaces between contours for a sense of the shape of the land-forms and the pattern of vacant lots. I discovered that we had·been driving back and forth across a long valley between two hills; most of the abandoned land was in that valley. When my students plotted the vacant lots on aerial photographs of the area several months later, they calculated that 90 percent of the lowest parts of the valley was vacant, 95 percent of the hillside properties was inhabited. The reason had to be water, water flowing down from the hills into the valley, saturating the soil, puddling after rain. Water now not visible except by inference. A stream once flowed there—it was the old boundary between the towns of Roxbury and Dorchester—and it still does, flowing underground in a sewer, carrying the community's wastes and rainfall. Consulting old atlases, I tracked the changes in the neighborhood from 1876 to 1886, 1892, 1903, 1910, 1922, 1934, 1948, 1964. Houses in the valley were built later than houses on the hills, many as apartments for poorer people. The first vacant lots in the valley were recorded in the early twentieth century, within twenty years of construction there. By 1964, large areas in the valley bottom had been abandoned.

Water, flowing and pooling, was not the whole story; such conditions could not be simply a matter of poor drainage. Someone I knew whose basement flooded after every heavy rain had installed a sump pump and built a drain around the foundation. His house, originally a worker's cottage, was built on marshy ground, as were his neighbors', but all of those houses were well maintained and freshly painted in pastel colors with white trim; there were no signs of drainage problems underground. But then his street was in Cambridge, a ten-minute walk from the Harvard campus, not in one of the poorest neighborhoods in Boston.

Initial abandonment of Boston's Dudley Street neighborhood was the product of several related processes: water flowing downhill, pooling in the valley; a stream sewered and buried; housing built and rented for short-term profit. That process of abandonment continued until the 1980s, accelerated by processes of decay, subsidence, industrial decline, unemployment, red-lining (denial of insurance and loans for homes and businesses in areas with older homes and immigrant or nonwhite population), arson. City planners commonly recognize the last set of problems without appreciating the existence and contributing effects of buried streams. Corresponding patterns exist in similar neighborhoods throughout Boston, as in many other American cities. In fact, I found exactly the same situation in West Philadelphia's Mill Creek just a few years later. Patterns seemingly unrelated, yet highly coincident—like abandonment and topography—should prompt the questions: do they correspond? if so, how, and why?

Processes connect, literally, physically, and figuratively; if we can read them, they make sense of events apparently unrelated: blazing wildfire, whipping wind, fleeing people; pouring rain, oozing mud, slumping hillsides; burning tissue, dying, then sprouting, flowering, animals returning, people rebuilding. Connections between material, form, and territory, the elements of landscape and language.

Hydrologic cycle: Patio de la Reja. The Alhambra. Spain.

Processes connect the organic and inorganic, the animate and inanimate, the physical world and the organisms that inhabit it. Leaves transpire and roots suck, animals breathe, drink, and excrete, all exchanging air and water between atmosphere, earth, and life. As plants and animals die and decay, organic tissue mingles with minerals and microorganisms to make soil, a living medium.

Processes overlap: water wears away stone, rolls rounded river cobbles, and dumps them downstream; people gather the smooth stones and lay them to form patterned pavement; footsteps over time wear them away. Some processes (movement, exchange, growth, and decay) overlap the organic and inorganic, animate and inanimate. Others (sensing, sustenance, birth, and death) are common to animate and inanimate alike, to organisms with mind and those without, while many like making/building, learning, playing, fighting, dreaming are the province of animate organisms alone, human and nonhuman, though human cultures differ in what is considered animate. Australian Aborigines believe animate ancestors shaped their landscape, including many plants and animals.

Process as Metaphor and Means to an End

Processes, like poems, are full of metaphors, relationships among significant details, such as lines, cycles, and circles. The hydrologic cycle describes water moving from ocean to air, from air to earth, from earth to river and sea, an exchange between heaven and earth powered by the sun: "All the rivers run into the sea, yet the sea is

Braided rivers and star. Patio de la Reja. The Alhambra. Spain.

not full; unto the place from whence the rivers come, thither they return again."[6]

Water spills from source in the fountain onto pavement, its sound amplified by surrounding walls. It puddles on the stone floor, evaporates, and cools the air. In the Alhambra in Granada, Patio de la Reja, a small enclosed patio, is an economical, elegant, and powerful statement about the qualities of water, a poetic description of the hydrologic cycle. Small, river-worn pebbles, each embodying the action of water over time, are set in packed earth that permits water to seep beneath them to irrigate the roots of the cedar trees planted at each corner of the courtyard. In a tightly organized geometric pattern, elongated black stones form flowing, braided rivers, rounded whitish-grey stones, alternately ground and stars. The whole forms a deep congruence between function, feeling, and meaning.

The hydrologic cycle is an idea shared by many cultures. It is taken for granted by most Western scientists as a fundamental concept; every textbook in geology and physical geography describes it, and yet, as the geographer Yi-Fu Tuan points out, the standard version, combining processes that occur within moments and others that take place over thousands of years, is so general that it is almost meaningless.[7] Tuan traces the history of the concept from 1700 to 1850 in natural philosophy and theology as evidence of the wisdom of God, of the economy of means and ends.

In the moss garden at Saihoji, in Kyoto, no leaf lies on the moss; any leaf that drops is raked up promptly. A rake propped against a tree and a pile of leaves nearby make the garden seem contrived, separate from the real forest. Decay and regeneration are here, but the steps in between that make rebirth possible are not—no seeds, no decaying leaves that create soil and fertilize the trees. The garden exists in a perplexing, steady state, time suspended, a complex metaphor.

Moving, exchanging, reproducing, growing, dying, the processes of life are understood and celebrated in terms of what one knows and values. Is growth good and decay bad? What, if anything, is the ideal state: movement or stasis? Is birth-life-death cyclical or linear? Are processes, is time, linear or cyclical? It depends. It depends, for example, on one's worldview and religion, Hindu, Jewish, Christian, Buddhist. Stephen Jay Gould describes the tension between seeing time as progressive or cyclical as the assertion of the uniqueness and contingency of history, on the one hand, and as the immanence and timelessness of law, on the other.[8] He observes that most cultures have viewed time as being cyclical; Jewish and Christian religions are exceptional in their emphasis on time as being linear. There is ample support in the world for both views, in phenomena like day and night and seasonal change, in the fact that water flowing over varying rock materials and steepness of slope cuts different patterns, just as the process of worship yields different forms of ritual paths and shrines in dissimilar cultures.

Flood, fire, earthquake have been seen as expressions of God's punishment for human sins, as Nature's revenge for human abuse, as a natural process prompted by rainfall, lightning, or colliding continental plates. Causes differ in the perception of differing cultures. In Genesis, humans are at the center of the story, as both stewards and exploiters, admonished to "be fruitful, and multiply, and replenish the earth, and subdue it." To Gaians the purpose of natural processes is the maintaining of the planet as a whole, its land, seas, atmosphere, together with all its life. Many scientists, it is sobering to remember, until quite recently believed that natural processes left to themselves would maintain what they saw as the inherent stability, balance, and harmony of Nature.[9]

Process, as a deliberate act by a conscious being, is a means to an end. All human processes are cultural, deliberate means by which humans sustain themselves, adapt to their environment, and relate to one another. Most basic are those processes essential for survival of individual and species: physical—moving, exchanging, sensing, reproducing, growing, and decaying; social—identifying, communicating, making/building, trading, playing, learning, competing, and fighting; spiritual—dreaming and worship. Human habitats—buildings, gardens, neighborhoods, towns, and cities—must satisfy all three of these kinds of basic human processes. Design, the imagining, making, adapting of human artifacts and settlements, has this express purpose.

"This course goes against everything I have learned about design," a student once complained to me. Like many others of my students, he had a hard time seeing the design of a *process* as a legitimate and essential aspect of his art and craft. This is difficult; it demands the ability to envision and anticipate evolving form rather than a single, finished form. Recently, I asked students to design a nursery for street trees, a living laboratory for middle school students, to be planted and maintained as part of a new curriculum in environmental education. My students' task was to design not merely an attractive nursery but one that reflected a new middle school curriculum and stimulated the process of learning. Furthermore, they had to design the process by which sites for planting the new trees are selected and secured (vacant lots and blocks for future planting), by which a program is promoted, trees planted, cared for, transplanted, and cared for in their new site. This required conceiving of change and phasing over a period of ten years and beyond—from conception, initiation, selecting sites, planting, caring for, and transplanting. All but a few students produced lovely drawings of a nursery but failed to design the curriculum it served or the processes by which it would be created, attract support, and be sustained over time.

Architects and landscape architects tend to focus not on process, but on form and material; when designs fail to be sustained in the real world, it is often because designers ignore the processes that shape them during and after construction. When the audience at the public meeting in Roxbury attacked the landscape architect's design for a new park in their neighborhood, they were undoubtedly thinking of other playgrounds built a few years before but not maintained, playgrounds filled with smashed glass that became scenes of crime. Material, form, and space are sensed and shaped by processes, by touching, seeing, moving and by erosion, fire, vandalism, care. Processes provide action. Neglecting pertinent processes can lead not only to failure of function and expression but even to destruction and death.

Matter: Sensual and Dynamic

Medium of Seeing, Smelling, Hearing, Touching, Tasting

Rock, Water, Wood, Air, Fire: Finland. Flying to Helsinki over the archipelago—water and rock—tiny islands in a dark, blue-black sea; later, over the mainland—water and trees—thousands of long, narrow lakes, all aligned north-south, surrounded by a vast forest. Gradually forest gives way to small farms and scattered woodlots. Then the city. As I walk around Helsinki, I look down a street and see sky and sea. Rocks rise out of the water, push up from under the ground, the soil a thin skin. Late spring air is fresh and cool, light brilliant—a sharp, low, blinding light that backlights birch leaves and rakes across stone buildings. Motoring out on the water, I pass dozens of islands, many little sauna houses, painted red, lining the shores. Late-evening light turns long, flat islands into glowing lines along the horizon—yellow, then rose.

On an island in the archipelago wind is still, water ripples gently, a silky, pearly grey. The sauna is perched on rocks, facing water. Outside, the cold is bracing; inside, dry heat penetrates skin and lungs. Scent of hot rocks and wood walls, floors, and roof permeates air; lungs draw in wood and rocks with each breath. I emerge from dry heat, swat skin with freshly cut birch switches, air that had seemed cold despite shirt, sweater, down vest, and jacket now seems comfortable in bare skin. I walk barefoot over smooth, round rocks, diving into the archipelago, the water cool, but not cold. Returning to the sauna, I ladle water over rocks, and sit in steamy mist. Air, rock, water, fire, wood, and body are joined. No wonder Finns speak of sauna with reverence.

We see, smell, hear, touch, and taste landscapes through materials; they are sensual. Gravel crunches underfoot, grass swishes, a wooden bridge thumps hollow. To a blind person, snow may give a sense of walking through an endless, undifferentiated nothing, for it muffles sound.[10] In some times and places, sense of sound seems heightened, discrete sounds amplified: when air carries sound farther at night, and in early morning; where ambient noise is low, in a quiet cloister, where sounds bounce off walls. The courtyard of the Hotel de Sully in Paris is a garden cloistered between the raucous Rue de Saint Antoine and the stately Place des Vosges, quiet, protected from street noise by massive stone buildings. Birds bring the space alive, chirping from within ivy on the walls, hidden but for their sudden flitting and the moving leaves.

Farmers sense soil with their fingers: sand is grainy, falls loosely; clay is fine, swells with water, shrinks when dry, rolls between fingers; humus, sponge of decayed plants, is springy when damp. Soil is mineral, vegetal, and animal, a living medium for growth: eroded, dissolved, ground-up rock; organisms, decayed and alive; water, and air. Vintners taste soil—slatey, gravelly—in wine; the French have a name for it: *terroir*. Brown, black, red, yellow, grey, blue, glittering mica are colors of earth particular to place: red comes from iron; mottled, blue-grey gley from seasonal water; green from serpentine. Adobe, bricks, and tiles are the colors of local soil, gravel, the colors of local rocks, crushed; Black Earth, Wisconsin, is aptly named. I was shocked thirty years ago when I first saw the bright red soil of Oklahoma; I had always assumed that Thomas Hart Benton (1889–1975) painted his red hills with artistic license.

Air—medium of light—is seen as life and spirit, celestial and ethereal not material, not real in itself. Ironically, the more evident its actual materiality (the more water and dust it contains) the more immaterial the world seems. Air filled with water and dust is misty and hazy, blurring the edges, dissolving the seeming solidity of things. Airborne water and dust reveal the colors of light's spectrum in rainbows, sunsets, and haloes. Humidity and dust change light's quality—its color, clarity, and brilliance—variously from place to place. A low, raking light shining through clear, dry air accentuates the texture of things and heightens a sense of materiality. Add reflective surfaces of the sea and a special light results: the iridescent light of southern California, the brilliant bounciness of winter light in Sydney, of late spring and early summer in Denmark and the Helsinki Archipelago.

The contrast between desert and oasis makes one conscious of air: dry desert air parches nose, lips, mouth, and sucks moisture from skin; moist, cool air in an oasis is palpable, invisible, but not intangible. Walled gardens and narrow, shady streets aligned to capture cool evening breezes are typical of old districts in desert cities like Jeddah. Screens that filter air and light and rooftop wind-catchers that funnel breezes through moist cloth to cool the interiors of building are common to traditional desert architecture.[11] The International Style, imported to desert countries like Saudi Arabia, displaced traditional design, substituting urban districts of high-rise buildings surrounded by hot, glaring pavement and cooled by air conditioners. In twentieth-century Europe and North America, most planners, designers, and builders ignore air as a material to be skillfully shaped: the result is noisy, windswept streets and plazas, cold in winter and hot in summer, and sealed buildings requiring heating or cooling even on the most temperate days. Tanner Fountain at Harvard University is a delightful exception: in summer its nozzles produce a fine mist, cooling air; warm steam once emerged in winter from underground pipes that heat university buildings. Unfortunately, the steam was discontinued after some objected that it was wasteful of energy.[12]

Sensations shift easily into feelings and emotions; witness the description of the Laguna fire, laden with empathetic response to the fire and its aftermath: hard, barren, gullied slopes, stubby, blackened stumps, acrid odor of burnt tissue, silenced birds and insects, their absence once noted, keenly felt. Response has much to do with memory. George Eliot in *The Mill on the Floss* wrote, "Our delight in the sunshine on the deep-bladed grass today" would be no more than a "faint perception," were it not for the "sunshine and grass of far-off years, which still live in us and transform our perception into love."[13] One whiff and one is transported back across the years. Memories are sensual, personal, place-specific. Asked to describe his home landscape, a student from Saudi Arabia spoke of the special, seldom smell of rain. My memories of childhood landscape are of big rocks and stone walls in the woods, the sour smell of smashed Osage orange, lilacs in May, fresh-cut grass, burning leaves, moldy soil, the tart, sweet taste of raspberries, apples, and sour grass.

The light in Japan is often green. One day in Kyoto, as I walk up the entrance path to Shisendo, the air is so humid I can feel its weight pressing against my body, its moisture clinging to my skin. The sun is bright but does not penetrate directly into the bamboo grove through which the entrance path leads. Sunlight filters through layers of leaves, each leaf absorbs light, leaving the light passing through one shade darker. The surrounding surfaces have a green cast, from the bamboo leaves and moss to the bluish-rosy green of the bamboo trunks; even in shadow the moss glows iridescent green. The air itself is saturated with green. Are the millions of microscopic water droplets hanging in the heavy air all reflecting green?

In a Japanese July the fullness of these greens reveals the presence of water in garden and forest, in city rice field. Light and water feed photosynthesis, the process by which green, the color of life, emerges. Water swells leaves, propels new growth with its distinctly lighter color, feeds grey-green fungus and lichens on tree and stone. The undulating, moss-covered ground of Saihoji seems fluid; roots and old stumps emerge from moss like rocks from a retreating wave, like flotsam riding a rolling swell.

In the gardens of Kyoto—in Shugakuin, in Katsura, in Shisendo, and, above all, in the moss garden of Saihoji—the overwhelming presence of the color green and the recession of others permit an appreciation of the range of shades and variations in texture. It is easiest to understand green in these gardens, but I begin to see the significance in the green mountains that form a backdrop to Japanese villages and cities and in the subtle, gentle green of the tatami mat upon which I sat, ate, and slept. The memory remained with me even in parts of the city where I could see no green. It remains with me still.

In Kobe city, at the end of an elegant lunch, I am served a single cup of green tea and, in a glass bowl, three cherries on ice. Perhaps it is the red of the cherries that draws my attention so sharply to the greenness of the tea. The tea seems like a distillation of the Japanese landscape; in drinking it, I drink the landscape.

Dynamic Medium of Process and Meaning

Rock erodes to sand, cemented sand becomes stone, erodes to sand once again. Fire consumes plants and releases seeds, ashes mix with soil to nourish new seedlings. Steel, forged from iron ore and fire, exposed to air and water, turns to rust. Stones cut from quarries, stacked to form walls, fall into ruin, and the rubble is used to build anew. Materials are dynamic, constant but constantly changing, moving, growing, decaying, transforming. Artists and craftsmen often say materials are living, that they have "an active presence, a character, a capacity for change."[14] To see materials as static is an illusion. If the human life span were a day, flowers might seem as enduring as rocks, if we lived a thousand years, rock might seem mobile.

Flowing, molding, pressing, hammering, forging, cementing, growing; dissolving, eroding, grinding, tumbling, cracking, crumbling, scuffing, decaying: materials manifest process. River cobbles and river-run gravel are tumbled smooth and rounded; quarry-cut cobbles and crushed stone have sharp, angular edges. Sedimentary rocks are laid down in layers, deposited by water or wind and carry the imprint of context: ripples, shells, leaves, seeds. Metal, concrete, and plastic flow into a mold and harden, taking the mold's shape. Bud scars on twigs and grain in wood are records of annual growth reflecting irregularities of context. Plants—pruned, pollarded, espaliered, clipped, left freely growing—are clues to social and cultural context. Materials are shaped by processes in context—material, formal, spatial, functional, social, and cultural.

Minerals assume an "angle of repose," the steepest slope they can sustain without reinforcement: grains of sand fall naturally into a gentle slope; clay can hold the sheer drop of a cliff until it shears off; the silty soil of Laguna's hillsides slips, slumps, and slides when wet. Joints and fractures in rock are the lines along which it erodes and breaks into blocks, chunks, or sheets. How long rock retains its shape depends upon its durability, its resistance to surface erosion and internal decay. Some rocks are harder than others; some dissolve. Harder rocks resist erosion to form hills; softer rocks erode to form valleys. Limestone landscapes in water-rich regions form gently rolling karst terrain with many sinkholes over underground channels and caverns. Materials give form potential and yet impose limits to corporality and meaning.

Air is breath, plants live and die, stone endures. Sand—countless tiny loose particles—records processes, the ebb and flow of tides, the passage of people or animals, but these traces are easily erased, thus sand's meaning of immeasurability and impermanence. Stone has mass and strength, and often stands for permanence, timelessness, and immortality. Political monuments are commonly made of stone; the shrines of wood at Ise, an exception, express the paradox of enduring impermanence. The meanings of materials are both inherent and invented, traditional and potential.

Water is paradoxical: yielding yet powerful, transparent yet reflective, a leveler, eroding mountains into plains, cutting valleys, smoothing stones. Seeking level, it fills valleys, forms flat, reflective planes. On the sea's horizon, it traces the horizontal line that orients and anchors. It flows, even as ice; glaciers flow down valleys between mountains of grey rock, break up into icebergs where they meet the sea. Water absorbs, carries, and releases other materials; it is a link among them—earth, air, and living tissue. Translucent, it takes on the color of air, of suspended sediments, of bottom. In Taoism, water expresses *wu-wei*, "the strength of weakness."[15] It cleanses, a symbol of spiritual purification used for ablution, holy water, baptism. Many natural springs in Ireland are seen as sacred and are adorned with flowers, rocks, and pictures of the Virgin Mary.[16]

Fire is comforting in hearth, candles, and campfire, and awesome in lightning, explosion, and forest fire. It consumes and destroys, transforms and renews; indeed, many types and groups of plants require fire to sustain them. Fire burns off woody growth in prairies and releases pine seeds in forests. After a fire has ravaged prairie or forest, green shoots emerge from the blackened earth. No wonder fire is a symbol of transformation and regeneration for many religions and cultures. At Notre Dame in Paris, thousands of candles burn in memory of the dead.

Trees and flowers live, grow, reproduce, and die. People impose meaning, as metaphor, upon flowers and trees. Flowers are laid on graves. And Dylan Thomas said of trees, "The force that through the green fuse drives the flower / Drives my green age; that blasts the roots of trees / Is my destroyer." But not all trees reproduce, a plastic tree, for instance. Only a human can create a plastic tree, for it cannot regenerate or make another tree. Plastic trees and flowers are used decoratively, but they are never *just* decorative, for cultural associations are too strong.[17] Martha Schwartz used plastic plants in her rooftop Splice Garden for the Whitehead Institute for Biomedical Research in Cambridge, Massachusetts. The garden is simultaneously lighthearted and serious, witty and chilling, a garden version of gene-splicing and artificial life. The thin brown trunks of the plastic trees with their imitation bark have protrusions like pruned branches. There are two "spliced" forms, one with a Japanese, one with a French garden motif, the two separated by a sharp line. The ground on either side is aquarium gravel in two shades of green, the Japanese blue-green, the French a dark green; the walls behind are painted two corresponding shades. Circles of raked gravel radiate from round, plastic shrubs on the Japanese side; large blocks in geometric shapes on the French side are covered with Astroturf, some topped with a basket of plastic flowers. In Splice Garden, material and form, together, express and reinforce meaning.

Materials arouse senses, carry meaning, pose limits. Deployed deliberately, to modify process and form and extend their meanings, materials furnish precision and nuance. Used in ways which contradict intended meaning, they may undermine and obscure it. Ignorance of craft, of materials, their properties, and performance in context can lead to unintended irony and to failure: when the stone facing of a monument or a plantation of trees, meant to endure, disintegrates or dies; when a masonry wall, shaken by an earthquake, collapses.

Form: Shape and Structure

Unyielding Axes, Disintegrated Grid: Chantilly

June 1992. The gardens of Chantilly, northwest of Paris, are a huge clearing in a forest that once covered thousands of acres. Laid out by André Le Nôtre, the designer of Vaux-le-Vicomte and Versailles, these gardens were the scene of great parties and pageants in the seventeenth and eighteenth centuries; the forests were the site of elaborate hunts. I stand on the terrace above the gardens, looking out over many great basins of water, rectangles and circles reflecting sky—the water parterres. The chateau behind me, fortified by moat and walls, was built in the early sixteenth century on a plateau above the river and looks out over a broad flat floodplain.

I walk down a long flight of steps from the terrace, along a water parterre lined on one side by rows of small trees with straight trunks, their crowns clipped into green globes like the plastic trees in Schwartz's Splice Garden. The path ends at the edge of a canal, reputed to be the largest garden canal in the world (more than a mile long); Le Nôtre worked at Chantilly for twenty years, realigning the Nonette River and digging the canal out of marshes in the 1670s. I walk to the end of the canal to see the basin I know is there, and it seems to take forever; old prints depict visitors of past generations, some walking, some riding on horseback, in carriages, or sailing up the canal. The scale is vast, not a garden one can see comfortably on foot; at walking pace, I find the views monotonous, changing too slowly. I pause at the end of the canal and take a different route back through the trees on a flood terrace above the canal.

Disintegrated grid. Chantilly, France.

I am here not only because Le Nôtre considered Chantilly one of his finest works, but because a student once gave me a photograph of the place, showing the forest on a misty morning with three straight paths leading off into the distance at angles to one another. The image has haunted me since. As I leave the bright gardens, sun reflecting off the canal and basins of the water parterre, I enter the shadowy forest on a straight path that crosses diagonally another straight path, both lines of light. Cutting straight paths through the forest was Le Nôtre's first act. Paths, broad and narrow, crisscross through the woods, going off in different directions, disorienting. The Piste des Lions is one of the broadest and once led straight through the forest for miles right up to the gate of the chateau. Trees along the widest avenues through the forest are sheared up, flat as a wall.

I walk up the Piste des Lions, a path of soft, deeply raked earth at least twenty feet wide, until I realize it is for horses, not people on foot, and move over to the wooded footpath alongside. To my left, through the border of trees, is the broad piste, lit by sunlight, to my right the darker woods. The footpath is narrow, just wide enough for a single person, and meanders, as if made by someone wandering in the woods. There is a main path, and smaller paths that wander off and come back (or not). This is a weird woods. Spooked by a sense of enchantment, I stop to reason why. Birds twitter, a cuckoo, at least six other songs overlaid. Except for a few beeches, the trees are lindens; all fairly young, they fan up together and bow out in clumps, like stump sprouts. Some clumps have one or two fat trunks with dozens of smaller trunks, mostly slender saplings. No rotted trunks are lying around, no stumps are visible among the thickets of trunks and saplings. But there is one clue in the occasional large holes six feet or more across and four feet deep, which seem to occur mostly along the piste, not further in. There is a strange quality to the shape of the trees and the structure of the wood. I begin to draw what I see and realize that the trees were originally planted in rows, each tree a node on a grid, then cut at about the same time—or did they die, gradually, within a decade or more of one another? New shoots had sprouted from the base of each stump, decaying the orthogonal grid. The bizarre overlay of geometries is a relief after the rigid Euclidean geometry of Le Nôtre's plan at Chantilly. A grid of planted trees established the forest's original structure, now altered by stumps sprouting randomly around the base. Paths for horses and riders cut straight through the woods; then people, wandering, made curving paths seemingly at random.

MARCH 1997. I return to the forest of Chantilly in early spring. With a map of the forest in my hand, and no new leaves yet on the trees, I find my way easily through the forest that was so disorienting to me before. The forest is divided into numbered plots, labeled on map and on signs on the trees. Each plot is different, from tall trees with stump sprouts cut, the strongest, biggest stem left to grow, to shrubby thickets. Some are planted on a grid, others seem not to be; in a few plots, there are signs of cutting. One huge tree, its stump six feet across, was cut within the last year, its former crown still visible in the vacuum it left in the forest canopy; trees around it bend away from where its branches once spread. In some sections are holes twenty feet across where trees have come down, in others newly planted allées of beech, trees sixteen to eighteen feet apart, branches trimmed up above head height.

Months later, I read that Chantilly is part of an old royal forest; near Paris, it was a popular place to hunt, managed for hundreds of years as a game preserve for deer, boar, and pheasants.[18] The strange geometry I saw was the consequence of coppicing, of cutting trees, permitting stumps to sprout, then cutting the sprouts at intervals to create a bushy woods with food and cover for beasts of the chase. The tall trees here and there, eight to ten an acre, are "tellers" left as source of seed. All in all, an artificial forest if ever there was such a thing, a forest of the chase. But the birds don't seem to care that the forest has been planted, cut, re-grown, an artifice.

Shape versus Structure

A leaf's shape may be ovoid or lobed, a tree's shape round or vaselike, but the leaf's and the tree's structure is axial and branching. A terrain's shape is flat or rolling, mounded or bowl-shaped, its structure layered or massive. Shape expresses form's surface contour, while structure is the relation of its parts to the whole—a flower and its bud, petals, stamen, incipient fruit; a mountain and its slopes, summit, underlying rock; a town and its streets, buildings, gardens.

Shape is the more obvious and tangible; structure may be concealed. In the Bluegrass region of Kentucky, the bedrock of flat, layered limestone is hidden beneath the paradox of rolling karst terrain—dissolved by water—and revealed in river-cut cliffs and road cuts, echoed in walls of flat, laid stone. One sometimes sees the same structure in limestone paving: flat-bedded sheets, eroded into little hills and hollows—a miniature landscape. Erosion, decay, and destruction uncover or highlight concealed or unrecognized structure: decay of tree exposes growth rings in its core; weathering exposes; fire reveals the infrastructure of streets after homes burn. Structure permits perception of a whole that might otherwise be seen as unrelated fragments, and of parts that would otherwise be intangible.

Shape may change while structure remains constant. The dogwood tree, where bud and flower are one, is another paradox. The hard grey bud opens and its four-part sheath separates, softens, and grows into a four-petaled, white flower; the structure is constant, the shape changes. So, too, the shape of a beach shifts, daily, seasonally, over the years; its structure (the relation of sediments to water level, wave height and length) endures.

Drive a peg into the ground, attach a string, and move the string around the peg—you have inscribed a circle in landscape, a shape of gathering and enclosure, the most efficient shape to bound an area, like Indians' kivas in the American Southwest, the Vikings' circular settlements at Trelleborg, or the amphitheater at Roskilde, both in Denmark. Structure describes how a shape (or any landscape element or feature) evolved, developed, or was made, the word *structure* from the Latin "structura," to build. It defines a shape's proportions (broad or narrow, symmetrical or asymmetrical) and its complexity (simple or compound, regular or irregular). Shape may be explicit or implied, the whole not present; in an arc the circle is implied, the mind completes the shape through knowledge of a circle's structure.

Circle and sphere, square and cube are simple shapes. Shape is a superficial form of similarity, a low order of pattern. The more irregular or complex shapes are, the more significant congruence among them. The shapes of rock crystals and coral reefs are compound, the gradual accretion of similar shapes. Trees and shrubs of different species, pruned into a complex, uniform arc by persistent wind, is a significant similarity. But the sun, ripples in a pond, tree rings, a wheel, a Viking fort, and a kiva have little in common besides a circular appearance: ripples and tree rings expand from a center; tree rings, forts, and kivas enclose interior space; wheels spin. The sun, we imagine, has a spinning interior.

Geometries of Process

In Australia's central desert, spheres and rings of green and grey spinifex stand out against red sand. What is the shape of a spinifex plant—and when? It is round and roughly spherical at first but, as the plant grows outward, its center dies; gradually, the plant forms an expanding ring around its hollow origins. A shape reflects, at a given moment, the limits and potential of its materials, the processes that shape it, and the particulars of its context. Sand dunes shift with wind, a shoreline shifts with water currents. Volcanoes spew molten rock, which hardens into new landforms, and scientists imagine jagged mountains eroding into gently sloping plains. Sheep and deer prune tree canopies into a flat-bottomed shape at the height of their reach; the clipped trees fill out again when browsing ceases. Trees, gardens, and towns are shaped by movement, growth, cultivation, exchange, and decay. Skylines of many American cities changed after 1960, when private developers began to build high-rise towers for downtown offices; the shape of inner-city neighborhoods changed too as houses and businesses, abandoned by owners moving from city to suburb, fell into ruin.

Shapes of mountain ranges, riverbanks, sand dunes, trees, and snow crystals are poised at a moment in time, their beauty lying in a peculiar combination of order and disorder, harmoniously arranged, form reflecting the processes that produced it. Benoit Mandelbrot calls such forms, and their congruence across scales of time and space, "fractal" geometry, "the geometry of nature." Fractal shapes come from complexity and turbulence, they are infinitely long and self-repeating, like Mandelbrot's description of a shoreline, or like traces of tidal rivers in mud, branching ferns, or the edge of a cloud. A sensibility steeped in classical geometry might see such forms as too complex to describe, as simply disordered, or, as Frank Lloyd Wright did earlier, as able to be abstracted into triangles and circles, grids and radiating lines. As fractals, such complex patterns can be described, with relative simplicity, through repetitive processes like bifurcation and development. Snow crystals, in their combination of stability and instability, of symmetry and randomness, of repetition and variety, are fractal forms. Each snowflake or ice crystal embodies both the process of its formation and all the changing weather patterns it has experienced. Water, crystallizing, forms a growing tip with a boundary that becomes unstable and sends off side branches. The structural similarity of snowflakes comes from limits and potential of its material, water; the seemingly infinite variety of shape is caused by variations in context, in the precise combinations of wind, sun, humidity, and temperature to which each is exposed as it forms. Knowing the structure of ice crystals and how their growth is affected by context, it is possible to read those contexts in the shape of each flake. And the same is true of larger landscapes.

Fractal geometry provides a way to describe and appreciate the complex form of villages and older urban districts admired for their variety and quality of wholeness. Such places evolved with a peculiar combination of order and disorder, through purposeful process and repetitive use of built forms, the shape of buildings, streets, and squares varying in response to differing conditions of context—physiographic, economic, cultural, and individual preference. In some new towns, on the other hand, the form of houses, and even such details as exterior paint color and landscaping, are prescribed. And redeveloped urban districts are often a hodgepodge of idiosyncratic buildings and leftover space.

Similar kinds of structure underlie landscapes and their features, both naturally occurring and designed. Axes—of snowflake's branching, river's flowing, city's streets—are lines of movement, whether actual or implied, straight, serpentine, or spiral, singular or branching; they depend on quality of movement, conditions of origin and growth. One major axis, a broad processional route paved with stone, oriented north-south, extended through Beijing, led straight through the Forbidden City connecting the throne room in the palace to the Temple of Heaven. The Champs-Élysées is an axis built by Louis XIV to accommodate the movement of his court back and forth between his Parisian palace, the Louvre, and Versailles, expressing the link between the two. The main street in Aspen Farms and Main Street in Disneyland are axes of movement and meeting. Two axes, at right angles, aligned to the compass, defined the Roman *castrum*—a military camp, and later, a square, fortified town—two roads crossed at the center, puncturing the walls at four gates. This pattern is still preserved in towns like Ljubljana in Slovenia and Cologne in Germany, both originally established as Roman castra.

A city's grid, like a spider's web, is made by overlapping lines of movement, a lattice structure regularly or irregularly shaped. A square grid, quickly surveyed and settled, was common in colonial towns and frontier territories from those of ancient Greece to the Americas: from the ancient Greek city of Priene, to Mexico City, Philadelphia, and the American Midwest. Like the Roman castrum, Philadelphia has two major north-south, east-west streets (Market and Broad) that are central axes within a grid of streets. Benjamin Franklin Parkway, built more than two hundred years after the grid was surveyed and settled, cuts diagonally across it, slicing squares into odd-shaped slivers; such breaks from underlying structure signify something.[19] In this case, the desire to transform an old neighborhood into a new district of cultural institutions and to link two important monuments: City Hall at the intersection of Market and Broad and the site of the new art museum on a hill across town. One can also see cities with a gridded street pattern like Philadelphia's as a modular structure, square-shaped blocks of land bounded by streets. Modular structure, in towns, buildings, tiles, and honeycombs, comes from packing together modules of similar shape.

Most human settlements, like all landscapes, are stratified, spatially and temporally: streets and buildings over underground sewers and basements; multistoried houses with street-level common rooms for entertaining visitors and second-floor private rooms; penthouses on upper floors of skyscrapers. Just as the layered structure of sandstone, shale, and limestone reflects their formation from successive depositing of sand, silt, and clay, so the ground under cities reveals layers of previous settlements. Nested structure, too, is a form of stratification: Imperial Beijing was structured by a series of concentric, rectangular, walled enclosures; the innermost precinct, surrounded by a moat, was the emperor's Forbidden City with the palace at the center; the Forbidden City was enclosed in turn by the walled, administrative imperial city. Nested landscape structure, one part enclosed within another, may also convey a sense of refuge as one moves progressively inward. Courtyard gardens within houses of dense city districts in Kyoto are secular havens, the fenced enclosures of Ise religious refuge; in both, there is a progressive contrast between outer, public realms and inner, private ones, between secular and sacred.

Certain settlement structures are more rigid and inflexible than others, others more open and flexible in accommodating change.[20] Those with circular structure pose particular problems and specific opportunities, for a circle is complete in itself. A circular park is the heart of the University of California-Irvine campus, bounded by a path, lined by buildings; the university has expanded greatly, but the park at its center remains sacrosanct. Had it been another shape, a rectangle, for example, it might have been encroached upon by buildings. In this case, inflexibility was an advantage. Like a circle, stratified structure is less adaptable for it can expand or contract only by accretion or erosion, one layer at a time. Modular structure expands through repetition, axial structure along lines of growth. The grid, on the other hand, is particularly flexible because it accommodates growth along multiple lines of movement.

Marker and Vessel of Experience and Meaning

Elms trees are tall and vase-shaped: long branches sprout high on the trunk, arching up and out like ribs in a Gothic vault. Parallel rows of elms, planted close so their branches meet, create a cathedral-like space beneath the trees. Cherry trees are short and branch close to the ground; an allée of closely planted cherries encloses an intimate space. The Naiku shrine at Ise is raised on a rectangular platform supported by enormous boulders; fences define its inner, most sacred spaces. Space is shaped and differentiated by the form of landscape features: a void enclosed by trees, hills, buildings; an area marked off as distinct or special or forbidden. Open or enclosed, monumental or intimate, such spatial qualities depend on the form and scale of bounding plants, landforms, or walls. In the beginning, according to Genesis, the earth was without form, and thus void. Form orders space: the poet Wallace Stevens describes how a jar placed on a hill reorders the landscape around it; buildings do the same.[21]

Shape, like material, is sensual—visible, tangible, even audible. Anyone who drives on a country road, up and down hills and around curves, *feels* the shape of the land or, sailing a boat, the shape of waves and wind. In landscape, shape is continuous, related, connected to other shapes. The sighted person perceives these as a whole; to the blind person, this continuity is invisible, seemingly fragmented, heard as "various broken sounds spread across a nothingness," until "rain presents the fullness of an entire situation all at once, a sense of perception of the actual relationships of one part of the world to another."[22] Shape has texture: fuzzy, spiky,

Geometry and function. Sonja Poll's Garden (1970). Denmark. (Plan drawn by Sonja Poll)

or smooth to touch, and it modulates movement: directing and deflecting running water or crowds of people, focusing and reflecting sound—amphitheaters are often bowl-shaped, to gather people and project sound.

Paths that follow cardinal directions, the rising and setting of the sun, or that link important landmarks provide a sense of orientation; mazelike paths engender confusion. Vitus Bering Park in Horsens, Denmark, both confuses and orients. A spiraling path leads to an elliptical lawn near the center, and two diagonal paths slice shortcuts across the park. The curving path is grass, lined by tall, dense rhododendrons all over eye height; straight paths are paved and flat. The effect is disturbing, yet reassuring; to encounter a straight path is to find a way out of the spiral. The whole can be experienced only by exploration, fitting for a park that honors the explorer and cartographer after whom the Bering Strait was named. C. Th. Sørensen designed it in 1954–56, anticipating by several decades later trends in landscape and urban design; which, like Vitus Bering Park, were inspired by the Russian constructivists. Parc de La Villette in Paris, which combines a meandering path with several straight ones, is an example.

Sonja Poll's garden at her house north of Copenhagen, designed by Sørensen (her father), has a complex geometric structure: ellipse, spiral, and circles of hedge, lawn, paths, patio, and flower beds play against the triangle of the property's boundaries and the rectangle of the house. The spiral path leads from the back door down to a small circular patio enclosed by a rounded bank that provides

Spiral path. Sonja Poll's garden. Denmark.

a sense of rest and refuge. The oddly shaped leftover space between elliptical hedge and boundary fence is a convenient place for vegetable garden, compost pile, tool-shed, and greenhouse; an awkwardly shaped property turned to advantage.

Geometry, for Frank Lloyd Wright, was "an aesthetic skeleton" that held symbolic meaning: "Certain geometric forms have come to symbolize for us and potently to suggest certain human ideas, moods, and sentiments—as for instance: the circle, infinity; the triangle, structural unity; the spire, aspiration; the spiral, organic progress; the square, integrity."[23] Through "subtle differentiations of these elemental geometric forms," and "a sense of [their] symbol-value," form could be made to *signify*, an idea he exploited for both buildings and gardens.[24]

A circle represents both movement, around a central point, and also stasis, a shape with no beginning and no end, T. S. Eliot's "still point of the turning world."[25] It is a paradox complicated by another paradox: a circle's outline has no hierarchy but its structure, with a center, has. Jens Jensen's "council rings" for parks and gardens in Illinois and Wisconsin were circles of stone with campfires in the center, where people could gather to talk, tell stories, perform. Jensen saw the council ring as a symbol of democracy and of "the brotherhood of all living things."[26] A circle is associated with heaven in many cultures, the annual cycle of seasons, with birth and death, change and becoming. There are more squares than circles in human-built landscapes, and more circles than squares in "natural" landscapes. Is this why squares so often represent reason and order?

In sacred architecture, circle and square, sphere and cube are often combined. The exterior of Woodland Chapel at Forest Cemetery is square and rustic; the interior is square, but within the square ceiling is a circle, and from that circle springs a dome, a half sphere with a central skylight. A circle of simple, Doric columns supports the circular opening in the ceiling under the dome. A soft light washes the dome and strikes the stone floor within the circle—an abstraction of a forest clearing. The body of the dead is placed here in the light under the dome; the mourners sit in shadow.

So, too, the plain buildings of the Shaker Village at Pleasant Hill, Kentucky, give no clue to the flights of ornament within. Who, seeing the austere exterior stone and brick walls, could imagine the arched doorways, vaults, and curving rails of Center House? or the elegant curves of the two spiral stairways in the Trustees' Office—except, perhaps, from a clue in the fantail over the door and the glazing in the third-floor window above the door? This structure is not coincidental; it represents the Shaker belief of a grace-filled inner life nurtured within a plain and austere exterior.

Mont-Saint-Michel's single pilgrimage path is a hierarchical structure, leading from worldly base to hilltop shrine, a spiraling, then a straight, vertical axis, and continues on inside the church, along the main axis from rear to front toward the rising sun. The parts of the whole are ordered along a gradient of importance. Indeed, all axial structure is hierarchical, each part subordinate to a dominant spine. Not surprising, then, that axes are common to religious and political landscapes. In Rome, Paris, and Washington, principal streets link cultural landmarks and political monuments—secular shrines.

The layered structure of Kansas City, Missouri, is hierarchical, the layers both horizontal and vertical: poorer people in inner city, in urban valleys; the wealthier in outer suburbs, on ridges. Anyone attending a convention in Kansas City need never encounter the tumbled down buildings and vacant lots of the valley between hotels and convention center. New hotels are on a bluff, connected to the downtown center by a viaduct that leapfrogs the poor districts, sight unseen, below.

In a coordinated structure like a grid, all parts that have similar importance carry equal weight, though certain orthogonal lines in the grid may be emphasized, for example, streets crossing at the center of a castrum or a city. A grid structure, easy to survey and plot, is sometimes seen as a sign of colonization, but a grid has also been a symbol of democracy. Paul Klee used a grid in paintings to give order to diversity. G. N. Brandt used a similar strategy in his design for Mariebjerg Cemetery, north of Copenhagen, where a grid of high evergreen hedges disguises changes in topography and unifies the whole. The visually separate, rectangular modules framed by the grid are landscape rooms for different styles of burials: wooden crosses marking graves within the dappled shade of a wooded meadow; family tombs set within ferns and ivy under the dense shade of evergreen trees; a serene space carpeted by clipped lawn where ashes are scattered; the graves of children in a place enclosed by lilacs under the spreading branches of an old oak; and many others. The repetitive structure of the grid emphasizes the different landscape styles within each precinct and the particular attitude about death exemplified in each.

Formal composition is fundamental to design, but form without substance, at odds with process, may fail to function, alienate those who use a place, and even put them at risk. Sørensen delighted in formal play; his compositions have complex and sophisticated geometry, but they do not neglect material, process, and performance. Great landscape authors like Sørensen and Brandt fashion forms and employ them to shape and structure space, to evoke feeling, hold meaning, and perform function.

Performance Space: Places of Need and Use

Uluru, Stourhead, Cooper's Place

The heart of Australia is a vast red desert thousands of miles across. To many who live in the cities and towns that hug Australia's coastline, the Center is a threatening chaos, but to Aborigines who dwell there, the Center is highly ordered, a complex mosaic of sand hills, claypans, dry channels, rock holes, and rocky outcrops, each with a precise relationship to water, plants, animals, and myth in a landscape rich in food and charged with meaning.

Bands of Aborigines move deliberately within this domain of food and water sources and sacred places defined by inherited song. Songs of how ancestors sang them into being, and with them the right to use the paths they relate, are passed from one generation to another. The continent of Australia is laced with these ancient paths, visible only to those who know the songs that describe the way, that tell of the relationships among rocks, water, animals, and humans, and that link present time with the forming of the world during the Dreamtime. The songs tell of movement and guide hunters and gatherers of food, legends of origin recalled in everyday rituals of digging for bush potatoes and witchetty grubs, gathering bush banana, hunting wallaby.

The small aboriginal bands have estates of sufficient size to support them with water and food, the fuzzy boundaries of each band's estate overlap adjacent ones; contiguous bands are joined by the songs they share. The locations of paths and sacred places are not fuzzy, however; trespass on a sacred site is forbidden except by those who "keep" the place and those they permit to accompany them.

Rituals celebrate landscape and reenact its formation through dance as well as song. Settings for rituals are created by clearing the ground, constructing a windbreak, and inscribing elaborate symbolic patterns in packed earth: a circle as a water hole, a camp site, or a food-bearing bush; wavy lines as a watercourse; arrows as a path.[27] In the 1970s, aboriginal artists from the central desert began to transfer these compositions to canvas, with methods and compositions strikingly

The climb. Uluru. Australia.

similar to those of traditional ritual art.[28] Typically, the artists work outdoors on canvas spread on the ground, often a group working on a painting together, an affirmation of shared territory and responsibility to the landscape they live in. Many artists begin with a red ground, then add concentric circles—perhaps a rock hole. These paintings and ritual settings are maps of territory as an Aborigine might see it. Walbiri see water underground, witchetty grubs and honey ants crawling in roots; they paint mythic landscapes with water, grubs, roots, terrain, branches, superimposed, fusing past, present, future. In *Witchetty Grub Dreaming at the Site of Mount Wedge*, four small witchetty bushes frame a larger, central bush, all five lying in a claypan surrounded by sand hills.[29] At each bush a woman sits with digging stick, rooting for witchetty grubs. The grubs are shown within the roots of the bush, below ground. Such paintings fuse mythical events with events of daily life, expressing a unity, across time, with natural processes and the landscape they shape.

Uluru rises out of this desert, like an island in the sea, like Australia itself—an immense monolith marking the center of a continent. Water streams off courses eroded into the rock, like rivers of a miniature continent, isolated by desert-sea as surely as Australia itself is surrounded by vast stretches of ocean. There is even a continental shelf of plant life around the base, supported by more abundant water there, the runoff. Of great significance to Aborigines are Uluru's several sacred sites, perhaps the oldest continuously revered place in the world.

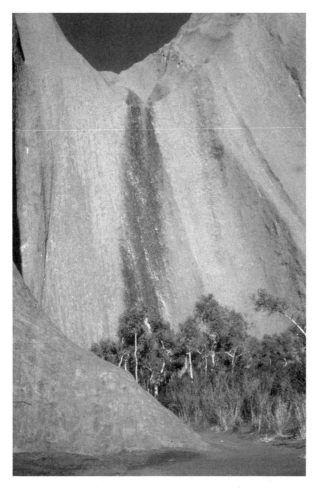

Refuge. Uluru. Australia.

The first white explorers who reached it in the late nineteenth century named it Ayre's Rock, but local Aborigines continued their subsistence culture until the 1940s, when cattle stations began to encroach upon their foraging territory, depleting water sources. Today the rock is a symbol of the outback for all Australians and the destination of tourists.

Some tourists to Uluru climb, many watch others climb, then take in the rock at sunset, but most see this landscape from an air-conditioned tour bus, mainly on the move, only its broad outlines visible. Those who step down from the tour bus and walk into the landscape, away from the road and parking lots, enter a different world of green foliage, blue and purple wildflowers, vivid, red-orange ground, with a base rhythm of humming flies punctuated by birdsong. None of this is visible or audible within the moving bus with its closed tinted windows.

Aboriginal rangers have built a path for visitors across the sand plain with its wildflowers and spinifex into a mulga grove and on to the base of Uluru. They lead small groups along the path and tell stories: how to gather spinifex, how to beat and heat it to form glue, how to make fire and find food, how the Liru warrior ancestors—poisonous snakes—came across this plain and threw their spears at the Kuniya ancestors, leaving the pockmarks one sees on the rock today. The tourist path, named Liru, recalls aspects of the dreaming tracks.

The English who colonized Australia were blind to the paths and signs that ordered the Aborigines' landscape. To them it was foreign, a chaotic wilderness. The landscape they introduced, still being built in the desert today, is a pastoral landscape, its roots in eighteenth-century English landscape gardens and their ancient precedents in Roman poetry. From the time that Joseph Addison, in the early 1700s, urged the English landowner to "make a pretty Landskip of his own Possessions," English gentry shaped their estates to express the integration of agriculture, art, property, power, and politics.[30] Their landscape gardens tell stories that can be decoded only by those who can read the signs. Stourhead, in southwestern England, is such a landscape garden. To the modern visitor with no intimate knowledge of classical literature, its landscape is merely picturesque; to an eighteenth-century English gentleman, it represented the power of privilege and empire.

At Stourhead, one descends from the house down wooded slopes to the lake below and enters a calm, carefully ordered world. Follow the path around the lake—now enclosed in woods, now open to a carefully framed, postcard-perfect view—and an allegory unfolds, for one who can read it. Sculptures and buildings embellish the story, and Latin inscriptions yield clues to their meaning: lines from Virgil's *Aeneid* refer to the founding of Rome, others to Alfred, the first English king, or to the builder and owner, the eighteenth-century banker Henry Hoare, a juxtaposing of classical and Gothic styles that parallels the links between ancient Rome and powerful, mercantile England.[31]

Stourhead is literally just that, the head of the river Stour, whose source is numerous springs within the valley. Monuments mark the springs: one is a Gothic cross, moved from its original location near St. Peter's Church in Bristol; another, a sleeping nymph and a river god who points the way to the Pantheon, presiding over a spring that wells up within a grotto. The statue recalls the story from the *Aeneid* in which "the God of the place, old Tiber himself," foretells the founding of Rome. The path leads to a replica of the Pantheon, past a hermit's cave to the Temple of Apollo, across a Palladian bridge to the Temple of Flora. Hoare, unlike many other landowners, who moved entire villages to make way for their landscape gardens, incorporated the village of Stourton into his Arcadian composition. The church spire and the cottages across the way compose a peaceful scene visible from the Pantheon across the lake. Stourhead's self-contained world was a refuge for Hoare and his family from the political turmoil of London and Europe. It stood for the owner, embodying, in his own words, "the fruits of industry and application to business and [showing] what great things can be done by it, the

Storied path. Stourhead. England.

envy of the indolent who have no claim to temples, grottos, bridges, rocks, exotic pines and ice in summer."[32]

This English landscape style spread throughout the British Empire and beyond. Nineteenth- and twentieth-century garden suburbs in England and North America adopted it, and so, more recently, have corporate office parks, asserting the power of property, the status of the owner, and alluding to the continuity of Western culture.

"Only land is power" reads a message scrawled across the wall of an abandoned building in Boston's Roxbury neighborhood. This message would not have been lost on eighteenth-century Englishmen, nor is it lost upon residents of North American inner cities who transform abandoned vacant lots into community gardens, only to be forced to relinquish them for parking lots or if land values rise, for buildings, nor is it lost upon those whose gardens are held more securely in common trust.

Forty people garden at Cooper's Place, a community garden in Roxbury. Each gardener has a plot and all tend a common rose garden with a sitting area open to the entire neighborhood. The sitting garden, reached through two gates under rose-covered arbors, is an anteroom to the allotments beyond, through another arbored gate. Behind the individual plots is a common herb garden and another sitting area for the gardeners, and, alongside, an orchard. Many of the plants the gardeners grow—peanuts, sweet potato, collards, and watermelon—reflect their southern origins. The sustenance provided by their land is spiritual as well as physical and social: as one gardener said, "I love to plant; I love to watch anything grow. I kneel down in that dirt and take up a handful of it. I say this is nature . . . this is God's thing and I enjoy it."[33] One gardener tells of how she goes out into the garden early in the morning, when all is calm and peaceful, to pray. Here, she says, she feels nearest to God.

Twenty years ago the garden was just another vacant lot, composed of four house lots whose property boundaries were invisible with no trace of the four original houses save the stone retaining wall along the sidewalk broken by steps that once led to the four front doors. In 1975, a group of local senior citizens transformed the lot into a community garden. For six years, the gardeners tended their plots, though they were aware that the ultimate destiny of the land they tilled was beyond their control. In 1981 they acquired the land, and two years later they secured funds for improvements from the city. In 1984 my graduate students in landscape architecture developed new designs for the garden, one of which was then built by unemployed youth enrolled in a landscape training program at a local community college.

I had to help six landscape architecture students at the Harvard Graduate School of Design—all white, middle-class, raised in suburbs—to enter the landscape dialogues of forty elderly urban gardeners—African American and Hispanic. Each student was asked to start the semester by staying with one of the gardeners for the weekend. The next week we met with the gardeners to discuss their dreams for the community garden my students were to design for them. My students and I had framed a series of questions to elicit our clients' hopes; one asked the gardeners what their favorite place in Boston was. The response was a surprising consensus: "The Fenway Rose Garden." "We want a rose garden!" Whereupon Beth Arndtsen, the student who had posed the question, visited the Fenway Rose Garden, but it was January and the garden was closed. Undeterred, she scaled the locked fence to study the place; her design for the new community garden adapted its white arbors, its climbing roses, its gravel paths and flat lawn. When each of the students presented a design three weeks later, the forty gardeners chose Arndtsen's. It was built and planted a month later, in March 1984, and it still thrives there.Had the question not been posed, we might never have realized how important a symbol the Fenway Rose Garden was for them. Ironically, the Fenway Rose Garden itself was then in jeopardy; landscape historians were petitioning for its removal from the Fens on the grounds that it was not part of Frederick Law Olmsted's original design for this landmark landscape.

From Linwood Street, in Roxbury, today, the white arches and vivid red and pink roses spilling out over the fence can be seen a block away; closer, the scent of roses fills the air. One enters the garden under a white, rose-covered arbor through an unlocked gate into a formal sitting garden, with a small panel of grass surrounded by a gravel path lined with flower beds. Cooper's Place, named for Ed

Territory reclaimed: Cooper's Place. Boston. (West Philadelphia Landscape Project)

Entrance, sign of welcome: Cooper's Place. Boston.

Cooper, a neighbor, gardener, and activist, is a local landmark. There have been weddings there, and it has stimulated neighborhood change. Before the garden was built, the apartment building next door and two houses across the street were vacant. They are now renovated, repainted, and repopulated. The gardeners had a dream of converting four empty garages at the rear of the garden into a center for canning fruits and vegetables and for environmental education. This seemed hopelessly beyond reach in 1984, but, in 1997, the group broke ground for the center; they had raised $450,000, mostly from foundations, to build it. The gardeners are extraordinary people, but the garden's design, too, was key to its success. The designer gave form to the power of the gardeners' dreams and created a place of beauty and refuge that inspired confidence, hope, and affection.

Despite differences of time, place, and culture, the landscapes of Uluru, Stourhead, and Cooper's Place are fundamentally similar. The phenomenon of territory, embodied in the use of land and the feeling of belonging to it, is common to all three. Australian Aborigines *are* their territory; they belong to their territory, not only the source of sustenance but also the repository of their history, a link to past and future generations. Aboriginal country consists of all those places that hold meaning through inheritance and personal experience. Aborigines separated from their country lose an essential part of their identity. The property of the English gentleman was the source of his power and his vote in Parliament; through the land's embellishment as a pastoral landscape he identified himself and his nation as the inheritor of Rome. His territory was not his own local property alone but England itself and the expanding empire. The land of Cooper's Place was hard-won; held in common it testifies to the achievement of individuals who worked together to achieve common goals. Each gardener shares ownership through use of the land; the plants grown there are a link not only to the past and to the larger community, but also to new hope for the future.

The boundary at Cooper's Place, a chain-link fence four feet high, is a more unambiguous demarcation of territory than exists at Stourhead or Uluru. One can see through the fence at Cooper's Place and talk across it; along with the carefully tended roses it signals that this area belongs to people who care for it. Vandals have left the garden untouched. The unlocked gate to the sitting area says this is private property where others are welcome. The locked gate to the allotments beyond marks them as private, with entrance by invitation only.

At Stourhead, unlike Cooper's Place, boundaries are often concealed. The ditch, or ha-ha, that keeps pasture in view and the sheep out of the garden is invisible from the house. The valley is a world in itself, with property boundaries invisible from within the valley since they lie beyond the enclosing hills or disguised behind dense planting. The inclusion of the village of Stourton within the view from the garden extends the boundaries of the estate beyond the territory it occupies. Thus is the larger world of the village and its inhabitants absorbed into the gentry's domain.

In aboriginal territory, there are no walls, fences, or gates at all. Overlapping boundaries between adjacent estates reflect the belief that many people together hold a country. Traditionally, one attains the right to a particular estate through prolonged association and care. Territory is defined by knowledge, by knowing the stories that plants, animals, and landforms embody. The paths that create territory are not just for traveling from place to place; they also express relationships and responsibilities across multiple, contiguous estates. Dreaming paths, some hundreds of miles long, trace ancestors' movements across the land, connecting significant places and sacred sites within the estates the path crosses. Places linked by a dreaming path are "one country."

Like the aboriginal dreaming paths, the path at Stourhead links a series of landmarks or signs that tell stories connecting the present with the past. The roses and white arbors at Cooper's Place are shared stories of past and present and link it to that other, well-tended public space, the Fenway Rose Garden. The Cooper's Place arbors have come to stand not for the community garden alone, but, beyond that, for a landmark that defines the larger neighborhood. At Stourhead, the Pantheon and the Temple of Apollo provide both a prospect from which to view and reflect upon the landscape and its stories and a refuge from sudden showers. The benches set under the rose arbors at Cooper's Place are likewise both prospect and refuge. Both are a refuge from the world outside just as the central desert of Uluru is now a refuge, for Aborigines, from Western culture.

Territory is established by the limits of the processes which create it. A watershed is a territory through which water flows to a particular stream or river; a tidal zone is the territory created by sea's ebb and flow. The boundaries of both are marked by extent of movement. A habitat is the area within which an animal forages and mates; a nation is the domain in which authority dictates that certain actions proceed in certain ways according to law. Paths, boundaries, and gateways are conditions, not things, spatial patterns defined by processes. Paths are places of movement, boundaries limits to movement, gateways places of passage and exchange. A path is maintained by movement. Once a process ceases, space becomes a shell of past practices.[34]

Places of Need and Use

I once spent a week walking footpaths in the Wye Valley of western England, armed with an ordinance survey. The first day's route was easy to follow: cutting through pastures, on stiles over fences, across wheat fields on narrow tracks through the grain, along the river Wye, then up, among a milling flock of sheep, to a hilltop pasture with views out over the rolling green and gold patchwork to the Black Mountains of Wales. The next day, my hosts sent me further afield, and the way was less easy to find and follow, though the path was clearly marked on the map. I walked along hedgerows through high grass, climbed over stiles blocked by wire fencing, crashed through cornfields, stumbled down a long slope

Territory, path, boundary, gateway, prospect, refuge, source, sign. Bedolina petroglyph (ca. 2500 B.C.)

covered in bracken, chased by a bull. My hosts were members of a local society dedicated to keeping footpaths open; they kept records of which paths had been walked, and when. The paths near their home were well maintained by their own frequent walking; they had made neat paths through nearby wheat fields by trampling a track when the plants were young and the farmer gone to town for the afternoon. Public footpaths on private land are remnants of an earlier landscape predating the Enclosure Acts. Public access, or right-of-way, is granted by English common law on the basis of traditional use; that right is relinquished if the path is not used at least once a year. My route was duly recorded, its right-of-way ensured for another year.

Most people tend to follow a path if there is one, as do cows and goats. On the large, sloping plaza at the foot of La Grande Arche, at La Défense in Paris, a straight, slanting path begins, ending nowhere special—Sven-Ingvar Andersson's whimsical stroke. The plaza is grey, of granite pavers, the path is white, of marble. I stood and watched people and path one late afternoon. Adults crossing the plaza altered their movement as they reached the white strip: either they changed course and walked up or down the path, or, as they crossed it, deflected their line of movement slightly. Two little girls bicycled down the marble strip and back up the plaza, again and again, for nearly an hour. Two older boys on roller blades came, set out cones of orange plastic along the path, and skated down, weaving in and out. Cyclists and skaters took turns.

Territory, boundary, path, gateway, meeting place, prospect, refuge, source, and sign are types of spaces basic to human habitats. I call them *performance spaces* to emphasize that they are generated by active processes and are not simply formal and fixed, as commonly seen.[35] My own approach sees space as a setting for performance of activities; it begins with the processes that generate places, rather than with their expression in particular forms, and then asks what settings are necessary to sustain these processes. Each kind of performance space is derived from archetypal needs and activities and the means invented to meet or accommodate them. Some needs and activities are basic to survival—moving, finding sustenance, stimulating senses, reproducing, growing, identifying, and controlling, and making/building. Others are social—belonging, communicating, trading, playing, learning, and conflict. Others, for humans, are spiritual needs—reflection, worship. The places we dwell in, gardens, homes, neighborhoods, towns, or cities, must, at the very least, satisfy these needs. This approach draws from the study of humans and culture and from landscape ecology and animal ethology. I have tested its relevance to landscapes of different cultures: from Uluru to Cooper's Place, from West Philadelphia to Japan, Versailles and Stourhead to Kongenshus in Denmark and Forest Cemetery in Stockholm. Performance spaces are also relevant to inorganic processes and other life forms to the extent that the processes that generate those spaces are shared.

There is a complex interplay between processes and the territories they engender. A simple path may be created by something moving—people, cows, a river—but most paths are not simple. A promenade path is for walking, meeting, talking, playing, displaying; a ritual path or pilgrimage route is for procession and worship. There are paths for every movement, for work, trade, invasion, teaching, learning, pleasure, travel. One place may be the setting for more than one archetypal activity: the channels of a tidal estuary are for moving and exchanging, but so is a trade route. Gateway denotes a threshold, a place of passage: a garden gate that opens and closes, a bridge point of entry into a city, a harbor of access to some hinterland. A sign may be words on a billboard or a post, but Uluru is also a sign, as are the roses at Cooper's Place and the monuments that mark the springs at Stourhead. All convey meaning. Patterns are of diverse scale: a garden, a building, a neighborhood, a city, a region, a nation, yet the functions served are the same; a garden wall, a building wall, a city wall, the wall of China, all are boundaries.

What I call performance spaces have been described by others, though not exactly in the same way; most others focus on a few types rather than many types or on form rather than process. Anthropologists and geographers are more likely to see such spaces as generated by cultural practices, architects more likely to see them as visible forms with process secondary, if there at all. In *The Experience of Landscape*, the geographer Jay Appleton, for example, examines the roots of refuge

Sign. Chaco Canyon. New Mexico.

and prospect in the adaptive behavior of humans and animals.[36] Christian Norberg-Shulz, an architectural theorist, refers to domain, path, and node as the archetypal elements of human settlements; Kevin Lynch, another theorist, refers to district, path, node, edge, and landmark.[37] In *Image of the City*, Lynch was concerned with identifying, wayfinding, and memory, his goal to define the elements people use to form mental images of a place by which they then find their way. He used these elements to assess and design the "legibility" or "imageability" of a place, to understand how well people could grasp and remember an image of the whole. Both Norberg-Schulz and Lynch compiled lists of elements from observing urban form and people's response to it. Architects and urban designers have used Lynch's list for decades, as if it were comprehensive (he never claimed that it was), though it omits certain important settings, like prospect, refuge, and source.

The architect and planner Christopher Alexander sees specific spaces for behavior as patterns that combine to create a "pattern language": global patterns on the scale of a region or town ("City Country Fingers," "Ring Roads," "Web of Shopping"); neighborhood patterns ("Green Streets," "Holy Ground"); building and garden patterns ("Entrance Room," "Zen View," "Tree Space"). The 253 patterns he describes in *A Pattern Language* are derived from his observations of places that, in his judgment, embody a quality of "wholeness," "the quality without a name."[38] Many of these patterns are wonderful and inspiring, others are idiosyncratic, formalistic, and formulaic. His insight that the character of a place

Gateway. Death Valley. California.

comes from patterns of events interlocked with geometric patterns in space is important and seminal, but his frequent focus on form rather than on the processes that shape it leads him to define patterns like "City Country Fingers," in which he stipulates that cities be no more than one mile wide, interspaced with farmland no smaller than one mile wide (so city residents can walk to it). He fails to take account of differences in terrain, soil fertility, drainage patterns, and so on. His dicta are sometimes vague, even mystical. Yet the problems that Alexander's theory poses and the gaps it contains challenge others to address them; his early work, less sweeping in both scope and claims than the later work, had a formative influence on my own thinking. His *A Pattern Language Which Generates Multi-Service Centers* identified all the functions of a community center, breaking them down into constituent parts; he drew formal and spatial relationships that made those activities possible and that evoked feelings.[39] His great contribution is his insight into the relationships among form, function, and feeling and his gathering of hundreds of examples of successful fit among these three.

When John Widrick went back to the drawing board to revise his design for a meeting place at Aspen Farms Community Garden, described earlier, he redefined the problem by focusing on the processes that would ultimately animate the space. He discarded his original proposal, a square area in the center of the garden, and began to consider the constellation of activities surrounding meeting: movement, exchange, gathering. This reformulation enabled him to envision the meeting place as a broad path with places to sit alongside, a main street running right through the garden rather than as a plaza. His success depended on the ability to move fluently between performance and space, between an understanding of general principles and of the particular context of the garden and its gardeners. To concentrate on formal qualities of space and neglect performance is to mistake the shell for the practices which shape and activate it; both are important.

Performance, Space, and Meaning

Many years ago, I heard René Dubos tell a group of landscape architects how "early man was imprinted by the soils, rocks, springs, and rivers among which he developed," "his mind and bodily responses . . . shaped by the information he derived from his senses," how humans, like all living organisms, "retain structural and functional evidences of their distant evolutionary past."[40] I chiefly remember his description of early humans and his discussion of the importance to their survival of refuge (a protected, secure, and comfortable place), of prospect (a vantage point that affords a broad view of prey and predators), and of water. His advice was to make a landscape to which people will be instinctively drawn: create a sense of refuge, provide a prospect and the presence of water.[41] His reflections on prospect and refuge made me take notice of such settings in landscape and made me wonder what other fundamental human, social, and cultural processes exist and what settings they might require.

Nourlangie Rock, an aboriginal dwelling now in Kakadu National Park, was occupied until the 1960s by people who lived as hunter-gatherers. It is a "found" dwelling, not a built one, reached by a hot climb through a dry, tropical woodland. There are only three narrow passages into a shelter created by an overhang and a tilted rock. It is shady, cool, and breezy, for the openings between the two rocks function as wind catchers, affording relief on a hot day. The roof is high, the interior spacious; walls are covered with rock paintings of animals, dangerous spirits, and Lightning Man, a fearsome, mythical figure. Rock paintings in Kakadu date as far back as nine thousand years or more, and as late as the 1960s.[42] As I stood looking, through an opening, out over the countryside, I thought of Dubos. As I did on another occasion in a very different place. The drive up South Mountain near Phoenix to the topmost overlook is several miles from the base; the view is of the valley below and cascades of mountain ranges beyond, one behind the other. Seen from above, the sprawling city seemed miniature and more comprehensible than when driving or walking within it. On a late afternoon, midweek, there were only a few cars, but the enormous parking lot indicated the many to come. By sunset, hundreds were there, couples sitting, arms around each other, families, groups of young men, black, white, Hispanic, Asian. Most just watched, quiet, as the sun went down and the city lights came on.

A prospect is not always pleasant. I sometimes think about the new residents of Åvangsgården—a doctor and a businessman—who tore out the hedges under the trees around the house to gain a view to the fields. The hedges had protected the farmhouse from strong Danish winds and driving rain, and perhaps the farmer, my Danish father, had welcomed a refuge, sacrificing prospect, since the balance between his income and his expense was so precarious. A prospect from West Terrace Park in Kansas City once made me feel elated, then depressed, and, ultimately, ambivalent. In searching for that park, I had passed through a neighborhood of vacant lots and dilapidated houses, onto a bridge over several layers of expressways and viaducts, through a renewal neighborhood to the remnants of the park; framed in the open arches of the refurbished hillside park was a vista of abandoned and decaying factories and warehouses.

Whether uplifting or depressing, the combination of refuge and prospect seems to encourage reflection, and places designed for meditation often combine the two. The verandah of the Ball House by Glenn Murcutt, near Sydney, Australia, is one such example, as are Shonantei, the teahouse at Saihoji, a Buddhist temple garden in Kyoto, and the Hill of Remembrance at Forest Cemetery in Stockholm. Like the Ball House, the teahouse at Saihoji is in a woods, its verandah elevated above the ground and protected on three sides—back, floor, roof. Here, though, the view is down to a lake, rather than out to distant mountains. On top of the Hill of Remembrance, the visitor is surrounded by a low wall of stone within a square of trees open to the sky at the center.

The form of a path may convey a message: straight is the shortest way between two points; a path that goes nowhere prompts a question; meandering invites a stroll. The Japanese stroll garden, with its sharp bends, pulls one's gaze downward; its twisting, turning path conceals then reveals views, giving a sense of flux and mutability. Paths may make allusions, intended or unintended: two paths diverging in a wood may remind one of Robert Frost's poem "The Path Not Taken." At Rousham, in England, the path tells a story; it winds through the garden leading the stroller from one carefully framed scene to another.

Paths, boundaries, gateways, prospects, refuges, and other territories have meaning even when dysfunctional. Two monumental arches on either side of the entrance to Newport Coast Road from Coastal Route 1 to Irvine, California, resemble victory arches, like the Arc de Triomphe in Paris, calling up associations with gates to European cities and triumphant armies. But they are signs, not gates; the six-lane road does not pass under them, nor can anyone walk through them since the other side is blocked by dense planting. They are hollow signs, literally; a rap on the surface brings not the solid sound of stone, but the hollow sound of empty space enclosed by plywood. Gates that permit one to pass by, but not to enter are, as it happens, an apt symbol here, for the road ahead is lined with gated communities, their entrances locked, presided over by guardhouses. The public highway runs past but the private communities are inaccessible to all but the residents and their guests.

So powerful are associations with elements like gateways that use at odds

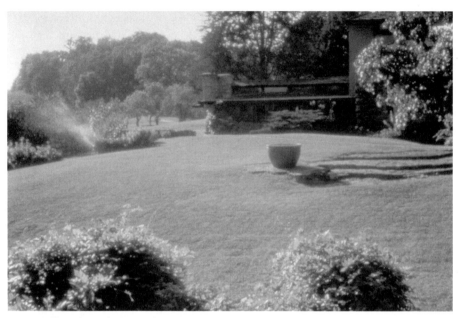

Hill Garden: Taliesin North. Wisconsin.

with their fundamental meanings may produce unintended responses. Fountain and spring are symbols strongly associated with life, health, and sustenance. Seneca urged ancient Romans to "raise altars to springs at head of rivers," and many urban fountains, from Trevi in Rome to Bethesda in New York, were built to celebrate a city's water supply. Fountains in contemporary hotels and shopping centers, on the other hand, sustain no life; they are nonfunctional, no one drinks from them. They smell of chemicals and mock the meaning of fountain as source. Dubos would probably agree that people are drawn to water, but that not all water sources are useful, comforting, or appealing.

The vocabulary of performance space is so pervasive, within and across cultures, that it is often taken for granted. Children learn it early in their own play and in organized activities. On a visit to a weekend scouting encampment in Denmark, I was struck by how quickly and effectively the ten-year-olds created a series of communities using a few simple materials. Each small group chose a site, pitched tents, built a table and bench for eating, dug a hole for garbage, strung up a boundary fence of twine, and hung a sign that announced the group's name. Territory, boundary, path, gate, source, gathering place, prospect, refuge, and sign: these settings encompass a common heritage that every culture embroiders upon, inventing forms to express its distinctiveness, even as they connect, through shared patterns, to the larger world.

THE NATURE OF MATERIAL, FORM, PROCESS, AND PERFORMANCE: FRANK LLOYD WRIGHT'S TALIESINS

Frank Lloyd Wright saw "land as architecture" and shaped its outward appearance to express his vision of its inner structure.[43] His writings, drawings, and built work all testify to his lifelong passion for nature and landscape. He wrote dozens of essays on the subject, more than any other architect, living or dead. He was a keen observer of natural form, an experienced architect of landscape; hundreds of drawings display his interest and insight: rhododendron and pine captured in a few pencil strokes, plans covered with detailed notes on planting and grading, sections showing deft modifications to terrain. Like the Japanese landscapes he admired, some of Wright's greatest works are large compositions of buildings and gardens, roads and waterways, fields and groves.[44]

Wright's understanding of nature was grounded in his family's Emersonian philosophy; he was steeped from early childhood in countless quotations, discussions, and sermons drawn from Emerson's writings.[45] His knowledge of landscape came from experience; observing and shaping landscapes were part of everyday life from the time he plowed, planted, hoed, and harvested fields as a boy, to when as a man he terraced hillsides, planted gardens and groves, dammed streams to generate power and make lakes and waterfalls, laid out contours for plowing that traced curving landforms, and selected sites for Sunday picnics.

The key to understanding Wright's approach to landscape lies in those places where he made his home over decades: the Jones Valley of southern Wisconsin and the desert of central Arizona. He was born to the first and chose the second, and the two must be seen together, as he experienced them, the one in contrast to, clarifying, the other. Taliesin North (1911–59) and Taliesin West (1937–59) are structured by similar principles but of different shape, each in dialogue with the other, each with its own landscape.

Buildings were central to Wright, his primary means of integrating varied landscape features in a unified composition. One cannot imagine Wright as the designer of a place like Stourhead, where the main event, the park in the valley, is a separate world from the house. Wright's landscapes are inconceivable without the structures that order the landscape even as they respond to it. The terraces and gardens of Taliesin emanate outward from the dwelling; the reverse is also true, landscape suggested the form of the buildings, the size and placement of windows. It is often impossible to say where building ends and landscape begins, his work part of a larger tradition of architecture that embraces the idea of landscape and building as continuous, where building interiors resemble landscapes.[46] When I am inside Wright's buildings, I find myself looking out to distant views of hills, lakes, trees, and buildings, following the plane of interior floor to exterior terrace, then, tracing the line of walls and roofs as they slide into terrain in a fusion of building and earth. I find myself, as Wright himself did with Japanese architecture, stumped to determine "where the garden leaves off and the garden begins . . . too delighted with the problem to attempt to solve it."[47]

Just as eighteenth-century English landowners embellished their estates—planting groves, damming streams to form lakes, moving villages, building landmarks to guide the gaze—so Wright transformed Jones Valley into a celebration of the landscape of southwestern Wisconsin. The landscape appears sculpted, and indeed it is. A grove of trees rounds off the angular top and ragged slopes of Midway Hill; curving roads and rows of crops accentuate the rolling landforms. Wright would certainly have agreed with Humphrey Repton's assertion that "to improve the scenery of a country, and to display its native beauties with advantage" is an art; Repton's three principles—utility, proportion, and unity—were among Wright's own.[48]

Over the years Wright changed the hill garden above the house radically, transforming it from rough pasture in a grove of trees into an open, rounded mound. By the late 1930s, the profile of the hill garden was a smooth curve covered with soft, closely clipped grass. Originally, the ridge was flatter on top, its form less perfectly round. Over the years, he removed the trees and their stumps, replaced the long grass with clipped lawn, inserted cut stones into the turf—an idealized version of limestone ledges—and rounded and smoothed the landform into a representation, an abstraction of a hilltop. So, too, he rounded off the valley as a whole through a gradual simplification of the given form. Ironically, like much of the rest of the landscape Wright graded and planted, the mounded slope and ledges of the hill garden have often been seen as naturally occurring rather than constructed. Many assume that the ledges and smooth terrain have just always been there. They are mistaken. The hill garden at Taliesin North is a rounded mound, like a breast or pregnant woman's swelling belly, enclosed by angular walls of stone and surmounted by a tower, which originally housed a dovecote.[49] Given Wright's belief in the symbolism of forms and also the association of doves with love and devotion, one can read the circular mound as feminine and the square enclosure as masculine, then interpret it further as a memorial to his murdered lover, Mamah, as representing the fertility of the valley embraced by the lover and architect.[50] The wall surrounding the hill garden sets it off from the surrounding landscape. From at least the 1920s, there was a distinct difference between the two; rough meadow of long grasses grew right up to the wall and was juxtaposed to the clipped grass within the enclosure. Wright often juxtaposed the ideal and the real, abstracted landscape form and given form, the cultivated and the wild. Experience of contrasts heightens each.

Wright was a performer and built each of his homes and gardens as a stage for the many daily, weekly, and seasonal rituals he designed for his family and apprentices. The tea circle, a semicircular niche with a bench halfway up the steps, is a pivotal place that negotiates a graceful transition between the lower courts and the hill garden. It is shady and breezy on a hot summer's day, a delight to the eye,

Prow garden and Taliesin West, 1949. Arizona. (Historical Collection of Herb and Dorothy McLaughlin)

to the body in movement. Taking tea in the tea circle became a daily practice at Taliesin from the 1930s if not before: "The four o'clock tea bell brings the Fellowship together for a welcomed respite from the day's work. Cooling sounds of ice rattling in tall glasses fall on ear as we climb the steps to the circular stone bench of the 'council ring.'"[51]

After 1938, Wright divided his life between Wisconsin and Arizona, journeying twice each year by automobile back and forth, his schedule driven by seasonal heat and cold, the cycle of spring planting and fall harvest. The juxtaposition of the two landscapes clarified each and kept his perceptions fresh. The property he bought for Taliesin West was near Phoenix at the foot of the McDowell Mountains on a gentle, south-facing slope with panoramic views over Paradise Valley to distant mountains. The hills behind have heaps of shattered rock at their base, all covered with desert varnish, black and red from many years' exposure to cycles of moisture and evaporation. The ground is hard, with rocks scattered across the surface as if cast there. Two deep washes structure the site, their steep sides, breadth, and long heaps of loose rocks and gravel clues to the violent force of waters crashing down the stony hillsides after rainstorms. Dozens of small, shallow washes lace the area. Wright sited Taliesin West up against a hill between a large wash to the west and a smaller wash to the east. Here, as he put it, "we decided to build ourselves into the life of the desert."[52]

His Taliesin West is a complex of buildings, courtyards, and gardens aligned, notched, and knit into the landscape: walls, roofs, pergolas, and paths catch sunlight and cast shadows; sight lines point to distant landforms; walls cut into, extend above, reach out to the immediate terrain. Segments of the main path and most of the buildings are aligned along a straight line—the spine of the complex—aligned so that the walls of the buildings receive both morning sun and afternoon light, and so that ends of the main path point to distant landforms. No isolated axis, this spine is embedded within two grids, as a line of one grid and a diagonal in the other. All the disparate parts of the place are held within the lattice structure formed by these two intersecting grids. Buildings, gardens, paths, and patios are set into the slope in some places, elevated on a platform above the desert in others. Lines of movement as one walks through Taliesin West zig and zag along the lines of the two interlocking grids. It is a landscape meant to be walked through.

I never feel a stronger fusion between patterns of landscape and life than I do at Taliesin West. As I walk back and forth between Guest Quarters or Sun Cottage, dining room, archives, library patio, and prow garden, shuttling along Taliesin's paths, I feel woven into the landscape, immediate and distant. Approaching and moving through the complex along the spine, I enter at grade, descend a few steps, turn and turn again, ascend, turn down the main path with a wall and the ground behind it at shoulder height, then turn to walk under a loggia, down a few steps, onto a platform elevated above the desert—the prow garden. As in a Japanese stroll garden, I am turning repeatedly, my eye drawn to the desert and the "borrowed" view of landmarks in the distant landscape.[53] As I walk through the garden, the paths bring a distant mountain into view again and again, at a bend in the path, framed by the loggia, repeatedly hidden and disclosed. Convinced this must be an important landmark for Wright, I asked its name. It is South Mountain, the site of Ocatillo, a temporary camp Wright designed in the 1930s that presaged important discoveries, and a new direction, in his work. At Taliesin North, too, Wright framed views of landmarks with personal significance: the Romeo and Juliet windmill, his first commission; Bryn Mawr, Bryn Canol, and Bryn Bach, local hills given Welsh names by his mother's family.

In Taliesin West, Wright took the materials of the desert and reordered them to construct walls and paths. Desert rocks—huge boulders, sharp-edged stones, rounded "goose-eggs" from the washes—were set in a rosy matrix of concrete made from desert sand to form the walls of platform and structures. The rocks float in this matrix, their positioning startling in its dynamism, unrelated to the positioning one would expect in a wall, prompting one to wonder about the processes of their formation. As Wright said, "Here in Arizona, one is much closer to the cataclysm," and it is just this sense of cataclysm that the walls convey.

The prow garden at Taliesin West is the counterpart of the hill garden at Taliesin North. Desert and garden meet at the wall in Taliesin West and the view is elevated, as in the Wisconsin hilltop garden; though here desert wilderness not fertile fields once surrounded the garden. The plants of the prow garden were those of the desert, massed as single species and reordered in planters and beds of angular shapes. Yucca fills a large bed next to a triangular-shaped pool in the sunken part of the garden. The garden is an oasis open to the desert, jutting out into it. The wall does not enclose the oasis but marks a boundary, inviting comparison between the domesticated and the wild, the human-built garden and what Wright called "this incomparable nature garden . . . a grand garden the likes of which in sheer beauty of space and pattern does not exist . . . in the world."[54]

Wright took care to distinguish between outer and inner form—shape and structure—but the irony is that he himself often fell into the trap of imitating external shape and ignoring inner structure. Jensen chided him for designing flat roofs that echoed the horizontality of the prairie's ground plane but were poorly adapted to the region's heavy snowfall. Hence the leaky roofs for which Wright is famous. Taliesin West was built into the land, the geometry of its plan inspired by the angles of the surrounding terrain, but floods that swept down off the nearby slopes sometimes washed right through the buildings. Whenever Wright responded only to landscape's surface form, rather than to the processes that shaped its underlying structure, he ran into trouble.

"Structure is the very basis of what I call reality," wrote Wright in 1937, the year before construction began on Taliesin West.[55] Years earlier, just after building Taliesin North, he had asserted that structure was "at the very beginning of any real knowledge of design. And at the beginning of structure lies always and everywhere geometry."[56] By structure, he meant the way elements are united into "a larger unity—a vital whole."[57] Though his definition of structure remained fundamentally the same, it evolved between 1912 and 1937, the years in which he first built Taliesin North and Taliesin West. In 1912 he was stressing that structure was "pure form, as arranged or fashioned and grouped to 'build' the Idea" and that geometry (Euclidean) was "the grammar of the form," "its architectural principle."[58] At Taliesin North from 1911 to 1914, he grouped the squares, rectangles, and circles of buildings, terraces, and gardens in a highly sophisticated play of shapes within a single grid. By 1937, when he declared, "Nature could not have static structure first if she would," he was emphasizing the organic, dynamic quality of structure: a product of creative process, unfolding, shaping and shaped by function.[59] At Taliesin West, he established a complex lattice, a structure of spine and grids that has accommodated changing needs and expansion relatively gracefully over the past half-century. The two Taliesins thus represent a profound shift in his strategy of structure, from static eternal geometry to dynamic organic structure.

There is often an unresolved tension in his works and texts between the two.

Wright returned each year to Arizona and Wisconsin full of ideas for change, seizing afresh the task of reshaping buildings and gardens: "It was pandemonium for two weeks—tearing out walls, rebuilding," recalls Bruce Pfeiffer, a member of the Taliesin Fellowship since 1949.[60] The Taliesins, brilliant essays on design to accommodate growth and change, were built and rebuilt, shaped and reshaped, in successive paroxysms of creative destruction. Their very essence was change, their current form the result of adding and subtracting, accretion and erosion, growth and decay. As one of his associates, Cornelia Brierly, observed, "Mr. Wright never cared about things lasting. He was satisfied just to see them take shape."[61]

Over his lifetime, Wright worked out a personal vocabulary and adapted it to many different places. Apart from his native terrain the landscapes that moved Wright most powerfully were those whose underlying structure is expressed clearly in the shape of their landforms and plants, as in deserts.[62] His work *had* to respond when he moved from the gently rounded deciduous trees and layered landforms of Wisconsin's Driftless Area to the spiky desert plants and angular landforms of the arid Southwest. How apt that the Wisconsin hill garden is a rounded mound enclosed by a square of layered limestone walls, the prow garden a triangle elevated by walls of rocks tumbled in mortar like talus at the base of desert mountains. The Taliesins are masterful compositions of landscape elements, influenced by Wright's own experience, ideas, and ideals, and those of his time and culture, further shaped by the context of place. As Wright said, speaking at Taliesin West, "In inhabiting the two places, you learn. You have the open book of nature. On the one page you have efflorescence, richness, ease . . . a form of decay. Perhaps this vegetation that grows all over so abundantly is a form of mold that comes upon the more accurate elements—the stone foundation of things. But when you get out here, you're back to the foundation."[63] In the landscapes of Taliesin North and Taliesin West, the same author speaks but with a different dialect in each.

5

Dynamic Weaving, Fabric of Stories:
Shaping Landscape Context

Context comes from the Latin word "contexere," to weave, an active root that belies its static common meaning. Context weaves patterns of events, materials, forms, and spaces. A tree, growing, is context—a weaving together—of leaf, branch, trunk, and root; decaying and transpiring, a tree shapes larger weavings of soil and atmosphere. A river, flowing, is context for water, sand, fish, and fishermen; flooding and ebbing, it shapes bars, banks, and valley. A gate is context for passage, its form determining how things flow through it: narrow gates constrict; gates of screens block large things and permit smaller ones to pass through. Context is a place where processes happen, a setting of dynamic relationships, *not* a collection of static features.

All snowflakes, snowdrifts, leaves, trees, gates, and towns would be identical if active context did not shape them; varying contexts create the seemingly infinite shapes of snowflakes, as of trees, rocks, and people. Abundant water swells living tissue; drought shrivels it. In shade, leaves grow larger than in full sun; crowding and shading by other trees force a tree to grow up not out; persistent wind bends branches and trunk. Pruning shears, and deer teeth too, cut branches to stubs from which twigs grow thickly; breeding for fruit causes more profuse flowering. Earthquakes crack and shift huge blocks, condensation and evaporation "varnish" desert rocks red and black, a sculptor cuts and polishes. Working shapes a body's posture—stooped or straight. No feature of landscape is immune.

Through context, materials acquire meaning. Stone is heavy; moved over long distances—taken out of context—it signifies force, power, or wealth. The pyramids of Egypt, each man-made mountain the tomb of a single man, a pharaoh, are impressive not only for their size, but for the enormous blocks of stone, cut, moved, and stacked by thousands of laborers. So, too, are the "sarsen" or "foreign" stones of Stonehenge and Avebury on the chalky Salisbury Plain, and the Travertine marble from Italy transplanted to modern corporate offices in New York and Los Angeles. Botanical and zoological gardens replete with plants and animals from the far reaches of empires in late nineteenth-century Britain and France and ancient Mesopotamia represent the far-reaching power of those civilizations. Not only culture, but individuals provide context and meaning. The Taliesins of Wisconsin and Arizona were shaped by, and acquire meaning within, the context of Frank Lloyd Wright's life and work. The meaning and impact of the Vietnam Veterans Memorial or of the Hill of Remembrance at Stockholm's Forest Cemetery depend, in part, upon the visitor's own context.

Six trees. Saihoji. Kyoto, Japan.

Mountain, Sea, River, Forest: Japan's Deep Context

Mountains rise out of the sea and form the islands that are Japan. Eighty percent of Japan is mountainous. Where mountain and sea meet, waves pound against steeply sloping rock. A narrow band of flatland emerges between mountain and sea, broadens out into plains at the mouths of large rivers to form a platform for Japan's largest cities. On this edge between mountain and sea, most Japanese live. For centuries, heavy rains have eroded the rock of steep hillsides, washing sediments down to the sea to form the coastal plain. Volcanoes like Mount Fuji created plains of lava and ash. Mountains are the source of land; no wonder Japanese revere them.

Mountains afford a prospect over the land that, from a distance, provides an illusion of control. But the landscape is in uneasy repose, its surface composure obscuring the violence that has forged it. The mountains of Japan are ranged along lines that trace the collision of continental plates. Earthquakes rock mountains and shake low-lying flatland like jelly. Volcanoes spew fire and ash. Typhoon-driven rain cuts into mountainsides, and tidal waves engulf coastal lowlands.

The mountains of Japan are steep and flatland is precious, hence the extreme density of settlement and the high cost of level land. Cities, towns, villages, farms, and industries compete for space on the scant flatland; nearly every piece is intensively used. Houses, stores, warehouses, and rice fields abut abruptly with no transition. Everything is worked-over. Even heavily forested hillsides are often terraced beneath the trees. The flatlands are managed, rivers restrained and confined, enclosed by levees that limit their floodplain and create more habitable land. Within the levees are vegetable plots, sports fields, and practice courses for driving. Like the prospect from mountain over land, the shaping and the managing of Japan's landscape convey a false sense of control. In densely packed Japanese cities most streets are narrow with little or no sidewalk; the gates or doors of houses and stores open directly onto streets shared by pedestrians, bicycles, and cars. Yet, even in dense urban districts, tiny gardens are wedged between buildings midblock, a luxury of use that is astonishing.

My *ryokan*, a small inn with three guest rooms, is crammed into the interior of a block in a dense maze of narrow streets in old Kyoto. Yet inside, one wall of my room looks into an enclosed garden, filled with shrubs, carefully pruned. Below the threshold is a large, round stone. Water fills a basin hollowed out of the rock, beside the water a bamboo dipper. A narrow gravel path leads between the shrubs to a shrine, and a small tree forms a canopy over the whole. The morning sun on the garden throws a yellow-green light into the room. The tiny garden is a green world. Two clogs wait on a stone beyond the sliding door—an invitation.

From humble urban garden to monastery and imperial estate, Japanese landscape literature compresses and condenses features and ideas, concentrates meaning in miniature, paradox, and detail. Though the courtyard garden at Ryoanji is only twenty-five yards long and ten yards wide, on many levels it stands for Japan. Fifteen rocks in five groups, each group surrounded by an apron of green moss, rise out of a sea of raked gravel, a distillation of Japan's deep landscape structure: the juxtaposition of mountain and sea, stone and water, with the narrow band of settlement between. The garden is at once microcosm and cosmos, like so many Japanese landscapes, a landscape of paradox. The stillness of stone is felt more deeply through juxtaposition to moving, rustling trees beyond the wall. The sand is still, yet raked lines imply motion. The composition seems open, yet at least one rock is always hidden. The garden is both clear and obscure, a difficult simplicity derived from complex ideas, reduced, rather than from an easy, simplistic statement. It is difficult to experience Ryoanji with the receptive and reflective mind it deserves. Unresolved contradictions intrude, jarring the senses.

I enter Ryoanji through a huge parking lot filled with cars and tour buses. Large groups, including masses of uniformed schoolchildren, throng the path between the parking lot and the gate into the park. The mood of the crowd is of an outing or a festival. The path is lined with souvenir shops, ice cream stands, and tea shops along one side, toilets on the other. The crowd fans out in the park beyond the gate, but converges again in the building adjoining the courtyard of stones. Inside the building, I pass a souvenir shop and then, unprepared, walk out onto a veranda overlooking the stone garden. I sit and try to absorb the garden. Though a few other visitors stand or sit alone, most are here in groups; a sign says, "Please be quiet," but a loudspeaker blares intermittently. Teenagers are jostling, joking, and chattering, the surge of their hormones at odds with the repose of the garden. I leave, disappointed.

A final paradox: I experience the garden more intensely in memory than I did in actuality. The image of rocks, moss, gravel, wall, and trees beyond is etched into my mind.

In Kyoto, I learn to look and listen for water. Water is present everywhere—in rain, rice fields, and rivers, in green leaves and gardens, in ponds and stone basins, as throughout mountainous, humid Japan. Streams flow through hillside gardens and rice fields, down into the city, along the streets in shallow, stone-lined canals, and on into the broad floodplain of the Kamo River. At dinner the first night, I am startled by the sound of ducks and moving water beneath the ryokan's window. I had entered the ryokan down a long, narrow path squeezed between two buildings in the dense, old Gion neighborhood, and, from the front, there had been no hint of the canal behind the house.

The next day, I see stone-lined canals threaded throughout the city below street level, alongside or behind the buildings. Many are neglected and without public access; most buildings turn their backs on them. Many canals have unsightly utilities along their banks, one exception, "Time," is a commercial building on a busy central corner designed by the architect Tadao Ando. Its lowest floor opens onto a broad, shallow water channel below street level; steps lead down to the water. The water flows over stones that have been laid on the bottom of the channel, tracing a rhythmic pattern on the surface. The water slows as the building curves inward, broadening the channel, then accelerates as it is constricted farther on. Water sounds muffle the street sounds above. It is a small, waterside refuge. Several blocks away, the dense maze of the city is interrupted by the Kamo River. People are walking, sitting along its banks on a summer evening. The outdoor terraces of restaurants nearby open to the expansive space. Here is an opportunity to achieve at a larger scale what "Time" has accomplished on a small scale, a promise not yet fulfilled. Nineteenth-century prints by Hiroshige show that some canals in Japanese cities were once lovely promenades lined with cherry trees; so could this be.

The City of Kobe built a river park along the course of the Toga, a river which streams down off the mountainside and through the city to Osaka Bay in a broad, stone channel. At low flow, water trickles along the base of the channel, and fountains on either side shoot arcs of water across the channel at the foot of the hill, just below the Shinkansen train station. Children and adults fish and swim in the channel; in flood, water fills the channel. The entire park is within the one-hundred-year floodplain; terraces mark the height of the average annual flood.

Forest envelops the mountains of Japan and once covered the lowlands as well. The forests are structured by light; straight trunks of the tallest trees carry their leafy canopy toward the sun, smaller trees reach long slender branches up through the shade of the canopy. Each part of the forest—from fern to shrub to canopy, from air and water to soil and life—is linked to other parts and to the whole, united by light and water. Forests are finely layered, leaf upon leaf, life upon life. Like the canopy of a tree, the roof of a traditional Japanese house extends well beyond the walls; the drip line on the ground below the eaves is like the drip line at the edge of a tree's canopy. Beneath a tree one is sheltered, but still outside; in a traditional Japanese house inside and outside merge in a similar way. In Japanese gardens, I looked through branches to sky and water, through water to reflections of trees, rocks, clouds, and sky. In garden, as in forest, each detail has its place within the whole, all linked by deliberate impulse, by idea. Parts of the whole may be distant or even absent: at Shugakuin, the mountains across the valley are part of the garden; at Ryoanji, water is present in its absence. In the Japanese garden, as in the forest, are many details, many layers.

Even a Japanese tea whisk is linked to landscape. The whisk is made from a single four-inch segment of unadorned bamboo, each filament straight and light, like a single trunk of bamboo; together they form a grove. Above a short, uncarved handle, its stem splits into 172 filaments that alternately lean in and fan out, curling at their tip, held separate by black thread woven between them at the point where they lean in or fan out from the handle. The eighty-six filaments that push in toward the center meet below their tip, forming a conical mass, then curl outward. The eighty-six long, slender filaments that arc out curl inward at their tip. Similar, but not identical, each filament stands out as a separate unit, yet together they shape the outer form of the whisk. The whisk is linked to landscape, too, through the greenness of the tea the whisk blends from teapowder and water. And it recalls the garden, the traditional setting for the tea ceremony. Such dialogues are the context of individual, group, and landscape over time.

Elemental Landscapes

Tree

An old tree stands in grass at a wood's edge, its trunk and branches thick, its bark deeply ridged. Older branches are low and spreading; younger branches, on the shady side, shoot straight up: half a wolf tree. The tree encompasses a moment and a lifetime. Each twig shoots forth new growth, extends its reach toward light. Buds swell and burst, from one bud a new leaf unfurls, first white, then green, from another a flower. Each flower in short-lived glory, petals separating, wilting, falling, leaves a budding fruit, a house of seed that will yield new life. The leaves, now full, face to sun, fill out the shape of the tree briefly, then shrivel and fall, expose the frame of trunk, branches, and twigs. Its fruit drops to earth and rots—a rich bed for seed within. Sprouting seed sends shoot to sun, root to soil; branching twig each year adds height and branches at growing tips. Each brief cycle adds to the tree's history: a small scar on a twig is a leaf stem that used to be; a large scar on its trunk marks a lost branch. Ridge upon ridge of each twig, rings within rings of trunk, mark the years; the length between each ridge, the width of each ring, tell the chapter of a growing season: years of abundant water, air, and nutrients;

years of drought, pollution, starvation. The tree itself, some day, will slough its bark, drop leaf and limb, die and decompose. Or cut, it may regenerate, send up saplings from the base of its stump.

A tree connects earth and sky by the sunlight it transforms into leaves and wood, the nutrients it draws from earth, the water and air it transpires, the energy it stores as potential fire and warmth, food in sap and fruit, refuge for the animals and other organisms it harbors. A tree canopy establishes a shadier domain, cooler and moister than the surrounds, the edge of its domain the outer reach of the leaves—the drip line. A tree modifies habitat to sustain itself and nurture its seedlings: decaying leaves alter soil chemistry and create a spongy humus that holds moisture, a soft medium for root growth. Some trees, like black walnut, release chemicals toxic to other plants or, like Norway maple, suck up so much water and nutrients that other plants cannot survive. Not only a context, not only a participant in, but a shaper of context, a tree modifies and orders environments to suit its needs and ensure survival.

A former field, open to sun, encouraged the old tree's spreading; the grove, grown up since on one side, gave it the partial, wolf-tree form. The grass beneath is clipped, so seedlings sprout but do not grow to trees. The old tree grows on a farm no longer, but is now surrounded by a grid of garden rooms in a cemetery north of Copenhagen—Mariebjerg, one of G. N. Brandt's masterworks. The tree, an oak, stands in a large, square, grassy room, enclosed by a frame of lilacs, blooming. The lilacs, open at the bottom, are a transparent screen of slender woody stems. A yew hedge forms an opaque, green frame around the whole. The space between the two hedges, lilac and yew, is an ambulatory around the little clearing with its graves. I enter the garden through an opening in the hedges, cross the grassy threshold between them, step into the clearing where small gravestones are set flat, flush in grass, within a large grid, only partly filled. Tiny white daisies grow in grass, and myrtle's clear blue-violet flowers beneath the pinks and purples of the lilacs. Sweet scent of lilacs, fresh smell of grass, birdsongs of many layers fill the clearing: a raucous, repetitive note, a long, melodic song with many variations, a dove's whooo / whooo / whooo. Birds in the hedges twitter and flit like children in the leaves. The old, broad-spread oak spreads branches over the graves, as if to protect them. The lilacs lean into the clearing, reaching for sun.

Planting the framework of hedges to encompass the old oak, *just so*—off center, at the edge of the clearing, the edge of the wood—was a master stroke, so was choosing this place for the burial of children. The small garden is just as poignant in late autumn, without leaves, with vivid contrast between big trunk and branches of the oak and twisted, slender lilac branches reaching into the clearing toward the tree. Beyond the oak tree's canopy, moss fills the space between the stone squares. "Sleep well, little Jan," say the words on one.

My association of lilac hedges with playing under rosebushes as a child is personal; so are the memories they prompt of children laughing in the leaves, unseen behind hedges in Eliot's poem, of Whitman's reference to lilacs by the dooryard blooming in his elegy on Lincoln's death.[1] But I am not the only child who has played beneath bushes. Verbal literature draws so heavily from landscape literature that it is difficult *not* to make such connections. Great landscape literature stirs personal memories, carries common meanings, and derives power from both.

The transformation of humans into trees, trees with human qualities, gods in trees are common stories: Philomen and Baucis, Daphne and Apollo, threatening forests in Grimm, *sakaki* ("plant-god") trees in Shinto temple precincts. Gerda Gollwitzer has collected illustrations of trees in art and literature from many regions of the world over three thousand years.[2] Words describe, prints and paintings depict Daphne growing into a tree, her hair and fingers sprouting branches, toes rooting, as Apollo, chasing, reaches out to grab her. The many parallels between trees (or plants and animals) and humans led scientists in the early twentieth century to describe forests as communities, to see in them human values, such as harmony, cooperation, invasion, dominance. Since the 1950s the view of plants as individuals with overlapping territories, favored by many American ecologists, is seen by some as a response to a shifting emphasis in the larger culture from community to individual.[3]

On a prairie, in a desert, a tree is a sign of water; a forest is a reservoir. A tree is a pump, powered by sunlight: sun evaporates water from leaves, sucking water and nutrients from soil via paths in roots, trunk, branches, and twigs. Where water is ample, forest is the norm, and a single, freestanding tree an anomaly, for trees tend to live in groups, branches and roots interlocking, big trees shading smaller ones. Forest alters habitat far more effectively than any single tree; it creates conditions for plants whose requirements (light levels, soil chemistry) and rhythms (time of leafing and flowering) are compatible with the trees' own. Trees are enormously successful organisms; on land, if they have light and water (ice or snow won't do) their domain is limited only by the activities of animals (grazing) and humans (burning, cutting). Out on the prairie, a green line of cottonwoods, visible from many miles away, announces a river; even with leaves off, these large, coarse trunks and many fine branches and twigs form distinctive silhouettes against the sky.

River

Water moves in a swirling helix, pushing a river into a series of sweeping curves that meander across the land. Its force swings against one bank, eroding and erasing, scooping a deep pool, sweeps across the other bank more slowly, releasing sediments from suspension, forming riffles, laying down new ground. A river moves across valley floor over time, cutting and dumping, cutting and dumping, shifting its course, cutting off channel fragments to form crescent lakes or "oxbows." Islands move slowly downstream as flowing water hits one end and,

River meander. Dinan, France.

deflected, erodes the shore, carrying sand and silt down river, released to sink in the eddies at the island's tip, a point bar.[4]

A river has form through time. It laps against, flows across land, its shore an elusive line, moving up and down and across the landscape. Swelling, it rises up and rages, cutting earth, dumping mud, then, dwindling, shrinks back within its banks, leaving terraces on the plain to mark the bounds of periodic flood. No rain, and yet the river flows, in drought, drawing underground water from rains of thousands of years ago; trees, still green and living, tell the presence of water underground. Lining the Todd River in Alice Springs, Australia, on a low, broad, meandering band of grey sand are big, spreading eucalyptus trees, the only sign of water for much of the year.

Rivers gather water from sky and land, from within earth and rock, carrying, concentrating, sorting grains of sand, silt, and gravel, the debris of the discarded and the dead. Places of concentration and exchange, fertile, rich in food and water, rivers connect destinations, charting paths into remote territory, their mouths gateways between sea and hinterland. Animals and people gather along them; all principal cities in the world were once on rivers: at mouth, confluence, or limit of navigable waters. Some are synonymous with civilizations: the fertile crescent formed by the Tigris and Euphrates, the Nile, the Tiber, the Yangtze. Rivers are boundaries, and can be barriers; bridges and ferries permit crossing and mark passage, real and mythical, like the passage from life to death over the river Charon.

Riverbank. Dinan, France.

In Dinan, France, a monumental arc of poplars marks the sweeping meander of the river Rance, the arc representing the *idea* of that sweep, smoothing out the irregularities of the riverbank. Through the abstraction and echo of the horizontal form in the vertical dimension, a line inscribed by humans on the landscape, the experience of the river is intensified. Individual trees set in a tight, evenly spaced row along the banks of the river assert their own quirky growth, more apparent in contrast to the regularity of their placement. Dinan's core is a fortified medieval town set on a hill, the river valley, once its trade route, now a park—a green chasm between the old city and its modern suburbs. The riverway is a precinct apart from the old and the new; its form is more sinuous, its tempo more leisurely, yet it is a landscape on the move: flowing, swinging, cutting into rock along the outer arc, laying down a broad terrace along the inner curve. The flat plain, its edge marked by the poplar arc, advances, accreting sediments carved from hillsides upriver. The rough green wall of woods rising beyond the poplars cloaks the steep slopes, cut by water flowing.

Water springs from rock and seeps from soil into pools, pools spill into streams, and streams converge to form larger streams and rivers deep and broad. A river flows from sources to sea. Gravity pulls a river down, from high ground to low: water tugs at rocks and roots, rushing streams strip stony slopes, swift currents run through rocky rapids, waterfalls plunge over cliffs. It slows on flatlands, spreads, and swings in broad, sweeping curves. Near its mouth, wide channels diverge within the estuary into wandering meanders—curves within curves within curves—engraved on shifting mudflats. The river dumps its load of silt among marshy grasses and watery earth, then spews out to sea the sediment it has ferried so far, staining seawater brown, tan, or red earthy tones, creating a broad sloping undersea shelf marked by shifting sea color—from light to deeper blue.

What is a river, then? Mountain spring, seep, rill, rapids, meanders, marsh, mudflats, mouth, shoals. Its bounds are the banks within which its waters ordinarily flow, the flatlands onto which its water floods, the upland ridges from which the water runs, the extent of the underground reservoir from which the river draws. A coastal river links land and sea; winds drive waves, tides tug the sea upriver.

Runners of rapids, stalkers of fish, and river watchers know what rivers signify. Mark Twain said knowledge prevented his experiencing the Mississippi poetically, but, for Norman Maclean, river knowledge is the source of poetry. He tells of "becoming the river" in watching it flow by and knowing how it was made: "As the heat mirages on the river in front of me danced with and through each other, I could feel patterns from my own life joining with them. . . . And I sensed that ahead I would meet something that would never erode so there would be a sharp turn, deep circles, a deposit, and quietness."[5]

Cloud

Out on the plains, as on the ocean, where the sky vault is vast, clouds approach, visible from great distance, pass overhead, transform: a cloud moves slowly across the sun, edge lit, sun disappears behind then reappears as the cloud moves on; shadows move across the land; a shaft of light breaks through, shines now on hill now on meadow. High clouds and low clouds: one flows quickly east, the other drifts slowly west—dizzying.

In clouds, as in rivers, water, air, and dust combine; sky, river, sea, mountain, and valley are contexts for cloud. Cloud color, shape, and structure reveal temperatures, speeds, directions of flowing air, and proportions of water and dust: heaped clouds and layered clouds; tall and short; high, feathery filaments—frozen ice particles; amorphous grey, white, black. Clouds describe the surface over which air flows—the quality of terrain: they hover over islands, roll like waves over mountain ridges, flow down valleys and lie in gentle dips and hollows. Morning mist rises over rivers, fog over seas. Sea of air, sea of water are one sea.

The artist James Turrell works with light and sky to design "sky spaces"—apertures in ceilings and walls, the bowl of a volcano crater—to frame a view of the sky, offering an experience of the sky alone. An artist cannot shape the sky, but Turrell shapes perception to "set up a situation to which I take you and let you see. It becomes your experience. . . . It's not taking from nature as much as placing you in contact with it."[6] Turrell's sky spaces recreate the experience of lying in an open meadow where the sky fills the view. One is absorbed as clouds scud past, lending depth, color shifting gradually, at dusk when blue becomes darker and deeper extending into violet, then pierced by the first star, all in a slow but steady succession toward black of night and emerging starlight. Turrell installed a series of works in the home of an Italian patron, where, through one small window framing a view of the sky, he was led to reflect on the physical laws that govern the universe, that connect his body and world to other worlds.[7] In city and forest, where buildings and trees crowd the horizon, such an experience of sky is rare except from a rooftop or in a meadow, or through a skylight. Turrell transformed the skylight into art that prompts contemplation of time, change, and the rhythmic dialogue between humans and nature.

Boundary between cloud and sky may seem distinct from a distance, but becomes wispy as one approaches; within the cloud all is edge, all wisp. The edge of a cloud is infinitely long—archetypal, fractal form. Walk up a mountainside into cloud, downhill into valley fog, sail into sea fog, and the boundary blurs into a zone, not an edge. Within a cloud, the world seems ethereal, elusive, without substance. No wonder the Hopi believe the clouds are the domain of the dead. A cloud cannot be touched, but it can be felt, cool and moist. In the Bible, clouds portend and conceal, they are the unseen hand of God, or God's apparition: "And the LORD said unto Moses, Lo, I come unto thee in a thick cloud."[8]

Mountain

Moses said he spoke with God on the mountain and saw the Promised Land beyond the river Jordan. Mountains, in many cultures, are where gods and humans meet, the axis mundi where earth rises to meet sky, where the human is dwarfed into insignificance, where otherworldly light seems to glow, haloes around backlit peaks, ridges silhouetted from behind by brilliant light.[9] At Roden Crater, an extinct volcano near Flagstaff, Arizona, Turrell is shaping a series of earthbound spaces to engage skylight from sun, moon, and stars. One among hundreds in a field of volcanoes, the red and black cone rises up out of the Painted Desert. Turrell chose it for the shape of its interior bowl, a curvilinear horizon framing the sky, inducing a sense of celestial vaulting, of the sky as dome. He is reshaping the bowl to intensify perception of sky's color and vaulting, is building chambers and tunnels within the mountain to reveal specific celestial phenomena and varied aspects of light in space. Roden Crater is both sacred space and astronomical observatory.[10]

Mountains emerge out of ancient, ongoing violence and inexorable, eternal erosion. The volcano field near Flagstaff is the scene of ancient explosions that threw up magma—or molten minerals—from inside the earth, leaving cones of red, purple, and brownish-black. Around Sunset Crater, the last to erupt, lava fields of spiky, blasted, black cinders are still barren more than nine hundred years later. The seismic shudders and jolts of California are still thrusting up mountains; the San Fernando earthquake of 1971 lifted the San Gabriel Mountains of Los Angeles six feet.[11] Uluru emerged as the rock around it in the center of Australia eroded away. The rounded, tree-cloaked slopes of the Smoky Mountains in

North Carolina and Tennessee are the remains of higher peaks whose eroded sediments form the Eastern Coastal Plain and Atlantic Shelf.

Mountains are context: colder at peak and on north flank, warmer at base, on south and west, more moist to north and east, dry to south and west. To go up a mountain, or from south slope to north, is to seem to travel hundreds, even thousands, of miles. In temperate climates, the tallest peaks may have arctic conditions at their summit where summer comes late and fall early, and plants of the tundra grow in alpine meadows. Drive down the Blue Ridge Parkway through North Carolina to the Smoky Mountains in late May, in and out of spring, as the road rises and falls, as it follows northern, then southern, slope, runs along a ridge, dips into a valley. The mountains' lowest slopes are deep green, the color lightens with height to pale lime just below the black-green coniferous forest. Deep green fingers follow mountain valleys up and fade into lime, a sign the valleys are warmer. In the lowlands, trees are fully leafed in their dark summer color; as one rises, their color becomes brighter, then paler, finally, there are only tightly furled buds and bare branches. White flowers of dogwood and pale-pink azaleas of mid-mountain spring furl back into winter. Topping a ridge, plunging down the mountainside, is to fall into summer.

The long road up from Denver over the Rockies through Kenosha Pass, gateway into South Park, is squeezed between mountain walls of overwhelming mass and scale; the driver feels gravity in rockslides along the road, in their angle of repose. Solid, crumbling, at rest, in motion, enduring, and changing. Plants on hot, dry southern and western slopes are sparse, with rocky soil exposed as reds, greys, browns. Dark green spruce stand, needles stiff, on moister, cooler northern slopes, and yellow aspens flicker; then, on a rise, at ten thousand feet, South Park stretches out, its vast meadow below rimmed by distant mountain peaks, jagged, snow-covered above timberline. Landforms and plants within the valley-park look soft, but feel hard and prickly. Soil is thin, plants sparse; rocky fragments and plants are sharp, even the grasses feel like pins. Aspens' yellow lines and patches trace disturbance: fire, landslides, mining. As people stop to see the view their voices carry, mingle with aspens' rustle, insects' clatter-buzz, wind across ears a noise like blowing in a seashell, sound of trucks in low gear coming up hill, whoosh of cars coasting downhill into the park, air horn of a truck bearing down on a car, its weight carrying it downhill.

The Rocky Mountains split the continent; the peaks along the western boundary of South Park are part of the Great Continental Divide. Like all mountains, they shed and store water, rain falling on their back slopes drains west to the Colorado River and the Pacific Ocean, its waters to be drunk in Utah, Arizona, Los Angeles; rain on the front slopes flows to the Mississippi via the Platte. The Rockies' thawing snowpack feeds streams and rivers of the drylands on either side. So, too, the Sierra Nevada in Spain divide Granada from the Mediterranean coast, a relationship of mountains, earth, and rivers that the gardens of the Alhambra pre-

Mountain, river, stage. Lovejoy Fountain. Portland, Oregon. (Maude Dorr, Courtesy Office of Lawrence Halprin)

sent in miniature; they are abstractions of a mountain stream. Water gushes from fountains in walls, spouts in thin streams from fountains in floors, flows softly from the basin in the Patio de la Reja, streams down from the hillside gardens to city and river below. Distant snow-covered peaks are the fountains' source.

Studies of water movement around rocks, of rocky slopes, with their planes, fracture lines, ledges, and talus, fill many pages of Lawrence Halprin's notebooks. In drawings, he records his observations of mountain streams in the Sierra Nevadas, and traces his transfer of understanding to the design for Lovejoy and Ira's Fountains in Portland, Oregon. At Ira's Fountain across from the Portland Auditorium, the progression from springs, to tributaries, to downstream waterfalls is telescoped into the space of a city block. The sheer volume and force of the falls and the mystery injected by the many water sources, some half-hidden, combined with the steep drop to the base of the fountain and the dense screen of pines contribute to an experience of water that echoes its importance as a source of electric power in this region of mountains and rushing rivers.

At the base of the fountain, waterfalls roar: water funneled down a shoot and over the edge falls free; water streams down the face of tall, slanted slabs; a thin stream, caught by a notch in lip's edge, arcs out—a line of light. Above the falls, water spouts from several sources, disappears, reemerges, clashes, mingles, flows over the edge. Water color and movement change: reddish brown over cobbles, dark green in deep places, white to light green in foaming waves and spray. Here

People as context: basketball moves. East Oakland, California. (Lewis Watts)

and there, running over rough conglomerate, water catches on protruding stones, tracing many white foamy lines, each stone a point of origin. The ground at the upper level slopes from side to side, top to bottom, tilts, and seems to shift. The expansion joints in the concrete are irregular, like joints in rock. Water's sound is lighter here, higher pitched.

Human

"Don't forget, the biggest attraction isn't here yet," said Walt Disney, the day before Disneyland opened in 1955. "What's that?" "People. You fill this place with people, and you'll really have a show."[12] No matter what one may think of Disney's theme parks, he had a point.

At Ira's Fountain, the landscape is truly theater, a stage, scene of action, not a static scene. Even without people, the fountain has drama in patterns of water and surface, light and ripples play off surfaces. Water movement invites action, the flat slabs at the base ask to be occupied. The plaza accommodates many players and watchers within its nooks and crannies. Within two hours one Saturday morning in early May, a limousine pulls up and a couple in wedding dress emerge to pose beneath the fountain for a photographer who balances his tripod on a sloping slab, a daring mountain biker rides up and down the steps and across the slabs below the falls, three women in wet suits pose in a kayak under the falls for a host of photographers, a man in a red-and-black-checked flannel shirt, jeans, and boots lies on his back, his bare belly rising to the sun, two children drop leaves in a stream, then chase to watch them flow under, over, around, and through. In Lawrence Halprin's works, people—walking, talking, sitting, dancing, playing—are part of the landscape; his designs require people to complete them. People animate his places, their movements an improvised dance within a choreographed framework. As Halprin said of the Portland fountain, "Though the environment itself is visually exciting it was conceived as a place for involvement. . . . The score for people's activities remains open and nonfixed. The composition was unfulfilled until it was occupied."[13]

People-watching is a popular pastime in virtually all cultures. Much of the attraction of tourism is the pleasure of watching the novelty and also the recognition of other people, for all cultures share common landscape genres—thoroughfares, homes, sacred landscapes—that also reveal each culture's distinctiveness. As actors on a stage (or gone from it, leaving it empty), people provide context. Where human settlement is dense, one might never see a landscape without a human figure, and there is scarcely any place on earth without mark of human occupation. The Scottish Highlands are a ghostly, emptied landscape in glen after glen, but stone walls and sheep pens on hillsides and a path are signs of habitation. Many are drawn to wilderness like this where they may walk for days and meet no other human; many are repulsed by other wildernesses recently abandoned in inner cities.

Statues of human figures populate some landscapes: mythical, heroic, and evocative characters like Hercules at Vaux, the "British Worthies" at Stowe, generals on horseback, the Little Mermaid on a rock in Copenhagen Harbor. Partially buried human forms evoke a sense of the horrific, like the open, toothy mouth of the giant at Bomarzzo, in Italy, through which one enters a cavelike room. A statue of three soldiers, looking like lost boys, stands near an entrance to the Vietnam Veterans Memorial in Washington, D.C. When the memorial was first proposed without human figures some people objected; the soldiers' statue by Hart was added a few years later. Hart believed that without the human figure Maya Lin's design was elitist and that his was populist, "for the figure is a necessary element if public art is . . . to be truly public."[14]

But is the unpeopled wall really unpeopled? And does it not touch fears? "It is what people do in the space and the things they leave there that moves me as a foreigner without any connection to the culture or war," said one of my students after visiting the Vietnam Veterans Memorial. The statue of the soldiers makes a statement; the wall invites reflection and initiates a dialogue. The intimacy of the personal objects at the base of the wall recalls mementos left at the feet of statues of saints in pilgrimage churches. The narrow path keeps people in close file, alongside the wall of engraved names, a ritual of respectful remembrance. The Lincoln and Washington monuments, visible at either end of the path's axis, are imposing and superhuman; the wall is more human in scale, more personal: the people honored here are connected to Lincoln and Washington by line of sight, and much more.

The human body is the basis for landscape's measurement, both relative in scale (micro, human, superhuman) and precise (foot, yard, mile). A day's journey on foot or horseback once measured land area. The Japanese land measurement was once the *tsubo*, the area of rice field required to feed a family for a year. Body's form embodies stories about the evolution of the species and the life history and habits of the individual, about place and culture. The human body and mind are both natural phenomena and cultural artifacts. Adornment tells stories of societies; people decorate their bodies with paint, precious metals, feathers, shells, bones, and fancy dress to advertise their social identity and status, attract mates, celebrate rites of passage and religious ritual. The feet of Chinese women were once bound to make them tiny. Current fashion in the West favors the skinny, yet the diets many savor are rich in fat. Human bodies are bound within the natural world, exchange with air, water, animals, plants in every breath, swallow, and bite.

Human evolution, Loren Eiseley said, is an "immense journey" from sea shallows to space beyond earth. Bodies and minds bear the marks of the contexts that shaped and shape them: sea and savanna, city and cyberspace. Of the body's many substances the primary is water: "The river is within us, the sea is all about us."[15] Eiseley describes human bodies as "little detached ponds," "sacks of sea water."[16] And the "most enormous extension of vision of which life is capable: the projection of itself into other lives. This is the lonely, magnificent power of humanity. It is, far more than any spatial adventure, the supreme epitome of the reaching out."[17]

Bird

"To you they are birds, to me they are voices in the forest," a Kaluli man told anthropologist Steven Feld.[18] In the Papua New Guinea rain forest, where the Kaluli make their home, are more than 150 different birds. Birds are ancestors named by their sounds. Kaluli sing with birds, insects, and running water; for them composing a melody is like "having a waterfall in your head," songs come from birds, and have trunks and branches.[19] Kaluli do not sing in unison, but, like birds, in response to one another. In ceremonies, dancers turn into birds. Kaluli aesthetics evolved within rain forest ecology; the concept of "lift-up-over-sounding" is important in Kaluli song, like layered birdsong, song echoes the layered forest. As Feld reminds us, many composers of music, from composers of the blues to Olivier Messiaen, have drawn similar inspiration from birds.[20] Stories of transformation—from human to bird to human—are common also among North American Indians, as are associations of specific birds with human qualities: eagles with power, hawks with aggression, ravens with trickery. Birds share many processes with humans: they speak, mate, nest, have territory, navigate, hunt, flock.

My closest experience of birds as voices in the forest occurred one early spring morning on a field trip taken to look for migrating birds; a class of twenty ten-year-olds and a half-dozen adults walked through Carpenter's Woods in Philadelphia, a place well known to birdwatchers. After some time, we found a place in the woods to sit and hold an informal Quaker meeting, since the children had missed the weekly meeting for worship back at school. For half an hour, I listened to layered birdsong shape an audible space that matched the layers of the forest, from sources in trees high above and down beneath bushes. Their songs were many and diverse: cheeps and chirps, tweets and twitters, buzzes and melodic phrases. Children, adults spoke, intermittently, between long pauses, as they were moved to, in varied voices, like the birds.

Rachel Carson opened *Silent Spring* with a chilling description of a spring when no birds sang: "There was a strange stillness. It was a spring without voices." [21] The passage from parking lot to the central plaza at the Salk Institute in La Jolla, designed by Louis Kahn, is a built analogue of Carson's fable. I approached as a pilgrim, prepared for epiphany by color photographs of the place, and found disappointment. I entered buildings and plaza through a stand of trees where birds were singing, across a carpet of grass and wildflowers between grove and gate, and stepped into a stark, glaring plaza of white stone. [22] Directly ahead, water ran into a long channel incised in the white stone, pointing to sea and horizon. Water was almost invisible and inaudible, unlike the Alhambra, where it had been omnipresent. I stayed several hours, and during that time, a few researchers in white lab coats hurried across the plaza from one building to another; two talked for a while, huddled under the building's overhang at plaza's edge. My only company on the plaza was an architecture student, photographing and taking notes. How devoid of life the plaza was, I realized most fully when I walked back through the gate into the grove full of birdsong. The oasis, the refuge, is not within the walls; it is outside, among the trees.

Unlike the Islamic precedents it draws from as models, Kahn's design is not an oasis at all, but, at the heart of the institute, a silent abstraction, with its gesture to the horizon, the ocean. The sterile white plaza resembles an ideal of a laboratory; yet when I peeked in the windows of the working laboratories inside, I saw a fertile clutter. Ideas arise out of obscurity and jumble, and only afterward seem crystal clear. The plaza may represent the product of scientific research; it does not reflect the process of discovery. Nobel laureates tell stories of how the context of a community, conversations, and even chance remarks were key in developing their ideas. But here was a rigid core devoid of life, sound, and movement in an institute devoted to medical research — to life. Later, I learned that Halprin was to have designed the plaza, but that he and Kahn had disagreed fundamentally over what its nature should be. Halprin felt it should have places to sit, meet, and meditate, be full of water's sound, birds' song and flutter. That would have made less of a visual impact perhaps, been less photogenic, but more delightful and fruitful, more in tune with the meaning and function of the place.

Dialogues in Context: Place

Where Mountains Meet Plains: Denver

Great, upright, red rocks, thrust from the earth, rising hundreds of feet, strike the boundary between mountain and plain along the Front Range of the Rockies. The red slabs are the ruined remnants of ancient mountain peaks, of rock layers that once arched high over the Rockies. My eye follows the angle of their thrust and completes that arc, transported millions of years into the past to an understanding of the powerful processes of mountain-building and erosion. Nestled up against these foothills, Denver rests on sediments many hundreds of feet deep, their fine grains eroded from slopes of ancient mountains once high above the Rockies. Beyond the foothills are suburbs, and beyond the suburbs, further east on the Plains, city, farm fields, and rangeland.

I find more magic in the fractured, tilted zone at the mountains' base than in the younger peaks of these mountains. Rocks rise high out of the ground, huge and dramatic; elsewhere, only a small surface is exposed, emerging from the grass. I walk over these submerged giants, imagine them extending downward to their foundation, waiting for erosion to wear away soil and plants, to expose them. The rock is soft, brittle, broken, the surface of the large strata smooth and rounded. Grasses grow in depressions of the rock faces, lichens, bright yellow-green and grey-green, climb the tilted flanks of red, rose, pink, and mauve rock; black streaks where water travels. Green cedars, rooted in the rock-strewn ground, are tough, their foliage coarse. Sun shines on smooth rocks, casts smooth, dark shadows; junipers cast many tiny, jagged shadows. Dialogues in color and form. In the open, on the foothills' flank, I look up to see thin, transparent clouds, ethereal against red rocks and blue sky, hovering overhead—mountain wave clouds flowing gently eastward. The wind, gusty and fierce coming off the mountains, almost blows me over the edge. It calms for a few seconds or minutes, then more gusts kick up red dust-devils. Whirlwinds whack my face with grit.

A path of red sand, ground from rocks, runs between two cedars, a gate, a sense of passage from one domain to another. I think how different this rocky terrain is from the domain across the road below with its soft rounded hills eroded by sharp gullies, windblown silt of the Plains. Three deer cross the slope ahead; I pick my way off the path to follow their track. The sound of water trickles down the swale, across the path.

Red Rocks Amphitheater is set up among these foothills west of Denver, facing east, its flat stage dwarfed by the red slabs that frame it and the panoramic view across the city and the Great Plains. The dialogues of material, form, and territory are those of the surrounding foothills. Concrete steps mixed with red sand give a

Identity of place: mountains, plains, Denver. Red Rocks Park.

rosy tint; in some places, red sandstone slabs. The cedars of the slopes are planted in rows in large stepped terraces; they line the steps down each side of the theater. The path from the lower parking lot leads around huge, tilted rocks, under ledges, down to the base of the amphitheater—a beautiful passage. Design in such a setting should be just this recessive, not calling attention to itself; it takes a self-confident designer to be so understated. The amphitheater was built in 1941; more recent additions are less successful; the new canopy is an eyesore, so are new steps of grey, untinted concrete. Gravel has been added to the parking lot, also grey; it is not of the place, not red. Traces of the earlier, red gravel are visible beneath the grey. All are jarring, misguided "improvements." The original designer, Burnham Hoyt, was more sure, more deferential.

Sitting, looking out over Denver and the Plains, I feel the hill at my back and the huge sweep of rocks to each side of the amphitheater, a sense of refuge. The sun is hot on my arm; its light catches the top of the foothills' parallel ridges. Beyond the hogback, a sharp, vertical ridge, the soft, eroded hills are clad with brown-green; beyond are the houses on the plain and the trees of the settlements where once was only grass. From the amphitheater is a view of the city and a prospect for reflecting upon the deep structure of the region and the place of humans within it.

A few days later, I sit on one mile of sediments in the Central Plains Experiment Station in Munn, Colorado, about eighty miles northeast of Red Rocks

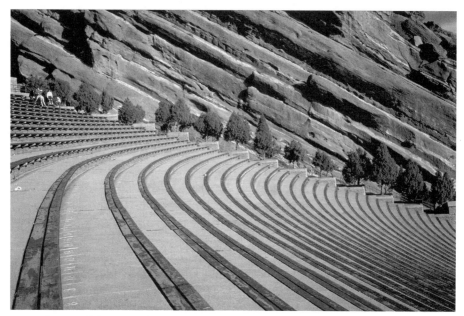

Contextual shaping: Red Rocks Amphitheater.

Amphitheater listening to stories of the place told by a University of Wyoming professor of range management clad in a shiny, blue nylon shirt, jeans, cowboy boots, and a tooled belt. During the worst storms of the Dust Bowl years, he is saying, soil from Colorado blew all the way to the Atlantic Ocean, and folks in eastern cities choked on it; it brought home to them what was going on in the Midwest. The semiarid climate of the High Plains supports a short-grass prairie; without irrigation, no trees grow except in floodplains and depressions. Eleven inches of rain per year—almost desert; cactus grow here: small, rounded barrel cactus and tiny prickly pear.

The grassland looks soft, but crunches underfoot; there is a crust on the soil. The prickly cacti are low, unobtrusive, an unwary walker may get a spine through the boot. Out here on the experimental range are no trees, even in the swales: "It is next to impossible," another professor is saying, "to generate runoff in this landscape, it is absorbed so rapidly into the soil." I discover how quickly air and wind parch skin, mouth, and nose. We are a group of fifty landscape ecologists and landscape architects out on the High Plains for an entire afternoon, and no one has thought to bring drinks.

The next day, I drive east out onto the Plains again, off the main road into the grassland, grazed and ungrazed. I drive for miles without seeing a single tree. My eyes adjust to the compressed spectrum of color and detail, to the subtle shifts in color across broad patches of landscape, a mosaic of pale greys, yellows, and browns of many fine-grained details—silver-grey dead leaves, pale green lichen, golden composites, straw-colored grasses, brown earth, fence posts weathered brown. The terrain is hilly, sometimes quite steep. Occasional gullies cut across the landscape, their edges sharp, steeply cut like a long rip torn in the land. The soil is soft silt, windblown—loess—piled up in places into rounded dunes. Coming down into a gully beside an eroded hill, I am shocked to see several trees, dark, bold, and coarse.

Roads reveal the landscape: bending around rock and curving with the slope of the foothills, straight and right-angled on the Plains, where the gridded system is important for wayfinding. At regular and reassuring intervals I know I will find another coordinate—even if the road is closed to passage, it means there are some people around somewhere, though it is hard to know what is public road and what is not. At one intersection (all gravel roads), a sign says, RD something. The road is on the map, but a cattle grate and a notice attached to a fence post say, PRIVATE PROPERTY—NO TRESPASSING. Off the main roads, I am turned back by such signs again and again.

Today, the weather is sunny with high clouds, cool and windy, the wind blowing off the mountains, sagebrush rolling wild, plastered against the mountain side of fences. The plains are about the sky—sun, clouds, wind. Wind blows across my ears and whisks clouds across the sky, their shadows racing across the landscape. What is golden one minute becomes charcoal grey or dull brown the next. There is only the sound of wind, and that is constant; wind pushes at me, slams the car door.

The Plains are open: the landscape is big, the sky vault vast, the scale of a single person (or even a group) dwarfed. Nothing is vertical except what people have introduced: a windmill, cruciform telephone/electric poles, a series of fence posts. I can see for miles across the rolling plains with no point of orientation. Up in the foothills the height, openness, and prospect were reassuring; I knew where I was, could see where I had come from and where I was going. There were refuges—behind rocks or junipers, in the protected overhang of a huge tilted stone. There were clear choices for routes: up, down, along the slope, down into a valley. Down on the Plains, I have no reason to chose one direction over another, except to avoid the low sun of late afternoon. Out here I feel compelled to head toward a ridge for a prospect.

Each farmhouse is planted round with trees, the huge older trees diminishing the houses, often bungalows no more than one floor high; trees are planted as close as ten feet from the house, straight vertical trunks in sharp contrast to the broad horizontal sweep, marking each a special place. The farmhouses stand against the sky, isolated, except for these trees. I understand why the settlers planted trees so close together and near the house, a detail one can latch onto. I drive back toward the city and see trees again; they tame the landscape, give to the openness a locus.

Denver and other cities along the Front Range Corridor—Fort Collins, Boulder, Colorado Springs—straddle the zone between Rocky Mountains and

Deep context: sky, wind, open, dry. High Plains. Colorado.

Great Plains. Denver, a city of trees, is an oasis of irrigated green within the arid landscape, a refuge from this wide open land. It is buffered from the extremes of mountains and Plains by the presence of both: from mountains' steep, rocky ravines by Plain's soft slopes; from Plain's drought by snowpack and mountain streams. To James Michener the South Platte River that flows through Denver is "a sad, bewildered nothing of a river. . . . It's a sand bottom, a wandering after-thought, a useless irritation, a frustration, and when you've said all that, it suddenly rises up, spreads out to a mile wide, engulfs your crops and lays waste your farms."[23] A wide river of shallow, braided channels, it is clogged with sediments carried down from the mountains. It flows through willow thickets and cotton-wood stands across the high dry plains to the Missouri and on down to the Mississippi and Gulf of Mexico. Long dry periods are punctuated by cloudbursts that swell streams and rivers and, especially when augmented by springtime snow melt from the mountains, swiftly convert dry creek and river beds to wide, raging torrents. These rhythms are part of the deep context of this place; they become part of each life that dwells here.

Rhythms of high peak flows separated by long periods of extremely low flow are a challenge for the designers of storm sewer systems. Denver's sewers were once open gulches; many were converted to underground pipes, but the enormous size required to accommodate peak storm flow made conversion often im-

Response to deep context: house in grove. High Plains. Colorado.

practical. Over the past twenty-five years, therefore, Denver has built a new storm drainage system of parks and parkways. The channels through which the stormwater flows are the paths through which people walk, ride, or kayak, the form congruent with the deep context of the region. The channels and the water flowing make this context and its rhythms legible within the city even as they link outlying farmland, suburbs, and downtown. It is a storm sewer/open space system that is not only functional and sustainable, but also beautiful and meaningful. Skyline Plaza, part of a downtown redevelopment project, steps down into a sunken garden that pools water after heavy rains; it prevents flooding downstream by letting the water seep gradually into the sewer. Harvard Gulch, a storm drainage channel and linear park, has replaced the narrow, dirt gulch that once flooded adjacent houses. The original plan called for an underground storm sewer; instead, the water now flows through a park whose sinuous landforms echo the movement of water, even when it is only a small trickle. Where the level of the channel drops, a weir breaks the water's erosive force. At high water the weir is exciting, but even at low flow, its sculptural form recalls the power of water at high flow. Where the South Platte River moves through downtown, at the confluence with Cherry Creek, there is a park and a plaza where people come to watch the kayak races and sit by the river. The plaza has another purpose, designed to absorb and deflect floodwaters, its broad terraces alternately submerged or exposed. At high water, lower terraces are ghosts whose form, under water, makes a trace on the surface.

The Enduring and the Ephemeral

Weather is the ephemeral expression of wind, rain, heat, and cold from minute to minute, day to day, season to season. Climate is the pattern of long-term variations; deserts, prairies, and forests express its enduring patterns. At continental and global scales, seasonal patterns of rain and drought, heat and cold, produce corresponding associations of plants: deserts, prairies, dry woodlands, temperate forests, coniferous forests, and tundra. Prairie grasslands, like the American Plains, grow in regions with moderate rainfall—more rain than in desert regions, less than in forested ones, all temperate grasslands have similar characteristics, so do deserts and forests.

Some contexts are more enduring than others. Still, *enduring* and *ephemeral* are relative terms: to human eyes, mountains seem unchanging—an illusion fostered by the perspective of human perception and life span; the sediments washed off eroding mountains onto the Great Plains are a mile deep east of Denver.

Cultural contexts may also be enduring: Thomas Jefferson is part of the landscape context of Charlottesville, Virginia, and of the American Midwest. The influence of Roman language, law, and literature on landscape extends way beyond the Mediterranean region and the territory Romans once occupied. The pastoral landscape, celebrated at least as early as in Roman literature, has been working itself out over millennia, further strengthened by the biblical tradition of pastoralism: "He maketh me to lie down in green pastures; he leadeth me beside the still waters."[24] It becomes deep, not permanent, not universally cross-cultural, but enduring, persistent, over time and place in Western cultures despite great differences of climate and terrain. Rolling lawns with groves of trees—in estates and suburban tracts, office parks and cemeteries—are evidence of the pastoral landscape's deep cultural context.

Even hunter-gatherers, through fire, change species composition and the pattern of plant communities. How closely the form of the visible, surficial, human-made landscape relates to the enduring context of geology and climate depends mostly on the extent and intensity of human activity and its congruence with deeper context. To many, farmland is a natural landscape, but all agricultural methods impose a cultural order.[25] To many, even most, cities are unnatural, but a more enduring natural environment is there, camouflaged by the surface of buildings, roads, sewers, and parks.

The grid, which in the nineteenth century was laid across the landscape of the American Midwest and West, an idea at first, then a real grid of fences and roads, a framework to domesticate the western wilderness is superficial, not deep, context. From the humid East to the drier West, the grid holds within it many settlement forms, all visible on a clear day if one travels by air, for example, from

Two contexts: beach ridges across the midwestern grid. North Dakota. (Alex S. MacLean/Land-slides)

Chicago to Denver: on the Nebraska prairie, wheat fields conceal older fields and small streams that erosion will deepen into gullies; in Colorado, pivot irrigation displays a pattern that seems bold and distinct. But, as with patches and corridors of forest, meadow, and fields of a single crop, both wheat fields and pivot irrigation reflect a particular culture more than deep context, the landscape surface a cultural artifact, many of its features ephemeral.

The hedgerow and small field landscape many English love was originally a response of ancient farmers to deep context. Size and shape of prehistoric fields varied, with larger, rectangular fields on gentle slopes and small, irregularly shaped fields on steeper, rougher terrain.[26] But changes to field boundaries over the centuries responded to shifts in ownership patterns, market demands, rural occupations. The landscape of today was created through a succession of enclosures to create pasture for sheep, some as early as the fourteenth century, some from the enclosure acts of the eighteenth and nineteenth centuries.[27] A shift from sheep to food crops and the introduction of large agricultural machinery are now transforming this landscape once again, from the patchwork of small enclosed pasture to large open areas. Still, surface structure is often ephemeral, disappearing after successive changes, while traces of an earlier cultural landscape and of a deeper structure remain. A stile over a fence and a path through a field mark footpaths that predate the enclosure acts and to which the public still retains the right of passage. Left unplowed, unmowed, or ungrazed, the landscape will be reclaimed by forest, but, on the downs of southern England, farming practices over millennia have so altered the soil's structure that it will no longer support forest. Deep context is enduring, its rate of change prolonged, but even deep context can be altered over time.

Sea is the deep context of the Netherlands, literally lowlands. Dialogues between seawater and land, flood tides and dikes, boats, travel, and trade have structured culture and settlements over hundreds of years. The polder landscape of canals and fields reclaimed from sea—from long and thin to broad and vast— were such dialogues, their forms shaped by changes in technology and new sources of power, from hands to windmill to bulldozer. Polders are part of the enduring context of the Netherlands, sustained through many years of labor, but now many are being flooded and returned to sea, reminders that agriculture may be deep, but not eternal. The context behind this profound change is not just the nation, but the European Community. And the sea itself. Some polderlands, like the Danish heath, are seen as marginal agricultural land in the context of Europe as a whole.

The deep context of a city is invisible to most, buried under layers of human constructions; and yet it exerts a powerful influence upon the urban landscape. Skyscrapers in Manhattan, built where bedrock is within reach of foundations, hide the rock, but the skyline reveals it. Boston's Lower Beacon Hill was tidal estuary until filled in the nineteenth century, with houses built on foundations of submerged wooden pilings, sound as long as they were under water. Modern residents forgot what Bostonians once knew: if groundwater drops below the pilings' tops, they rot and no longer support the buildings. When surface structure obscures or opposes deep context, only energy, materials, and information can sustain it.

Landscapes like the Alhambra in Granada mark fleeting human triumphs, but they also celebrate what endures: the mountains, rivers, and the warm, dry climate of Andalusia; the thousand-year presence of the Moors, their gardens, irrigation systems, and knowledge. The great gardens of Le Nôtre extol the deep context of the Île-de-France, physiographic and political, still a region of concentrated power to which resources of the country flow. Eighteenth-century English landscape gardens, like Stourhead, reveal, in contrast, not simply the rolling physiography and lush climate, but the power of gentry compared to royalty. Mariebjerg and Nærum present enduring aspects of Danish nature and culture, and Ryoanji represents deep contexts of Japan.

In the history of a place the deep contexts are constants that successive human generations must readdress. Traditions, values, and policies may change, but deep context remains key to the history and future of a place—why it was settled, its initial location, its transportation routes, its economic development, and the health and safety of its residents.

Anomalies: Things Out of Context

Landscape features may coexist, juxtaposed, and yet be unrelated, anomalies of material or form out of context, shaped by a different context from the one that predominates. Glacial erratics—anomalous boulders—were shaped by local conditions elsewhere, thousands of years ago, when glaciers flowed across the land, scraped chunks of rock, and carried them many miles to be left behind when the ice retreated. Stone walls and old building foundations engulfed by woods in New England are clues to changes in human use of land, just as hedgerows in England are artifacts of agricultural landscapes that no longer serve the original purposes. Like the wolf tree in a woodland of younger trees, so a mansion surrounded by tiny urban row houses may tell a story of abandonment and recolonization. Anomalies reveal variations in context otherwise hidden, disguised, unrecognized, or forgotten. On prairies, in deserts, trees in swales signal water underneath. Wooded thickets on vacant lots in American cities, on abandoned farm fields, and bombed ruins in Berlin are reminders that the larger context there is forest, and absence of forest an anomaly of culture.

A channel's width, depth, and shape describe the amount of water that normally flows and the height of regular and occasional floods. The signs are there even when no water flows: wadis, wide shallow dry boulder-strewn strips, are desert streambeds; seldom, but repeatedly, water rages down their broad reach. A wadi, its bed dry, is still a river, as anyone knows who has ever seen it full or dug into its gravelly channel to find water. In Phoenix, the huge, dry floodplain of the Salt River is not a wadi; its waters are diverted upstream by the Granite Reef Dam into the Northern and Southern Canals and dispersed into hundreds of miles of smaller irrigation canals and ditches.

"Sometimes I went south to visit our German neighbors and to admire their catalpa grove," says the narrator of Willa Cather's *My Ántonia*, "or to see the big elm tree that grew up out of a deep crack in the earth and had a hawk's nest in its branches. Trees were so rare in that country, and they had to make such a hard fight to grow, that we used to feel anxious about them, and visit them as if they were persons. It must have been the scarcity of detail in that tawny landscape that made detail seem so precious."[28] An anomaly is often a landmark; it may become sacred, like Australia's Uluru. Different cultures occupying the same landscape at different times often embrace the same significant landscape features: high points and churches in England, sacred springs and Christian shrines in Ireland, aboriginal sites (Uluru) and Australian tourist destinations (Ayre's Rock). Anomalies sharpen the perception of a larger context that might otherwise be taken for granted: a clearing in the forest, a grove on the prairie. Sometimes, even, anomalies or rarities are valued more highly than the common landscape. National parks in the United States and Great Britain often preserve the most extraordinary landscapes, remote from human settlement, anomalies of natural phenomena.

The geographer George Seddon calls this the crown jewel approach, in contrast to Denmark's, of preserving the most typical—whole everyday landscapes where many people live.[29] But then, Denmark is a relatively homogenous landscape; it has no Grand Canyon or Peak District. Surely it is important to preserve both rare and common landscapes.

An anomaly confounds expectation, a puzzle that prompts a story to explain it: a dry wadi or oasis in the desert, an island in the sea, a mountain on a plain, seashells on a mountaintop, poppies in a field of rape. How to explain anomalous patterns is at the heart of both myth and science. Erwin Panofsky, reflecting on the connections between Roman temples and medieval market crosses in English gardens, on the one hand, and Palladian temple front and romantic "Silver Lady" on the Rolls-Royce radiator, on the other, concludes that these apparently incongruous juxtapositions are clues to the character of English culture, the opposing forces of rationality and intuition, classicism and romanticism.[30]

As I walked through the woods in the Quabbin reservation of central Massachusetts some years ago, I stumbled across old stone walls and foundations half-buried in leaves and undergrowth and large trees growing out of old cellar holes. A paved road ran through the woods for several miles, then headed for the lake, disappearing beneath its waters. The road once led to seven towns in the flooded valley now occupied by Quabbin Reservoir, towns drowned to provide water for the city of Boston. If you did not know the story, you would be tempted, as I was, to find out. Or to speculate.

Identity: The Power of Place

A place is particular, a tapestry of woven contexts: enduring and ephemeral, local and global, related and unrelated, now and then, past and future. Landscape context is a fabric whose strands are narratives of landscape elements and features, both the persistent and the fleeting. Many stories have been shaped over tens of thousands of years, others over several human lifetimes, still others are just now emerging. There are deep stories, dialogues that have become interwoven, embedded, in place over time. Every place has ongoing stories, recognized, concealed, and lost. Some take longer to tell than others, some are short; some have an ending, others are open, still unfolding. All that has happened in a place, all the lives lived there contribute to a sense of place; identity is defined by the common and by the rare alike. An idiosyncratic anomaly like Watts Towers in Los Angeles, a fantasy built from discarded crockery and scraps of metal, can help define identity of a place.

When Dolores Hayden first moved to Los Angeles and set out to trace the history of her new urban landscape, she discovered many untold stories, and founded the Power of Place project to bring them to light. The result was a landmark project that tapped "the power of ordinary urban landscapes, to nurture citizens' public memory, to encompass shared time in the form of shared territory through walking tours, public art, and publications."[31] Hayden concentrated on

Los Angeles downtown, the site of the original Spanish pueblo founded next to a large Native American village, Yang-Na, and documented the successive activities that structured the landscape there: vineyards, citrus groves, flower fields, oil fields, manufacturing, and real estate development. Most traces of earlier activities have been erased, but remnants remain in street names, isolated citrus trees, a winery, a produce market, a flower market, an oil company. Hayden challenges designers and artists to envision new public spaces that would reveal these former urban landscapes and those who lived and worked in them, men, women, and children, Native Americans, Hispanic, Anglo, African, Chinese, and Japanese Americans. Many place stories here in Los Angeles (and everywhere) are concealed, forgotten, or uncelebrated, especially those of women, poor people, ethnic and racial minorities. Hayden's purpose is not to introduce competing stories into the public realm, but to celebrate the diversity of identities that have contributed to the American landscape, and to forge a new and fuller sense of place.

In the Mill Creek neighborhood in West Philadelphia, a place where my students and I have been working since 1987, as in most older American landscapes, is a rich fabric of stories. Its principal thoroughfare, Lancaster Avenue, was the nation's first turnpike, and before that an Indian trail that followed a ridgeline. From the Busti Mansion, built by one of the first large landowners, there is still a prospect over the valley below. The Pennsylvania Institute, a hospital on the opposite hill, was a nineteenth-century landmark of treatment for the mentally ill. Most houses standing today were built after 1876. A small African-American community already lived there then, served by an African Methodist Episcopal Church and a "home for colored orphans." At the turn of the century, European immigrants predominated, including Italians and Jews from Russia. A large Caucasian population remained until the 1970s; today the population is almost entirely African American. The story line of the Mill Creek itself, once visible from the windows of mansion, hospital, and orphans' home, is now buried in a sewer but is still powerfully present in its consequences.

There are painful stories in Mill Creek, stories just as important to remember as stories of mills, mansions, and immigration. A 1934 study of Philadelphia's housing, which became the basis for red-lining, documented building age and condition, race, income, and education of residents. Mill Creek's older houses (some in poor condition, some with flooded basements), its population of different races and ethnic origins (some with relatively low incomes), led to the lowest rating, red, for the entire neighborhood. Over the next fifty years, homeowners and businessmen there found it difficult, often impossible, to get mortgages, bank loans for improvement or expansion, and fire and theft insurance. Mill Creek is shaped by all the processes at work in inner-city America. New homes and businesses in suburban areas, subsidized by federal highway, mortgage, and infrastructure programs, fueled new construction beyond the city line in the headwaters of Mill Creek, funneling more runoff and sewage into the sewers, increasing floods, bursting pipes downstream in West Philadelphia. Segments of Mill Creek sewers have collapsed repeatedly since 1930, destroying homes and even lives, yet federal grants subsidize new suburban sewers, not the maintenance of old inner-city ones, including this one, which carries runoff from suburban development. The place was laid waste by the violence of neglect that Robert Kennedy called "slower, but just as deadly, destructive as the shot or bomb in the night . . . the violence of institutions; indifference and inaction and slow decay."[32]

"You mean there really *was* a *creek!*?" an eighth-grade student said as she examined a photograph from 1880 showing stream, mill, men dwarfed by the huge sewer they were building, new row homes in the distance. A map of 1915 indicated the spot where the photograph had been taken, and a 1961 newspaper photograph showed a deep, gaping hole, porches hanging, falling; a broken sewer, parts of houses, a truck down at the bottom. At the start of the school year, a teacher in Mill Creek's Sulzberger Middle School told me that her students called their neighborhood The Bottom. So they already know it's in a floodplain? "No, they mean it's at *the bottom.*" Both meanings of the word can be read in the area around the Sulzberger School: standing water after rain; slumping streets and sidewalks; tumbled-down buildings, some boarded up, some occupied; vacant house lots, rubble-strewn; whole square blocks of abandoned land, men standing around street corners on a workday afternoon, jobless.

Front and back doors of the middle school open on different worlds. The six front doors, in the solid, three-story, brick facade on high ground, face a small neighborhood of well-kept homes. Aspen Farms, the community garden designed by my students in 1988, is just a block away. The school's back door, a full story lower, is in the bottomland, so are the playfields and, across the street, the Mill Creek Housing Project, many units unoccupied, walls covered with graffiti, grass overgrown. The contrast between care and devastation is striking: drive down one street between well-kept homes; turn the corner onto fallen-in houses. The scene repeats as you turn, turn again: care, waste, care, waste. The islands of care are mainly on higher ground, where houses have well-used porches, many carpeted with plastic lawn, furnished with chairs and potted plants, where open lots are gardens or off-street parking. The sea of waste in between the islands is mostly in the bottomlands: houses with cracked foundations, buckled porch posts, tipped roofs, boarded-up buildings; vacant lots filled with rubble and trash, thickets of sumac and ailanthus trees.

In the 1997–98 school year, 130 sixth, seventh, and eighth graders at Sulzberger Middle School, together with my students at the University of Pennsylvania, learned to read the neighborhood's landscape, to trace its past to understand its present and envision its future. The tools they used were their own eyes and imagination, the place itself, and primary documents like maps, photographs, tax records, census tables, steam-railroad timetables. The students wrote and drew their visions for the future and a group of seventh graders even wrote and sang a rap: "Pipes BREAKING / Street, it be a-SHAKING / Houses, it be TAKING / Underground / Where rats run round . . . / . . . What are we going to do with the vacant land, ya'll? / We can build a boxing ring / So we can all / brawl / And play basketball. . . ." The ideas they proposed were published in a booklet, "Power of Place: Visions for Our Mill Creek Neighborhood"; some may actually be built.[33]

Reading the Mill Creek landscape is a skill anyone can learn. Even without maps of the topography or the sewer, one can follow the buried stream's course by connecting the low spots, keeping slopes to either side, walking from vacant lot/meadow to slumping playground to community garden to new homes built on "open" land. The children tracked the creek, proud of their special knowledge of things happening underground, unseen by most adults.

The Mill Creek Housing Project was designed by Louis Kahn, one of America's most famous architects, and built in 1954. The dark, tiny doorways of the project's row houses have no porches, no places to pause between sidewalk and house; neither prospect nor refuge, the doorways are used only for passage and concealment. Yet even the most modest older homes in the neighborhood—row houses with no porch or garden—offer a stoop, a place to sit and watch the street.

The City Planning Commission's Plan for West Philadelphia, published in 1994, made no mention of either the historic landscape or the buried river; a new project, Nehemiah Homes, was built in the bottomland downstream from the Mill Creek Housing Project, as an isolated enclave for first-time homeowners. Small groups of new houses within the established blocks of long-time homeowners, experienced in community building, would have appeared less heroic, certainly less visible, but would have been much more likely to survive.

In summer 1997, a group of Sulzberger Middle School students, teachers, community gardeners from Aspen Farms, and my research assistants from the University of Pennsylvania worked together to gather stories about the Mill Creek and its namesake neighborhood, and to find ways to tell those stories of the urban landscape in the school's curriculum. The students and teachers wore T-shirt advertisements of light blue; on the back, in black letters, they say, "ASK ME ABOUT THE MILL CREEK." And people did.

SUSTAINING THE FABRIC OF PLACE: JAPAN

For thousands of years the Japanese have integrated the traditional and the new. Shinto customs and shrines exist side by side with Buddhist temples, often combined; papers inscribed with wishes and tied to trees, a Shinto custom, are a common sight in Buddhist temple precincts. Buddhism came to Japan long after Shinto was established as the indigenous religion, but it prompted many changes in Shinto practices. In Shitennoji, a large Buddhist temple complex in Osaka, where there are many Shinto shrines, one, simple and beautiful, is dedicated to a god of the earth, its central feature a large stone, covered with soft, green moss.

Beneath the moss is a carved relief of Buddha.

At times, the contrast of old and new in Japan is extreme: in Tokyo, a man sweeps the street with a broom made from a branch and twigs; on an adjacent lot a construction worker in hard hat pushes earth with a bulldozer. Tea whisks and *tatami*—straw mats three feet by six feet and several inches thick—like much traditional Japanese design, are admired greatly, but they are now relics, no longer part of the flow of daily life for which they were fashioned. How to embrace the new while preserving and renewing the best of the traditional is a dilemma for Japan today. Some Japanese architects have successfully integrated tradition and innovation. With wedding receptions and honeymoons now big business and with weddings in Christian chapels a popular trend among young Japanese, many Japanese hotels have built wedding chapels. Tadao Ando's design for the chapel at the Rokko Oriental Hotel in Kobe fuses Shinto and Christian, traditional and modern, Japanese and Western. His Rokko chapel complex has a fan-shaped reception terrace, a corridor with an anteroom, and a small chapel. Built of concrete, glass, stone, and steel, not the old wood, tile, paper, and tatami, it seems very Western in style, recalling modern Finnish churches. And yet, fundamentally, it is Japanese, as I found out when I visited.

I step across the gap between the curved edge of the reception terrace and the straight edge of the corridor and enter a world apart. The long corridor—with walls and vaulted ceiling of blue-green, frosted glass and a floor of black stone—stretches into the distance to an open end that frames a distant view of green—trees, shrubs, and grass—like the view of the garden from the teahouse at Katsura. Translucent walls meet black stone floor flush, filling the corridor with a diffuse, disembodied light. I feel suspended in light, the green view at the end my only connection to the material world. A long way down the corridor, the door to a chapel opens abruptly to the right. I turn sharply into the small, dark anteroom to face a concrete wall that curves into a vertical strip of clear glass—the landscape beyond abstracted to a thin line of illuminated green. Another sharp right turn, and I stand at the chapel's threshold, the chapel walls are of warm, dove-grey concrete. The left wall of floor-to-ceiling glass faces the green hillside against which the chapel nestles. The floor of elegant black slate draws my eyes downward, and the green view beyond the glass wall pulls my gaze outward, a tension between interior floor and outdoor landscape reminiscent of the correspondence between tatami floor and garden at Shisendo, at the ryokan.

As I leave the chapel, I face the translucent, blue-green wall of the corridor, wall glowing with light reflected from the landscape beyond, visible only as blurred outlines with an intensification of green near the ground and blue toward the sky. Like a shoji screen or the white silk screen at Ise.

Modern architecture like Ando's is singular; a comparable integration of new and traditional has seldom been achieved in the larger landscape of contemporary Japan. Rather, far-reaching changes in valued landscapes—foundations of myth, art, and religion that connect modern Japan with its origins—are breaking the continuity of culture, in an engulfing wave of change that has not been resolved with the past. Only an understanding of the deep context of the Japanese landscape and a careful discarding and adapting can resolve this dilemma: how to find open recreational space in the city amid competing claims for the same, scarce land? How to accommodate automobiles without destroying city and countryside? How to weigh the relative importance of new housing and of rice fields?

A long workday, a six-day work week, and short annual vacations make urban open space essential to quality of life in Japan, but how, in the context of scarce open land, can space be found for playgrounds and ballfields, for places to stroll and sit, and for the increasingly popular but land-consuming sport of golf? Activities that extend over large areas in North American cities are compressed here. Gas stations are compact, with little pavement, no visible pumps. There are no vacant lots, for open space is precious. Every bit of land is used, even rooftops. Groups of workers perform daily calisthenics atop office buildings. Parks and sports fields compete with houses, businesses, industry, hospitals, schools, highways, and parking for the same scarce space. Many Japanese live in apartment buildings and have not even a tiny garden. But in and around Japanese cities are green open areas; the largest are temple grounds, rivers and riverbanks, and forested hillsides. Sacred sites have long been associated with water and hills, but so, too, have places for entertainment. In the Tokugawa era from the seventeenth to nineteenth centuries, along riverbanks and at bridges, in temple grounds and outside temple gates the rules governing behavior were more lenient than in ordinary urban areas. These sites attracted entertainments of many kinds and became a sort of free space "exempt from both conventional social norms and clear-cut property relationships. They were a kind of 'sacred' place where freedom and protection were assured."[34]

I step out of the Tennoji subway station in Osaka into a steady rain and wander around a dense district of old houses and narrow streets, packed with dozens of temples. The temple grounds are shady, green oases, enclosed by high stone walls. From the street the only hints of these gardens are the treetops poking above the high walls and occasional views through the gates. I pause at each gate and step beneath its wide, wooden canopy to peek into the garden within, glad for shelter. Despite the rain, one temple precinct is filled with children running and playing; preparations are under way for a festival later in the day. I return several hours later to find the festival in full swing, the grounds packed with people and booths of food and games that spill out through the gate onto the adjoining streets.

Small neighborhood temples, serving a local population, are an informal play space for children. Larger temples, with many priests or monks, have more formal, landscaped grounds, dignified and subdued—a place to stroll, not play. The fact that temples do not pay taxes on the land they occupy is a major concern of city government in cities like Kyoto, where temples are numerous, but so long as they permit public access, temple grounds are an important civic resource, a place for recreation and reflection, embodying and perpetuating cultural tradition, in dense urban districts a refuge. In Kyoto, the forests and gardens of hillside temples, monasteries, and imperial villas preserve forested hillsides and maintain the flow of cool air off the hills into the city on hot summer nights, but in other cities, development of hillsides for housing and resorts is eliminating space for recreation, destroying the traditional relationship between mountain and settlement, and blocking hill-to-valley breezes.

Automobile ownership in Japan is growing, and so is traffic congestion. In large Japanese cities, dense settlement, narrow roads, and irregular street patterns make the subway the most efficient mode of transportation. Efficient subways, thronged with people late into the night, busy, interior arcades, and the active street life of Japanese cities fill many Americans with nostalgia for the lost vitality of American central cities. But in smaller, less densely settled cities, as in the Mie prefecture, where bus and rail lines are less convenient than the car, parking on streets has become a major problem. The widening of streets and creation of space for parking is causing large-scale demolition of older buildings in such cities. Competition for space is not new, but what is new in Japan is not only the growing number of automobiles, but the importation of settlement patterns that require enormous amounts of space. So, for example, new urban districts in Tokyo and Osaka have become virtually indistinguishable from similar developments in Dallas and Houston. Where tradition and innovation once enriched one another in mutual readjustment in Japan, a growing gulf is now separating the old and the new. Rapid economic growth and the importation of Western styles of architecture and urban development, fueled by education of Asian designers and planners in the West and the increasingly international scope of professional practice in design and planning, all have contributed to the swift changes and to the lack of integration. The dilemma is one many cultures face: how to reconcile tradition and change.

One of the most startling sights to a Western visitor is the occasional rice field in Japanese cities—seemingly isolated anomalies, unrelated to anything around them. Like the tatami mat in a room, the green carpet of the rice field extends from boundary to boundary of the property, often with only a few inches between it and adjacent apartment houses, stores, or warehouses. An eye grown used to the greys and browns of streets and buildings and garish signs suddenly sees the rice field, an intense, living, growing green. How could it survive in the densely built city of extremely high land values? Rice must be important.[35]

The emperor grows rice within the grounds of the Imperial Palace. Rice is the offering brought to the shrines at Ise. Rice has structured the landscape of country and city. Rice and fish are the staples of Japanese diet, the one from the earth, the other from the sea. Historically, coastal fishing village and inland farm village formed a unit, and it was the demands of rice cultivation—flat terraces connected by water channels—that structured inland villages. Many Japanese cities are built on the rice fields of former villages, and contemporary urban form often reflects that earlier structure of field and village. City blocks may reflect the shape and size of the rice fields they replaced. Rice fields are a reminder of the origins of the Japanese measurement system, the basis of dimensions for room and house. The *tan*, a standard measure of land, was originally the area needed to produce rice to feed a family of four or five people for one year. Before the seventh century, the size of one tan depended upon the land's productivity; after the seventh century, the tan became a standard size, three hundred *tsubo*; one tsubo is the size of two tatami.[36] Traditional Japanese rooms are modular, composed of varying numbers of tatami, woven from a reed that covers the rice-stalk padding inside. The bowl of rice, tatami mat, room, house, and the block on which they are situated, all are related; all parts of a whole felt, but not seen in a single glance. The rice fields of city, country, and palace, the rice-straw ropes that bound and mark sacred places, the rice of thanksgiving offered at Ise, these are all part of that whole.

How, for example, to weigh the importance of new houses compared to the importance of a small rice field? The rice field yields rice for a single family or at most a few families, an apartment building would house many. On a deep level, the city's green rice fields yield more than food. They permit city dwellers, especially children, to appreciate the relationships among sun, earth, water, and plants; to see the connection between nature and food. These rice fields permit one to *feel* history, to understand, not just to know abstractly, the landscape history that structures the city blocks and streets of Japan. Such prompts help transcend the overwhelming concreteness of the present, serve as an aid to imagining the reality of other times, both past and future.

Foreign rice is less expensive than homegrown rice, but rice is more than food. In Japan, mountain, sea, and forest form the warp; rice is an important thread in the weft. Pull that one thread—rice—and a portion of the pattern that is Japanese culture unravels. No wonder urban, as well as rural, rice fields have government subsidy. Culture is a fabric, the deep context of the natural landscape, the warp against which the weft of human intervention and elaboration weaves a pattern.

Landscape context is complex and dynamic, woven of many strands, in multiple dimensions. In landscape, speaking in context demands more than using local materials and imitating forms common to the regional landscape. To speak in context is to distinguish deep and lasting contexts from those that are superficial and fleeting; it is to respond to the rhythms and histories of each and to project those contexts into the future. To guide such contextual expression is the function of the grammar of landscape.

6
Rules of Context:
Landscape Grammar

A leaf on a tree is similar to a noun in a sentence. Nouns are not green, and leaves are not words, but the relationships among leaf, its growing or wilting, its context in twig, branch, and tree are like the relationships of noun to verb to sentence. This insight is Gregory Bateson's: "Both grammar and biological structure are products of communicational and organizational process."[1] In other words, "Anatomy *must* contain an analogue of grammar because all anatomy is a transform of message material, which must be contextually shaped."[2] But Bateson limited this analogy to the "creatura," living things; he failed to see that entire landscapes and their features—rivers, clouds, and mountains, not only trees, birds, and people—might not only be analogous to, but even *embody*, grammar and language.

Through grammar, meanings are shared; grammar is an aid to reading and telling landscape more fluently, deeply, expressively, and gracefully. The language is living, so grammar—derived from speech and the literature of landscape—is timeless, yet not rigid, but evolving and various. There are formulas, rules—artifacts of inherited usage—but also free expression, the renewal of language through the invention of new patterns.

Readers do not use grammar the same way tellers do. Readers decode meaning, move from perception of an element to an appreciation of its function, to understanding. Tellers have a message to relate and search for ways to express its significance by the choice and ordering of landscape's elements.

Elements like water or path unite to form features, like river or fountain, and features, in turn, combine to create larger landscapes, grammatically ordered to convey "wider and more varied patterns of meaning than in and of themselves."[3] Such rules govern the creation of leaf, tree, and forest, gate and garden, street and town. Trees and birds participate in grammar; they do not choose to obey its rules, and cannot break them. People follow the rules some of the time, but sometimes break them and sometimes invent new grammars. Multiple, overlapping grammars coexisting is what makes human landscapes so interesting and complex.

Principles of Grammar

Landscape grammar has no right or wrong, despite its rules, except perhaps when function is impaired or when choice leads to a sickness or dying. Grammatical principles are descriptive, not prescriptive; they reflect usage, aid the reading and making of landscapes, but do not demand they be made in a single, specific way, though some ways may be more adaptive than others. Codifying landscape grammar is a daunting task because contexts are multiple and change continually. Consequences must be assessed. Certain landscape statements carry a price: a town in the path of a river's flood, or a house on a landslide-prone slope. Landscapes that do not agree with the enduring context of a place may be riskier or more costly to build and maintain. With no single appropriate answer to a decision to stress or underplay a particular tense in landscape, a mistake in tense is made only if chosen materials, forms, or processes deny, undermine, or fail to convey an intended meaning.

Combining Grid, Water, Path, Meeting: Ancient Priene

In Priene, a colonial city in Asia Minor built in the fourth century B.C., elements combine to create a larger landscape of function and meaning. Priene was constructed on a hillside above a river's floodplain, where it was well defended from both natural hazards and human enemies. It was originally a seaport settlement; the hill spur on which it stood jutted out into the sea that separated the city from Miletus, its neighbor across the water to the south. The site today is more than seven miles inland.

Priene's layout followed the then-current method of Greek town planning, a grid plan coordinated with the sloping terrain. Streets, houses, and public spaces were subordinate to the overall grid, with the acropolis on a hilltop high above the town, the whole surrounded by a wall. Priene, carefully sited on sloping ground, demonstrated the flexibility of the grid. The main streets ran, more or less level, along the line of the slopes, and the secondary streets—narrow alleys—stepped up and down the slopes; the grid was aligned so that one street ran down the center of the one long valley that cut into the hillside. The houses were sited, as Hippocrates and Aristotle recommended, on the south-facing hillside to capture sun; they stepped down the slope so sun could reach houses across the street.[4] Most public buildings and temples were built where slopes leveled out. Curving seats of the outdoor theater, facing out, open to the sky, were set into the hillside below the acropolis, and the long *stadion*, a racecourse, rested on more level ground below the town.[5]

The structure of the hills around Priene is layered rock—marble and schist; water trickles through cracks in marble, underground, and flows out as hillside springs. The ancient water supply was both natural springs (exposed within the town by the terraced terrain and marked by fountains at several intersections) and an aqueduct that tapped mountain springs behind the town. The water system, like the grid plan, was typical of towns built in Greece itself after the fourth century B.C. Engineer and scholar Doris Crouch thinks Greeks chose sites for their colonial towns that resembled the geological context of their native country, confident of their ability to adapt their familiar town planning and water management practices there.

The lines of Priene's grid followed patterns of events—water's flowing, above

Coordinating town and terrain: Priene. Mid-fourth century B.C. Turkey.
(Wiegand and Schrader, 1904)

and below ground, and people moving. Both lines of the grid and the movement
served function and meaning. Lines became paths for water and people, boundaries for buildings; points of intersection with springs became sources of fountains and spaces for public gathering. Just as a word's meaning is mere potential
until shaped by specific relationships with other words in context of phrase,
clause, or sentence, so the meaning of an element of landscape is merely imma-
nent until shaped by relationships with other elements in context. Flowing, water,
grid, path, boundary, and source (and the streets, drains, and fountains they comprise) pose potential relationships, suggesting combinations, permitting fusion,
or promoting integration. Paths as lines of movement are potential links between
disparate entities—people, animals, water. Grids and axes, both structured by
points and lines, have potential to coincide or intersect, as in Priene's (or Philadelphia's) street grid with embedded principal axes.

Water and air in Priene, as elsewhere, share the same components, in different proportions, as rivers, seas, skies, and clouds. Clouds, intermediate in water

composition between sea and sky, link the two; when fog forms, sea and sky are indistinguishable, seemingly fused, disorienting to anyone out on the water. When two or more elements are fused the many become one, but the parts retain their identity. Like Priene, the Vietnam Veterans Memorial in Washington, D.C., can be divided into phrases: the wall itself is like a noun phrase, moving along the path a verb phrase. Wall and movement are modified: the wall by the material, stone, as by an adjective; moving, by path's descending and rising, as by an adverb. Like any landscape text, the memorial is composed of many such phrases, both subordinate and coordinate (the stones are subordinate to the wall, but coordinate to each other and to the mortar). Like all landscapes it is a complex composition; qualities of embeddedness are shared by all landscapes and all other languages—verbal, graphic, mathematical, or musical.

A landscape has many contexts, interacting (contingent, coordinated, subordinated) or independent, with highly related (congruent, echoing, convergent), or loosely related, or even unrelated, patterns (discontinuous layers). These multiple contexts may be fused (node on a web or network, when a tree's wood and fruit are also part of a system of lumber and food production and distribution, when plants grow in a certain soil or when a road follows a ridgeline); parallel (when a road runs alongside a river); nested, overlaid, overlapping (edge as zone; forest edge, porch, and portico); intersecting, interwoven, interlocking, continuous, interrupted (nonconforming rock layers, 1960s urban renewal that tore down whole blocks).

Grammar of verbal language combines morphemes into words, words into phrases, phrases into clauses, and clauses into sentence, but too close a comparison between verbal and landscape grammar must be resisted. Yet, like landscape, verbal language is continuous, neither linear nor segmented. The segmenting of verbal discourse is a process of combining, of sentences into paragraphs or stanzas, into chapters, poems, and books, ordinarily the province of composition. Composition is also the process of the composing of landscape, of selecting and combining landscape elements in significant ways, according to rules of grammar and traditions of rhetoric and style. Style is a way of doing things, a characteristic system of expression an individual or group employs.[6]

Scale and Tense: Micro, Macro, Past, Future

Elements—water and stone, circle and grid, path and prospect, moving and growing—have no scale, but landscape contexts do. The scale of the Great Plains, unbounded by mountains and forests, is vast; up close, landscape features like trees and buildings give the Plains a more human scale. The Smoky Mountains, though tall, are cloaked in dense forest; small clearings in the hollows have an intimate scale. An overview, like the prospect over the Plains at Red Rocks Amphitheater in Colorado, conveys a sense of connection across space and time, a possibility of seeing past routes and future direction, how parts fit into a whole.

"The world at arm's length—roughly one meter in scale—is the world of most artifacts and of the most familiar living forms."[7] Thus begins *Powers of Ten: About the Relative Size of Things in the Universe*, a remarkable journey in photographs and text across the known world: zooming from beyond our galaxy down in scale to a proton, in forty-two progressive views, each representing a power of ten. A collaboration by the designers Charles and Ray Eames, the physicist Philip Morrison, and the educator Phylis Morrison, it is an essay on scale, the relative size of things in the universe. Of the distance traveled, imaginatively, only about a dozen of the scales—from the moon to the surface of our skin—have been directly experienced by humans, the others have been seen through telescopes, the transmissions of robot ships, through microscopes and traces left in experiments.

An area one meter square is at the heart of human experience, the scale of human companionship, conversation, touch, the size of a desktop, of a small gate and its threshold, a narrow sidewalk, a bench for one person or two, close together. The next smaller scale, exponentially—10^{-1}, or ten centimeters—is intimate, that of a hand close-up, the latch of a gate, an individual flower or leaf, the detail of tree bark, grain of marble, a frog, a small spiderweb. One step smaller—one centimeter—is the scale of a fingernail, a spider and a fly, the joining of materials as in metal latch to wooden gate or mortared joint between bricks.

Increasing dimensions to a space ten meters across, one arrives at a domestic scale: the size of a single house or small garden, the domain of a family in some parts of the world; one can hear a human voice clearly from ten meters away, though one cannot touch and can barely distinguish facial features. This is also the scale of a tree's territory—the height and breadth of its canopy, its drip line, and extent of its roots underground. The only animals larger than ten meters are whales.

An area one hundred meters square, just over two acres, is of civic or palatial scale: of a city block with buildings, yards, streets, and sidewalks, encompassing many homes or businesses, of a large plaza, a stadium, the base of a skyscraper. The Fenway Rose Garden in Boston, the lawn around it, and the basketball court nearby all fit within such a space, so does the Taj Mahal with its four minarets. In the countryside, two acres is the size of a small pasture or a garden that will support a family with food. The giant sequoia, the largest known individual organisms, reach one hundred meters in height.

In the view from one thousand meters (one kilometer) in the air, a height sustained by an airplane approaching a landing, individual people are not distinguishable, but cars, boats, gardens, buildings, a segment of highway are. One thousand meters (one kilometer) square, approximately two hundred acres, is the area of a neighborhood with many blocks, its network of streets and hundreds, even thousands of homes. It is the size of the Fens with all its paths and ponds, Rose Garden, sports fields, and parkway. Small farms, each with house, garden, barn, pasture, and fields, like Åvangsgården in Denmark, are two hundred acres, as are large gardens like Stourhead. The horizontal span of the George Washington Bridge in New York City is a thousand meters.

In a landscape ten kilometers across (about six miles), the layout of downtown and inner city is discernable, their neighborhoods, streets, highways, and blocks. Rivers and parks are visible at this scale, and one can still make out the largest individual buildings. Ten kilometers is a cruising altitude familiar to airplane passengers; Mount Everest reaches this height above sea level.

Looking down at a landscape one hundred kilometers across, the scale of the entire metropolitan region of Chicago or Philadelphia or a portion of Los Angeles, one can see the structure of principal streets and highways, river and park systems; no buildings are visible. This is the scale of a moderate-sized watershed, of Philadelphia's Schuylkill River or Boston's Charles; one can see the surficial traces of fault lines across the Los Angeles region. It is a vantage few people have seen except on maps or in photographs taken at high altitudes.

At one thousand kilometers across, larger patterns of rivers, lakes, clouds, mountains, and plains appear, but the mark of humans is more difficult to discern. This is the scale of the Great Plains, the Rocky Mountains, a large hurricane, or the watershed of a great river like the Missouri or the Ohio. Forests have been cut, rivers dammed, rock quarried, cities built, but from this perspective, little has changed in thousands of years. At ten thousand kilometers across, the earth itself fills the area, swirling clouds reveal air's movement; at one hundred thousand kilometers, the familiar picture of spaceship earth, seen from space, a sphere of blue sheathed in an atmosphere of swirling white.

Space is not segmented into scales, but continuous. A seed is part of fruit, fruit part of tree, tree part of forest. Path, garden, neighborhood, town, region, nation are nested contexts, each enclosed within a larger whole and context for features at smaller scales. This successive, sometimes hierarchical, relationship of parts and wholes in landscape gives its language a nested structure. Rules of grammar—modification, agreement, correspondence, subordination, and coordination—apply across scales, as well as within.

To be comprehended, patterns must be brought within human range by enlarging the micro and miniaturizing the macro. Designers' drawings and planners' maps represent landscapes enlarged or reduced; the scale they choose depends on the actions they intend. Urban designers typically work from the scale of building, street, and plaza to neighborhood, architects within the scale of a building, from doorknob to threshold to chair to exterior walls, with all its features and furnishings—scales at which environment can be seen, touched, smelled, heard. Planners work at the scale of an entire neighborhood, region, or even nation, ordinarily not concerned with sensual experience. Landscape architects work at scales from garden to metropolitan region, and thus bridge design and planning, a distinctive and important role. When professionals focus on a narrow range of scales (from gate handle to garden, for example) without addressing larger contexts of scale (neighborhood and region), they may introduce elements that do not agree with those contexts and may, therefore, be unsustainable. Similarly,

Correspondence across scales: cracking ice. Massachusetts. (Alex S. MacLean/Landslides)

when planners focus on scales of neighborhood or region and neglect domestic and local scales, their proposals may not agree with those smaller contexts and produce failures or unanticipated consequences.

A strength of Christopher Alexander's "pattern language" is that it reflects landscape's nested quality; his patterns are arranged from the metropolitan scale of "Distribution of Towns" to the intimate scale of "Half-inch Trim," though most of the patterns fall between the dimensions of one meter to one hundred meters: personal, domestic, civic, and neighborhood scales reflecting the architect's and urban designer's scope of concern. Alexander does not specify how to combine them, though he does advise the reader to pay attention to patterns at more than one scale.

A similar device to the Eames' and Morrisons' "Powers of Ten" could be constructed to illustrate scales of time: from the length of a deep breath, to the time spanning the lives of people known to a single person, to the time of the earliest surviving landscapes shaped by humans, to the age of fossils. Tense in landscape is relative; it is rare to find an entire landscape in a single tense. At Vizcaya, the former estate of John Deere in Florida, worn stairs of stone embedded with fossilized animals and vegetables resonate with the smell of rotting plants in the surrounding tidal swamp. Like the rounded river cobbles in the Patio de la Reja's fountain in the Alhambra, made smooth by years of running water, the worn steps, fossils, and smells at Vizcaya summon a sense of ongoing time and collapse the past and present. As do shoots sprouting from a cut stump. The tumbled-down houses and abandoned land in Philadelphia's Mill Creek, occupied by so many unemployed, convey a sense of past that has no part in the future.

Hadrian's Villa in Tivoli, east of Rome, is a rambling ruin that once housed thousands of people. Like the skeleton of a dead tree sticking out of one of the vaults, action here appears over, apart from the ongoing process of decay. But there are signs of repair, explanatory plaques, railings to protect visitors from falling, all introducing a sense of the present, some, depending on materials and form, calling attention to the contrast between the past life of the place and its present.

Loss of past can be self-inflicted. Dallas performed a lobotomy on itself when it destroyed all vestiges of its past downtown, replacing older buildings and squares with new commercial office buildings and a cultural district. Reconstructed colonial and pioneer villages are similarly disquieting. Both kinds of places seem in limbo, detached. East Berlin, in physical suspension for many years, is undergoing a shocking transformation, eradication of the recent past, replacement by the new. Not so in West Berlin after the war, where new construction was integrated into remains of old buildings damaged by bombs, as in the Kaiser Wilhelm Memorial Church. The East German government owned all the railroads, and because they used no more than a few lines, in many railyards and along rights-of-way tracks and land are now overgrown. Around East Berlin are many railroad bridges, now lush ruins. The Ruins, the eye-catcher visible from the courtyard behind Sanssouci, in Potsdam, is perched picturesquely high up on the hillside; it conceals a reservoir that feeds the fountains of the park, a built version of a late eighteenth-century German painting of a Roman aqueduct in ruin. "We have too many ruins now," said a German friend.

In Orange County, California's South Coast Plaza, Isamu Noguchi's sculpture *Lima Bean* is the only sign that the land now covered by mirrored-glass banks, office towers, parking garages, and lawns was, until recently, beanfields. A present tense, without obvious antecedents, pervades the freshly clipped, cleanly edged green grass, brightly colored flowers, polished metal fountains, and trendy signs and lamps. No spent flowers, dead leaves, or old buildings hint at past lives. Nor is there anticipation of the future, for southern California's mild climate produces no single time of blooming, no pronounced seasonality, just an ever-agreeable present.

In Philadelphia, spring moves by at fast forward; one day is cold and blustery, branches bare, then air is warm and breezy. One late afternoon in mid-April, the sun fills the air with brightly lit dots of color—greens, browns—leaves brightly backlit. Three days later, trees are almost fully leafed out. The air is full of falling bud cases and petals; insects zing around, light catches their wings. Every day sees major changes. I feel the future rushing toward me in landscapes like these.

Modifying, Agreeing, and Corresponding

At Parc de Sceaux, outside Paris, the ground is graded plane—flat and tilted— and trees are clipped into cubes and cones. Long parallel rows of sycamores,

Growth and form modified and subordinated: clipped allées. Sceaux. France.

lindens, and hornbeams are planted close, their leaves sheared into a solid green mass that frames the mansion and forms an entry to the park. Beyond the house, thirty-six cones of evergreen yew dot a tilted plane. Their sides show a lighter green, new bright green growth against deep-green, older growth and brown, where the yew has been cut back sharply. Clipping modifies the yew's growth, makes it bud more densely, become more opaque, and introduces a tension between outer form and internal, branching structure. This part of the garden is bounded on two sides by a long, clipped, rectangular wall of yew. Beyond the green wall, woodland trees grow freely.

Imagine how shocking it must have been when plants were first pruned into cones and cubes. Why would anyone modify plants' growing, so extremely, without a strong intent? To demonstrate mastery? Reveal an underlying ideal? Contrast reason and irrationality? Now it has become a formula: topiary. Some people find topiary repulsive, to others it is fashionable or fun. Sven-Ingvar Andersson takes it as serious fun, as he said in an essay of 1967 soon after he had planted Marnas, his "henyard" garden of hedges and topiary birds in southern Sweden. First he planted the birds as "eggs," young hawthorn trees cut "into tight balls, so that the birds will not grow bare-legged," then later, little by little, he shaped them into hens twelve feet high.[8] He described how he expected his garden to grow over the next forty years, said he knew a lot could go awry between then

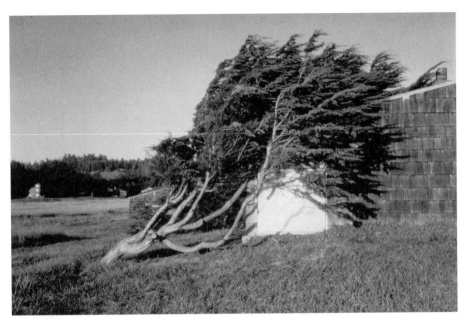

Agreement: wind, tree, house. Sea Ranch. California.

and now, but, despite the uncertainties, he was not worried about the outcome:

My confidence stems not so much from a sense of my own ability to manage the affair, but from two facts: the simple pattern of the planting and the material, hawthorn. If I always proceed with a respect for the placement of the hawthorns and their existence as living organisms, they will always form a clear pattern that can adapt to whatever serendipitous circumstances are introduced by myself and by time. The hawthorns, on the other hand, permit enormous variation, from the meter-high closely clipped to the freely growing twenty-foot tree. But not beyond those limits which lie in being a hawthorn, which means that every single cell, whether it sits in the roots or in the skin of the fruit has a predetermined number of chromosomes with a particular set of genes, which can vary a little bit and give each plant its unique individuality, yet still ensure similarities in form and mode of meeting external conditions.[9]

Is it right or wrong to clip trees, flatten and tilt slopes, lay a grid of streets on hilly ground? Neither right nor wrong, necessarily; it all depends on meaning and consequences. Limits are imposed not by a moral criterion, but by the materials, forms, processes, and behavior, depending on their nature.

At Sea Ranch, a residential development on the northern California coast, someone planted a tree against the exposed, windward corner of a house near cliff's edge, overlooking the Pacific Ocean. Dwarfed, pruned by wind, its branches splay back, embracing both sides of the home, as if protecting. The tree's form agrees with wind's force and direction and building's shape. To read protection in this requires an imaginative leap between outstretched branches and arms. The tree had no message for people, its dialogue was with wind and house.

The wide path up the Hill of Remembrance in Stockholm's Forest Cemetery is steep at first—climbing eased by low stone steps, deep, stone-dust treads, landings every dozen steps; then the slope tapers, steps pass between trees through an open gateway atop the hill, ending just inside low walls.[10] At the beginning of the ascent, steps are set into the hillside, so the slopes enfold the climber; at the end, frames of trees and wall enclose. Form and material shape the experience of path and refuge; all modify processes of movement and grieving, in agreement with the meaning its author intended: "To give form to a sorrow that cannot be told," an experience of difficulty, comforted.[11]

Shapes of valley floor and terraced slopes reveal where floods have been and where they will return. Shape of river's banks and the structure of its branching agree with patterns of rain falling and the qualities of material over which it flows: branched in uniform rock, trellised (parallel branches and sharp turns) in fractured terrain, braided rivulets over unconsolidated sediments, interrupted over limestone (a stream may disappear into underground channels dissolved in the rock). Channels straight and long are rivers modified to agree with human purpose, confined by design to direct water for human use.

Frank Lloyd Wright once laid out a grid of gardens on the Wisconsin hillside below Taliesin North; it faced the road, presented a vivid pattern, and people drove by just to look at them.[12] Unlike the grid of streets and drains at Priene, however, form and function did not agree; this was a poor location for such a layout and for gardens, the slope too steep, the soil too erodible. Wright soon replaced the gridded gardens with grass and trees. When first built, the prow garden at Taliesin West, composed of desert plants, agreed with the climate of Phoenix; now it is filled with grass and tropical flowers, which are at odds with the climate, and must be irrigated.

The Wisconsin River near Taliesin is dwarfed by the vast valley through which it flows. Where valley and river do not agree, the valley has been shaped by a different river or process, in this case, thousands of years ago by a glacial lake with far more water than the present river's flow. The Salt River, or Rio Salado, is an enormous grey, dry channel of gravel that divides Phoenix from Tempe. The river is empty, its waters distributed by hundreds of miles of canals into thousands of gardens and swimming pools. Forms of river and valley ordinarily agree; forms of valleys in the same rock and region correspond: agreement, in relationships between a landscape element or feature and the processes that shape it; correspondence, to analogies across entire landscapes, at micro and regional scales. The gridded streets of Denver correspond to the larger grid of the American Midwest; the process of surveying and settling links their disparate scales and locations. Water flowing through unconsolidated sediments produces the correspondence between patterns of sand in a gutter, along sandy banks of a river, in broad, braided channels of the South Platte River, hundreds of miles long.

In Phoenix, in September, it is more than one hundred degrees at midday and extremely dry. Animals' rustle, birds' song are still until after sunset. High, thick walls protect lush, garden oases. In the desert beyond the walls, plants are widely spaced to gather water, many emerge only after rainfall. Ocotillo is tall with long, tough, thorny stems that flare out from the base, as in a vase, leafing out after rain, blooming scarlet in spring. A fence of ocotillo stems looks dead brown until rain falls, and then, after a few days, it turns green—a living fence, memory of rain, barometer of the past. The rocks of Taliesin West, varnished bright orange-red and black, mark many years' exposure to daily cycles of heating and cooling, evaporation and condensation. To lack of water and strength of sun all desert plants and animals, rocks and rivers respond, giving the landscape a pervasive and powerful order. Not sameness, or even similarity, of material and form, but correspondence—tough skin, compact form, spaced for water, dormant between rains, nocturnal activity—gives a sense of coherence to deserts and to all landscapes.

Understanding landscape grammar provokes question, answer, and appropriate response. Failure to understand leads to misreading and inappropriate action. In the mid-1980s, when architects and urban planners failed to read the vacant blocks in Boston's Dudley Street neighborhood, the result, in part, of the blocks' location in an old floodplain, they proposed to build new houses in the bottom of the abandoned valley. My students and I proposed alternative designs in agreement with the landscape structure: houses on higher ground and parks and playgrounds over the buried stream and within its former floodplain. New houses and town commons sponsored since by the Dudley Street Neighborhood Initiative have followed this strategy.[13]

Order: Coordinating and Subordinating

W. G. Hoskins compared the English landscape to a symphony that "is possible to enjoy as an architectural mass of sound," but whose impact is greatest when: "we are able to isolate the themes as they enter, to see how one by one they are intricately woven together and by what magic new harmonies are produced, perceive the manifold subtle variations on a single theme, however disguised it may be."[14] Enduring landscape context is akin to symphonic theme and restatement, responses to that context by populations over time are like Haydn's many variations. But not all landscapes are harmonious. English footpaths with no relationship to either old sheep pastures or more recent wheat fields, that correspond, instead, to an even older pattern of common fields, are a Shostakovich landscape, full of clashing orders and discords, not the lush harmonies of Brahms.

Disorder, wrote Rudolf Arnheim, "is not the absence of all order but rather the clash of uncoordinated orders."[15] Arnheim defined order as "the degree and kind of lawfulness governing the relations among the parts of an entity" and com-

Correspondence and coordination: Ocatilla. Frank Lloyd Wright. (© 1998 The Frank Lloyd Wright Foundation)

plexity as the multiplicity of the relationships among those parts.[16] The greatest works of landscape literature, like great compositions of music or art, combine high order with high complexity, a difficult union, but: "complexity without order produces confusion; order without complexity produces boredom." The easiest way to achieve a sense of order is by repeated use of homogeneous landscape materials or forms—green lawn at Stourhead and Forest Cemetery. Hierarchy orders landscape by subordinating some features to others—the central axis at Versailles, nested domains at Ise. Coordination achieves order by granting elements similar importance—the grid of garden rooms at Mariebjerg, ellipses at Nærum. Chaotic order, not random, but seemingly accidental, is the most difficult of all; Halprin and his associates designed the surfaces over which water flows in Ira's Fountain in Portland to create specific patterns of turbulent flow.

Frank Lloyd Wright experimented with all four kinds of order—homogeneous, hierarchical, coordinated, and chaotic—to compose landscapes of high order and high complexity. In Taliesin North he used homogeneous material—local limestone and sandstone—for buildings and walls. His compositions, up until the 1920s, were coordinated by a single orthogonal grid, sometimes leading to problems on steeply sloping or irregularly shaped terrain, as in the gridded gardens at Taliesin North. Working in complex topography on large landscape compositions in the 1920s, he gradually adopted structural strategies more appropriate to irregular terrain. At the Johnson Compound in Death Valley, an unbuilt project of 1924, he provided hierarchy with several axes aligned in response to terrain and views. When he drew a new site plan in 1925 for vineyard, gardens, and farm buildings at Taliesin North, he coordinated them within a new grid oriented roughly perpendicular to the line of the slope, at a forty-five-degree angle to the grid of the earlier plan. At Ocatilla, a temporary desert camp where he lived for a few months, Wright overlaid two grids, each aligned with the terrain, sowing the seeds of design that would come to fruition in his Taliesin West. He often juxtaposed architectural form derived from Euclidean geometry to the complex, seemingly random, order of plants' growth: at Taliesin North in the cantilevered terrace over wild slopes below and hilltop garden enclosed by wall with freely growing grass beyond; at Taliesin West in the prow garden raised above the desert.

At Priene, in Asia Minor, points where water springs from the hillside are nodes around which fountains and important public spaces for meeting— temple, agora—are coordinated. Intersections in the lattice of Wright's Taliesin West are potential nodes, some activated by crossing paths, sculptural objects, entrances to buildings.

FOLLOWING AND BREAKING THE RULES

Local Dialects, Invented and Imported Grammars

Grammar is a living pattern reflecting both timeless rules and the contingencies of time and place. The deep context of a place is the foundation with which new expressions agree, correspond, are coordinated, subordinated, or not. Attending to the grammar of enduring context entails a response not only to the physical context of landforms, plants, and plant communities, but also to temporal context, to rhythmic daily and seasonal changes of light, temperatures, and water characteristic of a place, and to enduring aspects of cultural context. Design that reveals and agrees with deep context is likely to be more functional, more economical, more sustainable over time than design that disregards it.

Local landscape dialects emerge out of dialogue with enduring contexts of place; traditional vernacular landscapes are a consequence of collective learning, trial and error, finding what works and repeating it, refining through experience. They tend to correspond more closely to local conditions than do landscapes of cultures of highly developed technology. English hedgerows of hawthorn and beech; New England walls of glacial boulders dug from fields; layered limestone walls in Kentucky blue-grass country and the Driftless area of Wisconsin; split-rail fences in Virginia/North Carolina; barbed wire and wooden post fences in the Midwest: all are boundary types particular to the cultural and material context of place (property ownership, land use; local stone and plants). Vernacular landscapes may also include features that do not work in a place, such as those imported by immigrants. But the Hispano-Islamic gardens at the Alhambra in Granada are classical works in congenial dialogue with the natural and vernacular landscapes of Andalusia, with their mountains and rivers, their steep, terraced hillsides, fountains, cascades, pavements of river cobbles in flowing and geometrical patterns.

Glenn Murcutt studies a site for a building by observing its processes—wind blowing, sun shining, fire burning, animals moving, plants growing, water flowing. Then he designs in agreement with these processes, including the ways of his clients' lives. Form and materials of his buildings correspond to vernacular structures, not because he imitates, but in response to similar features of enduring context. Design attuned to enduring context can go beyond conventional understanding of regionalism's focus on indigenous materials and forms of vernacular settlements and buildings. In fact, as in Murcutt's buildings, imported materials and distinctly contemporary forms introduce a present tense and, thereby, heighten an awareness of layers of time.

Parc Sceaux and other seventeenth-century French gardens near Paris, like Vaux-le-Vicomte, Versailles, and Chantilly, were bold inventions. With their broad, flat terraces and sheets of water in basins and canals, these gardens were keyed to the floodplain landscape of the Île-de-France and the powers of their royal and aristocratic patrons. But the geometry and visual effects of Le Nôtre's designs relied also upon strict accuracy of measurement in design and construction. In the eighteenth century, the title "geometer" referred to all mathematicians, computation ability was a sign of intelligence, and many of the well educated were proud of their arithmetical computation.[17] The gardens also display an understanding of military engineering.[18] These gardens were ordered by a grammar invented not only as an expression of the deep structure of the landscape of the Île-de-France—the floodplains and canals—but the intellectual and political context of the time as well.

In composing landscapes, humans participate in, and elaborate on, dialects of place, perhaps even choosing to depart from and replace the rules with a grammar of a different place and time, or one simply invented, idiosyncratic. The landscape of every place engenders expectation. When form deviates from that norm there is a reason, conscious or unconscious, intended or unintended. Designers who know grammar may break the rules deliberately for the sake of meaning, for the sake of powerful new expression or new relationships. But designers who flout the rules without reason or in ignorance produce, at best, gibberish, a jumble of forms and materials, of meanings that add up to no meaning, like many landscapes today; at worst, potential catastrophe.

The International Style of architecture and planning, so influential in the twentieth century, is responsible for the proliferation of high-rise towers amid a broad, bland landscape of grass and concrete, appropriate to no place. In Jeddah, air-conditioned towers block sea breezes from penetrating the city; in New York City, it produced a no-man's-land of wind-swept plazas. In Mexico City, concrete buildings and pavement replaced three stones that had been quarried for buildings and pavement in the Valley of Mexico from pre-Columbian times. The black, the grey, and the red stone were formed concurrently in volcanic eruptions: the black stone is basalt, lava spewn from volcano mouth; red stone *tezontle* is rock that was molten but remained within the volcano. The lightweight red stone traditionally was used more in walls, the grey stone in details—ornament, frames, thresholds, the heavy black stone in pavement. Recently, Mexican architects and landscape architects, like Mario Schjetnan, have introduced stone from the Valley of Mexico once again in buildings and pavement.[19] Lack of correspondence between the pervasive concrete of International Style buildings and plazas and the indigenous volcanic stone used traditionally forfeit a story linking the built landscape to the vulcanism that shaped (and still shapes) the Valley of Mexico. Failure of agreement between the enduring context of vulcanism and landscapes and buildings designed in the International Style, ill-adapted to earthquakes, have had deadly consequences: pilotis, free plan (post-and-beam construction with non-bearing or curtain walls), separate stair shafts sheared off during earthquakes; roof gardens add weight at the top where it is most dangerous. The old pyramid form is very earthquake-resistant, so is the patio form that gives a rigidity and stability to the structure.[20]

The interior gardens and thick-walled buildings built by Spanish missionaries in Mexico and southwestern America, on the other hand, were oases in a hot, dry climate, learned from the Moorish culture of southern Spain, brought there, in turn, from northern Africa and the Middle East. But the green trees and lawns of the English landscape garden exported to India, Australia, and Africa as a sign of home, comforting to imperial bureaucrats and an assertion of British dominance over local cultures, were not so adaptable; to export is not necessarily to adapt. When built forms are repeated across the world without an understanding of the processes that originally generated them and in ignorance of the story lines of the place to which they are exported, their narrative can become boring, alienating, unsustainable, even disastrous.

Grammar Observed and Ignored: Chestnut Hill and Mill Creek

A big rock juts out of the Schuylkill River in Philadelphia just upstream from the East Falls Bridge. When the river is in flood, only the barest tip of the rock pokes above the water; once or twice a year, even the tip disappears, marked only by lines on water's surface. At low flow, the rock's stony ridges emerge, a warning to boaters of deeper rock below the surface. The rock is part of the fall zone, a series of waterfalls and rapids that mark the place where the soft sediments and gentle slopes of coastal plains meet the Piedmont's rocky hills—the end of navigable waters from the sea. From the vantage of a satellite one thousand kilometers above the earth, the Coastal Plain is clearly visible, as are the Appalachian Mountains and their foothills, the Piedmont. The rock in the Schuylkill is a part of this larger complex that structures the entire eastern seaboard of the United States from New Jersey to Georgia, as well as the Philadelphia metropolitan region.

William Penn sited the new town of Philadelphia in 1682 on a strip of relatively level, forested land between the Delaware and Schuylkill rivers just north of their confluence. Like the fourth-century builders of Priene, Penn aligned the lines of the grid—the city's future streets—with the landscape's structure: parallel to the two rivers and perpendicular, connecting them. The low, gently rolling plain and small creeks were no great obstacles, and the city grew within this frame of streets and squares. Penn's vision of Philadelphia as a "greene countrie towne" was influenced by current ideas in town planning. After the Fire of London in 1666, for example, John Evelyn and others put forward proposals for widening and straightening the streets, and for introducing a new grid of streets with squares filled with gardens and trees. Penn's plan for Philadelphia expressed those ideas.

Philadelphia's principal source of water from the early nineteenth century was the Schuylkill River. The fall zone was flooded by a dam built in 1821 to power the waterworks to pump river water to a reservoir atop Fairmount, from which it flowed by gravity through pipes to the city below. Philadelphia's Fairmount Park, one of the world's largest urban parks, was created along the banks of the Schuylkill and its tributary, Wissahickon Creek, to protect the water supply. Today one can walk eleven miles from City Hall, at the center of downtown, to the city's limits, without leaving park: up the sloping plain of the Franklin Parkway to Fairmount, now capped by the Philadelphia Museum of Art, on the broad walks along the banks of the Schuylkill, up a narrow trail in the steep, rocky, wooded Wissahickon Valley to northwest Philadelphia and Chestnut Hill, a "railroad suburb" built in the late nineteenth and early twentieth centuries. The path from downtown to Chestnut Hill tells a story of Coastal Plain and Piedmont, of flat plain, then rolling terrain, of houses and sidewalks of brick, then of stone, of cosmopolitan London plane trees, then native eastern hemlocks and beeches.

As the city expanded to north and west, and as the streets of the grid were extended, they hit the steeper slopes, deeper valleys, and broader streams of the Piedmont. In Chestnut Hill, the grid deforms and disintegrates as it approaches the slopes along the Wissahickon and its tributaries. Here, the park boundaries coincide with the valley's upper slopes; woods extend up tributary creeks into neighborhoods where houses, walls, and terraces are built of the native stone—Wissahickon schist—patterned after English Cotswold cottages and French villas, the gardens landscaped with plants native to the region's forest. Though styles of houses and gardens were imported, the designers responded to the grammar of deep context. Thus the grid is subordinate, deferring to the landscape's structure; stone and plants of gardens correspond to the materials of the region, the plants are in agreement with its climate and soil. The community's main street and spine,

Grammar observed: Wissahickon. Fairmount Park, Philadelphia.

Germantown Avenue, predates the extension of the city's grid and cuts across it, lined with older houses, part of the enduring cultural context. Before it became a park, the Wissahickon Valley was an industrial landscape, with more than thirty mills and numerous houses and inns. Most of the buildings have been removed, and, since the turn of the century, a forest of oak, beech, and hemlock has grown up protecting the city's water supply and the neighborhood's property values.

In a different neighborhood, another tributary to the Schuylkill, Mill Creek, became not park, but sewer. When the urban grid pressed westward from city center into the rolling hills and valleys of West Philadelphia in the 1880s, row houses packed the grid, in some sections with little or no yard at either front or back, and no parks to relieve the dense fabric. Anomalies, large properties—a mental hospital, a mansion, a large playground, a huge vacant block—either predated the city's expansion or resulted from development that ignored the grammar of deep context. Buried in a sewer, its floodplain filled in and built on, Mill Creek still drains and still carries all the stormwater as well as the wastes from half of West Philadelphia, but the size of the pipe, about twenty feet in diameter, is too small to agree with the huge quantity of sewage and stormwater it needs to convey. In consequence the wastewater cracks, then undermines the sewer, and, once or twice a year, sometimes more often, the sewer overflows, and brown water spouts from inlets and manhole covers.

For more than sixty years, in Mill Creek, the ground has fallen in, here and

Grammar ignored: burying Mill Creek (1880s). (Philadelphia Water Department)

there, along the line of the sewered stream. A playground was built by the city on the site where, in 1961, several blocks of housing had collapsed and been demolished. Now, sagging streets and sidewalks and cracked walls reveal ongoing shifting and foretell future cave-ins. For many years, the creek has ripped open the grid, undermined buildings and streets, slashed meandering diagonals of shifting foundations, tumbled buildings, and vacant land across the urban landscape. Young woodlands of ailanthus, sumac, and ash have grown up on older lots, urban meadows on lots recently vacated.

Most community gardens in this part of West Philadelphia lie within the old floodplain of Mill Creek. Gardeners at Aspen Farms know there is a buried stream in their neighborhood; they see its effects in and around their garden. Houses across from the garden have sunk several feet, and the plots in the back corner, where the garden slopes toward the old streambed, need water less frequently, since the soil there is often moist. The Spruce Hill Garden was built where a house collapsed over a tributary to the Mill Creek. A crack now spans the entire height of a house across the street from the garden; the building has sunk down over that same old streambed. Just one block away, 43rd Street, a low point, floods every time it rains.

After a heavy rain, the Schuylkill flows milky brown, the water surface glazed, oily, and lumpy, like a thick soup of sediment and sewage. Normally, rain falls,

Grammar ignored: houses built over sewer. (G. W. Bromley, 1927)

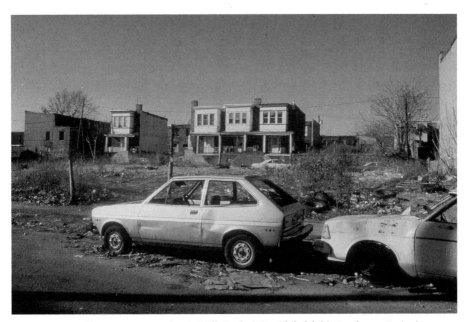

Consequences of ignorance: vacant lots in Mill Creek. (West Philadelphia Landscape Project)

flows quickly across the paved floodplain to the sewer, then on to a treatment plant for cleansing before discharge into the Schuylkill. After large rainstorms, there is too much sewage and some flows directly into the river—a combined sewer overflow. The mixture of sanitary sewage, stormwater runoff, and river water flows downstream past parks and docks into the Delaware River and its estuary. Mill Creek overflows past the place where Philadelphia draws its own water, but cities downstream, like Wilmington, Delaware, take in its discharge. The consequences of ignoring landscape grammar in the Mill Creek neighborhood and other communities extend far beyond their own boundaries.

Grammars of place embody collective wisdom accumulated over generations of life in a particular landscape; their rules are guides it is foolish to ignore. But grammar is a flexible system, not a straitjacket of dictums. It does not dictate how the language of landscape should be used or what meanings ought to be expressed. The methods by which authors combine individual elements to compose landscapes, the rhetoric they employ, and the ideological agendas they promote are the subject of pragmatics, poetics, and polemics of the language of landscape.

Three

Using the Language of Landscape:
Pragmatics, Poetics, and Polemics

For thus it was designed:
Controlled disorder at the heart
Of everything, the paradox, the old
Oxymoronic itch to set the formal strictures
Within a natural context, where the tension lectures
Us on our mortal state, and by controlled
Disorder, labors to keep art
From being too refined.

—Anthony Hecht, "The Gardens of
the Villa d'Este," *The Hard Hours*

The henyard at Marnas.

7
Shaping: Pragmatics
of Landscape Expression

CREATING A FRAME FOR STABILITY AND SERENDIPITY: MARNAS

Driving down a country road in Sönder Sandby, past fields of wheat and farm-steads tucked behind hedges of the broad, rolling cropfields and pastures of Skåne in southwestern Sweden, I see it would be easy to miss the tiny, old, half-timbered house. It is partly hidden by tall green hedges against the road. Four willow trees form a narrow gateway between house and hedge; slow and turn sharply to enter, pull past the hedge and enter a garden fantasy with clipped balls of privet, tall top-iary birds, and spherical purple flowers on long green stems. A coiled green hose and a basket of cut flowers lie on the path, catching the late afternoon sun, signs someone must be nearby. High, living walls of hawthorn bound and screen other garden rooms: sounds of shovel digging lead to where the gardener is, in floppy straw hat, wooden shoes, and overalls, planting yellow yarrow brought over from Lutyen's Deanery in England.

Marnas, named for Marna, an earlier tenant, is Sven-Ingvar Andersson's weekend home. The house is much as it was a hundred years ago, with no indoor plumbing and a stove to heat its three small rooms. The garden is a laboratory and workshop, where, for thirty years, Andersson has tested new ideas and pursued ancient practices: growing pears in bottles for brandy, clipping hedges, making soil from wastes. Tasks depicted in the Breughel print that hung opposite Andersson's desk at the Royal Academy of Fine Arts in Copenhagen are carried out here.[1] For him, traditional gardening is a link "through history to human ex-istence and evolution."[2] Marnas is a personal playground, too, with past projects and ongoing experiments: a woman of boards, a sculpture of branches, an over-grown wall of brick that was once a barbecue pit. The garden's grid of hawthorn hedges encloses eleven rooms, large and small: secret gardens, leafy passages, a garden room of strawberries and vegetables, another of compost, another of fire for burning woody refuse, one vacant, "an empty pot for useful things."[3] Six top-iary hens, twelve feet tall, clipped from hawthorn, sit in a "henyard"—a flowering parterre—the largest room, near the old house. Birds twitter; a hedgehog pokes out from under a hedge, waddles down the allée, ducks under another hedge.

When, in 1967, the editors of *Arkitekten* asked Andersson to write an essay on complexity, he sent in "A Letter from My Henyard." It was a reflection on the gar-den at Marnas, a philosophy of landscape and life, a manifesto, gentle, but pointed, light and deep, playful and critical, spontaneous and composed, a reminder that, in landscape, ideas are tangible and values have consequences.

Andersson foresaw the time when he no longer would have the strength "to hold clippers or clamber up ladders" and when it would be difficult to find folk to hire. He planned the garden's future form as a hawthorn grove, the grove it is now beginning to be, growing from gridded hedges. Though the trees were planted when he wrote, there were still no hens in the "henyard," since the hedges were only a foot high and the "hens" still "eggs"—clipped balls of hawthorn: "I have a definite idea of how my henyard will end, but that which lies between *now* and *then* is an open plan. . . . A lot can happen before the henyard becomes a hawthorn grove." The fixed framework of the hedges was in place, but many decisions were still to be made: how high should the hedges be ("It's hard to clip them if they are over four and a half feet, but I would like to enclose the henyard a bit better")? Should the tops be clipped horizontally or follow the terrain, or be cut at several different heights ("A plane at just the right level will make a completely enclosed space in the lower part of the garden, and a view out over distant hills and ridges from the higher hedge room")? What about the spaces between the rooms, should they be voids between the parts of the garden that "mean something" or rooms in themselves—leafy passages "filled with fine shade-loving plants or birdcages or moss-covered stones"? "From the rectangles one could peek in at these wonders through openings in the hedges." How consistent should the various parts of the garden be? There were many possibilities:

> positive and negative space structure, different room heights, open and closed spaces, spaces that gather themselves around something which happens on the ground plane or that open to the clouds; passages that follow the district's in-between spaces and passages that wind through the garden seemingly independent of the primary structure? Shall I perhaps make my playground into an illustration of "Complexity and Contradiction in Architecture" or shall I let form follow function in the hope that less is more? There are many "Intentions in Architecture" to choose from, and to the ecological requirements of the hawthorns I can add my own social needs.[4]

Or, he asked, should he simply yield to "the free play of forces and accept chaos as the aesthetic of our time"? Humans, "like hawthorns, are very adaptable, but still bound to their genetic structure" in whose "genetically fixed pattern there is a need for stability, on the one hand, and for freedom, growth, and individual development," on the other. "The task, then, is to find the balance." Plan only details that express the essential framework, let the others emerge—that was the answer he built into his garden. Leave room for impulse and serendipity. "The only ideal city planned in detail that still functions well is the botanical garden at Padua. . . . But then it is plants that are concerned there," not people.

Most people do not consider making a garden as speaking, and do not begin to garden by reflecting on what they want to say, and yet, nonetheless, they are

An open plan: Marnas (1967).
(Sven-Ingvar Andersson)

Legend: (1) road, (2) house,
(3) courtyard, (4) patio,
(5) apple orchard, (6) cars,
(7) henyard, (8) bonfire,
(9) strawberries,
(10) rabbits' place.

speaking, even praying, through their gardens. Though human capacity for language may be innate, we learn the language of landscape primarily through living in, building, caring for a place. How and why people choose to express themselves as they do, how to know what is appropriate, is the subject of pragmatics.

People need a place to shape their environment, writes Andersson. The need for self-expression is at the root of community gardens as it is of his own hawthorn hens. What rationale could justify the aesthetic double standard that asserts the architect's right to experiment, he asks, yet confines the user "behind a nice facade" and windows with "neutral curtains," and denies them the right to exuberant expression "that could be the true folklore of industrial society?"[5] Andersson's garden at Marnas embodies themes and strategy similar to those G. N. Brandt explored in Denmark at Mariebjerg Cemetery and C. Th. Sørensen at Nærum Garden Colony. All three demonstrate an interplay of order and complexity; in all three a fundamental structure establishes order, but time, circumstance, and the gardener's improvising add complexity.

Marnas celebrates transience within constancy, it is an open experiment steeped in tradition, changing as plants grow and as the gardener ages. In Andersson's essays, I read of his earlier garden with the leftover privet shrubs "that decided they

Elaborated framework: Marnas. (1976) (Sven-Ingvar Andersson)

Legend: (1) bonfires and sitting, (2) kitchen garden, (3) compost, (4) Beata's garden, (5) sun garden, (6) flower garden, (7) henyard, (8) tunnel arbor, (9) country road, (10) parking, (11) field, (12) outhouse and guest house, (13) old orchard with privet hedges, (14) patio, (15) house, (16) meadow.

wanted to become birds;" I discover his topiary garden, and learn how Marnas was designed to "hold the dream" of the gardener as an old man sitting under a hawthorn grove.[6] I read the plans from 1967 and 1976, and view a succession of photographs, recognizing the grid of hedges that enclose the many garden rooms. The birds clipped from hawthorn, now more than twelve feet tall, occupied their "henyard" from the beginning, but some of the early rooms are barely recognizable in the one I know now. His daughter's sunny little garden is now a shady room filled with lilies of the valley; his grandson's special place is not beneath the trees as Andersson imagined but under a structure of branches and old boards built to shelter tender plants. The "orchard" has become a guesthouse with a privy and a closed gazebo, its walls the old windows of the architecture school retrieved from the trashpile. One fruit tree survives; I sit under it, looking out, as Thomas Jefferson did from his gazebo at Monticello, toward the blue distance of a "sea" view.

Andersson had written in his 1967 essay, imagining his later years:

> If I am so fortunate to live to a patriarchal age and feeble senility, and if my henyard hasn't been torn down for a rocket launching pad or some other useful thing, sometime near the turn of the century, I will sit in a grove of hawthorns with a rug round my legs. Perhaps there is a little clearing which lets the sun reach the ground in a few

places, but mainly all that I have shaped has disintegrated now I no longer have the strength to hold clippers or clamber up ladders. My son-in-law has no interest for this sort of thing and folk cannot be hired for garden work. Nonetheless, I am satisfied. The hawthorns are grateful for the freedom to develop a lovely, healthy growth. In early summer all the branches are decked with masses of yellow-white flowers, like whipped cream, which later fall to the ground like a silent snowfall, leaving the crooked stems standing black against the white ground. In fall, the branches are weighed down by dark red fruits and by all the birds that thrive in the sheltered world of the thorn grove and enjoy its edible fall dress. If I am truly fortunate my great grandchild will dig holes under the trees.[7]

Between then and now was an open plan, one whose structure so far has been flexible enough to hold the dream.

AUTHORS' SOURCES

To make even a small garden, like Andersson's small garden—let alone a neighborhood or city—requires hundreds of decisions: which flowers, which vegetables, which fruits, shrubs, trees to plant, how to arrange them; whether to fence the garden and how, with what kind of entrance gate—material, hinge, handle, latch—with paths straight or curving; how to cultivate, mow, prune or permit plants to grow without shaping. The task is complex. Each choice limits further choice, raises questions, and presents other opportunities; each decision is significant, conveys meaning. How daunting then to set a frame for an entire neighborhood or city, one people will live in for dozens, even hundreds, of years. Where and how does one begin a landscape? There is no single "right" way, as Andersson made clear.

Composed landscapes are made from the landscape phrases of an author's experience not constructed laboriously from landscape elements, just as Northrop Frye and T. S. Eliot said poems come from poems, are made of poems, not words.[8] Sven-Ingvar Andersson's garden comes from his experience of birds, his family's farm, the hedges of Brandt at Mariebjerg and Sørensen at Horsens and Nærum, the clipped shrubs and raked gravel of Shisendo. So, also, Lawrence Halprin's Portland fountain comes from rocky streams in the Sierra Nevada Mountains, Murcutt's buildings from the Barcelona Pavilion and Farnsworth House of Mies van der Rohe, and from the eucalyptus trees, sun, wind, and water of Sydney harbor.

Every person belongs to a set of themes that connects each to lineages of experiences, values, beliefs, practices, and theories. Andersson's work is linked to that of Sørensen and Brandt, but also to that of Steen Eiler Rasmussen, Sven Hermelin, Frederik Magnus Piper, Pieter Breughel, Kazimir Malevich, Geoffrey Jellicoe, Kevin Lynch, medieval monks, anonymous farmers and gardeners.[9] Life themes shared across generations and cultures lead to landscapes and also forge friendships among teachers, students, and colleagues—living, dead, unborn.

Sørensen regarded Le Nôtre (1613–1700) and Ligorio (1500–83) as colleagues; he kept their portraits, like those of family, in his bedroom, and emulated the precision of their geometry, but more freely, with ellipses and spirals.[10] In the Philadelphia offices of Andropogon (named after a grass), a landscape architecture firm specializing in landscape restoration, hang photographs of Ian McHarg and the ecologist Jack McCormick. Among my own pantheon are Frederick Law Olmsted, Frank Lloyd Wright, C. Th. Sørensen, Paul Klee, T. S. Eliot, John Dewey, Patrick Geddes, Lewis Mumford, Ian McHarg, Lawrence Halprin, Kevin Lynch.

Reproduction and Adaptation

Many gardens imitate others: a mother's or a grandfather's, an English cottage garden, a Japanese rock garden, a wildflower meadow. They echo memories and lineages, a fondly remembered person or place, love of things English (or Italian or Japanese), desire for authority, reverence for the wild. It is easier to copy or adapt an existing pattern than to invent a new one, but one learns from copying; to make a self-reproducing landscape, for example, is to understand the processes that shape, structure, and sustain it. When Olmsted designed the Fens in Boston no one had ever built a marsh before, and the project yielded new knowledge and new techniques.[11] He had to figure out what to plant, how, and when; though he consulted with experts and engaged a contractor who assured him that he was up to the task the first attempt was an utter failure. Olmsted had based his design upon a general understanding of natural processes of water movement—tides, currents, and flooding—and plant growth and succession, gained from prior experience, but he had no existing built models to guide him. Nevertheless, he undertook this risky experiment on a public project very much in the spotlight. In collaboration with the city's engineer, he worked out a plan for the basin to receive rising floodwaters and for the tidal gate to enhance water circulation and regulate water exchange between the Fens and the river. He engaged Charles Sprague Sargent, director of the Arnold Arboretum, to advise him on plant selection and on methods for establishing the marsh. In the first phase, in 1883, more than a hundred thousand plants, grasses, flowers, shrubs, and vines were planted in a space of two and a half acres.[12] Many species, both native and exotic, were included so that if some died, the odds were that others would survive. Some plants were intended to play the role of "nurses" to shelter more tender plants from sun and wind until the more vulnerable could take hold. But, for some reason, almost all the plants died before the end of the first year and had to be replaced. Furious and mortified, Olmsted wrote the contractor, "The mere loss of so many plants is the smallest part of the disaster. The whole plan is a wreck."[13] The Fens were replanted; within ten years the new marsh looked as if it had been there forever.

Olmsted, understanding the significance of the Fens and Riverway, urged his partners to follow it carefully, day by day: "The aims are novel, the conditions are novel. You cannot trust to usage." As he said in 1893, the Boston projects would be "points to date from in the history of American landscape architecture, as much as Central Park. They will be the openings of new chapters of the art."[14] New chapters, yes, and yet, projects like Olmsted's Fens (1880s) and Aldo Leopold's Sand County farm in Wisconsin (1930s) were relatively rare until the 1970s, when such landscape architects as Darrel Morrison and Andropogon Associates began to specialize in landscape restoration, experimenting with seed collection and in planting and management methods like burning and seasonal or annual mowing. Landscape restoration is now a field in itself, though is more often practiced as a science than an art.

Architects, typically, focus on adapting their buildings only to the formal geometry of landscape, if they consider even that. In his book *Design Thinking*, Peter Rowe describes an architect who approached the design of a new health facility and hotel by adapting the layout of a "classical villa" as the point of departure, because of a "correspondence between the villa type and the problem at hand"; the architect did not engage landscape explicitly except to address the view toward a lake.[15] Rowe also describes the various working methods of other architects in designing building complexes and urban districts; few mention landscape at all. Architects like Glenn Murcutt are exceptional.

Landscape authors collect phrases to use. They gather small details, like the way two materials are joined, or how grasses grow in shallow water, how sun shines through backlit maple leaves, how a path is set into a hillside, how an edge of rough stones keeps walkers on an unfenced path. And they compile larger features from work that has preceded them: how the grid at Mariebjerg, Priene, or Philadelphia, and the ellipses at Nærum provide predictability yet flexibility. Laurie Olin's notebooks are full of such observations: drawings of details among sketches for projects under way.[16] Christopher Alexander's pattern language is a collection of such phrases, meant to be selected by a designer and adapted to a given situation. Reproducing and adapting are designers' strategies as they are of life itself. Adapting a phrase or "precedent" is like recombination (taking genes from two parents). The choices of model and what to adapt to are key. A designer may use an Italian hillside villa as a model for a project on a sloping site, or a mountain stream as a model for a fountain. A designer is foolish to adapt a plan to the form of a hillside or incorporate a nearby tree without taking account of the processes that shape them, unwise to adapt to weather since it will change tomorrow. A wise designer adapts to the enduring patterns of landscape.

Composing a landscape is so complex a task, it is no wonder many designers imitate precedent. Not a bad way to learn, unless the application becomes dogmatic and rigid. Or unless patterns are copied without returning to the original for inspiration, thus losing meaning. To use a form or phrase without knowing its roots is to miss the sense of the original discovery. The vocabulary of forms—streets, gardens, parks, and buildings—often deferred to as precedents, is not merely a reflection of enduring human needs; each represents a response to the particular cultural values and practices of its time. Some forms may still have the capacity to express contemporary purposes and values, but many do not. Geoffrey Jellicoe adapted historic motifs inventively, altering and juxtaposing them in surprising ways that made them seem fresh. "To copy a historic form of the past is to raise a corpse from the dead and pretend it is alive," says Jellicoe. "Only the spirit can be alive to activate the present."[17] There is need not only for continuity of tradition, for enduring precedents that still seem appropriate, but also for invention. Both are necessary if landscapes are to express contemporary cosmology, speak in an age when photographs of atomic particles and of galaxies are commonplace, when time and space are relative, not fixed.

Abstraction and Invention

Frank Lloyd Wright expressed his reverence for nature not by imitation, but by abstracting landscape features, as in the perfectly rounded form of the knoll in the hill garden and the steps/ledges cut to appear as layered bedrock but with edges straighter than those in an unbuilt landscape. Wright saw himself as bringing out the ideal, the inner nature, not imitating outward appearance; it was a process he equated with civilization, one that "the true artist *imposes* on natural forms."[18] For him, abstraction also meant a progressive geometrization of outward form; he saw natural features as underlain by "an essential geometry." At Taliesin West, he abstracted the formal structure of the landscape, the angles of mountain peaks and talus at the base of nearby hills; he applied that triangular geometry to the form of house and garden and to the structure of the whole. "Abstraction is stark form," he said in 1937, "in abstraction it is the structure or pattern of the thing that comes clear, stripped of all realistic effects, divested of any realism whatsoever."[19] Hill garden and prow garden at Taliesin North and West are each abstractions, the re-presentation of their landscapes.

Brandt, the author of Mariebjerg Cemetery, built his own garden as an abstraction of three archetypal landscapes—farm, garden, and wilderness—each, a small garden room. Nearest his house is an orchard garden with clipped grass lawn, a frame of apple trees and surrounding hedge, a small rustic teahouse built of branches, and green apples on the ground in summer—a serene combination of formality and informality. Next to the orchard is a water garden, after that a tiny woodland. At its best, abstraction teaches, presents a larger and more complex landscape idea in a compressed form.

Like Wright and Brandt, Halprin prefers abstraction to imitation, but he engages landscape processes more fully, distinguishing between "copying nature's pictures" and "using her tools of composition."[20] Ira's Fountain in Portland is not a mere visual copy of a river but an equivalent experience; it reproduces the ways water moves in a rocky, mountainous landscape, condensing a mountain stream into a single city block. The many variations in material and form of the surfaces over and through which water flows there produce a great variety of waves,

Author's sources: studying water movement. (Lawrence Halprin, Courtesy Office of Lawrence Halprin)

ripples, eddies, and sounds. Others have imitated the form of this fountain, but not the process by which it was conceived or which it represents, and without his attention to details of water flow; in consequence, their designs are far less engaging, often boring. In designing with process, in contrast, Halprin draws from arts like dance and music that share the dynamic qualities of landscape, particularly modern dance that entails improvised movement within a choreographed framework. Another fountain in this mode is the "beach" at Parc André Citroën in Paris, a large, inclined plane of stone, like the slope of a beach, with more than one hundred water jets, whose spouting varies, like waves breaking then running up the beach in the shifting zone between water and land, inviting play. An abstraction of a beach, provoking a similar response to water from players and observers.

Among landscape designers there has been much preoccupation about invention and the avant-garde in the late twentieth century, leading some authors to produce landscapes that are new and inventive for their own sake. The results have been mixed, among them some alienating or irrelevant public spaces and some successful experiments. In seeking the radically new, authors have introduced unconventional materials, imagery, and composition, but few have worked in fresh ways with landscape processes themselves.[21] Schwartz's Splice Garden uses conventional materials in shocking ways and materials like plastic not ordinarily associated with gardens. SITE employs common imagery in surprising, even surreal, ways, like the cars submerged in asphalt at the Ghost Parking Lot. The result of authors' borrowing of formal strategies, like montage and collage, from art has sometimes been a confusing collision of forms and materials. The better of these, however, such as the plan for Bernard Tschumi's Parc de La Villette in Paris, is more puzzling on paper—structured by seemingly unrelated axes, curves, and grid—than it is in fact. Much larger and more elaborate than Sørensen's Vitus Bering Park in Denmark, built thirty years earlier, the plan for Parc de La Villette, which resembles it, has follies—small, bright-red buildings—each a slightly different form, laid out on a grid. The follies stand out against green lawn, their bright color and varied character making them easy to spot as landmarks; the grid is oriented to the canal and the main promenade.

Murcutt uses metaphor to envision buildings that are like contraptions to engage landscape phenomena like sun, wind, rain, fire, plant growth, and animal movement. The Ball-Eastaway House is on a wooded site in the semiarid sandstone belt surrounding Sydney, and the house of corrugated iron seems, at first, a foreign object inserted into this ancient landscape, an alien spaceship on a large, rocky outcrop. But, gradually, the house tunes one in to this tough, scruffy landscape, prone to bushfires fed by the oil of eucalypt leaves. The iron walls form a thin, but tough, fire-resistant skin for the house. Sprinklers set into the iron punctuate the line of the house just under the roof, ready to spray the walls and roof in case of bushfire. The sprinklers are both fire extinguishers and sculptural ornaments. Murcutt saw the dry floodplains of rivers in the Sydney region, where rain falls seldom but comes in torrents when it does, as an analogy for the gutters of the building and designed them wide like the broad floodplains. The downspouts are large columns, their generous diameter in agreement with both the volume of water they must drain and the size of the eucalypt leaves that are swept along with the water, their round shape describing the spiraling movement of water. Downspouts end several feet above the ground, depositing the eucalypt leaves in a nest-like pile that softens the impact of water hitting the ground, preventing erosion. Water from one downspout falls onto a rock ledge that slopes away from the house, leaving a black streak like the marks left on Uluru and other rocks by waterfalls. Gutters and downspouts are neither imitations nor abstractions of natural form, but analogues, expressing and accommodating the movement of water.

Metaphor is a powerful aid to imagining new forms, but some metaphors and their translation into form are irrelevant, clichéd, incomplete, or inappropriate. The library at the University of California–San Diego has an awkward tree-like form, a too-literal imitation of an obvious metaphor: tree of knowledge. Jørn Utzon's church at Bagsværd, north of Copenhagen, expresses a metaphoric link between earth and sky; the corridors are roofed with glass vaults through which sky is visible. The rolling white ceiling resembles clouds, and you sense the sky, and look up to clouds. And yet the metaphor would have been more powerful had he used rainwater to reflect light and express actual connection, as in Murcutt's house at Bingie, between earth and sky. The drainpipes and gutters at Bagsværd are visible, but closed, the water not used, a missed opportunity.

There is a tradition of garden laboratories among Scandinavian landscape architects like Per Friberg, Sven-Ingvar Andersson, and Henrik Pøhlsgaard; successful experiments find their way into clients' landscapes, the failures remain unreplicated. Friberg's garden, in southern Sweden, is like an inventor's laboratory full of ongoing experiments; some have been in process for thirty years. Half-built projects and sculptures lie around; parts of the garden are like different episodes in an open-ended story. A few years ago, he began to experiment with the front lawn, laying out large square patches of lawn in a grid defined by mowed strips. He treats each patch differently, leaving grass at different heights, mowing at different times, sowing some with wildflower seeds. The American landscape architects Michael Van Valkenburgh and John Lyle also have made garden laboratories; so has the Scottish designer Ian Hamilton Finlay. Van Valkenburgh has strung mirrors in his garden, photographing them at different times of day; he sprayed a chain-link fence with water one winter to create an ice wall, trying diverse techniques and quantities of spray, then later used the idea in a commission. In design thinking, inventive solutions often emerge through a process of trial and error, of trying out alternatives, building and refining them. Frank Lloyd Wright certainly proceeded this way, building ideas at the Taliesins, then leaving some and tearing out others, but when he experimented with clients' buildings the results were sometimes less happy.

House in Palm Grove, Palm Grove in House

Driving up the Pacific coast north of Sydney, Australia, the architect Richard Le Plastrier described how he came to design the house he is taking me to. A man wanted to build a house in a palm grove. When Le Plastrier went to the place he found a tall man gardening in the palm grove; the man wanted to build a house so he could live in his palm garden, but was stumped how to do it and reluctant to start. Le Plastrier designed a house in a garden and a garden in a house.

In the cove, the sun glints on palms growing on the hillside in the center of a little valley. The house looks more like a walled garden with palms inside and outside than a house. Around its periphery are walls of deep red, rammed earth; the path to the door turns sharply around and under large cabbage palms, through a gate into a narrow vestibule with glass and slat roof, then into a small open, roofed area, and then to the door into the house.

The whole is garden, sailboat, and Japanese house combined. The house is open, the conventional separation of house and garden broken down; the interior walls of sail canvas can be rolled up or down. The tight galley, bath, and storage space are ranged along one wall, the bedroom is next to a pool with a large window that looks out over dark water in which goldfish swim. Sailcloth moves in the wind, catching silhouettes of palm fronds in sunlight; other sailcoth walls are furled, as along a boom. The woodwork is especially beautiful, like the most finely crafted sailboat, and fitted, without nails or screws. A Japanese house: sliding screens, rooms like platforms, open, with few doors. Along the inner side, facing the garden, the walls dissolve into columns matching the columns of the palm trees, whose segmented trunks are echoed in the segmented wood columns and vaults of the roof over the living room. The parallel is intentional, the perfect home for a devoted gardener. The references to boats and Japan are not incidental. Le Plastrier was once the Australian national champion for single sail-craft racing, and studied, worked, and lived in Japan after working for Utzon on the Sydney Opera House.

For Le Plastrier, landscape comes first, the building must grow from it: "Landscape is everything, the broad structure, as well as the details." He often begins a job by spending a week or so living on the site and drawing. He builds the houses himself, with the help of contractors, and continues to refine the design throughout the process of building. The vault of the palm house was not resolved until the building was in process; Le Plastrier walked every day among the palms, searching for a solution. Yet landscape is not truly everything, for each building also grows from the patterns of the client's life. He spends time with the people for whom he designs so that he can understand better how they live. Like Murcutt, who does the same, many of his closest friends are former clients.

Thinking, Building, Caring

Designers who express themselves in the vernacular landscape of everyday speech tend to shape landscapes directly with their own hands and tools. Formal speech, reserved for special situations, is employed primarily by professional designers, usually in the service of a client who expects artful expression. Professionals tend to speak more indirectly than those who are not professionals, using drawings, plans, and specifications to tell others how to carry out the design. Landscape architects structure future form not only by direct shaping of material, form, and space, but also, indirectly, through anticipating how process will continue to mold landscape, and by devising a plan for management of change over time. The great challenge of landscape expression is the complexity of the medium and the fact of its abiding change. The smaller the scale, the greater the role of direct shaping through working drawings and on-site adjustments; the larger the scale, the greater the role of indirect shaping through guidelines and policies. The most indirect shaping (often with no intention of landscape expression) is through policies that create a context that shapes landscapes, in turn.

Shaping Directly: Trial and Error

I stroll through the big garden-to-be, south of San Francisco, along paths between curving white lines of plastic pipe, flexible as a garden hose. Some large boulders have already been installed, partly buried, next to the future fountain; the rest of the garden is still bare dirt. Workmen have staked the flexible pipe following Halprin's plans and now stand by, ready to move them on command. As I walk on the paths and look down the lines they trace around, up, and down gentle hills and valleys, Halprin signals adjustments. "You can't do this in public work," he explains to me. "When contractors have bid on a project they won't stand for this, and it damages the way you design. The design becomes a paper design, more geometric, less is changed in the field. And it's not easy to work with curves, since horizontal and vertical curves need to be adjusted carefully in place. Contours on surveys are never exact enough."[22]

I am reminded of one of the most successful gardens of curves ever made, the Donnell Garden, north of San Francisco in Sonoma. Halprin worked on this garden as a young associate of Thomas Church in the late 1940s, one of the last projects he undertook with Church before opening his own office. He worked on site using a garden hose to lay out paths and edges of beds. Perhaps "Capability" Brown worked at Bowood in England this way in the eighteenth century, on site, to achieve the cinematic curving landforms. The landscape architect A. E. Bye tells how he designed a long, curving entry road to an estate by driving a truck across the fields where he felt it should go, then staking the tracks he had made in the long grass. Many of the gardens Bye has designed have large, undulating lawns, their subtle curves emphasized in low light and melting snow. They were shaped directly on site by bulldozers directed by Bye or his staff. He rarely makes construction drawings, preferring instead to start construction with an idea, then work it out in dialogues with site, builders, and clients: "So often the unexpected occurs in garden construction. While moving soil on the Hering property [in Connecticut] we suddenly exposed limestone rock formations of astonishing complexity and drama . . . we stopped there."[23] Such direct shaping by an author is uncommon among designers today, and students seldom learn it.

The architecture studio Kinya Muriyama taught at the University of Pennsylvania one year was an exception. He asked his students each to design and build a portable teahouse, full scale, then to form small groups and site their houses together. The culmination of the studio was to set the tiny houses in a landscape, drink tea in them, and reflect. The students were startled when they took their houses outside for the first time and found that the ground sloped and undulated; it was not flat like the desktop, paper, and floor they had designed and built their structures upon. One group, drawn to a lovely grove of pines on a small rise in the middle of an open field, struggled to place their houses without destroying what had attracted them to the grove in the first place, yet many architects view a landscape or "site" as a passive foundation waiting to receive significance through a building.

Learning through doing was an important part of Wright's Taliesin Fellowship, and still is, after his death. At Taliesin West, apprentices select a site in the desert, put up a tent, and build a foundation platform or more elaborate dwelling. Some such buildings have been continuously adapted and inhabited over the years. Apprentices learn through living on that site, selecting it, constructing their

Author's sources: Thinking about a field for parking or agriculture. (Laurie Olin)

own shelter with materials at hand (gravel, sand, rock from desert, and wood, metal, glass scrounged from the workshop) and discovering the consequences: one shelter recently built down in a wash will flood to about three feet in a big storm. Wright himself built things over and over, or the apprentices did, until they got it right; there are no drawings or other records of many changes made at the Taliesins during Wright's lifetime.

Unlike Bye and Le Plastrier, who work on residential projects for individuals or families, most landscape authors today do not build the landscapes they design unless, like Wright, it is their own; instead, they work out ideas through drawings and models and direct others' labor through drawings and text. This is especially true when projects are public or of great scope: parks, plazas, entire new communities. In large firms, designers may not even make their own construction, or "working," drawings, and landscapes may be translated by intermediaries from drawings to reality with little or no dialogue between designer and laborer.

The Map Is Not the Place: Virtual Landscapes

While Murcutt does not construct buildings himself, several builders work with him repeatedly; he prepares all the drawings himself, from initial sketches to working drawings, and, in the drawing, works his way toward the making. Then he refines the design, making small adjustments while construction is under way. Françoise Fromonot calls Murcutt a craftsman because he is a sole practitioner whose drawing is an instrument of making.[24]

Drawing is a way of knowing and thinking, not just a diversion or even a medium of artistic expression; it is as natural for some people as speaking and writing is for others.[25] Making notes in the form of maps and sketches leads the author to see significant details and relationships. Even those who shape landscape directly use drawing to advance thinking and communicate ideas; Le Plastrier starts to design a building by drawing the landscape on site. Professional landscape authors commonly draw on sheets of transparent tracing paper to simulate, think about, develop, test, and refine their designs, laying one sheet over another, drawing over and over the sheets, copying some things from the sheet below, discarding others, a process of recapitulation, trial and error, a condensation of the vernacular method without the expense of actual building. The process calls for recursive passes until a "mutation" (creative breakthrough) occurs (and is recognized). As in the role of accident and serendipity in evolution, further trial and error in context, at enlarged and reduced scales, determines survival of a design. Designers inhabited such virtual landscapes long before computers were invented and they now inhabit digital drawings and maps.

Drawings and maps also permit one to construct views not presently visible to the eye or to present selective information. Topographic maps and section drawings, used together, are aids to the understanding and the modifying of landscape. Contour lines, representing points of equivalent elevation, enable one to envision landform and test modifications. It was by plotting the vacant lots on a contour map of the Dudley Street neighborhood in Boston, that I was first able to understand the correlation between low spots and vacancy. Identifying similar low-lying areas in other neighborhoods, before actually visiting them in person, permitted me to predict where concentrations of vacancies would occur. Through a section drawing, a "cut" through a landscape along a line drawn on a topographic map, one can see the slope of the ground plane and the relationships of soil, rock, and artifacts underground to things above ground.

Building and studying a physical model is an aid to developing, testing, and refining landscape designs in three-dimensional space, and also in time, particularly effective in visualizing complex processes like water and air flow through a landscape of complex shape, like a town. Take a model of the entire downtown of Dayton, Ohio, with all of its buildings and streets, then cover the surface with plastic pellets, and put the model in a wind tunnel, as my students and I once did, and watch bare areas—windy spots—and piles of pellets—places with poor ventilation—emerge, often in unexpected places but with an underlying pattern whose cause can be deciphered through experiment. Add new buildings and trees to streets and parking lots in the model, test it again in the wind tunnel, and solutions to many seemingly intractable wind problems can be found. Without model and

SECTION - LATITUDE 12½° S
LONGITUDE 137

Thinking about a house for an aboriginal artist and her family. Eastern Arnhem Land. Australia.
(Glenn Murcutt)

wind tunnel these problems would be felt in place, but the cause would be invisible, and the pattern impossible to appreciate, especially for an entire downtown.

And yet the drawing, map, or model is not the place. The same year I discovered, by plotting on a contour map, the connection between buried stream and vacant blocks in the Dudley Street neighborhood, architects for a local community development corporation were already designing several hundred new houses to be built on that same vacant land. The maps they were using contained no topographic information! When I first pointed out to them that the stream is a contributing cause of the original deterioration and abandonment, they found the idea difficult to believe. Unable to read contour maps, they had not been able to see the pattern in the first place, then found it difficult to incorporate that understanding into their work. Later, after reviewing my students' drawings and revisiting the site, they conceded the point and changed their plans. The information that is included on, or omitted from, maps and drawings limits what is expressed. One problem with the kind of drawing architects use to conceive buildings' mass and relationships, a "figure-ground" diagram, in which buildings are shaded black and their context left as white, is its implication that landscape context is blank. Similarly, functional diagrams or "space planning" drawings can lead to neglect of meaning, feeling, and art.

Drawing and model building are no substitute for fieldwork. I once was asked by planners at the Boston Redevelopment Authority to review their plan for Roxbury, about to be unveiled in a press conference. The planning process had been criticized in the community and controversy was anticipated. When I walked into the room that held their huge model of the neighborhood and scanned it, I saw new houses erected on the site of the garden of Cooper's Place, already a local landmark and the site of at least one wedding! Fortunately, the Boston Natural Areas Fund had already acquired the property from the city (the property map the planners had used was out of date), so the garden was not in jeopardy. But the error revealed problems with the planning process itself, which had relied too heavily upon secondhand information, too little on local knowledge.

Shaping Context Itself

As design through time, landscapes may entail a succession of designs, sometimes requiring alteration or even deliberate destruction of early phases through growth, succession, or thinning. This is particularly true of the restored "native" landscapes—wildflower meadows, marshes, and woodlands—that Andropogon Associates design, each requiring unconventional methods of maintenance—burning, for example, or selective thinning. In such landscapes, many vigorous plants may look like weeds and be destroyed unwittingly. Well-meaning clients may undermine the landscapes they originally chose by failing to care for them appropriately. In 1984, after ten years in the business of design, Andropogon had completed few landscapes they were still proud of. As a consequence of their experiences, the Andropogon partners changed the way they practiced and decided to insist, as a condition of their contract, on consulting not with the property's owners alone but also with the workers who shape it directly, those who mow, fertilize, prune, and rake it. Whenever possible, they go on advising and training staff, fine-tuning the landscape design for years after its construction. Landscapes are not finished when they have been constructed. It may take years to implement a design, for it to evolve; the way a landscape is managed can change it fundamentally over time. Shaping the context in which landscape is shaped is an act of design.

A landscape author can work alone at small-scale design, say for a garden, but cities and regions are, necessarily, collective cultural projects, accretions of millions of decisions, actions, and events, coordinated and uncoordinated, planned and unanticipated. All too often, such larger landscapes grow by regulation that restricts without enabling, or by default, rather than by expression of a common vision. Here lies the heart of the long-time tension between designers and planners. Planners of large landscapes typically rely upon regulation as a tool of shaping, while designers chafe against regulations since rules limit scope to invent. The best designers and planners discover new solutions by redefining the problem. Charles Eames was once asked if design admitted constraints; his answer: "Design depends largely upon constraints." Had he ever been forced to compromise? "I have never been forced to accept compromise but I have willingly accepted constraints." [26]

Sanibel, a city and barrier island of fabled beaches off the Gulf Coast of Florida, is a seashell-hunter's and bird-watcher's paradise. Half of the island is national wildlife refuge; by 1974, the other half was rapidly being engulfed by newly built resorts. Residents and environmentalists, on one side, and developers, on the other, were poised to do battle. Wallace McHarg Roberts and Todd, the firm I worked for at the time, was hired to prepare a comprehensive land use plan for Sanibel that would, among other things, have to hold up in court. I began by preparing maps of the island, "virtual" images of the place drawn from published sources, aerial photographs, and others' field surveys showing topography, geological development, water regime, flood zones, plant associations, wildlife habitat, historic settlement, land use, zoning. Then I entered into a dialogue with the place itself. A clear pattern emerged from the place on my first visit, reinforced by the maps.

Residents of Sanibel thought that the city's problem was the outside developers who were building a swath of condominiums along the gulf beach. The problem turned out to be far more complex. Hurricane floodtides for the ten-year storm, that is, a storm with a statistical probability of recurring once every ten years, were ten feet above sea level, but no storm that severe had occurred in thirty years, long before most people had moved there. No hurricane had hit the island since the causeway from the mainland was built in the 1960s. In the 1920s storm tides twenty-five feet high had swept over the island, yet no place on the island was above ten feet in elevation; the two beach ridges were only five feet above sea level, except for a few isolated higher spots. The few old-timers who had survived the last one told me it hadn't been too bad, but when I mapped the historic buildings that remained in Sanibel on the topography map, I saw that they all stood on the highest points on the island (between five and ten feet above sea level) and, even so, were up on stilts! The houses most residents lived in had been built at grade on lower elevations, and were sure to be inundated in the next, overdue ten-year storm.

A single main street ran the length of Sanibel Island along a ridge, with mangrove swamp and muddy bay beach on one side, freshwater wetland and gulf beach on the other. The mangrove swamp was principally a wildlife refuge for alligators, pelicans, herons, roseate spoonbills, and dozens of other bird species. The interior wetland was a freshwater reservoir, filled by rainfall; it supplied the island's drinking water, and the lagoons and sloughs that were home to alligators and other wildlife. The gulf beach ridge was a low dune between the Gulf of Mexico's saltwater and the freshwater wetland; the gulf beach of white sand was perfectly oriented to the currents so that new seashells washed up with each high tide. It was a nesting ground for enormous sea turtles that hauled themselves up the beach, laid their eggs, and returned to the sea. At one end of the island was a low-lying place of shifting sands, a guzzle breached by hurricanes. These eight physiographic and ecological zones structured the island, its human history and land use, its nonhuman populations, as well. Each zone supported the island's human and nonhuman populations in important ways: protection against flood, prevention of saltwater intrusion into the freshwater lens, sustenance of marine and other wildlife.[27]

The new zoning we proposed to the city was based upon the landscape's value for the health, safety, and welfare of Sanibel's residents. Regulations governing new development stipulated performance requirements that must be met in order to sustain that value: storm protection, for example. This type of zoning is much harder to administer than the conventional kind, which stipulates precisely what type and density of use are allowed and which are prohibited. Performance zoning, however, is more flexible; it permits a skilled designer to overcome problems with an inventive solution.

WEAVING A FABRIC

I have a shawl woven mostly of silk, with some wool and cotton, whose fabric reminds me of landscape. It has the colors, shapes, and complex structure of Wright's Taliesin West, the fixed framework and fanciful serendipity of Andersson's Marnas. Like landscape, my shawl was a collective project. One weaver, Randall Darwall, chose the materials, dyed the yarns, strung the warp, and set the vocabulary; another weaver, Fayette Watkis, wove the weft, composing and improvising within the prepared context.[28] The exact same warp yielded several other shawls that looked like very different cloth; although the underlying context was the same, the improvisations in the weft produced new patterns. The finished fabric of my shawl shimmers, not alone from the silk threaded through, but from the play of hues; threads transforming color, brown at one end, slipping through green, to purple at the other end, many stories or one story line with many phases; the shawl ends in a palette of knotted twists. Once you have seen such a fabric others seem routine and regimented. Darwall is like a landscape author who sets the frame within which the future landscape will develop, to be shaped by many others.

Sea Ranch, a condominium community on the north California coast built in the 1960s and 1970s, is like a Darwall shawl. Lawrence Halprin identified the warp; his plan for Sea Ranch was a score, a framework delineated in accord with the seacoast landscape of sun, wind, fog, beach, eroding cliffs, wind-pruned trees, open meadows, and drainage ways. The score provided a roadway, areas for clustered housing, and a set of rules for building. Order and experiment were both part of the plan, as the individual actors, human and not—designers, builders, owners, plants, winds, cliffs—improvised within these constraints. The designers who wove the weft (Joseph Esherick, Charles Moore, Donlyn Lyndon, among others) responded to the rules, each in their own way; the result was extraordinary.

In landscapes, particularly ones where there are many authors, the key is to establish a framework that provides overall structure—a structure not arbitrary but congruent with the deep context of a place, to define a vocabulary of forms that expresses the natural and cultural processes of the place, and then to encourage a symphony of responses to the conditions of the place and the needs of the specific people there. The result should be a dynamic fabric, complex but coherent, that will evolve to meet changing needs and desires, connecting past and present.[29]

Framework, Themes, Improvisation: West Philadelphia

Rows of brick houses with stoops line Westminster Street west of Lancaster Avenue in West Philadelphia; none have gardens, there are no street trees, and on a sunny summer day, the light is glaring, the street hot. In 1987 the narrow lot on the corner of Westminster and May streets had been vacant for many years, full of trash, junkies' needles, and an abandoned car. Ten years later, in 1997, a canopy of big green leaves spans the narrow lot, sheltering a garden room beneath, a dark, shady oasis. From a distance, the canopy looks like a tree, but from the gate at the sidewalk one can see that the leaves are growing on vines, supported by, entwined on, a wooden structure. Four posts are the corners of the room, four beams connect them, holding up the ceiling of green. Westminster Community Garden does not look designed, but it was, deliberately, by a landscape architect, not as a finished design though, rather as a framework, a warp, for eight gardeners to weave their weft upon. The neighbors who care for it had never gardened before, they simply wanted to get rid of the vacant lot eyesore across the street. They asked for an outdoor room to sit in, with flowers and vegetables, a barbecue pit, a tool-

Bottom-up: rebuilding community. (West Philadelphia Landscape Project)

shed. Ruth Loewe, one of my research assistants, designed an enclosed outdoor room, a garden with a curved path flanked by flower beds leading to a large, square wooden frame—an arbor—like the frame of a house. Beyond are the "backyard" vegetable plots. Within days of its construction in 1988, the framework was embellished. One neighbor brought treasures culled from flea markets: a ceramic dragon, a pedestal birdbath, a concrete bench with a lion's claw base, an old metal porch chair, a grill, a shade umbrella. Neighbors installed two sections of wrought-iron fence to create a gateway at the entrance, angled out like outstretched arms, and put up an old mailbox next to the white gate. They nailed a horseshoe and hung an American flag over the arbor's entrance, and installed a big, black iron kettle at the back, a reminder, to one, of her childhood in the South. One of the designer's greatest contributions in an inner-city neighborhood like Mill Creek is the translation of others' dreams into a form they can build upon and adapt, making it their own. The importance of the garden goes beyond an agreeable place to sit or to grow flowers or vegetables in; as one person said, "It's doing something for the neighborhood. Even the drunks want to help us do another one." Westminster was one of the first gardens built as part of the West Philadelphia Landscape Project.[30]

The designs for the Westminster garden and Aspen Farms are emblematic of the West Philadelphia Landscape Project as a whole; they embody its goals: to build an urban landscape that is a symbol of pride and hope, that reveals natural

Top-down: restoring water quality. Schuylkill River. Philadelphia. (Alex S. MacLean/Landslides)

processes and local resources, improves environmental quality, stimulates other initiatives, and builds skills and knowledge within the community that will lead to economic opportunity. Community gardens are apt models, tangible examples of transforming nuisance into beauty. They provide the opportunity for people to create their own place, to develop and display skills, knowledge, and accomplishments. Gardens create local heroes, leaders who become a source of advice and counsel for others with similar dreams. Adept at reading landscape, community gardeners teach others such literacy.

From 1987 to 1991, while Loewe, Widrick, and other research assistants worked with neighborhood residents and staff of Philadelphia Green to design and build gardens, I searched for, designed, and tested ways to approach rebuilding the larger urban landscape that would combine a comprehensive overview with a grass-roots perspective.[31] Conventional, top-down planning had not worked well in the past. Although public investments had been made, the results were not sustained: new houses, playgrounds, and streets were poorly maintained and often vandalized; none altered the underlying social conditions of unemployment, poverty, and abandonment. The neighborhood's many success stories were largely the result of private initiatives by groups and individuals within the community: vacant lots transformed into gardens, improvements to homes and residential blocks. Still, the bottom-up approach was likely to miss broader issues, such as the relationship of the Mill Creek sewer to regional water quality.

I started by defining a framework that was in agreement with the deep context of Mill Creek, the watershed and the community, then identified a vocabulary of landscape improvements appropriate to the context, and cited models of success that already existed in the neighborhood.[32] I called the product a framework for action, not a plan, for it is an open-ended guide that identifies opportunities for change; it does not prescribe a particular method or outcome or scheduled period of time. Like Aspen Farms' main street and the structure of Westminster, it is meant to be filled in through the actions of a host of individuals and groups: schools, churches, businesses, and public agencies. The framework of floodplain, traffic corridors, and grid of streets is inscribed by water flowing in valley bottoms and sewers, by people driving and walking along streets and sidewalks, building and settling blocks of homes. Water, flowing from north to south, cut the valley, undermined buildings, and created open land. People, moving east-west between city and country, made the primary paths, drawing commerce; settling and building, people plotted the city's grid, filled the blocks with homes, churches, schools, businesses.

At the heart of this proposal is the Mill Creek floodplain, to be designated as a special district in which low-lying land, once vacant, would be used to hold rainwater, which would then seep gradually into the sewer, preventing combined sewer overflows in the Schuylkill River. Not all the property in the new district need be public property; some could be owned by community groups or by businesses that tolerate, and even benefit from, periodic local flooding: a garden center and nursery or a miniature golf course. Revealing the presence of the buried creek is an important part of the proposal because many who live here do not even know the creek exists despite its persistent influence on their lives. The floodplain district would structure an urban landscape in agreement with the neighborhood's enduring context, analogous to such greenways and plazas as Harvard Gulch and Skyline Plaza in Denver and Olmsted's Fens and Riverway in Boston.

Within the framework of floodplain, traffic corridors, and city grid is the potential for improvisation. Originally built with block after block of rows of identical houses, with few variations, there are now gaps—large and small, connected or not—that were created after one or more houses were abandoned and destroyed. These vacant lots are a resource for reshaping small neighborhoods to meet the needs and suit the taste of the people who live there: gardens, orchards, outdoor workshops, sitting areas, play lots, and parking spots between houses on blocks where once there was no outdoor space at all except street, sidewalk, and porches. Reinvestment is likely to proceed house by house, block by block, variations on a theme. To aid this process, my research assistants and I defined a vocabulary of block types and vacant land types and produced dozens of sketches of possibilities intended to inspire people to imagine and invent.[33] These ideas were refined and tested in Aspen Farms, Westminster, and dozens of other community landscape projects designed and built between 1987 and 1991. What was learned in the process of talking with people and evaluating built products informed the planning, which, in turn, influenced the design of other projects.

Since 1990, my students and I have developed this framework further and worked within it. We created a digital database that fits the top-down/bottom-up approach, linking the scale of the city to that of the street corner, making available to the general public information and tools that were once accessible only to large public agencies and institutions.[34] One can look at a map of West Philadelphia on the computer screen, then zoom in on a smaller area, down to the scale of a few blocks or a single property, finding increasingly detailed information about land use, vacant land, buildings, sewer, floodplain, topography, and population. The database runs on a personal computer and was designed for use by both governmental and grass-roots organizations; an atlas of selected maps is also available on the Internet.[35] Among other uses, the database is providing course material for a new curriculum for a local middle school.

To be sustainable, community development in an inner-city neighborhood like West Philadelphia must address the issue of education, leadership, and employment prospects for youth. In 1995, my students and I, with gardeners from Aspen Farms, began to work with teachers and students at the Sulzberger Middle School to develop a new curriculum in which the neighborhood is an extension of the classroom. Children from sixth to eighth grades, working with students from the University of Pennsylvania, study their community's natural and social history and design and build outdoor classrooms on vacant lots. In summer 1997, one group of twelve- to fourteen-year-olds constructed a model of the Mill Creek watershed, built a pond and butterfly garden at Aspen Farms, created their own website, where they published descriptions of their landscape projects.[36] In fall 1997, a class of sixth graders studied neighborhood trees as part of their science studies, and planted and tended a nursery for street trees. In 1997–98, an eighth-grade class worked on a proposal for a miniature golf course in which water hazards store stormwater after rains and the eighteen holes tell Mill Creek's history. Students chose and wrote the stories, designed the golf course, and developed a business plan as part of their social studies, language, science, and math curriculum. At the end of the year, they will present their proposal to community leaders and staff of the West Philadelphia Empowerment Zone.

Landscape projects alone cannot solve problems like poverty, unemployment, and the physical deterioration of housing and public infrastructure, but even small, incremental improvements to the urban landscape significantly improve how neighborhoods look and function and the quality of urban life. Successful landscape projects serve as catalysts for other community development projects and as important adjuncts to social programs such as education, job training, and employment. Such projects have given Sulzberger and Penn students the opportunity to apply knowledge they are learning in the classroom and to effect tangible change in the neighborhood. And they give Penn students like

Loewe and Widrick the opportunity to learn by testing theory in action and to appreciate the complexity of the idea and reality of community. As Hayward Ford, president of Aspen Farms, told Widrick, "It isn't all a bed of roses. There are fifty different people, with fifty different ways of seeing things and fifty different ways of doing things. And everybody, of course, is always right."[37]

The West Philadelphia Landscape Project is atypical in many respects. It is a research project, the staff are faculty and students at the University of Pennsylvania, and there is no client in the conventional sense. This has advantages and disadvantages. Though the planning work has no official standing, neither is it bound by political expedience. We work with partners who wish to collaborate—community gardeners, teachers and students, public officials—and we make available the results to anyone who is interested. But we have no authority to implement our plans. Staff of the Philadelphia City Planning Commission and of the Philadelphia Redevelopment Authority attended presentations of our work and received copies of our reports, but no mention of the Mill Creek appeared in the city's *Plan for West Philadelphia* in 1994![38] The Philadelphia Water Department, on the other hand, made the Mill Creek Watershed an area for special study, and we hope to work together on demonstration projects that prevent flooding, improve water quality, and enhance environmental education and community development.

My work establishes a landscape structure, as Andersson's garden at Marnas does, that lends stability and welcomes change. Like Murcutt's Ball House and the house at Bingie, it is an actual and metaphorical expression of natural processes and the patterns of people's lives. Like Le Plastrier's house in a palm grove, it seeks to dissolve boundaries between human artifacts and nonhuman phenomena; the act of construction becomes part of the creative process. It has a score like Halprin's that inspires the creative contribution of others. Yet mine is a different sort of practice from any of these. I choose my clients, and they do not pay me. I influence how people think and act, but I have little control over the precise shape that their built products take—their houses, their gardens, their neighborhoods. The products I am most proud of are the people I have taught to read and speak the language of landscape and the frameworks I have composed to inspire and order their creative contributions.

8

A Rose Is Rarely Just a Rose:
Poetics of Landscape

Landscape materials, phenomena, and forms are emphatic, paradoxical, analogical: wind is an exaggerated breeze, water is yielding yet erosive, roses bloom and wither, so do humans. A rose is rarely just a rose; it is encrusted with meaning accreted through centuries of poetry, painting, gardens, and rituals of everyday life. And still roses are mined for fresh meanings by reformulation, surprising and provocative juxtapositions and combinations.

In Western cultures, where words have primacy over images and other symbols, figures of speech and rhetorical devices such as emphasis, metaphor, paradox, irony, address have been codified elaborately, even excessively, in literature but are rarely applied to landscape.[1] The failure to recognize the potential figurative power of landscape in its own right, not simply as a backdrop or a frame for a building, is common. Yet all but a few figures and tropes, some of which turn specifically on wordplay (onomatopoeia), are present in landscape literature.

Thomas Jefferson employed the figurative qualities of landscape masterfully; later architects have modified and weakened his remarkable vision. His design for the University of Virginia at Charlottesville used two parallel rows of pavilions and colonnades to define a central lawn and frame a view to the Blue Mountains. One end was left open, the other closed by a large building, the library, facing the mountains. Thus Jefferson linked two sources of knowledge: books and nature. When, in the 1890s, the university's board of visitors elected to close the open end of the space with a new building by the architect Stanford White, the view to the mountains was blotted out, and the Lawn became an enclosed space, internally oriented, losing the reference to nature Jefferson had intended and provided.[2] Some architects have lobbied to remove the trees from the Lawn so that the buildings can be seen more clearly, but it is the trees that intensify the experience of the buildings.[3] The contrast of the trees' branching, fractal form to the crisply Euclidean geometry of the architecture initiates a dialogue: in early morning, in late afternoon, low light casts shadows of branches against the smooth round white columns—a dialogue between organic and inorganic, romantic and classical, metaphor and source.

FIGURES OF SPEECH AND RHETORIC

Landscapes designed by Martha Schwartz are laden with overlapping figures and rhetorical devices, provocative and disturbing in their effect. The courtyard of the

Metaphor and source. University of Virginia.

Rio Shopping Center in Atlanta employs various figures of speech: hundreds of gilded frogs, larger than life, sit, equally spaced, facing a forty-foot-high geodesic globe and a central fountain that would otherwise be insignificant. Here there is anachorism (a form of anomaly), interrogation (a form of address), and, for emphasis, placement, exaggeration, and parallelism. The effect is surreal. Why frogs? Why facing the fountain? Schwartz calls the choice of frogs serendipitous; they were one of the least expensive garden ornaments available in Atlanta.[4] But a frog is not just a frog; it is a potent symbol, a sign of fertility in certain cultures, linked to water in most. It has a dark meaning, to some Christians, of avarice, a grasping at worldly pleasures.[5] Was this an ironic message in a place devoted to shopping? Some years after construction of the Rio Shopping Center, the *New York Times* published a story entitled "Silence of the Frogs."[6] It reported that, all over the world, frogs are disappearing, for reasons unknown, though some speculate that loss of habitat, environmental poisons, and the thinning ozone layer are causes. When I think about the Rio courtyard, I am haunted by the silence of the frogs. Landscape as language, richly figurative, attracts meaning beyond that originally intended and foreseen.

Emphasis

Placing emphasis on one thing requires downplaying the importance of something else, and this raises questions. Why emphasize one thing over another? And to

Placement, framing, parallelism, address: Katsura. Kyoto, Japan.

what end? Emphasis without meaning is boring; repetition without variation may become monotonous. Overuse of emphasis creates confusion: when one building and landscape after another strives to be bigger, brighter, more ornate, or more distorted than the ones that preceded or that surround it, the result is cacophony.

PLACEMENT. To set something first or last, as a manor house at the end of a long avenue of trees, establishes a hierarchy. Planting a grove of trees atop a hill makes the hill seem higher. Siting a monument or building on a mountaintop or hilltop stresses the structure's importance (the statue of Christ, the Corcovado, at Rio de Janeiro, Greek temples, Christian churches on older sacred sites); so does putting a fountain at the center of a garden or a piazza at the center of a town. Placing the Statue of Liberty at the entrance to New York Harbor at a time when most immigrants arrived there by ship gave it far more significance than if it had been erected in the middle of Central Park. The position of Louis XIV's bedroom and the statue of Apollo along the same central axis at Versailles implies a commonality between the two. So does the placement of Philadelphia's City Hall and Art Museum at either end of a broad tree-lined parkway, the significant connection between civics and culture.

FRAMING. Framing brackets; it separates from context, focuses attention by screening undesired or irrelevant views, by directing the gaze. Gates, walls, hedges, and groves of trees may frame objects, scenes, or distant prospects by enclosing with distinctive color, texture, sound, or scent. Low, protruding roofs of Japanese teahouses direct the gaze downward, evoking humility; windows in buildings and arcades at the Alhambra frame expansive views to distant hills and sky, conveying a sense of power. Richard Long and James Turrell play upon and within, and twist this tradition of framing: in "England 1967," Long placed a freestanding frame of dark wood in rolling parkland; in his "skyspaces" and at Roden Crater, Turrell frames the sky, isolating shifting light and clouds to focus contemplation.[7]

CONTRAST. An oasis in the desert, an island in the sea, a grove on the prairie, a clearing in the forest—all contrast with context. The more homogeneous and extensive the context, the more powerful the potential contrast: hot and cool, wet and dry, light and dark, colored and monotone, open and enclosed, large and small, loud and soft, rough and smooth, pungent and sweet. Freestanding elements on a plain become landmarks, even icons: the windmills and hedgerows of Holland, grain elevators on the High Plains, stone pillars at Stonehenge on Salisbury Plain, Uluru in Australia's Red Center. Bright, reflective surfaces in landscapes with dark, overcast, or misty climates are mirrors, signs, beacons. Well-watered urban landscapes in the arid American Southwest lose impact when too prevalent, when the line between irrigated and dry is haphazard. In an oasis, less can be more.

EXAGGERATION. Mountain is an exaggeration of hill, wind of breeze. The wind's force is increased when funneled through a small opening—the Venturi effect. Plants bred to exaggerate a desired form, color, scent heighten effect, so do "weeping" beeches in arboreta and neon-bright azaleas in suburban yards. Which attributes are selected for exaggeration is significant. Steps or paving stones far wider than human gait make one feel smaller; if the contrast is of superhuman or extrahuman scale a person may feel insignificant. A person feels more comfortable, important, or powerful when a landscape feature is a smaller than normal scale: the bridge over the pond in Boston's Public Garden; Denmark's Legoland, a combination of miniaturization and exaggeration with diminutive buildings, landscapes, and towns constructed from little Lego blocks. Exaggeration can also deceive: steepening a slope creates a sensation of height, forced perspective an illusion of distance, magnifying size in contrast to surroundings, a surreal effect. "Homage to the Magnolia," a walk in the garden at Sutton Place, an estate near Guildford, England, is a surreal landscape inspired by the painter Magritte.[8] There, five "monster Roman vases" frame and "herald" the view to a magnolia tree "too small and tender . . . to terminate such a lengthy vista." In the words of the walk's designer Geoffrey Jellicoe, "The purpose is to disorganise the mind by a deliberate incongruity in the juxtaposition of disparate objects, preparing it for the tranquility of the Nicholson wall," an abstract sculpture in a garden room beyond the walk (see *Allegory* below).[9] Toward the end of his career, Jellicoe was fascinated with the unconscious and explored landscape design "the unreasoned fantasia of the subconscious, released in all their fun, oddity, and awesomeness."[10]

Exaggeration in religious and political landscapes diminishes the individual and heightens a god, ruler, hero, country or state. The vast scale of the gardens at Versailles—the time it takes to walk from one end to another, the broad avenues, the long staircases, the canal that stretches into the distance—underscores the power of their builder, Louis XIV. The Mall in Washington, D.C., with long, flat sheets of water and stretches of lawn, has a breadth, length, and openness that make gauging distance difficult; it takes much longer to walk from place to place than one anticipates. At the Lincoln Memorial, one feels dwarfed by the many steps, the superhuman statue, and the high pedestal. Gigantic representations of human features emerging from ground or water herald the heroic or monstrous: the huge head and arm of Titan emerging from the middle of a pool in a fountain at Versailles; a gateway at the entrance of Oral Roberts University in Oklahoma formed by a cast of the founder's hands, clasped in prayer. The attribute chosen for exaggeration is significant. In Baghdad, two enormous swords cross over an avenue to form a Victory Arch more than 130 feet high, the entry to a military parade ground; the hands that hold the swords, modeled on a cast of Saddam Hussein's forearms with a sword in each fist, seem to explode out of the earth.[11]

The roots of landscape hyperbole may lie in phenomena like the awesome height of the Alps and dangerous force of storms. Frequent use diminishes its effect. In the seventeenth century, the jet of water on the Titan fountain at Versailles was unusual and dramatic, but higher jets of water now surge up, hundreds of feet, from lakes all over the world, so commonplace they fail to impress. A desert town, Fountain Hills, Arizona, boasts "the world's tallest fountain."

Distortion. A twisted or misshapen condition has been more fashionable in some eras than others, chic in sixteenth-century Mannerism and in twentieth-century postmodernism, with twisted axes common in buildings and streets. Distortion seems more disturbing in living things than in buildings, plazas, or streets, perhaps because of the association with genetic birth defects or mutations caused by radiation or toxic chemicals. In southern Sweden, there is a forest of naturally deformed beech trees (*Fagus sylvatica tortuosa*), their trunks and branches twisted and misshapen like the forest trees of Disneyland's Snow White ride. Some of the beeches, with their sharply bent branches, resemble Japanese calligraphy; others have curved, drooping branches that spring from the trunk at odd angles. Huge stones mark the boundary, frame the place in monumental scale. On a summer evening the low light, filtered through leaves, is reddish-brown. This is a profoundly disturbing place. Sven-Ingvar Andersson, who took me there, reports that the trees' deformed condition is genetically determined. Because it is so rare, the forest is protected by law. Once, he says, few other trees grew here, and there was little to distract from the trees and their bizarre forms. Now, ironically, with the forest protected by law, other trees have appeared, eliminating the uniformity of species that made the variety of distorted forms even more apparent. Andersson first visited this place at the age of twenty, and it depressed him greatly for he could not imagine being able to design a place as powerful as this; but why not plant a grove of them?[12]

ALLITERATION, ECHOISM, ASSONANCE. Arching fountains at Generalife in the Alhambra that repeat both sound and shape are alliterative. The wind in the poplars at Åbenrå in Denmark echoes and alludes to the sound of rushing water; this is echoism, as is the sound of the artificial sea at North Point Preserve in San Diego's Sea World, ironic since the real sea is just beyond, though invisible and inaudible. Repeating shapes of trees or landforms, as in roofs that echo treetops in Murcutt's Ball House or mountains at Taliesin West and Denver's Harlequin Plaza, is also echoism. Rattling leaves of bamboo and dry leaves of beech hedges is assonance, "a resemblance or correspondence of sound or shape," providing a kind of rhyme between sounds or shapes that echo, but do not allude to each other.

On a walk through Parc de La Villette in Paris a few years ago, I heard birds in song, but saw only one bird. As I moved forward, the sounds grew louder, and, at a turn in the path, I saw a row of speakers, spaced evenly, set among the plants in a garden border, and sat down to listen, entranced, to the wonderful music, a mix of instrumental music and sounds of the world, composed in what seemed a random blend and sequence. The music incorporated surrounding sounds as if they were an intentional part of the whole—birdsong, rustling leaves, the rushing traffic of the *boulevard périphérique*, the sound of feet walking on the bridge overhead, faraway voices and clapping.[13] I continued to hear the music as I moved on (or did I?), more aware of the tone, rhythm, and orchestration of sounds around me, no longer certain whether I was hearing music or just perceiving ambient sounds in a new way. I was tuned into the sounds of the city and heard an order, the underlying base tones of traffic, then repetitive and random sounds in combination, a passing train, construction hammers. That was the first time I had experienced what R. Murray Schafer calls a "soundscape," the characteristic sound, frequency, and rhythms of a place, alliteration, echoism, assonance. Since that day, I am more aware how sound shapes context, and sounds became less ephemeral, more easily recalled.

RHYTHM. Rhythm is a succession of accented beats or pulses, a pattern of sounds, sights, or sensations, a periodic recurrence or regular alternation with interval, meter, cadence: parallelism, epanaphora, epanalepsis. Rhythms emerge out of a contextual background; they go with or against, in counterpoint. In landscape, the rhythm of movement is most visible when documented on film or video, then viewed at a faster speed than normal. In Disneyland, the stroll is the rhythm, in basketball the dribble, the run, and the jump.

PARALLELISM. Parallelism repeats a formula or structural pattern to create order, establish a rhythm, emphasize a feature that departs from the pattern (an anomaly). Trees in an allée or avenue direct attention to a monument at the end, as the trees along the Franklin Parkway in Philadelphia direct attention to City Hall and the Art Museum at either end; when the trees were replaced recently, there was a controversy over whether species should be varied, for the sake of ecological diversity, or whether all the trees should be the same species, for the sake of visual effect, a conflict between the pragmatic and the rhetorical. In the end, a mixture of species was planted. Alexander Pope satirized gardens in which such repetition is taken to an extreme: "Grove nods at Grove, each Alley has a Brother, / And half the Platform just reflects the Other."[14] The pattern need not be, literally, parallel: at Nærum Garden Colony, the many freestanding elliptical hedges of hawthorn and beech reveal the rolling topography, rescuing the scheme from monotony. The repetition of bright red follies at Parc de La Villette, all about the same size and set on a grid, heightens the differences among the follies. The uniformity of parallel colonnades linking the pavilions that flank the Lawn at the University of Virginia highlights the variations among the pavilions. In the square-shaped Villa Rotondo in Vicenza, the repetitive symmetry of identical facades emphasizes each of the varied landscapes that confronts each loggia: formal garden on one side, then woodland; orchard and vineyard; distant fields and floodplain. Though the plan of the building is frequently reproduced, its landscape context is rarely shown. Yet Andrea Palladio, the villa's designer, cites its landscape context as the reason for this unusual four-part symmetry. The building is a foil for the landscape:

> The site is as pleasant and as delightful as can be found; because it is upon a small hill, of very easy access, and is watered on one side by the Bacchiglione, a navigable river; and on the other it is encompassed with most pleasant risings, which look like a very great theater, and are all cultivated, and abound with most excellent fruits, and most exquisite vines: and therefore, as it enjoys from every part most beautiful views, some of which are limited, some more extended, and others that terminate with the horizon; there are loggias made in all the four fronts.[15]

EPANAPHORA AND EPANALEPSIS. Disney's gates to each land in the Magic Kingdom repeat to signal a beginning; equidistant road markers announce the beginning of a new segment. Bands of stone headers at intervals across a brick sidewalk that mark the beginning of each segment of pavement provide variety that sets up a visual and audible rhythm. Progressive passage through a ritual landscape is often signaled by a series of walls, gates, shrines, or signs. At Ise, a succession of gates into nested enclosures marks the entry to increasingly more sacred domains; pilgrims may not proceed beyond to the innermost. A million pilgrims a year journey to Juazeiro, Brazil, home of a Roman Catholic "holy man" who died in 1934, climbing two miles up a steep hill on the Rua do Hortoa to a huge statue of Padre Cicero. Concrete statues along the route mark each Station of the Cross and prompt a prayer or action; pilgrims tie ribbons and drape flowers around the statues of Christ, slap or spit at the figures of Judas and Herod's soldiers.[16] All of these

Placement, framing, parallelism, address, metonymy: Sceaux. France.

landscapes are epanaphora, repeating an element to mark the beginning of a series of segments or motifs.

In epanalepsis an element or combination of elements is stressed through repetition, such as notes in birdsong, words in a refrain, or the diverse fountains at the Alhambra and Generalife, each similar in sight and sound—the low bubbler, the arc, the wall gusher. Many of the low bubblers are in small courtyards and under porticos in shade, where their soft sound is amplified, their shifting shape expanding in ripples. Arcs in larger, open courts are transformed by sun into curving lines of light, their splashing sound bright; gushers spout from terrace walls and rush into basins. The visitor moves through the gardens to these water refrains, variations on a theme.

Climax and Anticlimax

CLIMAX. In climax, the "highest or most intense point in an experience or series of events," intensity and significance increase step by step. When a canoist runs a river, toward a waterfall, water flows faster, the rushing roar grows louder, then comes the climactic drop into crashing water. So, too, a view or monument at the top of an ascending path (the church at Mont-Saint-Michel, the grove on the Hill of Remembrance in Forest Cemetery). Ecologists once saw a succession in plants' growing mounting to a "climax" in a sequence of stages: from a cut forest a meadow grows, then woody seedlings of shrubs and trees emerge, sun-loving trees grow into shady woodland, which die off, in turn, as forest trees grow higher. The perception of climax as the ideal of progression was in part a human idea projected onto landscape.

ANTICLIMAX. In anticlimax, there is a failure to live up to expectations: when the end of a journey disappoints, when no water is discovered in a desert waterhole, when no view and nothing else of significance appears at the end of a long, ascending path. The eye-catching ruins atop a distant hill, seen from Sanssoucci (the palace that lends its name to a grand estate in Potsdam outside Berlin), draw the eye; up close, after a long ascent, the climber finds no ruins at all, simply columns placed artfully akilter, to hide the reservoir that feeds the fountains of the park. Jellicoe prevented such a letdown in his design for the long walk at Sutton Place, whose terminus in an insignificant magnolia is not anticlimactic but provocatively surreal. After nineteenth-century tourists to Niagara Falls complained that "the Falls fail to astonish," Frederick Law Olmsted was hired, in 1886, to prepare a plan to redress the disappointment. He changed the rhythm and varied the sequence of visitors' experience.[17]

Anomaly

Landscape that is incongruous is anomalous; taking something out of time or place provokes notice and promotes discovery. To take something out of context on purpose can be crucial to invention and humor.

ANACHRONISM. In anachronism, the antique is placed out of time, in a modern setting, or vice versa. Replicas of gas lamps, benches, railings, and fences from the nineteenth and early twentieth centuries, common in American parks of the late twentieth century prompt questions. Why reproduce the old? Why not simply adapt it? Or invent anew, as in Paris and Barcelona, where lamps, benches, and fences in new parks are frankly contemporary, as the celebrated Paris Métro entrances once were? Battery Park City, a new residential and commercial neighborhood at the tip of Lower Manhattan, combines sleek modern buildings with a landscape that reflects nineteenth- and early twentieth-century style, but is surrounded by the city's crumbling infrastructure: potholes, decaying parks, aging subways. Perhaps the ubiquitous reproductions in the United States are expressions of nostalgia for a period when more substantial investments were made in the urban public realm.

The use of modern materials like plastic, steel, and concrete or of frankly contemporary styles to reconstruct or interpret historic landscapes is also anachronistic. Andersson advocates such an approach when the purpose is renovation or renewal, but not when it is reconstruction (which must, by definition, employ historically accurate materials and construction techniques). Renovation, he sees as guided by an understanding of the original conception and the elements that contributed to its artistic quality, not a copy, but an artful translation. Free renewal, as defined by Andersson, preserves not the form itself, nor even the spirit, but rather the original's artistic quality, an approach he supports when documentation or funding are inadequate to make reconstruction possible and when too little of the original is left to support renovation. Better a new form with a strong artistic concept than an imitation devoid of the aesthetic qualities that made the original memorable.[18] His design for Urienborg, Tycho Brahe's observatory and garden on the island of Ven, between Sweden and Denmark, is a fusion of all three, reconstruction, renovation, and free renewal.[19]

PROCHRONISM. World's fairs and expositions typically display a representation of something in the future as if it exists already. Disney's EPCOT (Experimental Prototype Community of Tomorrow), intended to "entertain, inform, and inspire," was envisioned as a showcase for American industry and research.[20] In "Future World," each exhibit is sponsored by a big corporation: "Wonders of Life" by Metropolitan Life Insurance, "The Living Seas" by United Technologies, "Universe of Energy" by Exxon, "Horizons" by General Electric, "Journey into Imagination" by Kodak, "CommuniCore" by UNISYS, "World of Motion" by General Motors. All demonstrate the conviction that environmental and social problems can be resolved by technology. In Kraft Foods' "The Land," a film titled *Symbiosis* praises "working in harmony with nature and listening to the land," implying that pollution has been overcome. The film ends with a lone farmer, hands in back pockets, staring across a field of grain, as if the family farmer is still alive and well, but then the camera pulls up to show development nearby. Since the category "farmer" has now been dropped from the U.S. census, this scene is deeply ironic. The landscape and buildings at EPCOT recall those of the 1939 New York World's Fair. This is yesterday's tomorrow, an anachronism whose landscape, with its swirling bands of brilliant blooms, is meant to reassure the visitor that the future will be a happy place.

ANACHORISM. An anachorism is a foreign element, something out of place rather than out of time. Exotic plants transported in the late nineteenth century from the outposts of the British Empire to the Royal Botanical Garden at Kew are anachorisms, so are the pastoral parks and gardens with green lawns and groves exported from Britain to Australia, India, Africa, and, today, to the American Southwest.

ANASTROPHE. Anastrophe is an inversion of the normal or expected order for emphasis, or humor, or priority. Thus, casts of human legs, upside down, stick up out of the pavement in SITE's plaza outside the railroad station in Yokohama, Japan. The sponsor, the Isuzu Corporation, wanted the plaza to feature their cars and allude to their work in high technology for outer space. Inspired by photographs of astronauts floating upside down in space capsules, SITE designed an inverted plaza with upside-down cars and legs cast from citizens of Yokohama. A field of Texas bluebonnets, the state flower, hangs upside down from the ceiling of Austin's airport, waving in the breezes of the ventilation system. "The Hanging Texas Blue-

Metaphor and simile: Harlequin Plaza. Colorado.

bonnet Field" is part of a larger commission of hedgerows, windbreaks, and allées designed by Martha Schwartz to lead travelers from the airport's parking lots and roads to the entry.

Metaphor

Metaphor involves a transfer of meaning from one thing or phenomenon to another, an "imaginative, often unexpected, comparison between basically dissimilar things."[21] Seen broadly, "all figures of speech that achieve their affect through association, comparison, and resemblance"; seen more narrowly, "a figure of speech that concisely compares two things by saying that one is the other."[22] Is the distinction between simile and metaphor relevant in landscape? What would landscape examples be of *simile*, a direct comparison, and *metaphor*, a condensed simile? Is it a matter of how literal the comparison? Is the gravel at Ryoanji, raked in wavy lines to look like water, a simile? Is Astroturf a simile for grass? Are ruins as memento mori, a reminder of human mortality, or Patio de la Reja, as the hydrologic cycle, metaphors? And is a metaphor the same as representation? Ryoanji and Harlequin Plaza, in an office park outside Denver, represent landscape, are they similes or metaphors? Mirror-clad pyramids at Harlequin Plaza echo the form of Rocky Mountain peaks, the checkerboard paving echoes the midwestern grid. What transfer of meaning is here, a "fanciful or unrealistic comparison"? Harlequin Plaza was once highly controversial, regarded by many as a polemical landscape that asserted the authority of art, flaunted concerns for function, and failed to respond appropriately to its context. But the designer George Hargreaves took elements of the office park's "anyplace" character and used them inventively, calling attention to the distant mountains and highlighting the unsettling character of the new development. The plaza is a metaphor that can be read on several levels.

Tree of life, tree of knowledge, tree as man or woman—are all metaphor or are they simile? At the heart of the campus at Århus University in Denmark, oaks, long-lived trees of strong wood and native to Denmark, are a symbol of the nation. Here are multiple metaphorical dimensions. The landscape architect C. Th. Sørensen proposed planting acorns instead of larger trees at the university, symbolic, in economic terms, of construction beginning just after the Depression and during the German Occupation. Sørensen said, "When my newborn daughter Sonja is eighteen, she will walk under the oak trees"; and she did.[23] The oak tree has become the symbol of the university; a large ceramic relief of an oak, *The Tree of Knowledge*, hangs at the main entrance, the only explicit reference to the landscape's metaphorical meaning.

SYNECDOCHE. A part that stands for the whole, a synecdoche, is often a landmark, a clue that points to an entire landscape, city, or nation: Half Dome for Yosemite, Eiffel Tower for Paris, Empire State Building for New York, the Mall in Washington, D.C., for the nation. The fountains built by American cities at the end of the nineteenth century, like Bethesda Fountain in New York's Central Park, symbolized and celebrated new public water systems. The name Bethesda alludes to the pool in Jerusalem where an infirm person "was made whole of whatsoever disease he had," making explicit an implicit link between water and health.[24] Today's windmill fields and powerlines, parts of the networks of power on which modern culture depends so heavily, render that network visible.

METONYMY. When an attribute of a person or thing stands for the thing itself, it is a metonymy. As a child, I thought the Iron Curtain was an actual metal drape drawn across the landscape of Europe, casting a long, dark shadow. For many people the Berlin Wall came to represent just such an idea. Buckingham Palace and Westminster stand for the British monarchy and parliament, much as the White House stands for the presidency and Lafayette Park and the Ellipse are now known as President's Park, or as the Hill represents Congress. A New England village green stands for the town; Disneyland's fairy castle for Fantasyland, Main Street for the midwestern small town. Landscapes have often been seen as representing the people who occupy them. In the early twentieth century, the Prairie Style of landscape and architectural design celebrated "the prairie spirit" where prairie plants and landscape stood for "native beauty," and the "independence and progressiveness of the pioneer" who settled the prairie.[25]

Houses and gardens built to represent their owners are employed by art and literature, as well. In Jane Austen's *Pride and Prejudice*, Elizabeth Bennet dates her love for Mr. Darcy from her first view of his estate: "Pemberley House was a large, handsome stone building, standing well on rising ground, and backed by a ridge of high woody hills; and in front, a stream of some natural importance was swelled into greater, but without any artificial appearance. Its banks were neither formal nor falsely adorned. She had never seen a place for which nature had done more, or where natural beauty had been so little counteracted by an awkward taste."[26] "A man's home is his castle" was a sixteenth-century English reference to Roman law.[27] Such nineteenth-century landscape designers and authors as J. C. Loudon in England and Andrew Jackson Downing in the United States advised how a middle-class villa garden could be landscaped in the style of an eighteenth-century English estate.[28] There is a direct link between the design of such English estates, with house and garden standing for owner and rustic cottage for rural ideal, and the design of American suburban grounds as pastoral ministates. Is the separation of the workplace and the home that is dictated by modern zoning an extension of the idea of Everyman's home as his/her "castle"?

PERSONIFICATION. Personification, identifying the nonhuman with the human (a tree is like a man, but not the reverse), abounds in popular culture: the Old Man of the Mountain in a rocky cliff, the willows that weep in cemeteries, the ravages of fires, floods, and earthquakes as Mother Nature's revenge. In gardens, allusions to classical literature are personified in sculpture: at Vaux-le-Vicomte, two statues overlook the central canal, the god of the Anqueil, the local river, and the god of the Tiber. Are we, thereby, invited to compare Vaux with the great Italian gardens or France under Louis XIV with the Roman Empire? It was the god of the Tiber who foretold the founding of Rome and reassured Aeneas of his future victory. At Stourhead, the statue of the god of the Tiber is an explicit reference to this passage from the *Aeneid*.[29]

EUPHEMISM. A landscape euphemism dresses up nasty things or things people prefer not to confront, the dress or screen standing for the thing screened, for example, garbage bins and service areas around large office buildings behind a green screen of shrubs or trees. A planted island in an intersection in River Oaks, a wealthy Houston suburb, a "designer" pump station that pumps sewage to a treatment plant rather than dumping it into Houston's Buffalo Bayou, a pudgy putto holding a basin on his head, drapery concealing his groin. Resort landscapes are euphemisms designed for play, with no signs of work save by those who wait on those who play. What a society chooses to screen in euphemism is a clue to its values and its anxieties.

CONCEIT. Schwartz's Splice Garden, on the roof of the Whitehead Institute in Cambridge, Massachusetts, relating the act of gene-splicing to the juxtaposition of French and Japanese garden styles, is a conceit: the relating of two quite dissimilar things—the plants representing living things, the inorganic plastic material standing for artificiality. The Splice Garden can be read as an allegory, as well, for the plastic cannot reproduce itself; after ten years it is faded and brittle, essentially dead.

ALLEGORY. An allegory is an extended metaphor, a story that can be read on more than one level, whose purpose is to enlighten and instruct. Mazes have been built as allegorical objects of amusement and means of religious experience. The maze at the Shaker settlement in New Harmony, Indiana, was described in 1822 as "a most elegant flower garden with various hedgerows disposed in such a manner as to puzzle people to get into the little temple, emblematical of Harmony, in the middle. The Labyrinth represents the difficulty of arriving at Harmony."[30] Parallels have been drawn between the maze and life's hazards: "The world's lab'rinth, whose enfractious ways are all compos'd of rubs and crooked meanders."[31]

The landscape of Sutton Place, designed by Jellicoe, is an elaborate allegory of "Creation (the lake landscape), Life (the gardens), and Aspiration (the Nicholson Wall) . . . and like all allegories, is intended to lift the spirit for a brief period out of the present."[32] The lake, in a shape suggestive of a fish, was conceived as the beginning of the allegory, with three hills representing father, mother, and child. Around the house are a kitchen garden, a swimming pool garden, a wild garden, a surrealist garden, a paradise garden. To reach the paradise garden from the house, one must cross a moat with lily pads on stepping-stones, for, says Jellicoe, "the allegory is that you must have a hazardous journey if you are to reach" paradise.[33] The secret garden, "the heart of the allegory," was inspired by *Midsummer Night*, a painting in the client's collection by Atkinson Grimshaw (1876), of a fairy and woodland. The Nicholson Wall, thirty-two feet long, sixteen feet high, is a carved abstract relief sculpture of white marble by Ben Nicholson that stands at the end of a dark reflecting pool in a garden room framed by hedges.

CLICHÉ. As twisted axes and fragmented spaces became fashionable in postmodern landscapes and buildings they lost their original bite and became clichés. As symbols of rebellion against modernism and as commentary on the fragmentation and chaos of contemporary life, they were metaphors whose power was eroded through overuse. A concrete path rolled up at the end like a carpet is a pun; seen more than once, it is a cliché, the standard fate of obvious puns, which lose impact and become annoying with repetition. However, when Peter Walker and Martha Schwartz used Astroturf to clad sloping planes of plywood, alluding to Le Nôtre's inclined planes of clipped grass, and in the context of other, similar allusions, in their roof garden in Boston, they reclaimed the lost meaning through reformulation and novel use.

Paradox and Irony

Paradox and irony, the one contradictory yet true, the other an incongruity between what is and what seems to be—expected and actual, expressed and intended—are closely related and often combined. Both are dualisms, but irony contrasts surface meaning and underlying reality. Denver's Rocky Mountain

Arsenal is both: a toxic dump, contaminated by nerve gas and abandoned, yet a wildlife refuge rich with a diversity of plants and animals.[34]

Denmark in June: blue sky, no clouds, clear air, bright sun, white light, cool breeze, cool air, hot skin; Konza Prairie, Kansas, in October: how soft the hills look to lie in, light yellow grass stems softly curving; close up, sharp limestone chips on the ground, grass stiff and prickly. Both are paradox. So is water, both solid and gas, visible and invisible; so, too, are built landscapes, like parks or planted prairies, that are commonly seen to be naturally occurring, while natural meadows on vacant urban lots, unplanted and untended, are perceived as artificial. Both, in fact, are natural and both are constructed. The false idea of natural as excluding the human causes this error. Every landscape is inherently paradoxical, a fusion of the managed and the wild.

Japan is a landscape of paradox. Violence and repose, discord and harmony, excess and economy, complex and simple, hidden and revealed, large and small, extraordinary and everyday, enduring and ephemeral, traditional and new. Juxtaposed, each contrast prompts contradiction and confusion; fused, they have rare depth and resonance, the simultaneous presence of contradictory qualities that enhance the experience of each. Japanese gardens are especially renowned for this phenomenon, but it is present, too, in villages and shrines of traditional character. Today, the fusion is disappearing, while juxtaposition remains, the consequence of a growing sense of unresolved contradiction and cultural confusion.

ANTITHESIS AND OXYMORON. Antithesis opposes antithetical elements by placing them in a balanced, parallel structure; oxymoron fuses contradictory elements in a single expression. It is easier for opposed elements to make each more striking and more significant, the juxtaposition of clipped and uninhibited growing like the three parallel rows of lindens framing an interior ring of freely growing horse chestnuts in the Place des Vosges in Paris, or the branches of elms at the center of Kongens Nytorv in Copenhagen encircled by rigid, stubby twigs of clipped elms. A view of a city skyline seen against a leafy foreground is also antithesis: Boston from Mount Auburn Cemetery; Philadelphia from Belmont Plateau in Fairmount Park; Houston from Buffalo Bayou.

Stone seems the antithesis of decay, but fossiliferous limestone, composed of plant and animal remains, is an oxymoron. Vizcaya, an estate near Miami, Florida, is surrounded by dense, subtropical forest. Its house, terraces, steps, railings, and paths are built of limestone that teems with fossils, animal and vegetable, including large corals, resembling slices of brain. The garden air is full of the dank smell of rotted organic matter. Schwartz's Splice Garden employs both antithesis and oxymoron: Japanese and French garden motifs are juxtaposed; all the plants are plastic. A plastic flower is an oxymoron, a condensed paradox that owes its effectiveness to synthesis, not juxtaposition, of contrasts; so is a roof garden, for gardens embody a sense of groundedness and a garden absorbs water while the pur-

Paradox, oxymoron, conceit: Splice Garden. Cambridge, Massachusetts. (Alan Ward)

pose of a roof is to shed it. Richard Long's circles of rocks and branches seem to deny the circle's structure; circular in shape and chaotic in structure, they are oxymorons. The disintegrated grid of the woods at Chantilly owes its magical quality to the fusion of planted grid, chaotic regeneration, and random dispersal of seed.

The curving line of poplar trees along the river Rance in Dinan in northwestern France is both antithesis in the contrast of arc and meander and oxymoron in the paradox of chaotic growth of trees planted in a precise arc. These are among the oldest devices in garden design, as Anthony Hecht reminds us in "The Gardens of the Villa d'Este."[35] Even an unbuilt landscape, like inert rock formed by flowing minerals, can be so read. Alexander Pope criticized gardens for lacking such contrast: "No pleasing Intricacies intervene, / No artful Wilderness to perplex the Scene."[36] If ever strictly true or not, it is no longer so, for with few armies of gardeners to clip, pluck, plant, and mow, even Versailles now has its wild, vegetative ruins.

Community gardens in the Mill Creek floodplain are both paradoxical and ironic: they stem from lack of use and also from preservation, from closed opportunities for investment and from new reconstruction. The successional meadows on vacant lots—both nuisance and resource—are also paradox. To be appreciated as a resource, the paradox must be seen: the meadow must show signs of use, of care, for example, through a carefully designed and maintained edge or fence, a frame of care that helps viewers perceive beauty.

ANTIPHRASIS. In antiphrasis, a material or form is used in a manner contrary to the expected, the expression contrasting sharply with what is meant. Schwartz employed this form of irony in her proposal for a New York City roof garden.[37] It looks like any other garden until its 897 daffodils bloom in spring, their bold yellow spelling IGNORANCE before they fade, leaving green, then brown leaves. In summer, purple Greek anemones spell EVIL, in early fall, Peruvian lilies emerge as orange MONEY, followed by BLISS in blazing red amaryllis. Flowers are used incongruously to challenge their common association with purity, beauty, and love.

LITOTES. A litotes is an affirmation of something through understatement, through the negative of its opposite (e.g., she is no fool). The opposite of hyperbole, it is an ironic understatement of the negative of its opposite: "Less is more," said Mies van der Rohe; "less is a bore," declared Robert Venturi. His firm's design for Franklin Court, on the site of Benjamin Franklin's house and print shop in Philadelphia's Independence Park, is not a mere replica; a white steel frame outlines the house that was once there, another the print shop. Franklin Court is a litotes, the understatement in the "ghost" structure, the white steel frame that outlines the house that was once there, the irony in incongruity within a historic district, the mocking of more literal historic reconstruction.

MEIOSIS. Meiosis is an understatement that belittles by using materials or forms "that make something seem less significant than it really is or ought to be." Schwartz's experiments with materials normally not associated with gardens, not only plastic flowers and Astroturf, but Plexiglass, wire glass, colored aquarium gravel, chicken wire, fish netting, and bagels, have been read by some as meiosis, as attempts to belittle, to undermine the meanings of gardens. The cover of *Landscape Architecture* magazine for January 1980, which featured a photograph of Schwartz's Bagel Garden, provoked an immediate, and virulent, reaction; letters to the editor filled pages of the magazine for many months with protests. Some landscape architects suspected she was poking fun at *them*, not at the garden itself. The Bagel Garden had low boxwood hedges in two squares, one inside the other, with purple flowers in the center, and ninety-six weatherproofed bagels sitting on a square strip of purple gravel. Schwartz said she was taken aback by the reaction: "Why are you all taking this so seriously? I was just having fun." The Bagel Garden (and much of her other work) employs rhetorical devices familiar to twentieth-century art—collage, Dada, Pop Art—long since no surprise to the art world, but an outrage to some lovers of gardens.

DRAMATIC IRONY. In dramatic irony's double vision of the future observers see what's coming, actors are blind to it. Overviews of a maze where viewers watch others wandering and can anticipate the dead end the wanderers will reach or their successful emergence, these are a form of dramatic irony. So are tricks in gardens where water shoots out unexpectedly, drenching the passerby, while others watch knowingly.

Irony: gateway to Newport Coast. Orange County, California.

Irony can also be in the eye of the beholder, unremarkable to some, ironical to others. To me southern California is steeped in irony and paradox: a paradise with perfect climate, iridescent sky, ocean beaches, snow-capped mountains, freedom of movement across a region laced with freeways, but an apparently idyllic landscape subject to violent ruptures of earthquake, wildfire, mudslide, riot. The outsider there sees the future as predictable and inevitable, homes destroyed on unstable hillsides or fault lines; the insider ignores the danger or assumes it won't happen to them. The population of Orange County has generally opposed governmental interference and control, yet neighborhood codes in Irvine limit what color owners can paint their houses. The triumphal arches on either side of a public roadway to gated communities are an irony, so is Fort Pendleton, a de facto nature preserve where soldiers learn means of destruction.

Address

At Disneyland, a visitor is addressed by a statue of Disney, himself, hand in hand with Mickey Mouse: "I think most of all what I want Disneyland to be is a happy place . . . where parents and children can have fun, together." Address announces, appeals, or prays to someone or something not present or unable to answer: a place, an idea, a supernatural being, a dead person. Laying flowers on a grave addresses the dead, while the dead address the living through gravestones.

APOSTROPHE. Sharp turns in paths of Japanese and Chinese gardens, an interruption for effect, focus attention on a view, increase awareness of the process of

Address. Mariebjerg Cemetery. Denmark.

walking, are apostrophes, whose original meaning from the Greek is "turning away." At the Vale of the White Horse in southwestern England the horse's outline, scraped into the chalky bedrock, faces the sky above not the valley below (most photographs of this monument are taken from the air, a view unattainable by those who first traced its outline thousands of years ago). Shrines with lit candles and offerings in churches and at roadside shrines address Mary. At Ise, coin box and rope are a shrine to the winds: throw coin into box, pull gong, bow twice, clap twice, bow, and back away. Trees within Japanese temple precincts covered with twisted paper and wooden plaques tied to branches are pleas for help in passing university exams or for the health of a child.

Aposiopesis. In aposiopesis a statement or address is broken off, to be completed in the imagination: an eroded cliff whose former outline can be visualized; a path or line with continuation implied; a path to the edge of a cliff or to a prospect whose continuation is the view, an incomplete circle to be completed by viewer. House and churches were moved and graves disinterred before the Quabbin Valley in central Massachusetts was flooded in 1928 to create the Quabbin reservoir; the roads remain, leading hikers through the woods of the Quabbin Reservation past old stone walls overgrown to the lake's edge, where one continues in imagination on a road leading under water, past former farms and homes, to old towns. The frame outlining the former silhouette of Benjamin Franklin's house at Franklin Court in Philadelphia, not a reconstruction, is an aposiopesis, in this case, less is more, and in no way a bore. Andersson's design for Urienborg, Tycho Brahe's garden on an island between Sweden and Denmark, is also aposiopesis. The original formal garden had a four-part symmetry, and Andersson chose to reconstruct one quarter only. It is deliberately incomplete, suggestive rather than exhaustive. An invitation to imagine.

EXCLAMATION AND INTERROGATION. On New Year's Eve of 1903, when Isabella Stewart Gardner welcomed her first guests to Fenway Court, a version of a Venetian palazzo (built with architectural details transported from Italy to Boston), they were enchanted by the garden within the house. There is no sign of it from the entrance or through the dark, narrow vestibule; the visitor emerges into a covered courtyard garden, three storys high, filled with light and the brilliant color and scent of flowers year round. This is exclamation, a strong statement standing out from its context. When designers say a building or garden makes a statement, they usually mean it embodies an exclamation. Interrogation resembles it, something unexpected but one prompting a question (!?), an anomaly, a path that ends in a wall, an unexpected juxtaposition like the golden frogs at the Rio Shopping Center or the huge vases in Sutton Place.

EXPRESSIVE CONTEXT: EUPHONY, CACOPHONY, MOOD, MYSTERY

If personification attributes feelings, thoughts, intentions to the nonhuman world, expressive context attributes the ability to evoke or amplify human feeling to landscape features and phenomena. Life-threatening events, such as wildfire, flood, hurricanes, and tornadoes seem to elicit similar feelings from people of different times and cultures. Sunlight and darkness, heat and cold, evoke common responses that vary from culture to culture and within a culture. But do landscapes embody gloom, mystery, confusion, calm? Or do they merely receive projected humans feelings? Authors and artists use landscape to signify or reinforce mood: many stories, written and painted, portray a dark pine forest, a sunny meadow, or a "looming" mountain to establish an atmosphere of gloom, cheer, fear. Poussin, Claude, and many other painters depict Aeneas meeting Dido in the cave as a thunderstorm pours rain and hail; "booming sea" and "howling" treetops are a stormy setting for the turning point in Yukio Mishima's *Sound of the Waves*.

A sense of melancholy or pathos, influenced by English poet-philosophers and their landscape gardens, fashionable in early nineteenth-century United States, was cultivated in that century in new "rural" cemeteries like Mount Auburn near Boston. Mount Auburn's designers sought to evoke sadness and promote reflection through "winding paths leading from sunny lawns through areas of cool dark woods, . . . dark and reflective water bodies, flowing streams, material evidence of the ravages of nature such as blasted tree trunks or of deciduous plants displaying nature's cycle of symbolic seasons, and vistas of great distance, height, or depths."[38] Many nineteenth-century cemeteries seem maudlin today.

In euphony landscape patterns are perceived as harmonious, in cacophony as discordant. At Paley Park, a narrow park on East 53rd Street in New York, a waterfall masks the cacophonous traffic noise on the street. The Villa d'Este in Tivoli and the Villa Lante in Bagnaia, both in Italy, employ water for euphonious effect. Jellicoe describes how, inspired by the Villas d'Este and Lante, he designed four cascades for the garden at Shute House in England meant to create a harmonic water chord as the water moves downstream through successive cascades striking trebles, altos, tenors, and bass.[39]

How one arrives at or enters a place, the transition between outside and inside, the nature of boundaries and gates, is critical to mood. So is sequence: the order of experience, the rhythm of movement, anticipation and the element of surprise.

MAGIC KINGDOMS: DISNEY'S WORLDS

Walt Disney told designers what he wanted visitors to feel: "I want them, when they leave, to have smiles on their faces. Just remember that; it's all I ask of you as a designer."[40]

Arrival at Disney World outside Orlando, Florida, is designed to put "guests" in a carefree mood, to create the sense of entering a world apart. Off the highway at the Disney World Exit, one drives for miles through Disney-owned territory, manicured parkland with signs in brilliant red, green, purple, and yellow that are unlike real highway signs. Park the car, then ride a tram to the ticket booth, buy tickets, and board a steamboat bound for the Magic Kingdom. There, a journey begins, across water, to an apparent island. Landmarks stimulate anticipation; the spires of Cinderella's Castle suggest a royal domain, synecdoche for the Magic Kingdom. At the dock one walks up a red path, under a sign that says, "Here you leave today and enter the world of yesterday, tomorrow, and fantasy," through a short, dark tunnel to the Town Square, full of bright shades and sounds, and roaming actors in costume. Munchkin land. It is as though, like Dorothy in *The Wizard of Oz*, having gone to sleep in real black and white, one wakes up to Technicolor and fantasy! In both Disneyland in Anaheim, California, and Disney World in Florida, red, yellow, and orange flowers, red paths, nostalgic music in major key create an upbeat setting; diminutive buildings suggest that one is a giant, ruler of the kingdom. California and Florida as their sites are no accidental choice; both are warm, sunny vacationlands.

Main Street, in both places, is a straight axis with a Victorian train station at one end and Cinderella's castle at the other, framing views to both. Seen from Town Square, the castle is a lure, an eye-catcher in garden terms, or "wienie," as Disney called it. Cars, buildings, lampposts, even trees are smaller than normal. One feels larger than life. On Main Street the buildings decrease in scale with height: the ground floor is 90 percent of normal height, the second floor 80 percent, and the third floor 60 percent.[41] Anachronisms are deliberate, so are the prochronisms of Tomorrowland, presenting the future as the present. Victorian materials and motifs like the exaggerated ornament on Main Street stores and the soundtrack of old tunes like "School Days" evoke nostalgia. Tomorrowland, with its sleek chrome rockets, its moving sidewalks (the "WED-way People Mover"), and a landscape swirling patterns of colored flowers reminiscent of Roberto Burle Marx's gardens of the 1940s in Brazil, is a dated fantasy, neither then nor tomorrow.[42] A bronze plaque at the entrance to Disneyland underscores the intention: "To all who come to this happy place: welcome. Disneyland is your land. Here, age relives fond memories of the past . . . and here youth may savor the challenge and promise of the future."[43]

Just as Disney's cartoons use exaggeration and distortion to evoke response in the audience, so the Magic Kingdom's landscape functions as expressive context. In Mickey Mouse's Birthdayland (Disney World), enlarged lawnmower, garden hose, windowboxes, shutters, picket fence, clothesline, watering can, rake, paths are neither awesome nor threatening, but comforting, familiar icons of American suburbia of the 1950s. In comparison to the miniature scale of house and yard, these huge objects make one feel simultaneously small and big, a child again yet an adult. Mickey and Minnie's car is parked in front of a garage with a huge lock. Why a lock? What's inside? The simulated landscape of the rides (trees with twisted trunks and branches in Snow White) titillate fearful delight in young children, the only kind of intended paradox in the park. The rides are allusions to cartoons and movies; as Disney said, "We're trying to tell a story in those rides."[44] Artists drew storyboards of the rides, and Disney "described the entire Snow White ride as if it were a movie cartoon, visualizing all the park's attractions for the designers just as he had brought cartoons to life for his animators."[45]

"If you can keep a place clean," said Disney, "people will respect it; if you let it get dirty, they'll make it worse."[46] A staff of six hundred copes with Disneyland's dirt; during the day, white-clad sweepers eliminate spills and litter; every night after closing, crews hose down the entire park, pluck faded blooms, replace trampled plants.[47] "Just make [the park] beautiful and you'll appeal to the best side of people. They all have it; all you have to do is bring it out."[48] Perhaps Disney was right, at least about Americans; as funds for maintenance of urban parks shrank in the 1980s and parks became littered, vandalism seemed to increase. Boston's Public Garden—fenced, well maintained, with swan boats and miniature bridge, and formal flower beds changing by season—seemed to inspire decorum and discourage mischief, while Boston Common—tattered and littered, its frog pond often dry—seemed to attract litter and graffiti.[49]

Still, obsessive cleanliness accompanied by much euphemism can seem cloying and oppressive, like the white painters' cart and the white cleaners' carts at Disney World with their tools, paint, soap, and disinfectants and, no doubt also, deodorizers for tidying up after the (real) horses that defecate and urinate on Main Street. Those who maintain and clean the park are themselves dressed up in sparkling white costumes. Other maintenance is hidden or tucked away on the perimeters, unacknowledged. There is an underground city that supports the domains above, reached through doorways with signs that say, "Members of the Cast Only." On the perimeter of Walt Disney World in Florida, a sign says, "You are now leaving WDW." But you aren't really. The warehouses and fire station that service Walt Disney World, all color-coded, are just outside next to the road, though there is no sign of any connection to WDW.

Disney regretted that he had not controlled the land surrounding the original Disneyland in California; the hotels, restaurants, and bars that grew up around his theme park created a "honky-tonk" context at odds with the park's family atmosphere. He also realized that there was more profit to be made in food and lodging than in the park itself. The purchase of 27,500 acres in Florida, more than 150 times the size of his California Disneyland, provided greater scope to shape the visitors' context and extend it through hotels and campgrounds, each with its own fantasy theme.

For James Rouse, developer of Columbia, Maryland, Baltimore's Harborplace, and Boston's Quincy Market, as for many other developers, Disneyland is a model. In 1963, he told the graduating class at Harvard's Graduate School of Design,

> I hold a view that may be shocking to an audience as sophisticated as this, and that is, that the greatest piece of design in the United States today is Disneyland. If you think about Disneyland and think of its performance in relation to its purpose—its meaning to people more than its meaning to the process of development—you will find it the outstanding piece of urban design in the United States. It took an area of activity —the amusement park—and lifted it to a standard so high in its performance, in its respect for people, in its functioning for people, that it really became a brand-new thing. It fulfills the functions that it set out to accomplish unself-consciously, usefully, and profitably. I find more to learn in the standards that have been achieved in the development of Disneyland than in any other single piece of development in the country.[50]

Disney's Magic Kingdoms are expressive landscapes with the power to move people. Designers and developers of new residential communities and shopping centers have learned much from Disney, and many parts of southern California, and of America, now resemble this world: themed communities and shopping malls with vivid flowers, turn-of-the-century lamps and benches, outdoor soundtracks of upbeat music. Bounded domains with guarded gates, kingdoms unto themselves managed by central authorities, invite prospective residents to live out their fantasies and leave crime and the poor outside. There is danger in longing to inhabit fantasyland, to forget real life, the mistakes of the past and the problems of the present, the genuine promises and risks of the future.

In fall 1993, I took part in a one-day workshop to advise the National Park Service on the future "Site Character" of the White House landscape, newly dubbed President's Park. Traffic and trees, monuments and barriers, sights and sounds were all discussed in the context of the presidency, the state of the nation, and Walt Disney. Advisors were asked to prepare statements beforehand about goals for the "desired future" of President's Park twenty years from now, and these were compiled in a document circulated o all participants. Disney's influence was pervasive. "The appearance of the White House grounds at President's Park are at least at the standard maintained by Disney at its theme parks," was one participant's stated goal. Another was, "There are no visually intrusive landscape elements, permanent or temporary. . . . Eliminate, wherever possible, above-ground utilities, mismatched sidewalks (no asphalt), the homeless, cars parked around the Ellipse."[51]

Reportedly, Walt Disney's body lies frozen in a cryogenic institute in Irvine, California, as Snow White's did in the enchanted forest, waiting. If he awoke tomorrow and stepped outside, he might think he was in Disney World.

It is easy to praise Disneyland and Disney World, and easy to condemn them, but no matter whether one is an admirer or a critic, both are models of rhetorical expression. To know landscape poetics is to understand how such settings are fashioned and how they achieve their effects. To use figurative language well is to create landscape literature that is imaginative, affecting, and eloquent.

9

Polemical Landscapes

Berlin, July 1993. I had driven through Potsdamer and Leipziger Platz without even knowing it. There was no "place" there, no sense of deliberately shaped space, just huge tracts of vacant, uneven ground covered with weedy plants. The walls of abandoned old buildings were scarred with unpatched bullet holes. The street I was looking for, Stresemannstrasse, was on the map but did not seem to be where the map said it should be. I parked next to the old German War Ministry and walked down Wilhelmstrasse, rounded a corner, my first glimpse of the Berlin Wall—still standing. A truck was dumping new cobbles on Niederkirchnerstrasse for workers to lay. Until recently this had been part of the no-man's-land between East and West. Thick slabs of smooth granite were stacked for a new sidewalk—a very expensive material. On the side of the street opposite the Wall, a fresh bouquet of red flowers was attached to the facing wall. Later I learned that this street had been Prinz-Albrecht-Strasse; No. 8 was headquarters of the SS and Gestapo, once the most dreaded address in Berlin. The flowers faced the former entry and basement cells where prisoners were brought and held.

This block was the center of institutionalized Nazi terror from 1933 to 1945: the headquarters of the Gestapo, the SS, and the Reich Security Main Office. Warrants leading to incarceration in concentration camps were issued here, all Gestapo activities were masterminded in its offices, genocide was planned and organized here. The buildings were still standing after the war, but in 1949, 1953, 1956, and 1962, they were blown up, one by one, until only two remained. Prinz-Albrecht-Strasse itself has disappeared; its new name, Niederkirchnerstrasse, was adopted in 1951 in honor of a Communist resistance fighter, a seamstress, executed by the SS.[1]

I stepped through a hole in the Wall into a big vacant lot and looked down into a deep trench running the length of the Wall—the cells where prisoners were kept. Two tall mounds—building rubble—rose in the center of the block, overgrown with meadow plants, their yellow flowers bright in the grey misty afternoon. On the other side of the mound was a small museum, The Topography of Terrors, with an exhibit of the history of this block of land, of the Gestapo and the Holocaust. Nearby, under a canopy, was a space filled with sand: the basement where prisoners were tortured. The museum opened in the 1970s, and, in 1982, the West German House of Representatives voted to erect a memorial on the site. A

Destroying the past: Berlin Wall near Prinz-Albrecht-Strasse 8 (1993).

competition was held in 1984, but the winning scheme was, in the end, not built. So what will be? The museum had a temporary quality, as ephemeral as the Wall itself had become; there have been proposals to build a heliport here or a new expressway. Part of the block where a famous palace by the architect Karl Friedrich Schinkel once stood is now a place where people without a driver's license can come to practice their driving; the building rubble is graded into hills and curving roadways.

I stumbled on the Topography of Terrors while looking for the site of the old Anhalter and Potsdam railroad station, the largest passenger station in Europe before it was destroyed by bombs in the Second World War. On the site, left undeveloped for more than fifty years, a woodland had grown up on the rubble, its flora diverse, including many rare and endangered species that had earlier disappeared from the city. I had read an article about the site years ago and cited it in my book *The Granite Garden*, but I had never seen it. I continued to search for the place; it was not on my map. I finally found the site, down the street from the Topography of Terrors, now with only a fragment of the old facade of the station still standing: in front were neat gardens, behind were soccer fields, where once passenger trains pulled in under a great arched shed. I walked way back, hundreds of yards behind the fragment of facade, into a wood of poplar, birch, and locust growing out of parallel ditches, their canopies creating leafy tunnels. I scraped the leaves and moss with my toe and exposed asphalt beneath, then looked down into the ditches and saw I was walking on one of the old railroad platforms. The trees were growing up out of the old tracks, not ditches at all, the yellow brick of the platform walls still visible in spots. These were the freight platforms, backed up to the Landwehr Canal where goods were transferred between barges and trains. Under some trees at the edge of a clearing a group of young people was hanging out, a fire burning. The fringe area was a "wilderness" preserved by West Berliners.

Later, I walked around what used to be walled-off no-man's-land between the Brandenburg Gate and the canal on the south; after the construction of the Wall, this area was mined, and vegetation kept low and open. Parts of it were inhabited now: an area with junked trucks and an old airplane, a place where dismantled sections of the Wall, all spray-painted, were stacked and standing. A hand-drawn sign said, "Bring your passport and get it stamped with the old German Democratic Republic border stamp." A new apartment building with landscaped parking lot and play areas, a new landscape, extended out into no-man's-land and stopped. Even with maps and postcards of the area before and after the Wall was built, it was hard to discover where the Wall once stood.

BERLIN, AUGUST 1966. We crossed on foot into East Berlin at Checkpoint Charlie, left the American sector, walked past the guard post, around barriers across the road, under gunpoint. An East German border guard motioned us toward a white prefabricated trailer, my Danish friend spoke briefly, in German, to the guard who then followed us into the trailer and took our passports. Inside were a few seats and a closed door leading to another room. We waited for what seemed an eternity. My friend (now a diplomat), pretending he couldn't speak German well, had deliberately insulted the East German soldier, and there we sat with no passports. Finally we were allowed to leave, and we wandered all afternoon through grim streets with buildings still riddled with gunshot holes from the war, with horse-drawn wagons, and uniformed men with machine guns standing about. At the end of the day, we crossed back into West Berlin on the U-Bahn, in a train that traveled slowly, creeping through closed-up, dimly lit, abandoned stations patrolled by dogs and soldiers armed with machine guns.

BERLIN, JULY 1993. Standing on Zimmerstrasse at Checkpoint Charlie, I tried to reorient myself and remember how I had felt in 1966. Nothing seemed the same except some signs and a guard tower, but the tower had been moved from the middle of the street to inside a fence along the side and was now a thriving tourist attraction selling T-shirts and other paraphernalia. New office buildings and stores were visible along Friedrichstrasse, just beyond Checkpoint Charlie, in the old eastern sector, and in the distance was a Benneton store, just like one in an American shopping mall. What a landscape of memory this is: old Potsdamer and Leipziger Platz, Gestapo offices, the Wall, Checkpoint Charlie. But it is largely hidden memory. There is potential here for powerful memorials, but instead the past is being erased, the Wall precinct built over. The old no-man's-land along Zimmerstrasse is filling up with newly built apartments.

From the Brandenburg Gate I walked along Unter den Linden to the mu-

Recreating the past: The Schloss (1993). Berlin.

seum island in Mitte. Traces of the Wall were already removed from the Brandenburg, a reconstruction of the prewar landscape installed. The rain was misting
steadily. Many postwar buildings lined the street, some prewar, once pocked, now
patched, the larger holes with blocks of lighter stone and the smaller pits with
what looks like plaster, like a ravaged face covered with makeup. The statue of
Frederick the Great on horseback was back in place where it stood before the war;
it was put back in the late years of the German Democratic Republic, as that
regime came to terms with earlier German history. In 1951, the municipality of
East Berlin blew up the Schloss, the residential palace designed by Schinkel. I was
surprised, therefore, to see what looked like the yellow-orange facade of the
Schloss in the distance. But its yellow walls billowed and flapped, the building an
elaborate full-scale replica on painted canvas, facing the river Spree and Unter den
Linden. There was a carnival outside, with roller coaster and booths. Young couples dressed in period costumes were handing out flyers in German and English,
announcing some businessmen's plan to reconstruct the Schloss on Marx-Engels
Platz across from the Dom (the burial cathedral of the Hohenzollern family built
in the 1890s). This would obliterate the plaza and mean demolishing a postwar
building, now closed because of asbestos contamination. Many East Berliners
were saying then that they did not want the 1950s building torn down.

The boundaries between East and West that dictated the fates of Berlin
neighborhoods for half a century are being eradicated rapidly. Everywhere the
names of streets and squares are being changed. Even the pedestrian stoplights

with the tiny "worker" image have been replaced by the banal, nondescript figures standard in West Berlin. Any tourist with a map made before 1990 is in trouble. On one building, a plaque (dedicated June 1993, just one month before I came) commemorates a workers' uprising in 1953, the plaque made deliberately to look old. It is dangerous to erase the past. It prevents dealing with memories and forfeits the possibility of transformation.

POLEMICAL DIALOGUES

Competing ideologies govern the ways landscapes are shaped. Ideologies based on loyalty to a primary authority set the terms of dialogues: the authority of nature, an appeal to the natural; the authority of the past, an appeal to tradition; the authority of art, an appeal to invention; the authority of expedience and efficient function, an appeal to economics and the practical, the authority of power, an assertion of strength, force, or wealth. Design follows from ideology: imitation of nature, rejection of the exotic; reliance upon precedent, rejection of contemporary invention; search for new expression at the expense of tradition; translation of functional diagrams into form at the expense of grace and meaning. All too often each of these is pursued in isolation, with the landscape an arena of polemical monologues. The authority of the past is ranged against the functional present, landscape as art against landscape as expedience, nature as resource against nature as sacred. Tradition is opposed to innovation, function to meaning, ecology to art. Is nature sacred *or* profane? *Can* tradition and innovation be reconciled? Should landscape be shaped as *art* or as *sustaining habitat*? The answer to each of these questions is the same, yes and yes and yes. For these apparent dichotomies are neither incompatible nor antithetical. What is the use of beautiful gardens if the larger landscape is degraded and the planet is dying? Of what benefit to humans is the health of the planet if the everyday world is barren?

Among the vital questions, posed and repeated, are these: Is nature a sacred entity and are humans one with all living creatures, or is nature a wilderness refuge requiring protection from the ravages of humankind? Or is nature just a reservoir of resources intended for human use? Is nature a web of processes that link garden, city, and globe? Is there a history common to all in a society or is there no shared past? Whose history should be remembered and celebrated in public places? Is art separate from the everyday, or rooted in the normal processes of living? Is art the province of the expert, or can, and does, everyone participate? Should places assert or exert power over people or empower them? The opposing answers to such questions lead to opposing natures, histories, arts, powers.

Tensions and contradictions in landscape architecture also stem from the intellectual biases and unresolved conflicts among the disciplines it draws from: agriculture (gardening, horticulture, forestry), engineering, architecture and fine arts, science (ecology), each based upon disparate ideas about the relationships of human to the nonhuman. Agriculture, engineering, and architecture rest upon the concept that nature can be improved upon, ecologists rely on the role of observing, rather than acting upon, nature. To gardeners (and by extension to farmers, horticulturalists, and foresters), humans are stewards charged with managing plants, animals, and their habitats for human ends, for sustenance and pleasure, and nature is both material and process, something to be reckoned with. To most engineers, nature consists of forces to be controlled or overcome. To artists and architects, nature is generally not an active agent but something to perceive, a source of inspiration and of symbolic forms to be drawn upon, a scene to be represented, a site to occupy and transform. To many ecologists, all of the above are interlopers in nature, human disturbers deflecting nature from its ideal, self-regulating state. Fortunately, there are exceptions. Engineers like Ken Wright of Denver have devised drainage and floodways that deflect or adjust to flowing water. Architects like Glenn Murcutt and Richard Le Plastrier regard landscape processes as active agents and design their buildings to respond to wind, water, light, and heat. Artists like Robert Smithson, James Turrell, Alan Sonfist, Newton and Helen Harrison, and Doug Hollis have engaged processes of erosion, water flow, light, wind, sound, and plant growth in their works.

Further accentuating these differences among disciplines is their recognition of, and homage to, different types of authorities in their understanding of the world and in justifying their actions. Most derive authority to some degree from tradition, from systems of rules, and from charismatic leadership, but give each differing weight. Historians of science have shown that science, too, is tradition-bound (until the next paradigm shift), its course swayed by powerful personalities and political and socioeconomic forces, not reason alone; nevertheless, science claims to recognize only rational proofs as a legitimate authority. Architecture, for its part, has long acknowledged the traditional authority of certain exemplary buildings (the Pantheon, the Villa Savoye) and of certain styles (for example, classicism and the vernacular), and most architects seek legitimacy through reference to a stylistic tradition or an original model. Artists, today, claim greater license to flaunt authority than do architects or scientists, and society responds by granting them greater freedom; artists are seldom held as accountable for their works as architects or engineers are.

Landscape architects draw from each of these and from other disciplines, often without examining and reconciling the contradictory beliefs and traditions. This habit of borrowing and applying theory and methods without resolution often places disparate ways of knowing and working in hostile juxtaposition.[2] In programs of landscape architecture, it is not unusual to find students with backgrounds in horticulture, art, architecture, engineering, and ecology all in the same class, with the department's faculty including members of several of these disciplines. Mating these fields in a single faculty is, at best, a rich marriage of ideas, at worst, a shotgun wedding, and few schools or individuals have succeeded in combining these diverse sources critically and inventively. As a result, too few built landscapes fuse the potential contributions of art, science, gardening, engineering. In 1957, Sylvia Crowe described landscape architecture as a bridge between science and art, a profession whose greatest task is to "heal" the "breach between science and humanism, and between aesthetics and technology."[3] Forty years later, landscape architecture is still struggling to integrate its diverse roots.

The Authority of Nature

Reinhold Tuexen, head of the Central Office for Vegetation Mapping of the German Reich, declared, in 1939, that it was necessary to "cleanse the German landscape of unharmonious foreign substance." Subsequently, a team of botanists declared "a war of extermination" against the small forest plant *Impatiens parviflora*, saying, "As with the fight against Bolshevism, our entire occidental culture is at stake, so with the fight against this Mongolian invader, an essential element of this culture, namely, the beauty of our home forest [is at stake]."[4] Under National Socialism, earlier ideas of the natural garden were taken up and their political implications expanded; one designer described, in 1936, an obligation to design "blood-and-soil-connected gardens."[5] These ideas became part of official policy as "Rules for the Design of the Landscape" developed by Heinrich Himmler's staff in 1942 for the so-called Incorporated Eastern Territories of Germany (taken from Poland in 1939): "It is not sufficient to settle our people in those areas and to eliminate foreign people. Instead the area must be given a structure which corresponds to our type of being."[6]

Such exploitation ought to have dispelled forever the illusion of innocence surrounding "nature," one of the most powerfully loaded, ideological words in the English and the German languages. Those who cite nature and the natural to justify their designs or to evoke a sense of goodness rarely examine precisely what such words mean to them. Most are ignorant of the ideological minefields they tread.

"Attack of the Killer Weeds," announced the cover of the Philadelphia *Inquirer*'s Sunday magazine in 1996, alluding to the lead article, "Aliens Among Us."[7] The conflict over the use of native versus "exotic" plants, debated over nearly one hundred years among landscape architects and environmentalists, and among ecological restorationists and horticulturists, has grown increasingly strident. Once confined to the pages of professional journals, it has now spilled over into the popular press. Is it a coincidence that there is a growing movement to support "native" plants and eradicate exotic "invaders," like the Norway maple, just at the time of mounting anger at illegal immigrants and at multinational corporations that move U.S. factories and jobs away to countries with low pay scales? Polemical rhetoric plays on fear of the alien, provokes opposition as well as support, and ironically obscures the real problems some species pose.[8]

Landscape authors who call their work natural or ecological cite the authority of nature to justify their selection of some materials or plants and the exclusion of others, and to support their decisions to arrange material in certain patterns, and to tend the result in certain ways. To call a landscape natural implies the existence of other, unnatural, landscapes that are, presumably, wrong. Yet quite different sorts of landscape designs have been cited by others as natural, much as God is claimed by opposing nations. In fact some designs invoke nature as if it were divine authority. To Frank Lloyd Wright, nature was the manifestation of God: "Nature should be spelled with a capital 'N,' not because Nature is God but because all that we can learn of God we will learn from the body of God, which we call Nature."[9] But for Wright, nature included humans, and the aim of his designs was "truly no less than the creation of man as a perfect 'flower of Nature.'"[10] For many people today, nature is devoid of humans and human constructions.

So, too, the authority of science is cited to augment or substitute for the authority of nature or God. To most landscape architects ecological science is a vital source of principles for landscape design; indeed, the adoption of ideas from ecology contributed to a renewal of that discipline in the 1960s. But, for some, ecology is the primary authority for determining the natural, and, therefore, the only correct way to design landscapes. To these, ecology's most extreme practitioners, ecological design is deterministic; the laws they cite are couched in terms that recall religious dogma. In recent years, debates over what constitutes a "truly ecological practice of landscape architecture" have escalated with certain groups accusing others of "nonecological" behavior.[11] Bitter quarrels have ensued over the proper materials, styles, and methods of ecological landscape design, some advocating the exclusive use of native, and rejection of naturalized, plants, some urging eradication of exotic invaders and condemning planting of foreign species. Some labor to conceal the artifice of their works; others celebrate the human capacity to transform the landscape. Some honor the role of reason in design and promote science as the sole source of truth about nature; others trust personal intuition or even revelation and reject science as a reliable way of knowing.

Such conflicts about competing sources of authority and conflicting ideas of nature engender confusion about certain issues: whether humans are outside or inside nature, whether human influence is, inevitably, destructive or, potentially, beneficial, whether one can know an objective nature apart from human values. Does authority come from principles, tradition, and precedent, from the way things have always been done or were done in some idealized past or by exemplary earlier models, or does authority rest in a rational system of rules or laws, which can be tested, proved, or explained? Some trust the claims of a charismatic leader.[12] Such differences in basic assumptions are so fundamental that resolving these conflicts seems impossible. And yet, clarifying some differences and dispelling confusion is not impossible. Not impossible, that is, if those engaged in the debate define their terms. If someone invokes the authority of nature, implying the right to speak for nature, who has conferred that privilege and why? And what is nature anyway? And how determine its authority? Or balance conflicting claims made in nature's name?

Nature is an abstraction, a set of ideas for which many cultures have no one name, "a singular name for the real multiplicity of things and living processes."[13] A. O. Lovejoy found sixty-six meanings of the words *nature* and *natural* in literature and philosophy from the time of the ancient Greeks to the eighteenth century.[14] The abstract quality of the word also tends to deny the role of the nonhuman as exerting an active force upon the world, on the one hand, while inviting personification (Nature's revenge) of nature, on the other.

The competing claims conceal real paradox. Nature is, in fact, both given and constructed. *Nature*, Raymond Williams called "perhaps the most complex word in the language," "the inherent force which directs either the world or human beings or both" and "the material world itself, taken as including or not including human beings."[15] From the Latin *natura*, which comes from *nasci*, to be born, nature is linked to other words from the same root, *nascent, innate, native, nation*; in English, as in French and Latin, nature originally described the essential or given character of something and only later did it become an independent noun.

As human cultures describe themselves as reflections of nature, so their ideas of nature mirror that culture, their concept of normal or abnormal, right or wrong. The idea of the Fall, of humanity expelled from paradise, assumes that a state of grace within nature is no longer available to human beings. Nor has science been immune; ecologists who describe the "harmony" of nature and the succession of plant "communities" from pioneers to stable climax forest assume an implicit model for human society.[16] Ecology, anthropology, and garden design are laced with Edenic narratives, nostalgic stories of an original state in which humans and nonhumans lived in peace, perfection, and innocence, followed by a state of expulsion, of humans anyway, from nature. In some such scenarios, the most "primitive," least "civilized" "native" peoples are seen as more worthy and as morally superior to the more "civilized" in their relation to nature.[17]

Even in a particular time and place, no agreement exists on the natural way of doing things. Wright and Jens Jensen, fellow residents of Chicago and Wisconsin, friends throughout most of their lives, agreed that nature was *the* authority for design and sought to articulate the moral messages or "sermons" they read in hills and valleys, rivers and trees. And yet the two "argued incessantly about the nature of nature," about what form a natural garden should take.[18] Wright had contempt for "some sentimental feeling about animals and grass and trees and out-of-doors generally," but revered nature as an internal ideal, the very "'nature' of God."[19] It was the task of the architect to bring the outer, often imperfect, form into closer conformity with an inner ideal, its nature, its essence. Wright derived his principles for design from what he saw as the underlying structure of flowers, trees, and terrain; his landscape designs were often abstract versions of actual regional landscapes of prairie or desert.

Jensen's obsession, on the other hand, was to protect and promote the native features of regional landscapes. He saw a correspondence between a region's climate, physiography, and flora and its human inhabitants; landscape, he believed, fostered, then symbolized, a relationship between people and place. His published works do not suggest that he believed humans could improve upon the native landscape: "Nature talks more finely and more deeply when left alone."[20] He revered the primitive, and found his "main source of inspiration . . . in the unadulterated, untouched work of the great Master."[21] Jensen sought to imitate the outward appearance of the local landscape, its meadows, woodlands, and riverbanks: "Through generations of evolution our native landscape becomes a part of us, and out of this we may form fitting compositions for our people."[22] Many of his ideas, such as a correlation between nature and nation and his advocacy of native plants were common in Europe and North America.[23] Contemporary ecological theories drew parallels between plant and animal communities and human communities.[24] German landscape architects under National Socialism carried the relationship between native plants and folk to ideological extremes, using native plants and natural gardens to represent the Nazi political agenda, and there is some evidence that Jensen was sympathetic to at least some of these ideas.[25]

Whatever nature means to landscape architects, they tend to care about it, for the beliefs and values it represents tend to lie at the heart of their decision to enter the profession. For the past seven years, I have asked my graduate students, "What is nature?" Among their responses are clashing perspectives: nature was given as a trust to humans by God; nature is trees and rocks, everything except humans and the things humans make; nature is a place where one cannot see the hand of humans, a place to be alone; nature consists of creative and life-sustaining processes which connect everything in the physical and biological worlds, including humans; nature is a cultural construct with no meaning or existence outside human society; nature is something that cannot be known; Nature is God. The experiential and spiritual aspects of nature are cited frequently, and nature as material resource is seldom mentioned.[26]

Ian McHarg's *Design with Nature*, published in 1969, stimulated fundamental changes in the teaching and practice of landscape architecture. McHarg advocated systematic application of a set of rules derived from ecological science and demonstrated its value in professional projects.[27] His charismatic personality and polemical power captured the attention of the profession and the public; he was instrumental in the acceptance of ideas others had also explored. Today, more than thirty years later, many of these innovations, once seen as radical, are common practice. However, his claim that science is the only defensible authority for landscape design has provoked equally dogmatic reactions from those who seek to promote landscape architecture as an art form and who have set that approach in opposition to "the ecological movement and its detrimental consequences for design."[28]

Is ecology a science (a way of describing the world)? Is it a cause (a mandate for moral action)? An aesthetic (a norm for beauty)? It is important to distinguish the insights of ecology, the science, from ecology as a source of prescriptive principles and aesthetic values. The perception of the world as a complex network of relations, with humans as but one part of that web, has been a significant contribution of ecology, but there has been a tendency to jump from such insights to prescription and proscription, to cite ecology as an authority much as nature was cited in the past as the source of laws for landscape design and as providing a single norm. To Laurie Olin this approach is "a new deterministic and doctrinaire view of what is 'natural' and 'beautiful'" reflecting a "chilling, close-minded stance of moral certitude." [29]

The Authority of the Past

Appeal to the past for authority is as problematic as appeal to nature. Because the history of twentieth-century landscape architecture has been told largely as a history of forms rather than of ideas and expression, especially in the history of naturalistic or ecological design, implicit motives and values implicit in design have generally remained unexamined. Gardens built to imitate nature may appear similar yet express different, even divergent, values and concepts. Although the Fens and Riverway in Boston and Columbus Park in Chicago were built to resemble scenery native to their region, and although both are frequently cited as precedents for landscape restoration today, the motivations that underlay them were different in important ways not usually understood. [30]

The Fens and Riverway, designed by Frederick Law Olmsted and built in the 1880s to 1890s, were revolutionary in function and form, their so-called wild appearance in contrast to prevailing formal and pastoral styles. [31] Built on the site of polluted tidal flats and floodplains, they were designed to purify water and protect adjacent land from flooding. They incorporated an interceptor sewer, a parkway, and Boston's first streetcar line, and together formed a landscape *system* to accommodate the flow of water, removal of wastes, and movement of people. Olmsted conceived them as a new type of integrated, multifunctional, urban open space, one he took care to distinguish from a park. This skeleton of woods and wetland, road, sewer, and public transit structured the growing city and its suburbs. The Fens and Riverway were a fusion of art, agriculture, engineering, and science.

Jensen, designing Columbus Park (1916) in Chicago thirty years later to symbolize a prairie landscape, created a large meadow, excavated a meandering lagoon, and planted groves of trees to represent the Illinois landscape: prairie, prairie river, and forest edge. [32] All the plants used in the park were native to Illinois; they belonged, as Jensen put it. [33] In outward appearance, the prairie river looked much like the Fens, as photographs within about a decade of construction testify. Like Olmsted, Jensen intended his project to expose city residents to the beneficial influence of rural scenery, particularly those unable to travel to faroff places or unwelcome in "neighboring fields, woods, pond-sides, river-banks, valleys, or hills."[34] Yet Jensen's aims and his goals were quite different from Olmsted's. His agenda at Columbus Park, as elsewhere, was to bring people, especially "the growing minds" of youth, into contact with their "home environment," for "We are molded into a people by the thing we live with day after day."[35] Every region ought to display the beauty of its local landscape: "This encourages each race, each country, each state, and each county to bring out the best within its borders."[36] In *Siftings*, Jensen elaborated on environmental influences, attributing certain characteristics among populations of European countries and American regions to the influence of their landscapes. He claimed to see each regional landscape as beautiful in its own way, but he repeatedly exposed a prejudice for the superiority of northern regions and their peoples: "Environmental influences of the hot south have almost destroyed the strong and hardy characteristics of . . . northern people."[37] He drew parallels between people and plants and advocated that only species native to a place be used: "To me no plant is more refined than that which belongs. There is no comparison between native plants and those imported from foreign shores which are, and shall always remain so, novelties."[38]

Olmsted, too, believed that environment influenced human behavior, convinced that contemplation of "natural scenery" had beneficial physical, mental, and moral effects, and that lack of such opportunity could lead to depression and mental illness.[39] But in constructing such scenery, he advocated the use of hardy, exotic plants along with native species, arguing with Charles Sprague Sargent, who opposed using nonnative plants in the Riverway.[40] The upshot was that only native species were planted on the Brookline side of the Riverway (where Sargent had the authority of approval), but a mixture of native and nonnative species was planted on the Boston side (where Olmsted did). The primary purpose of the Riverway was "to abate existing nuisances, avoid threatened dangers and provide for the permanent, wholesome and seemly disposition of the drainage of Muddy River Valley."[41] Jensen's work posed no such goals.

The natural garden movement of the early part of the twentieth century, which Jensen supported, and today's ecological design movement seem to have much in common. Both stress native plants and plant communities as material and model for garden design. And yet, deep differences in the ideas of nature have guided the two movements. In the United States, natural garden design in the early part of the century was part of a larger context of regionalism expressed in art, literature, and politics, a populist movement promoting local roots over the increasing power of the federal government, the growth of national corporations, and the influence of foreign styles.[42] Jensen, in his focus on regional landscapes and native plants, never discussed the value of plants, animals, or biological and physical processes apart from human purpose; his anthropocentric perspective is a contrast to late twentieth-century environmentalism, in which animals, plants, and ecosystems have been accorded value, even legal rights, not for their worth to humans alone, but for themselves.[43]

Among landscape architects the most bitter recent debates have been waged over the authority of nature versus that of art; the authority of past landscapes has been cited mainly in defense of one or the other position, each side constructing its own pantheon of past authorities: "Capability" Brown, Olmsted, and Jensen, for example, versus Le Nôtre, Daniel Burnham, and Thomas Church. The classical tradition of architecture has occupied a similar position among Western architects to that of nature among landscape architects. Much as different landscape architects are inspired by and appeal to nature for authority, so architects appeal to the authority of a classical style in buildings and landscapes, including particular exemplary models. Architects have returned to classical buildings and spaces repeatedly for inspiration and authority, from Palladio to Jefferson to Gunnar Asplund to Albert Speer to Robert Venturi. A classical style has been employed at different times and places for quite different purposes, all appealing to the past for authority, and serving primarily to identify the client with Greece and Rome. But as inheritor of what aspects of those cultures? Art? Philosophy? Democracy? Empire?

I was unprepared for the heated polemical debates among jurists on the Minnesota State Capitol Competition in 1986 over whether or not the new landscape should be in a classical style. "You are an ideologue," accused a fellow juror, a European architect, on the last day of the panel's deliberations for the Minnesota State Capitol Competition, following my support of a scheme he abhorred. By this time I had become inured to such attacks. At the first meeting of the jury, as we prepared to introduce ourselves, he had requested that we each identify our ideological positions so each would know where the others stood before the debate began. Expecting him to lay out a political position of some sort, I was surprised when he and another juror (also a European architect) professed their ideology as classicism.

The entries we had come to judge were proposals for the grounds of the Minnesota State Capitol Building, which had been built in the 1890s in neoclassical style. There were eleven members on the jury: two landscape architects, three architects, a city planner, and several politicians and local businessmen. This was a two-stage review: the first meeting was for two days, its object to select five finalists who would then develop their designs further; the second meeting would be several months later, to select the one to be built. There were more than three hundred entries, each consisting of two panels of drawings illustrating the design, all displayed on easels set up in the National Guard armory. We spent the first day reviewing all entries before assembling to compare notes toward the end of the afternoon and proceeding to narrow the field by eliminating many contestants from further consideration. The subsequent debates were among the least substantive and rational I have ever experienced on a competition jury, which normally affords the most challenging, stimulating, and heated of professional discussions. The two classicists supported those proposals that were in accord with their canon and dismissed those to which they were opposed, including any design in a modernist or contemporary style. The one proposal the classicists favored most was not a bad design, but several others they rejected out of hand were also worthy of consideration; their principal strategy seemed to be to eliminate competing schemes from consideration through appeals to the authority of the past, and further to flatter, ridicule, or intimidate other jurors to win support or cow the opposition, as needed. In the end, the Minnesota Capitol got a classical landscape.

Landscapes of memory are often polemical. Most reconstructions of past landscapes—Sturbridge Village in Massachusetts, Williamsburg in Virginia, and Disney's Main Street—take their authority from the past, but present a sanitized, sentimentalized version of past and present. So do places from which the past has been selectively stripped, like Philadelphia's Independence National Park, a zone of suspended time in a busy city. The core of that park is six large city blocks from which all traces of activity that occurred between 1800 and the 1970s are expunged, all of those buildings—factories, warehouses, stores, tenements—demolished. The remaining buildings, built before 1800 (or reconstructions), are scattered like headstones in a cemetery surrounded by a pastoral landscape of lawn and trees in one section of the park, and isolated within a monumental mall in the other. "Independence," as the National Park Service calls it, is the product of decades of bitter battles over what is significant about the past and how it should be represented. In the late nineteenth and early twentieth centuries, the focus was on Independence Hall and the Liberty Bell as national icons: first, on the reconstruction of the building itself, then, on creation of a proper setting for it. Proposals offered between 1915 and 1930 ranged from modest plazas across the street to a formal vista several blocks long to frame the building, with the Liberty Bell on a sort of altar in the center of a "Great Marble Court" surrounded by neoclassical buildings. From the 1930s on, the idea of a unified historic district grew, seen by some as a tool for revitalizing the surrounding area. Throughout the controversies two things remained constant: the regard for Independence and Carpenters' halls as national shrines. All the plans put forward for Independence included both buildings as foci. The landscape of Independence reflects changing ideas over the course of a century, of history, the nature of the authority it confers, and the role of historic preservation.

The Authority of Function and Expedience

Designers of the modernist architecture and urban design that dominated the landscape of American cities redeveloped from the 1950s through the 1970s invoked the authority of function to overhaul what they saw as "obsolete" neighborhoods and city centers. Entire blocks of older buildings were torn down, in some cases entire neighborhoods; streets were obliterated, and new high-rise buildings went up, surrounded by large, open, windswept plazas. Every city I have ever visited, with the exception of Copenhagen, has many such barren places. Copenhagen avoided similar mistakes by deliberately excluding massive redevelopment from the city's center, and by deciding not to build expressways on the site of the lakes that ring the city along the old fortifications; for years the city looked old-fashioned, with its low skyline punctuated by church steeples and spires of public buildings; now it is recognized as being particularly livable.

Ironically, single-purpose public works, like highways and housing, when pursued in single-minded concern for narrowly defined functional efficiency, often produce dysfunctional conditions. New expressways built between suburbs and central cities from the 1950s on destroyed many old neighborhoods and funneled traffic onto downtown streets, leading to more congestion and demolition downtown to provide more parking. Whole neighborhoods were deemed outmoded and unfit for modern living: "an obsolete neighborhood . . . and a new plan," declared one report. In this case, the authority of function was invoked to condemn lower-income housing in Boston's West End, a neighborhood described as "a defect to the city in terms of cost of services versus tax revenue," to make way for more "efficient apartments," open lawn, and parking lots in Charles River Park, a new upper-income development.[44] Houses were "machines for living," and from the 1940s through the 1960s, old houses in urban neighborhoods were torn down and replaced with new public housing in high-rise towers surrounded by parking lots and lawn. By the 1970s, many of these were deemed unlivable and hence demolished; the most infamous case, the award-winning Pruitt-Igo Public Housing Project in St. Louis, consisting of high-rise towers designed by the architect Minoru Yamasaki, was deliberately blown up in 1976.

It is difficult to convey the emotional impact of such wholesale destruction wrought by urban renewal to someone who did not experience it firsthand. I visited West Philadelphia in June 1969 to look for an apartment, and when I returned to begin graduate school at the University of Pennsylvania in September, entire blocks of homes between campus and my apartment were gone, and cranes were in place, building new towers. During the next year dozens of additional blocks were erased, the empty tracts bounded by temporary white rail fences, the ubiquitous sign of the Philadelphia Redevelopment Authority. In those years, white, wooden rails and open land seemed to be everywhere around the city. Many vacant blocks were not to be built on for twenty years; some are empty today. A friend told me of the trauma of losing her neighborhood, still strongly felt after thirty years. She had grown up in West Philadelphia on a block of rowhouses where she knew everyone; all of her friends lived within a few blocks of each other. At fourteen, after a trip to Boston in summer of 1968, she was shocked when her mother met her at the train station and took her home to North Philadelphia, an entirely different part of the city. Her home and entire community had been wrecked and cleared, people scattered; all that remained of the many blocks was one huge open lot, no streets, not even a brick left. "My mother must have known before I left for Boston, but never told me. I never saw my friends again. I still don't understand why it happened." The lot remained open for many years, until a small shopping mall was built. Such events happened in cities all over the United States in the 1950s and 1960s; the sociologist Herbert Gans estimates that at least a million families were displaced and low-cost dwellings demolished between 1950 and 1980 (not including households removed by urban expressway construction).[45] Many forced to move felt grief for their lost homes even when their physical living conditions were improved.[46] So much was destroyed so fast, so many historic buildings and districts, so many social networks and place memories; the reaction was not long in coming.

In 1961, Jane Jacobs opened *The Death and Life of Great American Cities* with a salvo: "This book is an attack on current city planning and rebuilding."[47] Her book documents examples of functionalism run amok in urban landscapes, and recounts tales of protest, including her own street's campaign to prevent city engineers from lopping ten feet off the sidewalks in order to widen the road and improve traffic flow. In many cities, protests against clearances halted highway construction, but a residue of distrust for planners and city officials still remains in inner-city neighborhoods. Highways and high-rise towers are still read, in some places, as polemical landscapes, as symbols of urban renewal. So are grass and parks: lands cleared were frequently sowed with grass seed; parks were sometimes built as compensation for properties taken for highways, many on the sites of former homes.[48]

Suburban landscapes, too, exhibit the pursuit of function and expedience at the expense of livability: short cul-de-sacs are barren expanses of asphalt, their dimensions dictated by the space it takes for a fire engine to turn rather than by the demands of sociability or play. Designers and residents in many places have successfully protested such regulations (fire engines are told to back up). Local commercial and corporate landscapes increasingly are versions of the chain-store phenomenon, with attendant uniformity of product. Laurie Olin describes how designs for new office parks, rooted in the identity of their region's landscapes, have been foiled by fast-track, large-scale construction firms that work for the same client corporations all over the country and, citing the authority of expedience, are unwilling or unable to adopt local materials and motifs.[49]

The Authority of Art

Richard Serra's *Tilted Arc* was a curving, tilted wall of steel plate, 120 feet long and 12 feet high; it spanned Jacob Javits Plaza at the base of a federal office building in Manhattan. Designed specifically for the site and built with public funds as part of a public arts program in 1981, it was removed just eight years later, following hearings, convened in 1985, provoked by opponents of the work who claimed that workers in the office building despised it as menacing and ugly. In the hearings, the artist and his supporters invoked the authority of art: since it was site-specific to remove it would be to destroy it as a work of art, to render it a mere heap of rusted steel; to do so would be an act of vandalism. The opposition maintained that this space was the only outdoor place in which workers could sit and eat lunch, that the occupation of the space by the sculpture precluded other uses. The attack on *Tilted Arc* in the name of function was ironic since the sculpture was itself a critique of the plaza built in 1967. Like many such spaces, Jacob Javits Plaza was large, paved, and open, elevated above the surrounding sidewalks, cut off by planters and walls, the only sunny spot occupied by an empty fountain (turned off to prevent water, whipped by winds, from spraying passersby). The old plaza asserted the power of bureaucracy, the new one that of a cultural elite. Users were well served by neither.

On one level the celebrated controversy pitted the authority of art against that of function, but it was also a clash of political power and ideas over the role of public art and who should control it.[50] Serra and his supporters advocated the autonomy of art, that public art should not be bound by practical and political considerations external to the work itself. In interviews, Serra has described how he strives to create "anti-environments" and how, with *Tilted Arc*, he intended "to dislocate or alter the decorative function of the plaza" so that once it was installed the space would be "understood primarily as a function of the sculpture."[51] Those who opposed *Tilted Arc* on political grounds did so for different reasons: some objected that it failed to symbolize patriotic values or justify civic authority; others protested the use of public funds for art.[52] In the 1980s, such criticisms were not limited to *Tilted Arc*. Critics used many of the same arguments to denounce the design for the Vietnam Veterans Memorial, proposed in 1981, the same year *Tilted Arc* was installed, mistaking similarities in style—abstract, nonfigurative, simplified form—for kindred meanings.[53] Ultimately, the public embraced one and rejected the other.

Tilted Arc was a watershed for many public artists; as Martha Schwartz comments, "The use of the plaza was subverted for the artist's vision, and whether that subversion is appropriate for public art turned out to be a very valuable discussion. I changed my mind during that sequence of events about what public art should be. The best public art is art that can speak on many levels, and if you choose not to be engaged with it, you don't have to be."[54] Schwartz, the landscape architect/artist chosen to redesign Javits Plaza, intended her work to be "the antithesis of *Tilted Arc*—less self-important and self-referential." Rather than highlighting the alienating aspects of the open plaza at the base of the office tower, she remade the place entirely to redress the dreary conditions to which Serra had so strongly responded.[55]

Schwartz, herself, designs polemical landscapes and cites avant-garde artists as her inspiration and authority (not Serra); she and others who have promoted landscape as art describe their opposition to function or nature as sole authority.[56] Compared to *Tilted Arc*, her work has elicited tame public reaction. The professional response is another story. Her Bagel Garden provoked outrage when it was featured on the cover of *Landscape Architecture* in 1980; it was accused of being elitist, called an insult. Many objections to it were similar to those raised later against *Tilted Arc* and the Vietnam Veterans Memorial, even though the Bagel Garden was her own garden not a public place. Much of Schwartz's work has been for private clients, as has that of Peter Walker, one of the most influential advocates of landscape as art. His corporate clients have given him scope to realize vast landscapes inspired by Vaux, Versailles, and Chantilly, such as the office estates in Texas for IBM at Solano and Clearlake. The clients reap the prestige such art confers; like Louis XIV, IBM has territorial ambitions, and the landscapes attest to its power.

The Authority of Power

Powerful patrons have long employed the authority of nature, of the past, of function and expedience, and of art in landscapes to demonstrate and legitimize their claims. They have also used landscape to display their dominance and wealth: through the construction of lavish gardens, parks, palaces, and temples to which they control entry; through the erection of monuments of superhuman scale that make an ordinary person seem insignificant and powerless, or powerful only as a member of a group; through the foreclosure of private property or enclosure of common ground for private purposes. English gentry who enclosed lands once open and used communally and then prohibited entry were invoking the authority of power; the hedges, landscape gardens, and sheep pastures they made were symbols of that authority. It was the same when Napoleon III and his prefect Baron Haussmann had entire sections of Paris demolished for new boulevards and buildings to be built in their place.

Mussolini's First World War Memorial and Cemetery at Redipuglia was designed to display the authority of power, as were the Mall in Washington, D.C., the palace and gardens of Versailles, and the Escorial in Spain. In all such places, composition points to the source of power, axial symmetry is usually the principal clue. At Redipuglia, a link is made between the glory of Italy, its military power, and God, as defined by the axis between carved words at the entrance, the tomb of the general at the base of the terraces, and the cross at the top. At Versailles, the king's bedroom was at the center and the chapel to one side; in the Escorial, palace of the Spanish kings, "the royal apartments were arranged around the chancel," conveying the message that "power, to be legitimate, requires piety and orthodoxy."[57] On the Mall in Washington, the Capitol, not the White House, is at the head of the primary axis, an indication that the primary power is vested in the collective, elected representatives of the nation's citizens. At Versailles Louis XIV entertained guests and impressed them with French military prowess; the gardens were displays of engineering incorporating the vocabulary of siege warfare: patterns of terracing like battlement walls, sequences of elevations and ditches, canals resembling moats. Louis XIV, who centralized and professionalized the French army, deployed soldiers as laborers to construct the gardens of Versailles.[58]

In the 1980s, Boston's inner neighborhoods were riddled with vacant land, abandoned buildings, closed fire stations and libraries. The state of these neighbor-

Cultivating paradox: Bird Sanctuary. Bloedel Reserve. Bainbridge Island, Washington.

hoods was invisible from downtown, but downtown prosperity, symbolized by gleaming new towers, could readily be seen from the neighborhoods, providing a stark and disturbing juxtaposition. The new towers, in times of high unemployment and declining local social services, were a daily reminder to residents of inner-city neighborhoods that they had not shared in Boston's economic growth. But the boom was a mixed blessing even downtown. Most new buildings that transformed Boston's skyline in the 1970s and 1980s were private projects constructed in a vacuum of public vision. Rather than contributing to the public realm, they often degraded it, creating dark, windy canyons and barren plazas, icy and windswept in winter, sun-baked in summer. Some buildings, ostensibly public, were and are still really private enclaves guarded by private police. The sumptuous materials lavished on their interiors contrasted vividly with the potholed, trash-filled streets and narrow, broken sidewalks outside.

The political scientist Harold Lasswell, late in his life, warned of the consequences of what he calls "the architecture of opulence—of sleek and commanding office buildings, apartment houses, and other structures"—to contribute to "long-run political destabilization" in that such architecture operates on a worldwide scale to reassure the rich, the strong, and the self-confident and to provoke and radicalize the poor and the weak.[59] He alludes to examples in the past in which powerful ruling elites were lulled by the landscapes of power they inhabited into supposing that the system supporting their privileges was equally robust;

they were, in consequence, unaware of how fragile their base of power. "The disaffected multitudes of our day," Lasswell writes, "are no novelty in the history of civilized systems of public order, save that they are stimulated by instant communication to act in concert on a widening scale."[60]

Landscape polemics at first may win attention for a neglected issue of significance, but, persisting, they harden into dogma, polarizing and leading to loss and fragmentation. Modernist dogma, which claimed to worship function and re jected history, ridiculed tradition, ignored memory, and banned ornament, provoked the historicist polemics of the classicists at the Minnesota State Capitol Competition. The single-minded pursuit of function and expedience that produced the urban clearances of the 1950s and 1960s sparked urban riots, in turn. Environmentalist dogma, which claimed nature as the sole determinant and authority for landscape design, incited others to proclaim the authority of art instead. Polemics spawn polemics. Polemical landscapes produce a counterreaction, if not immediately, then in subsequent generations. The purpose of polemics is not simply to persuade, but to mobilize the converted and set them apart. Today's struggles to redefine nature, history, and art, the efforts of others to follow the course of expedience alone and to invest as little as possible—all are reflected in landscape. There is contest without consensus.

Transcending Polemics

Nature, Art, Past, Function: Bloedel

In a forest, on an island, in a sound, near a city are a series of gardens within a garden devoted to environmental education. The Bird Sanctuary, Anteroom, Garden of Reflection, and Garden of Planes at Bloedel Reserve near Seattle tell stories about identity and difference, freedom and control, tradition and invention, use, abuse, and renewal.

A path leads through meadow, down through woods to a dredged pond edged by trees—the Bird Sanctuary, set between forest and meadow. Small islands make the pond appear larger and more mysterious. By the shore, the water is deep, brownish-black; further out, wind-driven ripples, swan/duck-swimming ripples collide, fracturing its surface into kaleidoscopic greens. Red alders line the shore in clumps of twos, threes, fours, and fives—like sprouts sprung up from the same old stump. As soil slides into the pond, trees lean in, then struggle to stay erect, reaching up to light, their leaves flickering. The trees mark a refuge at the edge of an open meadow that slopes up to sky. The way islands lie, poplars clump, meadow slopes looks deliberate; a feeling mind was at work in their creation. The Bird Sanctuary is an "artful wilderness to perplex the scene," dug, planted, inhabited.[61]

A path in the sanctuary leads from pond through forest to the Anteroom, a wooded moss garden, where it winds around enormous tree stumps. Clumps of alders grow out of the stumps, their many overlapping roots grasping woody car-

Cultivating paradox: Anteroom. Bloedel Reserve. Bainbridge Island, Washington.

casses and fallen branches. Ground, stumps, lower trunks are covered by thick moss: bright green, deep green, upright, creeping, shaggy green growing down from bark. Layers of soft, fuzzy growth, some of long fuzzy tendrils, other mosses branched like tiny leaves or twigs, form a thick cushion. The place has a graveyard air; branches lie like bones buried beneath moss.

The garden is both memento mori and memorial to the forest that was logged so long ago. It juxtaposes decay and rebirth; it celebrates both artful construction and organic regeneration, the power of life to renew a forest once cut for timber. And the paradox grows the more one knows. Bloedel Reserve is funded by a family fortune derived from the timber industry, the site first logged to fund a Territorial University for Washington, with the sale of timber paying for some of the original buildings on the new campus. When the property was sold, the proceeds were used to finance the university's first academic programs.

From the Anteroom's moss garden, the path leads in to the Reflection Garden, a clearing in the forest bounded by a rectangular frame of clipped yew hedges, a mythic space of water set in grass within yew within forest. The top of the hedge, sheared flat, catches a line of light. The long rectangular pool reflects the dark forest and reveals the groundwater beneath the spongy turf. A tree with three trunks holds the eye, an icon at one end. Like the trees beyond the wall at Ryoanji, in Kyoto, the trees of the forest beyond the hedge press into the space.

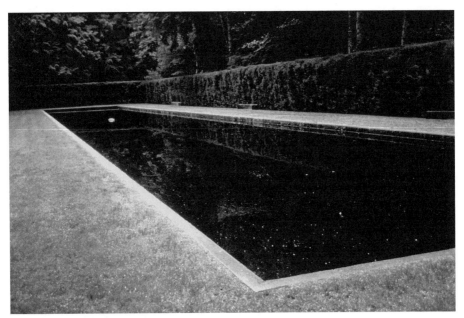

Cultivating paradox: Reflection Garden. Bloedel Reserve. Bainbridge Island, Washington.

Like pools in French gardens, for example, the one in Courances, dark water brims against green grass. The hedge, clipped on one side, grows freely on the other—an oxymoron. Many individual yews make one, clipped, mass; thousands of branches and twigs intermingle and merge to form walls both massive and opaque, yet delicate and transparent. Viewed obliquely, the plane of yews is dense green; seen head on, it is but a screen, the colors and shapes of plants beyond clearly visible through branches and twigs. The gardens' designer, Richard Haag, calls this a Zen space, and it is paradoxical indeed, a container of emptiness.

Beyond, the Garden of Planes, like the Anteroom and the Garden of Reflection, was once a fusion of Japanese tradition and contemporary Western art. In contrast to the "Don't worry, be happy" story of World Showcase at Disney's EPCOT, where the tensions between identity and diversity have been denied recognition, the Garden of Planes, in its original version, was perplexing, too difficult for visitors to understand. Several years ago the union of identities was erased, and the garden recast into a trite version of a Japanese garden. There is now no perplexity, no difficult questions posed, no responses prompted—except in the contrast between the clichéd banality of this garden and the other three.

The first three gardens at Bloedel are stories about the use, abuse, and renewal of landscape. They do not return the site to some imagined, ideal condition before humans cut the forest, but create a garden in which the evidence of human use—the tree stumps, for example—is incorporated into the whole. These three gardens draw their power from ideas of nature, from past garden traditions, from art, transcending polemics, making the case for an artful, humanist environmentalism, an antidote to the self-hate that underlies so much environmentalism, its misanthropy. They present paradox, thereby provoking reflection.

Cultivating Paradox

Now is a time for telling new tales, for retelling old dilemmas: how to live in the world *and* preserve it; how to sustain tradition *and* foster invention; how to promote freedom *and* cultivate order; how to forge identity *and* value difference; how to appreciate the parts *and* grasp the whole. Paradox, the fusion of seeming contradictions, has never been more critical. Apparent oppositions need to be seen not as unsolvable dilemmas but as part of a larger whole; they need to be fused in undisguised dynamic tension without loss of distinctions, avoiding the tendency to reduce the discomfort that tension engenders. This is a function of art. For humans invent new stories and recover old ones to cope with threats to survival, and relate them in new landscapes. Stories compel, capture imagination, change attitudes and actions, bring about dramatic shifts within a single generation. Landscape stories explain the world, define a place in it, justify actions, guide behavior, reinforce through experience. Art amplifies the power of these stories, making them memorable.

Using / Keeping. Across Puget Sound from Bainbridge Island and Bloedel Reserve in Seattle, Gasworks Park artfully reclaims a derelict industrial site for a public park. Olmsted advocated removing all artificial constructions in projects such as Niagara, but the landscape architect Richard Haag proposed retaining many of the ghost structures of the old gas plant, some tall and rusting, like reminders or warnings, some painted red, blue, and yellow—sculptural landmarks and play structures, all surrounded by grass. Bloedel and Gasworks are two chapters in the same story, both exploited for energy and materials—vegetable and mineral—then reclaimed, both optimistic, affirming stories about landscape's use, abuse, and renewal. Neither tries to disguise the artifice; the use of antithesis in both is effective. The sites are gardens in which the remnants of human use—the rusting towers at Gasworks, the tree stumps at Bloedel—are incorporated into the whole, the one juxtaposed to green lawn and children's play, the other to plants' growth. Without continued reminding, people readily forget that constructed landscapes can appear wholly the product of nonhuman process. Antithesis reminds that people used the land, then helped build "natural" landscapes; oxymoron prompts the realization that humans participate in many of the world's processes, both destructive and creative.

Sustaining / Inventing. There is always a tension between the attachment to the familiar and traditional and the impulse to start fresh, invent, and revolt; in different times and places, one or the other may be emphasized. Urban renewal of American cities in the 1950s and 1960s broke with the past, ignored ongoing story lines—the context of place—and often failed to reproduce landscapes as habitable and lasting as the ones they replaced. Which traditional landscapes are chosen for preservation or destruction is significant: in Independence National Historical Park in Philadelphia only the structures built before 1800 were preserved, the rest destroyed; in what was East Berlin, much of the landscape built after 1945 and before 1989 is being eliminated. Tradition without invention is stultifying; invention without tradition is alienating. One looks to the past and sacrifices the future, the other breaks with the past and focuses on the future; both neglect and impoverish the present. Haag's Bloedel, G. N. Brandt's Mariebjerg Cemetery, and C. Th. Sørensen's Nærum Garden Colony—oxymorons all—both reinterpret tradition and invent. Bloedel fuses traditional garden motifs (formal pool, bounded outdoor room, moss garden) with the plants and history of the temperate rain forest of the Pacific Northwest. Brandt and Sørensen take the elements of the Danish landscape (grove, meadow, and hedge) and use them freely in strikingly inventive ways. Bloedel, Mariebjerg, and Nærum are landscape expressions that permit the visitor to feel simultaneously the rootedness of tradition and the stimulus of invention.

FREEING / CONTROLLING. Public housing projects like Mill Creek forbid those who live in them to alter them, but then so do the covenant-enforced regulations in affluent Irvine, California, that prescribe color of house (bland earth tones) and curtains (white).[62] Designers must learn how (and when) to relinquish control (whether to enable others to express themselves or to permit nature's processes to take their course) while still maintaining order. *Tree Nursery*, a painting by Paul Klee, shows one answer to this dilemma; it is a framework of horizontal lines within which much variety is accommodated without an overall chaotic effect. Klee was struck by what he called the "patchwork rhythm" of gardens in a landscape. The organization of community gardens like Aspen Farms in Philadelphia depends upon a similar gridded framework of plots, each garden plot a whole in itself, an improvisation on similar themes by different individuals, yet all part of a larger whole unified by materials, structure, and processes. In Granada, Spain, allotment gardens lie within the Alhambra/Generalife, a national landmark, held within a highly organized framework of walls and terraces, enlivening not detracting, complementing the formal gardens and courtyards, where vegetables and nut and fruit trees are planted among flowers and vines. In the Moorish garden no arbitrary boundaries separate the ornamental from the productive, the pleasurable from the pragmatic, the sacred from the secular.

FOSTERING IDENTITY / TREASURING DIVERSITY. Splice Garden presents two garden traditions, Japanese and French, in uneasy juxtaposition—a paradox; the Bloedel Garden of Reflection merges them in a single landscape—an oxymoron—that recalls, simultaneously, Ryoanji and Courances. Schwartz's garden holds no promise of reconciliation between the two identities; Haag presents the possibility of a new identity born out of diverse origins. For me, Schwartz's is a cautionary tale, Haag's an optimistic story. But fusing several identities into a new one is not the only way, nor is it, often, even preferable. It is easiest to appreciate diversity when that diversity does not impinge on one's own identity. Sørensen's design for Nærum Garden Colony and Brandt's design for Mariebjerg Cemetery are landscapes that foster identity and encourage the valuing of diversity. At Nærum, Sørensen resolved the most common source of conflict among gardeners in such communities: how high the common hedge should be clipped. In the normal layout, a grid, each garden shares a fence or hedge with three other gardens, one to either side and one at the back. By proposing freestanding elliptical gardens bounded by hedges, Sørensen permitted each gardener to make a choice, yet gave the overall community its own, striking identity. Brandt accomplished a similar purpose by providing a landscape frame (allées of trees, hedges bounding burial "rooms") that establishes a strong identity for the whole while allowing for the expression of different identities within each room.

At the scale of an entire downtown, Hayden's Power of Place project in Los Angeles interprets the urban landscape as an expression of the histories of many different peoples; it seeks to forge a new identity out of a recognition of diversity rather than celebrate a single history that leaves out many others. The dark side of identity is that it is often defined not by what people have in common, but against those others who are uncommon, those seen as different and, by implication, inferior or unimportant. Perceiving difference seems to be easier than sensing similarity. The human habit of constructing dualisms runs deep: us and them, city and wilderness, nature and culture. But, similarity and difference need to be held simultaneously: the us in the them and the them in the us; the role of natural processes in cities and of human imagination in wilderness; the symbiosis of nature and culture. We need to shift from a focus on the Other to a reverence for all life, to a delight in diversity.

The language of landscape highlights similarities while both acknowledging difference and permitting the assertion of individual and culture within a framework of commonality. Landscapes themselves harbor both genetic and cultural diversity, and collectively, human habitats comprise a record of diverse adaptations to similar conditions. That diversity of response is a resource to be treasured. Some day we may have to sift through the human repertoire for answers to difficult questions.

Dividing/Uniting. Children bused miles away to visit nature when all around them are the products of natural processes: water flowing, earth subsiding, wildflowers and sumacs growing in vacant lots, making soil from rubble and detritus. Such an absurdity comes from dividing the world into pieces, nature/not nature, and so on, habits that prevent a grasp of the whole. Children are being taught to value places outside their neighborhood, faraway places they might someday see. Or never.

To see similarities among disparate things is at the heart of creativity. Oxymorons enable us to achieve a difficult unity while experiencing the separateness of the parts. To deny oppositions, therefore, is not to avoid distinctions; to distinguish one need not oppose. Prospects are important to seeing and making things whole, perhaps a reason why sages and prophets climb hilltops to gain perspective. Now satellites have given us a view of Earth from space, from which to conceive the whole in new ways.

"Why are you here?" a neighborhood child challenged me one day. "It's not your neighborhood." "It depends on what you call a neighborhood," I replied. "It can be the block you live on or the place you work or the city you live in, or even your country. I don't live in Mill Creek, but my office is less than a five-minute drive away; I want my city to be the best place it can be, I want my country to offer all its children the same chance to learn and work." Later I heard her explain to her classmates, "She thinks the whole world is her neighborhood. She wants us to be the best we can be."

REAL/IDEAL. Utopias can be dark. Plants hanging from wires in Disney World's EPCOT, or native landscapes that are racially pure, are reminders that one person's ideal may be another's nightmare. Mill Creek Public Housing, and other such projects of the 1960s, now decaying, abandoned, or demolished, remind us that one person's paradise may be another's inferno, that one group's search for personal paradise may condemn others, that the paradise sought by one generation may create a hell for the next. Italo Calvino warned that we live in an inferno of our own creation, "that we form by being together," and that to escape, we must "seek and learn to recognize who and what in the midst of the inferno are not inferno, then make them endure, give them space."[63] William James said those who would change the world must hold the ideal and the real as dynamically contiguous. Community gardens in Mill Creek's old floodplain, rivers restored in Denver, give tangible hope that we may yet achieve a more collective paradise. The park along the river Rance in Dinan, the patio in the Alhambra, serve as landscapes of meaning and value for other places and times. Make them endure, give them space.

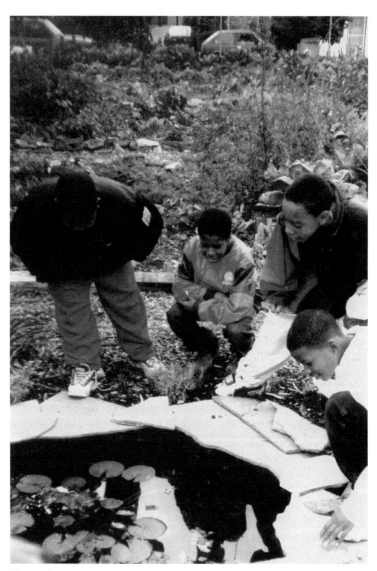

The pond at Aspen Farms. (Martin Knox, West Philadelphia Landscape Project)

Epilogue:
Reimagining Mill Creek

Designers are storytellers. Design is a way of imagining and telling new stories and reviving old ones, a process of spinning out visions of landscapes that pose alternatives from which to choose, describing the shape of a possible future. The products of design—gardens, homes, road and water systems, neighborhoods, and cities—are settings for living that convey meaning, express a society's values. We extend these meanings further through processes of construction and cultivation, use and neglect, as we dwell in what began as dreams.

Dream One. Mill Creek Parks

After rains, Mill Creek comes alive above ground, water pooling, forming shallow ponds, flowing through channels into riverine plazas, lingering for a few hours or days, then gradually disappearing, seeping into the sewer below. When the water is invisible, the creek's presence underground can still be seen. In early spring, carpets of blue scilla bloom in grass and under groves throughout the Mill Creek parks. Rows of red maples mark the course of the underground sewer; are rooted in the damp soil of the old floodplain. In spring, their buds swell dark red, leaf out green; in fall, leaves flame red, drop, blow across bricks, onto porches. Artists have designed water fountains there now, spray pools, even manhole covers.

Mill Creek parks meander through West Philadelphia, their diverse character reflecting their sponsors and contexts. Where blocks of rowhouses afford little or no outdoor space except street and sidewalk, there are ball courts, playgrounds, and play fields, sitting gardens, and community gardens, all intensively used. Mill Creek Mini-Golf and the West Philadelphia Garden Center, in the commercial district between Market and Walnut streets, are also among the parks. The parks are not continuous; they are most numerous north of Walnut Street, where there were once many vacant properties. South of Walnut, the parks are fewer.

People of Mill Creek call their neighborhood the Bottoms, using the term differently from their meaning years ago when it was known pejoratively as "The Bottom." Now they read it as fertile bottomlands, a place that regenerates continuously within the context of the creek and its history. They inscribe their own stories, improvising within the frame of creek and streets.

Every schoolchild knows the story and can read the landscape of Mill Creek: where it once flowed on the land, where its shore was the site of a large Indian settlement, where it powered mills to grind wheat and corn, then to weave cotton and wool, where it was buried in a sewer and built upon, where the force of the creek's waters broke through the sewer to flood basements, crumble foundations, and cave in streets. Where the land above the sewer became open once again, a gash of vacant land, trashed and abandoned. There Mill Creek parks were built, and rain now runs off rooftops, streets, and sidewalks into ponds in the parks, ponds that contain the water and slow its passage to the sewer, the treatment plant, and the river. Every schoolchild knows the connection between parks and river and water to drink.

Schools are at the heart of the community's reconstruction. Students' studies focus on the stream, the sewer, the community. They learn science, social studies, history, mathematics, art, and literature in the context of the neighborhood's past, present, and future. They learn the arts of citizenship: how to know a place, how to envision and build its future, how to care for it. Knowing, imagining, building, and caring, they teach their elders and younger children.

Schools have living laboratories—meadows, wooded groves, and ponds, once vacant lots—children care for and study them all as part of their science classes. In the hall is a display of photographs taken every year for the past fifteen showing the once-vacant lots and the growth of meadow and forest occurring over time. Students keep records of plant species growing there, and mount an exhibit every year of their discoveries. A big pond was dug on one vacant property, planted as a wetland, and stocked with frogs, salamanders, and other animals. Seen in the larger context, these outdoor classrooms are islands in the urban fabric, links for migrating birds in fall and spring between the wetlands along the Schuylkill River, the woods and meadows of Clark Park, Cathedral Cemetery, and Fairmount Park.

Mill Creek parks are now models of community development, environmental education, and water management, the first sewered, urban floodplain to be mapped in the United States, the first use of inner-city vacant land for stormwater detention to prevent combined sewer overflows, the pilot for many other projects in Philadelphia that saved millions of dollars. Teams of public officials, engineers, planners, and designers from other cities come to study the parks and the Mill Creek Center at a middle school in the bottomlands. Tours of the park start at the school, where sixth to eighth grade guides demonstrate a model of the watershed in the form of a fountain. The fountain was a collaboration between teachers, children, and artists, and many features were ideas first suggested by a child. It is like no watershed ever seen before: slanted copper panels stained blue-green by water represent roofs; it has basins (water barrels); sloping stone (streets and sidewalks); runnels (gutters); transparent columns of sand, of rock (soil); beds of water plants (wetlands); funnels and pipes (downspouts and sewers); a pool (river). The water enters the fountain in two ways, by rainfall or pipe. When rains come, the three-story school building spouts water off its roof into pools and pipes, running smaller fountains. When it rains really hard, children and teachers grab their raincoats and run outside to watch. And the water can also be turned on, filling the fountain from a pipe.

The play of water in the fountain is never the same. The fountain's pumps, check dams, spigots, and nozzles are controlled at will; some can be pushed, slid, or turned by a single child, others by the combined strength of two or more people. Water is concentrated or dispersed, patterns of flow are varied, as pumps lift the water, as check dams are shifted or slid into place, as spigots are opened or closed, as nozzles are turned to produce a fine mist or a line. Sometimes the play of water is a riot of random patterns, sometimes orchestrated through the coordinated efforts of the players. Water leaves the fountain along runnels that feed a series of pools in a large, sunken section of the school grounds. Usually only the lowest pools are filled, but after a storm the entire lower basin fills with runoff from the roof and school grounds. The magnitude of a rainstorm can always be gauged by how high the water reaches in the stepped basin. Only once in the last ten years has the water reached the top step.

Dream Two. Mill Creek Art Folk Park and Mini-Golf

After many years of planning and waiting, new buildings are being constructed now in the Walnut-Market Corridor, the commercial district and principal commuting route between downtown Philadelphia and the suburbs. Its renewal promises jobs and educational opportunities for West Philadelphia. During all those years, a temporary landscape grew and matured into a striking setting that drew private investment; new buildings were designed to fit within that landscape. The Market-Walnut Corridor intersects the Mill Creek floodplain between 42nd and 47th streets, where the original course of the stream was relatively flat and meandering, with small branches and ponds; by the 1990s, there were many vacant properties here. The new businesses that came are those that can tolerate waterlogged soil and periodic flooding: outdoor markets and parking lots, for example, where rainwater is ponded deliberately. The Art Folk Park was the first new enterprise built here, followed by several large commercial enterprises, the Mill Creek Garden Center and Nursery and the Mill Creek Miniature Golf Course; the popularity of each, in turn, boosted support for other investments.

The Mill Creek Art Folk Park, a large, open meadow visible from passing cars and buses, where artists construct and display their works, has attracted much attention and many visitors. The works change continually; with no formal selection process, most of the artists are little known, except locally, though occasionally a well-known artist creates a piece. Many of the works are quite whimsical, others more serious. There are works by sculptors, painters, muralists, dumpster divas, cartoonists, doll-makers, garden artists; on weekends the park draws photographers, fabric artists, hair-braiders, storytellers, griots, mimes, dancers, musicians, makers of musical instruments, poets. The place has brought together a magnificent local resource, previously unrecognized, once many individuals working alone, scattered throughout the community. The park itself was the outgrowth of an arts program to create new landmarks along the course of the creek, to reveal and celebrate it. The first work built at the Mill Creek Art Folk Park is the only commissioned work there: a fence, whose design was chosen in a widely publicized competition that also served to announce the art park. The fence was to mark and enclose the place, but also to permit those driving by to see the art works within, to allow people to move freely in and out, to be durable and inexpensive to construct. Hundreds of proposals submitted by artists from all over the country were judged by a jury of artists, community leaders, and members of the Art Commission and the Redevelopment Authority's Fine Arts Committee. After the jury's decision, a selection of the best ideas was displayed at the Institute for Contemporary Art. Many of these have since been built elsewhere.

The Mill Creek Garden Center and Nursery occupies several large properties, the principal retail center designed like a garden; here flowers, vegetables, and garden supplies are displayed and sold. Small trees and shrubs are for sale in lots nearby. The garden center and nursery is the largest in the city; its unusual and beautiful design draws customers from around the city and the western suburbs. It is prominently located along a major commuting corridor, and many stop by on the way home. It is a nonprofit organization whose programs are supported by proceeds from retail sales; the nursery and sales staff are youth from West Philadelphia working in an educational and job-training program. Many students work weekends and summers while still in high school, then continue in a full-time two-year program in horticulture and landscape management affiliated with a local community college.

Golfers at the Mill Creek Miniature Golf Course have five sets of holes to choose from—"Piedmont Forest," "Mills and Mansions," "Streetcar Suburb," "Cave-In!" and "Visions." All were programed and designed as part of the Mill Creek Watershed curriculum at the local middle school. In "Piedmont Forest," golfers tee off from a low point into a steep valley cut into the hillside, then gradually make their way up to the top, past springs, enclosed by oak and hickory trees, mountain laurel, ferns, mayapple, and past slopes of exposed grey rock flecked with shiny flakes of mica—Wissahickon Schist. "Mills and Mansions," a round of nine holes, tells the story of the colonial settlement of Mill Creek, with replicas of the cotton mill on Haverford Avenue, the drovers' inn along Lancaster, a slaughterhouse, and the Busti mansion. It leads into "Streetcar Suburb," another nine-hole round that tracks the development of the neighborhood from the Civil War to 1930, each successive hole another decade. The favorite part of this course is the reconstructed segment of Lancaster Avenue with all the stores shown in miniature, and the streetcar terminal. In "Cave-In," each hole represents an actual cave-in event from the 1930s to the 1990s, depicted in a posted newspaper account. Golfers tee off through scale-models of blocks of homes, trying to avoid water hazards and cave-in to reach the green and sink the ball safely into each hole. "Cave-In," in the lowest part of the site, incorporates several stormwater detention ponds; after rainstorms water comes splashing down the hillside into ponds and water hazards. There are unexpected squirts of waters and jets of air—golfers beware. "Visions" vies with "Cave-In" as the most popular course at Mill Creek Miniature Golf; it is an experimental course, a showcase of ideas for the future of the neighborhood where the "landscape" of each hole presents a separate proposal.

Many changes to Mill Creek in recent years were inspired by "Visions," the new plaza next to the old Arena Stage site, for example. Anyone can submit to a selection panel an idea for a new hole in the golf course. The propositions are submitted in miniature models; they range from the pragmatic to the fanciful, inciting crowds to voice their approval or dissent. Other proposals, such as showing Sulzberger Middle School in 2400 A.D. as a ruin, are fantasies. Some engender serious debate over days and weeks, provoking additional submissions in response. Plans for the vacant lot at 48th and Market were extremely controversial and prompted many alternative visions over the course of several years. The golf course began with an idea from one person, a member of the community. University and middle school students developed the idea, produced designs and a business plan, then presented their work to local leaders who decided to make it real. It is typical of the way things work.

Dream Three. The Urban Forest

From the air the neighborhood looks like an urban forest, on the ground, streets are shady, green corridors. A massive reforestation has occurred, block by block; even the narrowest streets are planted with trees. Streets that used to bake all day in the hot summer sun are now shaded; the trees have made streets and homes more comfortable on summer afternoons and evenings. The street is still a stage, but the action is cooler. Students grow the new trees right in the neighborhood in street-tree nurseries on former vacant lots: sixth graders plant small trees in the fall, tend them over the next two years, choose the street where they will be planted, teach residents about tree care, and transplant the trees to streets when they are ready to graduate from eighth grade. The trees are densely planted, and the weaker trees are thinned out to make room for the more vigorous. Each fall, the park commission brings truckloads of leaves collected from city streets for students to spread as a thick mulch, preventing the growth of weeds, keeping the soil moist and soft. Trees from the school's nursery survive much better than ordinary nursery stock.

West Philadelphia's Mill Creek has been the focus of a twenty-year study on the effects of trees on urban microclimate, a collaboration between students, teachers, and university faculty. Before new trees were planted, measurements of temperatures on treeless blocks throughout the community were taken as part of school and university school classes, then continued annually thereafter. Researchers have published papers demonstrating the marked difference in microclimate and human comfort on these streets within ten to twenty years after the trees were planted. Treeless neighborhoods were once ten degrees Fahrenheit hotter on summer evenings than suburban neighborhoods only a few miles away; now evening and nighttime temperatures in Mill Creek are ten degrees cooler than before, as cool as in the suburbs. This urban forestry project brought international attention to Mill Creek, and the dramatic aesthetic transformation has prompted many other cities to imitate it even before the results of the microclimate study became known.

Dream Four. The Grove

A grove of trees enfolds a school, branches reaching, buds unleafing. Leaves, soaking up light, drying, dropping, rotting, make roots' fertile bed. Year by year the grove has grown, ten more trees for every class. Each child, learning, prunes twigs back spurring growth, records changes, tells stories of straight-trunked tulip, multi-stemmed maple, dappled brawny plane, sturdy stocky oaks—red, white, and black—long-limbed yellowwood, delicate dogwood, billowy shadblow, eccentric gingko: many trees, one grove.

Behind the trees, walls of brick, baked yellow clay, rise high. A school sits on a limestone base, built in 1923, say numbers cut in its cornerstone. Windows broad and tall look out: trunks like columns frame the sixth grade's first-floor view, in September a green world closely canopied, then winter's open tracery and spring's pubescent bud, soft stem, downy underleaf. Seventh graders look down from the second floor into dogwood's creamy flowers, tulip tree's green-orange tulips and through branches where birds nest, flitter, flutter, sweep, chitter, stutter, cheep: many motions, one dance; many voices, one sound. From the top floor, eighth graders look out beyond the grove to houses and gardens, to rows of maples, strings of gingko, each line a sign, leading back to the school where they learned to make their mark.

Smell of sun heralds the new year on dry leaves, on apples, on pears along the warm south wall. Fragrant rain signals the coming of the end, as scents unfold, rhythms quicken. By the doors of the school, six yellowwood stand, their blooms blowing across the walk, white confetti in early June. Through this arbored gateway, students pass. They have learned to read what sloping valleys and flowing water tell, what bud scars say. They speak the language that holds life in place. Knowing, they shape the landscape to hold their dreams.

Notes

Full citations are given for all sources not listed in the bibliography. Travel journals, which I have been keeping since 1988, are not cited specifically because they have been used extensively throughout the book; see Sources for details on places and dates. All descriptions in the text in present tense are directly from the journals.

INTRODUCTION

1   See, for example, Spirn, *West Philadelphia Landscape Plan.*

2   See, for example, my essays: "Architecture and Landscape"; "Introduction," in Andersson and Høyer, *Sørensen*; "Texts, Landscapes, and Life," in Høyer, *Andersson.*

3   Unless otherwise noted, all photographs in this book are my own. See also *Telling Landscape,* a book of my photographs, also in preparation.

4   See, for example, my essays "Constructing Nature: The Legacy of Frederick Law Olmsted," in Cronon, *Uncommon Ground,* and "Frank Lloyd Wright: Architect of Landscape," in De Long, *Frank Lloyd Wright.*

1 THE LANGUAGE OF LANDSCAPE

1   See, for example, the tablet of Enannatum I, governor of Lagash, which records the delivery of cedar trees to roof a temple, Mesopotamia, ca. 2900 B.C., and other examples in Gyorgy Kepes, ed. *Sign, Image, Symbol* (New York: George Braziller, 1966). For a review of the literature on evolution of human cognition, see Donald, *Origins of Mind.*

2   Roland Barthes, *Elements of Semiology* (New York: Farrar, Straus and Giroux, 1968), 16.

3   Lakoff and Johnson, *Metaphors We Live By.* Each developed these ideas further in subsequent books: Lakoff, *Women, Fire, and Dangerous Things;* Johnson, *Body in the Mind.*

4   Stilgoe, *Shallow-Water Dictionary* and *Alongshore.* While I admire Stilgoe's work on the language of the estuary, I reject his definition of landscape as including only land, not water, and countryside, not city.

5   Brown (1716–83), Olmsted (1822–1903), Wright (1867–1959), Halprin (b. 1916), Schwartz (b. 1950).

6   Heidegger, "Building Dwelling Thinking," 145–47. Some of these implications have been explored by others, including the geographer Relph, *Place and Placelessness,* and the architectural theorist Christian Norberg-Schulz, *Concept of Dwelling.*

7   Verner Dahlerup, *Ordbog over det Danske Sprog* (Copenhagen: Nordisk, 1931), Jacob Grimm and Wilhelm Grimm, *Deutsches Worterbuch* (Verlag von S. Hirzel, 1885), Arther R. Borden, Jr., *A Comprehensive Old English Dictionary* (University Press of America, 1982). For a review of the histories of the words *landscape, nature, land,* and *country* in English, German, and Scandinavian languages, see Olwig, "Nature of Landscape." See also Jackson, "The Word Itself" in *Vernacular Landscape,* 3– 8. I am grateful to Andre Wink for the translation and interpretation of J. Heinsios, *Woordenboek der Nederlandsche Taale* (Martinus Nijhoff, A. W. Sijthoff, 1916).

8   Webster's *New Universal Unabridged Dictionary* (New York: Simon and Schuster, 1983) and *Oxford English Dictionary* (Oxford: Oxford University Press, 1989).

9   Anthony Hecht, "Gardens of the Villa d'Este," in *Hard Hours* (New York: Atheneum, 1967), 95.

10 Maclean, *River Runs*, 61.

11 Lakoff and Johnson, *Metaphors*. See also Ralph Waldo Emerson, "Nature," in *Essays and Lectures* (New York: Library of America, 1983), 7–49.

12 Stilgoe, *Shallow-Water Dictionary*, 23, 28.

13 Many cultures have no single name or notion for *nature*. The singular quality of the English word masks a real multiplicity and implies falsely that there is a single definition. See Raymond Williams, "Ideas of Nature," in *Materialism and Culture*, 67–85.

14 Jackson, in "The Word Itself," limits the definition of *landscape* to deliberately created, "man-made systems"; Stilgoe, in *Common Landscape*, narrows the definition further, to human-made, nonurban land.

15 Berger and Mohr, *Another Way of Telling*.

16 Bateson, *Sacred Unity*, 310–11, 253–57.

17 Leopold, *Sand County Almanac*, 129–33.

2 Reading and Telling the Meanings of Landscape

1   The passages quoted are from Twain, *Mississippi*, 280–83. Samuel Clemens spent 1857–61 on the Mississippi, first as a cub pilot under the tutelage of Horace Bixby, then as a licensed steamboat pilot. His pseudonym, Mark Twain, refers to water two fathoms deep.

2   It is ironic, given its history, that this Danish province is commonly referred to in English by its German name, Schleswig, rather than by its Danish name, Slesvig.

3   Helge Seidelin Jacobsen, *An Outline History of Denmark* (Copenhagen, Høst & Son, 1993), 101, 105.

4   For a social and cultural history of the Danish heath and its transformation, see Olwig, *Nature's Ideological Landscape*. The Danish edition of the book has additional material on European Union policies on marginal lands as they will affect farmlands previously reclaimed from the heath: *Hedens Natur* (Copenhagen: Teknisk Forlag, 1986). Olwig related these themes to the American landscape in "Reinventing Common Nature," in *Uncommon Ground*, edited by Cronon.

5   Hans Christian Andersen, "Jylland mellem tvende have," *Folkehøjskolens Sangbog* (Odense, DK: Foreningens Forlag, 1964), 712–13. See Introduction for a description of the circumstances surrounding my stay in Denmark.

6   Olwig, *Nature's Ideological Landscape*, 67.

7   Johannes Iverson, *The Development of Denmark's Nature Since the Last Glacial* (Copenhagen: C. A. Reitzels, 1973). Iverson summarizes research on the relationships among geology, soil, plants, and human occupation of landscape in Denmark.

8   From Cicero, *De natura deorum*, quoted and translated by John Dixon Hunt, "The Idea of the Garden and the Three Natures," *Zum Naturbegriff de Gegenwart* (Stuttgart, 1993), 312.

9   Hunt, "Idea of the Garden," 325.

10 John McCrae, "In Flanders Fields," in *The Oxford Book of War Poetry*, edited by Jon Stallworthy (Oxford: Oxford University Press, 1984), 165.

11 I. A. Richards, *The Philosophy of Rhetoric* (Oxford: Oxford University Press, 1936).

12 The east end of the allée was replanted in the 1980s. This is Steen Høyer's observation.

13 The U.S. Soil Conservation Service, one of the most successful federal agencies, owes that success to a balance between local knowledge and expert advice.

14 For a classic essay on the subject, see Meinig, "The Beholding Eye: Ten Versions of the Same Scene," in *Ordinary Landscapes*.

15 John M. Hull, *Touching the Rock: An Experience of Blindness* (New York: Vintage, 1992), 29–30.

16 Watts, *Reading the Landscape of America*, v. See also her *Reading the Landscape of Europe*.

17 "What the Frog's Eye Tells the Frog's Brain," in Warren S. McCulloch, *Embodiments of Mind* (Cambridge: MIT Press, 1988), 231, 254.

18 See, for example, Griffin, *Animal Thinking*, von Frisch, *Animal Architecture*, Sebeok, *Sign and Its Masters*.

19 See, for example, Moshe Barasch, *Modern Theories of Art* (New York: New York University Press, 1990), and Charles Rosen and Henri Zerner, "Caspar David Friedrich and the Language of Landscape," in *Romanticism and Realism: The Mythology of Nineteenth Century Art* (New York: W. W. Norton, 1984).

20 Kathleen Morner and Ralph Rausch, *Dictionary of Literary Terms* (Lincolnwood, Ill.: National Textbook Company, 1991), 163.

21 William Cronon, "Authority, Tradition, and the Future of Disciplines: A Comment [On Beans]," *Yale Journal of Criticism* 5:2 (Spring 1992). See also Anderson, *Plants, Man, and Life*.

22 Cronon, *Nature's Metropolis*.

23 John McPhee, "Los Angeles Against the Mountains," in *Control of Nature*.

24 Riley, "Square to Road."

25 Andersson, "En trädgård efter fem år," 27.

26 Philadelphia Museum of Art.

27 Paul Klee, *The Thinking Eye: Notebooks of Paul Klee*, vol. 1, edited by Jürg Spiller (London: Lund Humphries, 1961), 63.

28 Andersson, "Karlsplatz," 17. My translation.

29 All are unpublished professional texts. Henrik Pøhlsgaard brought these texts to my attention and shared his experience and insights about their use and significance in Andersson's practice.

30 See Halprin, *RSVP Cycles*, and Halprin and Burns, *Taking Part*.

31 Eiseley, "Flow of the River," in *Immense Journey*, 15–27.

32 Maclean, *River Runs*, 92.

33 *Webster's New International Dictionary of the English Language*, unabridged 2d ed. (Springfield, Mass.: Merriam, 1955).

3 The Literature of Landscape

1 Revelation 12:7–9.

2 Adams, *Mont-Saint-Michel*.

3 Henry Decaens, Adrien Goetz, Gerard Baylis, Gerard Guiller, and Maylis Mayle, *L'ABCdaire du Mont-Saint-Michel* (Paris: Flammarion, 1996).

4 Pfeiffer, personal communication, March 2, 1995. The other two chapters, says Pfeiffer, are Taliesin North and Taliesin East (Wright's apartment in the Plaza Hotel in New York).

5 Wright, *Writings, 1930–1932*, 226.

6 Ackerman, *Villa*, 286, 12. See also Williams, *Country and the City*.

7 Cronon, "A Place for Stories."

8 Tom McArthur, ed., *Oxford Companion to the English Language* (Oxford: Oxford University Press, 1992), 343. An elegy can also mourn the passing of a way of life or express a general sense of mortality.

9 Steen Eiler Rasmussen, "Haven, det langsomme skuespil," in *Essays gennem mange aar* (Copenhagen: Gyldendal, 1968), 101–14.

10 Shakespeare, *As You Like It*, 2.7.139.

11 *SITE*, 28.

12 See Thompson, *Bryant Park.*

13 Olin, "Regionalism," 256.

14 Charles Bradley, "The Leopold Memorial Reserve," in Thomas Tanner, ed., *Aldo Leopold: The Man and His Legacy* (Ankeny, Iowa: Soil Conservation Society of America, 1987), 162.

15 Nina Leopold Bradley, quoted in ibid., 171.

16 This and other passages on Olmsted are adapted from Spirn, "Olmsted."

17 I employ the term *genre* both in its general sense—kind—and in its specific use in literature and art to refer to type of subject or performance and body of related conventions. This is akin both to Northrop Frye's idea of genre as corresponding to archetypal human responses and Barthes' and others' notion of genre as sets of conventions that change from one place and period to another. See Frye, *Anatomy of Criticism* (Princeton: Princeton University Press, 1957), and McArthur, *English Language,* 435.

18 Huth, *Nature and the American,* 151.

19 Jon Else, "Yosemite: The Fate of Heaven" (Sundance Institute and Yosemite Association, 1989), 58-min. video.

20 There were times when the court was too poor to pay for the rebuilding. Anne Walthall, personal communication.

21 Eliade, *Sacred and Profane.*

22 I am grateful to Shunsaku Miyagi for identifying the plant and its meaning.

23 Michelin, *Paris* (Clermont-Ferrand: Michelin, 1985), 174.

24 Attributed to Asplund by Sven-Ingvar Andersson, personal communication, May 21, 1990.

25 Sven-Ingvar Andersson, personal communication, June 4, 1990.

26 Lowenthal, *Past Is a Foreign Country,* 197.

27 Huizinga, *Homo Ludens,* 10.

28 The building is Gund Hall, home of Harvard University's Graduate School of Design, designed by the Australian architect John Andrews.

29 Alan Lukashok and Kevin Lynch, "Childhood Memories of the City," *Journal of the American Institute of Planners* 23:3 (Summer 1956), 146–52. Clare Cooper Marcus, "Environmental Autobiography," Working Paper 301 (Berkeley, 1979). I use Marcus's techniques in exercises with my students. See also Marcus, *House as Mirror of Self.*

30 Lukashok and Lynch, "Childhood Memories," 145.

31 Cranz, *Politics of Park Design.*

32 Sørensen, *Parkpolitik,* 54.

33 Sørensen, *Haver,* 140.

34 See Hurtwood, *Planning for Play.*

35 Lady Allen of Hurtwood and Susan Jellicoe, *The Things We See: Gardens* (Harmondswoth, Middlesex: Penguin Books, 1953), 46.

36 Halprin, *Freeways,* 17.

37 Ibid., 37.

38 Chang, *Lawrence Halprin,* 230. Angela Danadjieva was a principal designer on this project.

39 Material on rice cultivation from Richard D. Porcher, *A Teacher's Field Guide to the Natural History of the Bluff Plantation Wildlife Sanctuary* (New Orleans: Kathleen O'Brain Foundation, 1985).

40 *Middleton Place* (Charleston: Middleton Place Foundation, 1976), 26.

41 Ibid., 15.

42 George Perkins Marsh, *Man and Nature* (1865; repr. Cambridge: Harvard University Press, 1965), 35.

43 The Ramble at Central Park was planted to appear "wild," but it was only a small part of the park. William Robinson, an English acquaintance of Olmsted, published his book *The Wild Garden* in 1870. Olmsted was undoubtedly also aware of Martin Johnson Heade's contemporary paintings depicting marshes along Boston's North Shore (I am grateful to William Cronon and Neil Levine for this reference).

44 Olmsted, "Parks, Parkways," 253.

45 See, for example, Ashihara's description of Japanese space in *Hidden Order.*

46 Thayer, "Personal Dreams and Pagan Rituals," in Francis and Hester, eds., *Meaning of Gardens,* 194–97.

47 Wilhelm Miller, "The Prairie Spirit in Landscape Gardening," Circular no. 184 (Urbana: Agricultural Experiment Station, Department of Horticulture, University of Illinois, 1916).

48 Sun Xiaoxiang, personal communication.

49 This style was fashionable in Elizabethan prose; the term refers to Euphues, the principal character in a prose romance by John Lyly. See McArthur, *English Language,* 387–88.

50 And thus one gets books such as Margaret Drabble, *A Writer's Britain: Landscape in Literature* (New York: Thames and Hudson, 1987), that trace these reciprocal allusions.

51 Suzanne K. Langer, *Feeling and Form* (New York: Charles Scribner's Sons, 1953), 40; *Problems of Art* (New York: Charles Scribner's Sons, 1957), 25.

52 There is also significance in the plaza's location—the site of the house where William Penn granted the "Charter of Privileges" in 1701.

4 ELEMENTS OF LANDSCAPE AND LANGUAGE

1 J. M. Moreno and W. C. Oechel, "A Simple Method for Estimating Fire Intensity after a Burn in California Chaparral," *Acta Oecologica/Oecologia Plantarum* 10:1 (1989). I am grateful to Michael Barbour for this reference.

2 Nita Lelyveld, "Desire for Scenic Beauty in California Leads to Disaster for Homeowners," *Philadelphia Inquirer,* March 9, 1998, 1, 8.

3 Stephen Davis, *The Hunter for All Seasons: An Aboriginal Perspective on the Natural Environ* (Northern Territory: Milingimbi School Literature Production Centre, 1984), 9.

4 Anthony F. Aveni, *Empires of Time* (New York: Basic Books, 1989), 73–75.

5 Halprin, *Freeways,* 23.

6 Ecclesiastes 1:7.

7 Yi-Fu Tuan, *The Hydrologic Cycle and the Wisdom of God: A Theme in Geoteleology* (Toronto: University of Toronto Press, 1968), 3–4.

8 Gould, *Time's Arrow, Time's Cycle.*

9 For Gaia theory, see James E. Lovelock, *Gaia* (New York: Oxford University Press, 1987); for challenge to the idea of harmony as nature's norm, see Botkin, *Discordant Harmonies.*

10 John M. Hull, *Touching the Rock: An Experience of Blindness* (New York: Vintage, 1992), 45.

11 James Steele, *Hassan Fathy* (London: Academy Editions, St. Martin's Press, 1988).

12 Joan Brigham, personal communication, April 6, 1997.

13 George Eliot, *Mill on the Floss* (1860; repr. London: Penguin Books, 1985), 94.

14 Andrews, *Living Materials,* 1.

15 Cooper, *Symbols.*

16 Walter L. Brenneman, "The Circle and the Cross: Loric and Sacred Space in the Holy Wells of Ireland," in Seamon and Mugerauer, *Dwelling.*

17 Krieger, "Up the Plastic Tree."

18 J. L. Reed, *Forests of France* (London: Faber and Faber, n.d.), 116–18.

19 Clay, *Close-Up*, on the significance of "breaks."

20 Lynch, "Environmental Adaptability," in *City Sense*.

21 Wallace Stevens, "Anecdote of the Jar," *Collected Poems* (New York: Knopf, 1991), 76.

22 Hull, *Touching the Rock*, 30–31.

23 Wright, *Writings, 1894–1930*, 117.

24 Ibid., 118.

25 T. S. Eliot, "Burnt Norton," from *Four Quartets*, in *The Complete Poems and Plays: 1909–1950* (New York: Harcourt, Brace, 1952).

26 Jensen, *Siftings*, 63; for discussion of Jensen's council rings, see also Engel, *Sacred Sands*, 200–01.

27 Munn, *Walbiri Iconography*.

28 Sutton et al., *Dreamings*.

29 Author's collection.

30 Addison, 1712, reproduced in Hunt and Willis, *Genius of Place*, 142.

31 Woodbridge, *Stourhead Landscape*.

32 Henry Hoare, in a letter to his nephew, quoted in ibid., 17.

33 Victor Pomare, quoted in Warner, *To Dwell Is to Garden*, 50.

34 Parts of this section are drawn from Spirn, "Uluru to Cooper's Place."

35 The term *performance* also acknowledges Halprin's *RSVP Cycles*. Kenneth Helphand referred me to Mayer Spivak's essay "Archetypal Place," *Architectural Forum* 140:3 (October 1973), 44–49. My performance spaces and Spivak's archetypal places differ, but there are important commonalities, especially in our emphasis on behavior patterns that generate spatial settings.

36 Appleton, *Experience of Landscape* and *Symbolism of Habitat*.

37 Norberg-Schulz, *Concept of Dwelling*. Lynch, *Image of the City*. Lynch's work has been particularly influential on the design and planning professions; this book is now in its twenty-third printing.

38 Alexander, *Pattern Language* and *Timeless Way*.

39 Alexander, *Multi-Service Centers*.

40 Dubos, *Man Adapting*, 9, and *So Human an Animal*, 70.

41 American Society of Landscape Architects Annual Meeting in Atlanta, 1978.

42 Jennifer Isaacs, *Arts of Dreaming*, 175–77.

43 Wright made numerous references in this vein, for example: "The land is the simplest form of architecture," in Brownell and Wright, *Architecture and Modern Life*, 17.

44 This text is adapted from a longer treatment of Wright's landscape design in Spirn, "Wright."

45 See Cronon, "Inconstant Unity," in Riley and Reed, *Frank Lloyd Wright*, 9–14.

46 See, for example, the traditional architecture of Japan, the work of Alvar Aalto, Adèle Naudé Santos, Glenn Murcutt, and Richard Le Plastrier.

47 Wright, *Writings, 1930–1932*, 246.

48 Repton, *Landscape Gardening*, 3, 69.

49 These associations are not far-fetched. Wright's Uncle Jenkin compared Tower Hill to a woman's breast in a sermon; see Graham, *Gospel of the Farm*. See also Biedermann, *Symbolism*, 100–02.

50 Wright described the symbolism of forms in "The Japanese Print," *Writings, 1894–1930*, 117, and he used a red square as his emblem. The hill garden, however, is merely a representation of fertility, for hilltops are not fertile here, the valley bottoms are. Mamah Borthwick Cheney was the wife of a client with whom Wright lived in Europe and built Taliesin; she was murdered at Taliesin in 1914.

51 Randall C. Henning, *At Taliesin* (Carbondale: Southern Illinois University Press, 1992), 68.

52 Wright, "Living in the Desert," 12.
53 Wright was strongly influenced by the gardens he saw during his visits to Japan. For a description of the principle of borrowed scenery (*shakkei*), see Itoh, *Space and Illusion*. For a description of the stroll garden, its relation to interior architectural space, and the concept of "movement-oriented architectural space," see Inoue, *Space in Japanese Architecture*.
54 Wright, "To Arizona," in *Writings, 1939–1949*, 34.
55 Brownell and Wright, *Architecture and Modern Life*, 277. The last chapter, a dialogue between Wright and Brownell, contains an extended reflection on the meaning of structure.
56 Wright, *Writings, 1894–1930*, 117.
57 Ibid.
58 Ibid.
59 Brownell and Wright, *Architecture and Modern Life*, 278–81. Wright used the big, blue Ming tea jar in the garden at Taliesin to illustrate his idea of structure as fusing "ideal" of function and purpose, process of formation, form and use.
60 Bruce Brooks Pfeiffer, personal communication, February 17, 1995. Apparently Wright worked these out in his head, then built directly; there are few drawings documenting these successive changes.
61 Brierly, personal communication, August 24, 1994.
62 Wright, *Writings, 1939–1949*, 33–36, and *Writings, 1931–1939*, 175–78.
63 Wright, *Living Voice*, 177.

5 Shaping Landscape Context

1 T. S. Eliot, "Burnt Norton," *Four Quartets*, in *The Complete Poems and Plays: 1909–1950* (New York: Harcourt, Brace, 1952).
2 Gollwitzer, *Bäume*.
3 For a discussion of the development of these ideas, the changing paradigm, and the relation of both to prevailing political values, see Michael Barbour, "Ecological Fragmentation in the Fifties," in Cronon, *Uncommon Ground*.
4 For a charming description of this phenomenon, see Watts, "Watching the Islands Go By," in *Reading the Landscape of America*. For wonderful, detailed descriptions of river phenomena and their significance, see Twain, *Mississippi*.
5 Maclean, *River Runs*, 61–63.
6 Brown, *Occluded Front*, 22.
7 Count Giuseppe Panza di Biumo, "Artist of the Sky," in Brown, *Occluded Front*, 61–88.
8 Exodus 19:9.
9 The mountaineer Galen Rowell has photographed these and other phenomena of mountain light: Rowell, *Mountain Light*.
10 For a detailed description of the Roden Crater project, see Adcock, *James Turrell*.
11 Hill, *California Landscape*, 146.
12 Thomas, *Disney*, viii.
13 Halprin, *RSVP Cycles*, 58.
14 E. Hess, "A Tale of Two Memorials," *Art in America* 71 (April 1983).
15 Eliot, "The Dry Salvages," in *Four Quartets*.
16 Eiseley, *Immense Journey*, 20.
17 Ibid., 46.
18 Feld, *Sound and Sentiment*, 45.

19   Feld, liner notes to *Voices of the Rainforest* CD-ROM (Salem, Mass.: Rykodisc, 1991); *Sound and Sentiment.*

20   Feld, *Sound and Sentiment,* 23.

21   Rachel Carson, *Silent Spring* (Boston: Houghton, Mifflin, 1962), 2.

22   The institute has expanded, and the stand of trees is no more.

23   James Michener, *Centennial* (New York: Fawcett Crest, 1975), 47.

24   Psalms 23:2.

25   Hoskins, *Making of English Landscape;* Taylor, *Fields;* Cronon, *Changes in Land.*

26   Taylor, *Fields.*

27   Hoskins, *Making of English Landscape;* Taylor, *Fields,* 1975.

28   Cather, *My Ántonia,* 29.

29   Seddon, Conference on the Contribution of Landscape Planning to Environmental Protection, Hannover, Germany, June 6, 1990.

30   Panofsky, "Rolls-Royce Radiator."

31   Hayden, *Power of Place,* 9.

32   Robert Kennedy, quoted in Peter Medoff and Holly Sklar, *Streets of Hope* (Boston: South End Press, 1994), 245.

33   The drawings and text are online. See "Publications" at www.upenn.edu/wplp/sms.

34   Hidenobu Jinnai, "The Spatial Structure of Edo," in *Tokugawa Japan,* edited by Chie Nakane and Shinzaburo Oishi (Tokyo: University of Tokyo, 1990). I am grateful to Anne Walthall for bringing this essay to my attention.

35   Tax laws make it advantageous to keep some land in agriculture, for if you qualify for status as a farmer your taxes may be much lower than if you are merely holding land for development. Kazuhiko Takeuchi and Shunsaku Miyagi, personal communication, July 9, 1990.

36   Takamasa Miyazaki, personal communication.

6   LANDSCAPE GRAMMAR

1   Bateson, *Ecology of Mind,* 154.

2   Bateson, *Mind and Nature,* 18.

3   David Crystal, *The Cambridge Encyclopedia of Language* (Cambridge: Cambridge University Press, 1987), 82.

4   Hippocrates, *Airs, Waters, and Places,* in *Hippocrates,* vol. 1, Loeb Classical Library, edited by T. E. Page (Cambridge: Harvard University Press, 1962), iii–vi; Aristotle, *Politics,* VII.xi.

5   The description of Priene is based on accounts in the following sources: Weigand and Schrader, *Priene;* R. E. Wycherley, *How the Greeks Built Cities* (Garden City, N.Y.: Anchor, 1962); and Crouch, *Water Management.*

6   See Schapiro's classic essay, "Style."

7   The description of scales is based on Morrison and Eames, *Powers of Ten.* The book was preceded by two animated film versions.

8   Andersson, "Brev fra hønsegård," my translation.

9   Ibid.

10   The treads are ca. twelve inches, the risers exactly one-half the tread, with a landing ca. thirty inches every twelve steps.

11   Attributed to Gunnar Asplund by Sven-Ingvar Andersson, personal communication, May 21, 1990.

12   William Weston told this to John deKoven Hill, who related the story to me. The grid gardens were planted ca. 1912.

13 Landscape architecture studio course at Harvard University, Spring 1985. For the subsequent development, see Peter Medoff and Holly Sklar, *Streets of Hope* (Boston: South End Press, 1994).

14 Hoskins, *English Landscape*, 20.

15 Arnheim, "Order and Complexity," 125.

16 Ibid., 123.

17 Lorraine Daston, personal communication, July 27, 1993.

18 Mukerji, *Territorial Ambitions.*

19 Schjetnan first told me of the traditional uses of these stones.

20 I am grateful to Mario Schjetnan for these examples.

7 PRAGMATICS OF LANDSCAPE EXPRESSION

1 *Spring*, by Pieter Breughel the Elder. Engraved by Petrus a Merica, 1570. Andersson was professor of landscape architecture there until his retirement in 1995; now he devotes full time to his professional practice.

2 Andersson, "My Definition of My Profession This Year," paper at European Conference of Landscape Architectural Schools, Ljubljana, Slovenia, August 1992, 3.

3 Andersson, "Brev fra hønsegård." Unless noted otherwise, quotations are from this article. The translations are mine.

4 These are references to two influential theorists and their books: Robert Venturi, *Complexity and Contradiction in Architecture* (New York: Museum of Modern Art, 1966); Norberg-Schulz, *Intentions in Architecture.*

5 Andersson, "Brev fra hønsegård."

6 Andersson has written about his garden, both explicitly and implicitly, in many essays; among those referred to here are "Trädgård efter fem år," "Brev fra hønsegård," and "Häckar och höns." For a complete list, see Spirn, "Texts, Landscapes, Life."

7 "Brev fra hønsegård," 581.

8 Adapted from T. S. Eliot and Northrop Frye.

9 These are all people he knew or wrote about. Steen Eiler Rasmussen was a Danish architect and historian, Sven Hermelin (1900–84), a Swedish landscape architect and one of Andersson's teachers, Frederik Magnus Piper (1746–1824), a Swedish architect who introduced the English landscape style into Sweden, Kazimir Malevich (1878–1935), a Russian painter, Geoffrey Jellicoe (1900–96) an English architect and landscape architect, and Kevin Lynch (1918–84), an American urban designer and theorist.

10 Andersson and Høyer, *Sørensen*, 5.

11 For a description of these projects in the overall context of Boston and Olmsted's work, see Spirn, *Granite Garden* and "Constructing Nature." For a description of how basin and tidal gate were intended to work, see Olmsted's account of his dialogue with the city's engineer in a lecture to the Boston Society of Architects, "The Problem and Its Solution" in 1886. The handwritten notes for this lecture are in the Olmsted Papers at the Library of Congress. They were transcribed by Cynthia Zaitzevsky and reprinted in her doctoral dissertation, "Frederick Law Olmsted and the Boston Park System" (Harvard University, 1975), 295–306, and excerpted in her book of the same title (Cambridge: Harvard University Press, 1982). For a description of how the flood control function worked, see E. W. Howe, "The Back Bay Park, Boston," a speech to the Boston Society of Civil Engineers on March 16, 1881.

12 Zaitzevsky, *Olmsted*, 188.

13 Letter to F. L. Temple, March 15, 1886, Olmsted Papers, Library of Congress. Temple was the

landscape gardener Olmsted had hired to plant the Fens. Of the one hundred thousand plants, only thirty-five thousand survived, many of which were "nurse" plants actually intended to die. Of the plant species intended to predominate over time, 75–95 percent were dead. See also Zaitzevsky, *Olmsted*, 187–90.

14 Letter to Charles Eliot and John Charles Olmsted, October 28, 1893, Olmsted Papers, Library of Congress.

15 Rowe, *Design Thinking*, 15.

16 Olin, *Transforming the Common Place*.

17 Jellicoe, *Guelph Lectures*, 178.

18 Wright, *Writings, 1894–1930*, 124 (emphasis added).

19 Brownell and Wright, *Architecture and Modern Life*, 275.

20 Halprin, *RSVP Cycles*, 104.

21 See Laurie Olin's discussion of this point, which he elaborates in "Form, Meaning, and Expression."

22 Halprin, personal communication, August 16, 1989.

23 Bye, *Art into Landscape*, 155.

24 Françoise Fromonot, personal communication, May 13, 1993.

25 This is true not just for landscape authors. See, for example, descriptions of the essential roles visualization plays in engineering, science, and invention in McKim, *Visual Thinking*, or any of Tufte's books, such as *Envisioning Information*.

26 "What Is Design?" in Neuhart and Eames, *Eames Design*, 15.

27 For a more detailed description of this work, see John R. Clark, *The Sanibel Report* (Washington, D.C.: Conservation Foundation, 1976).

28 Randall Darwall and Fayette Watkis, "Shawl," eight-harness summer and winter twill weave handwoven of hand-dyed silk, wool, and cotton, dip-dyed warp, 100 by 24 inches, 1994. I have collected several sets of scarves, of different weaves, that are variations on a single warp. Darwall's fabrics are in the collection of the American Craft Museum. He exhibits each year at the leading American craft shows. See also Julie Dale, *Art to Wear* (Abbeville Press, 1986); Karen Searle, "The Scarves of Randall Darwall: The Consummate Cloth," *Ornament* 14:1 (Autumn 1990), 22–25, 63; Margo Mensing, "Randall Darwall: Infusing Function with Life," *Fiberarts* (March/April 1995), 40–44.

29 I described an early version of this approach of improvisation within a framework, likening it to jazz, in Spirn, "Poetics."

30 From 1987 to 1990, this work was funded by a grant from the J. N. Pew Charitable Trust, a collaboration between the Department of Landscape Architecture and Regional Planning at the University of Pennsylvania, the Organization and Management Group, and Philadelphia Green, an organization devoted to the promotion and support of community gardens and other local landscape projects that is part of the Pennsylvania Horticultural Society. Since 1991, it has been supported by grants from Penn's Center for Community Partnerships, the Philadelphia Urban Resources Partnership, the Kellogg Foundation, and the U.S. Department of Housing and Urban Development.

31 See Spirn, *West Philadelphia Landscape Plan*.

32 See Spirn and Marcucci, *Models of Success*.

33 See Spirn and Cameron, *Shaping the Block*, and Spirn, Cameron, and Pollio, *Vacant Land*.

34 See Spirn and Cheetham, *Digital Database*.

35 On the project's website at www.upenn.edu/wplp.

36 Pennsylvania Governor Tom Ridge featured this work as part of his Budget Address to the state legislature on February 3, 1998. The teacher Glenn Campbell, eighth grader Keith Sisco, and

seventh grader Oneil Hall presented the work via satellite, as part of the governor's speech, and received a standing ovation from the entire assembly.

37 Spirn and Pollio, *Garden Is a Town*.

38 Philadelphia City Planning Commission, the *Plan for West Philadelphia* (Philadelphia, 1994). There is a brief mention of the Mill Creek sewer collapse of 1961, in which more than one hundred homes were destroyed, but no indication of present or future problems related to the creek and sewer.

8 POETICS OF LANDSCAPE

1 Definitions of figures and tropes discussed in this chapter are drawn from several sources, especially Tom McArthur, ed., *Oxford Companion to the English Language* (Oxford: Oxford University Press, 1992). Other sources are H. W. Fowler, *Modern English Usage* (Oxford: Oxford University Press, 1965); Wilson Follett, *Modern American Usage* (New York: Hill and Wang, 1966); Kathleen Morner and Ralph Rausch, *Dictionary of Literary Terms* (Lincolnwood, Ill.: National Textbook Company, 1991); and Edward P. J. Corbett, *Classical Rhetoric for the Modern Student* (Oxford: Oxford University Press, 1971).

2 Hogan, *Lawn*, 70.

3 Including Philip Johnson (who reportedly remains on the lawn advisory board for this purpose). Will Rieley, personal communication, April 17, 1989.

4 When the budget for the courtyard was cut, Schwartz had to change the design; she found the frogs in a garden supply store, where they were available in large quantities at low cost. Martha Schwartz, personal communication, December 13, 1993.

5 Cirlot, *Symbols*, 114–15. Cooper, *Symbols*, 72.

6 Emily Yoffe, "Silence of the Frogs," *New York Times Sunday Magazine*, December 13, 1992, 36–38, 64, 66, 76. See also "What the Frogs Are Telling Us," *New York Times*, March 6, 1994.

7 See Fuchs, *Richard Long*, and Brown, *Occluded Front*.

8 Jellicoe himself gave the walk this title; others, such as Michael Spens, refer to it as the "Magritte Walk."

9 Jellicoe, *Guelph Lectures*, 168.

10 Ibid., 149.

11 Al-Khalil, *Monument*.

12 Current preservation law does not permit transplanting the trees, which grow only in this place.

13 This was one of a series of sound compositions produced by six artists for particular sites in Parc de La Villette as part of a program called "Le chemin à l'oreille: Parcours sonores," May 30–October 31, 1992. The artist who composed this piece was Raoul de Pesters.

14 Alexander Pope, "An Epistle to Lord Birmingham," 1731, reprinted in Hunt and Willis, *Genius*, 213.

15 Palladio, *Architecture*, 41.

16 Candace Slater, *Trail of Miracles: Stories from a Pilgrimage in Northeast Brazil* (Berkeley: University of California Press, 1986), 5–6, 67–69.

17 See Olmsted, *Niagara*.

18 Andersson, "Principper for bevaring."

19 Andersson, "Tycho Brahes trädgård," *ale: Historisk tidskrift för Skåneland* (1992/2), 26–32; "Uraniborgs renässansträdgård: restaureringsprojektets förutsättningar och hypoteser," *Stencil* (1993/7), 13–20.

20 Opening speech at EPCOT, quoted in Holliss and Sibley, *Disney Studio*, 102. See also Walt Disney on planning for EPCOT, quoted in Thomas, *Disney*, 375.

21 Morner and Rausch, *Literary Terms*, 8.

22 McArthur, *English Language*, 653.

23 Sørensen, *Haver*, 165.

24 John 5:4.

25 Wilhelm Miller, "The Prairie Spirit in Landscape Gardening," Circular no. 184 (Urbana: Agricultural Experiment Station, Department of Horticulture, University of Illinois, 1916).

26 Jane Austen, *Pride and Prejudice* (New York: Signet Classics, 1961), 204.

27 John Bartlett, *Familiar Quotations* (Boston: Little, Brown, 1955), 110.

28 Loudon, *Suburban Gardener*, and Downing, *Landscape Gardening*.

29 Woodbridge, *Stourhead Landscape*, 19.

30 Janet Bord, *Mazes and Labyrinths of the World* (New York: E. P. Dutton, 1976), 141.

31 Quarles, *Emblems Divine and Moral, Together with Hieroglyphics of the Life of Man*, 1777, quoted in Bord, *Mazes and Labyrinths*, 7. Mazes are not always associated with confusion or difficulties; in the Italian Renaissance garden, for instance, they may refer to "order and human skill," Lazzaro, *Italian Garden*, 51–55.

32 Jellicoe, *Guelph Lectures*, 149.

33 Ibid., 172.

34 Cronon, *Uncommon Ground*, 59–66.

35 Anthony Hecht, "The Gardens of the Villa d'Este," *Hard Hours* (New York: Atheneum, 1967).

36 Quoted in Hunt and Willis, *Genius*, 213.

37 Van Valkenburgh, *Transforming the American Garden*, 16–19.

38 Linden-Ward, *Silent City*, 58.

39 Spens, *Jellicoe at Shute*, 55.

40 Thomas, *Disney*, 279.

41 Ibid., 264. These figures apply to Disneyland; the scale at Disney World is slightly different, the miniaturization more exaggerated from first to third storys.

42 See Corn and Horrigan, *Yesterday's Tomorrows*, and Adams, *Burle Marx*.

43 Walt Disney, speech at opening ceremonies for Disneyland, July 17, 1955, quoted in Holliss and Sibley, *Disney Studio*, 70.

44 Thomas, *Disney*, 280.

45 Ibid., 253.

46 Ibid., 289.

47 Leonard Shannon, *Disneyland: Dreams, Traditions, and Transitions* (Walt Disney Company, n.d.), 151.

48 Thomas, *Disney*, 281.

49 The frog pond has since been refurbished.

50 Quoted in Thomas, *Disney*, 387.

51 "The Comprehensive Design Plan for the White House: Desired Futures" (National Park Service, October 1993), 43

9 POLEMICAL LANDSCAPES

1 Reinhard Rürup, ed., *Topography of Terror* (Berlin: Arenhövel, 1991), 197.

2 Riley and Brown have addressed this topic in "Analogy and Authority: Beyond Chaos and Kudzu," *Landscape Journal* 14:1 (1995), 87–92.

3 Crowe, "Presidential Address," *Journal of the Institute of Landscape Architects* (November 1957), 4.

4 Quoted in Gröning and Wolschke-Bulmahn, "Mania for Native Plants," 123–24.

5 Quoted in ibid., 121.

6   Quoted in ibid., 122.

7   Tanya Barrientos, "Aliens Among Us," *Inquirer: Philadelphia Inquirer Magazine*, June 30, 1996.

8   For a balanced view of the conundrums, see John Rodman, "Restoring Nature: Natives and Exotics," in *In the Nature of Things*, edited by Jane Bennett and William Chaloupka (Minneapolis: University of Minesota Press, 1993).

9   Quoted by Brendan Gill in *Many Masks* (New York: Ballantine, 1987), 22. Another version, almost word for word, is transcribed from a tape of August 4, 1957, in Wright, *Living Voice*, 88. Wright told Mike Wallace the following in a television interview in 1957: "I've always considered myself deeply religious," said Wright. "Do you go to any specific church?" asked Wallace. Wright replied, "My church [pause], I put a capital 'N' on Nature and go there."

10 Letter from Wright to Lewis Mumford, January 7, 1929, University of Pennsylvania Library, Special Collections, Mumford Papers, folder 5477. Wright, *Living Voice*, 88. See also Spirn, "Wright."

11 See Thompson and Steiner, *Ecological Design*. The phrase *nonecological* is used in this volume by several authors with divergent views on the nature of ecological design whose essays reveal the pitfalls of appealing to "ecology" or "nature" for authority in landscape design.

12 See Max Weber's analysis of three forms of authority—traditional, legal-rational, and charismatic—in *Economy and Society* (Berkeley: University of California Press, 1978).

13 Williams, "Ideas of Nature."

14 Arthur O. Lovejoy, "Meanings of 'Nature,'" in *A Documentary History of Primitivism and Other Ideas* (Baltimore: Johns Hopkins University Press, 1935).

15 Williams, *Keywords*, 219. Many essays and entire books have been written on the origins, history, use, and significance of the word *nature*. See, for example, Williams, "Ideas of Nature"; C. S. Lewis, "Nature," in *Studies in Words*; Lovejoy, "Meanings of 'Nature,'" and "Nature as Aesthetic Norm," in *Essays in the History of Ideas* (Baltimore, 1948); R. G. Collingwood, *The Idea of Nature* (London, 1945); Glacken, *Rhodian Shore*; Evernden, *Social Creation of Nature*; Cronon, *Uncommon Ground*.

16 See Worster, *Nature's Economy*; Botkin, *Discordant Harmonies*; Golley, *Ecosystem Concept*; and Gregg Mitman, *The State of Nature: Ecology, Community, and American Social Thought 1900–1950* (Chicago: University of Chicago Press, 1992).

17 Candace Slater, "Amazonia as Edenic Narrative," in Cronon, *Uncommon Ground*. Slater traces Edenic narratives as they relate to the biblical story of Genesis, but points out that such notions are not unique to the Judeo-Christian tradition. For a discussion of other religious traditions, see Poul Pedersen, "Nature, Religion, and Cultural Identity: The Religious Environmentalist Paradigm," in *Asian Perceptions of Nature*, edited by Arne Kalland and Ole Bruun (Richmond, Surrey: Curzon, 1995).

18 ". . . a sermon which awakens the best in the human soul." Jensen, *Siftings*, 63. Edgar Tafel, *Apprentice to Genius* (New York: Dover, 1985), 152, and Cornelia Brierly, personal communication, August 24, 1994. Brierly was assigned to assist Jensen when he visited Taliesin.

19 Wright, *Writings 1930–1932*, 163.

20 Jensen, *Siftings*, 94.

21 Ibid., 23.

22 Ibid., 21.

23 Jensen was born of a Danish-speaking family in the Slesvig region, the contested border zone of northern Germany and southern Denmark. For perspectives on contemporary Danish and German ideas of nature and natural gardens, see Kenneth Olwig, "Historical Geography and the Society/Nature Problematic: The Perspective of J. F. Schouw, George Perkins Marsh and E. Reclus," *Journal of Historical Geography* 6:1 (1980), and *Nature's Ideological Landscape*; Joachim

Wolschke-Bulmahn, "The Peculiar Garden: The Advent and Destruction of Modernism in German Garden Design," in *Masters of American Garden Design III: The Modern Garden in Europe and the United States*, edited by Rachel Karson (Proceedings of the Garden Conservancy Symposium, 1993). See also Frank Waugh, *The Natural Style in Landscape Gardening* (Boston: Richard G. Badger, 1917), for a North American perspective and Ruff, *Holland*, for an introduction to the work of Jacques Thijsse, J. Landwehr, and the Dutch *Heem* ("home") parks.

24 See Mitman, *State of Nature*, for a history of the Chicago school of ecology and the interplay between science and a social philosophy that stressed the value of cooperation over conflict.

25 For Jensen's relationship to these ideas, see Wolschke-Bulmahn, "The Peculiar Garden," and his review of Grese, *Jensen*, in *Journal of Garden History* 15 (1995), 54–55.

26 On the first day of class, I often ask students to define *nature*. Sometimes, at the end of the course I ask them to write a short paper defining *nature* once again. Their later answers are more articulate and reflective, but rarely change in substance from their first brief statement. I have concluded that ideas of nature are deeply held beliefs, closely tied to religious values, even for those who do not consider themselves religious. By the age of twenty-five, most students' ideas of nature seem set or at least not modified greatly by a single course on the subject (they range in age from twenty-two to fifty; most are in their mid to late twenties). While largely North American, approximately one-third have been from other parts of the world, including Europe, the Middle East, Africa, Asia, South America, and Australia. Of the North Americans, most grew up in the suburbs or in rural areas; a higher proportion of foreign students are from cities.

27 Ian McHarg, "Ecology and Design," in Thompson and Steiner, *Ecological Design*, 321.

28 One article included gratuitous, unfounded attacks, some from critics who chose to remain anonymous, such as: "The so-called Penn School led by McHarg produced a generation of landscape graduates who did not build." Daralice Boles, "The New American Landscape," *Progressive Architecture* (July 1989), 53. Statements such as these were retracted by the editors in a subsequent issue of the journal in response to letters to the editor.

29 Olin, "Form, Meaning, and Expression," 150.

30 Grese, *Jensen*, presents a useful comparison of the work of Olmsted and Jensen in this and other respects, but emphasizes similarities and does not probe their ideological differences.

31 The Ramble at Central Park was planted to appear wild, but it was only a small part of the park. William Robinson, an English acquaintance of Olmsted, published his book *The Wild Garden* in 1870. Olmsted was undoubtedly also aware of Martin Johnson Heade's contemporary paintings depicting marshes along Boston's North Shore.

32 Jensen, *Siftings*, 76.

33 Ibid., 77.

34 Olmsted, "Parks, Parkways and Pleasure Grounds," 253–54.

35 Jensen, *Siftings*, 83.

36 Ibid., 46.

37 Ibid., 35.

38 Ibid., 45.

39 Such views were common at the time, and Olmsted discussed them frequently in relation to his work. See, for example, *Niagara*.

40 Olmsted preferred to follow William Robinson's practice of mixing native and hardy exotic plants, described in *The Wild Garden* (1870). See Zaitzevsky, *Olmsted*, 196, for quotations of Olmsted's and Sargent's disagreement on this subject.

41 Olmsted, "General Plan for the Sanitary Improvement of Muddy River and for Completing a Continuous Promenade between Boston Common and Jamaica Pond" (Boston, 1881).

42 Robert Dorman, *Revolt of the Provinces: The Regionalist Movement in America* (Chapel Hill: University of North Carolina Press, 1993).

43 See Donald Scherer and Thomas Attig, eds., *Ethics and the Environment* (Englewood Cliffs: Prentice-Hall, 1983).

44 From the report for the West End Redevelopment Scheme, part of the Boston General Plan of 1950, reproduced on a slide in the Fisher Fine Arts Library, University of Pennsylvania.

45 Gans, *Urban Villagers*, 386.

46 Marc Fried, "Grieving for a Lost Home," in Leonard Duhl, ed., *The Urban Condition* (New York: Basic Books, 1963), 151–71.

47 Jacobs, *Death and Life*, 3.

48 See Walter Hood's documentation of the history of four small parks in Oakland, California, in *Urban Diaries*.

49 Olin, "Regionalism."

50 See Casey Blake, "An Atmosphere of Effrontery: Richard Serra, *Tilted Arc*, and the Crisis of Public Art," in *Power of Culture*, edited by Richard Wightman Fox and T. J. Jackson Lears (Chicago: University of Chicago Press, 1993).

51 Ibid., 253, 264.

52 Ibid.

53 The Vietnam Veterans Memorial, however, was built with private funds.

54. Interview in Landecker, *Martha Schwartz*, 109.

55 Ibid., 149.

56 Schwartz, "Bagel Garden," 45–46. Schwartz, "Author-Designer Responds," *Landscape Architecture* (May 1980), 320. Daralice Boles, "New American Landscape," *Progressive Architecture* (July 1989).

57 Lasswell, *Signature of Power*, 7.

58 This description is from Mukerji, *Territorial Ambitions*, 46–48.

59 Lasswell, *Signature of Power*, 57.

60 Ibid.

61 A phrase used by Alexander Pope in "An Epistle to Lord Birmingham," 1731, repr. in Hunt and Willis, *Genius*, 213.

62 Dean MacCannell, *Empty Meeting Grounds* (London: Routledge, 1992), 81–82, cites numerous restrictions on house color and landscaping described in literature he received from Irvine's Chamber of Commerce: various covenants stipulate that houses must be painted with bland, earth tones. My rental agreement when I lived in Irvine in 1994 prohibited me from replacing the sheer, white curtains provided on all windows.

63 Italo Calvino, *Invisible Cities* (New York: Harcourt Brace Jovanovich, 1972), 165.

Sources

Sources acknowledge influential works, open the field to those interested in exploring it further, and reveal untrodden ground. This compilation is multidisciplinary, but is neither comprehensive nor exhaustive. It includes nonverbal sources not ordinarily cited in a bibliography, such as landscapes, maps, and photographs. As outlined above, the sources are divided into three major parts: landscapes, authors of landscape, and general references on reading and telling landscape. Primary sources—places themselves, materials consulted in archives, and interviews with landscape authors—are listed separately from secondary sources; landscapes, maps, photographs, and paintings studied in reproduction are under published sources. This selective list cites works of particular significance in shaping my ideas and others that will introduce readers to sources for further study of landscape as language. For more sources on specific topics, see the chapter notes.

LANDSCAPES

Nothing can replace direct encounter with the literature of landscape—places themselves, their sounds, smells, colors, textures, views, spatial sequences and relationships, feel of sun and wind. I am often familiar with a place I visit for the first time, have studied it in texts, plans, drawings, and photographs; yet I always discover the unforeseen and sometimes revise my views entirely after experiencing a place firsthand. Some places are disappointing (Salk Institute in La Jolla); others a delightful surprise (Villa Rotunda in Italy). Several telling differences between the work of "Capability" Brown and William Kent emerged only after visits to Bowood and Rousham in England. At the Villa Lante, I was unprepared for the significance of sound—lush, rhythmic, harmonic, melodic, symphonic sounds of waters gushing, roaring, rustling, spraying, splashing, dripping, resonating within manifold containers shaped to project, amplify, and even to silence. Fieldwork is essential to fluency in landscape language, and it shapes ideas. But experience alone is rarely sufficient to fully understand a place; depictions of places in maps, photographs, and paintings enable deeper readings, as do written guides. And one cannot visit every place; published sources are valuable substitutes to direct encounter, though not equivalents. It is best to be explicit about which landscapes one has read directly, and which one has experienced only through secondary sources.

Places: Fieldwork

The landscape sources listed below are organized alphabetically, by continent, country, and, in the United States, by state. The list is of places cited in the text or particularly influential in shaping my ideas. Since 1988, I have kept travel journals; transcribed into computer text in 1993, indexed by keywords, they were sources for refining key concepts as related to particular places. I have experienced some over many years. I have shaped others: community gardens in West Philadelphia and the Dorchester and Roxbury neighborhoods of Boston; the Toronto Central Waterfront; Woodlands, Texas; Sanibel Island, Florida. I have visited all types of biomes except tropical rain forest and arctic tundra, though not all continents or all great landscapes or works by all important authors. Many places I have not experienced directly are included among published sources.

Asia: Japan. 1990, by train from Osaka to Kyoto, Kobe, Ise, Toba, and Tokyo. Startling juxtapositions between traditional and new landscapes: in Osaka the Shitennoji temple district, the castle park, and the modern central city; in Tokyo, Asakusa, Shinjuku, Ginza, and the Meiji Shrine; in Kyoto, Gion, Tadao Ando's Time I, and the Kamo River, imperial villas of Katsura and Shugakuin, gardens in monasteries and temples (Saihoji, Ryoanji, Shisendo, Daitokuji). In Kobe, recently built landscapes: a floodplain park, a new town and winery behind the mountains, Port Island, newly built on fill, and Tadao Ando's Chapel at the Mt. Rokko Hotel.

Australia. 1987, from the tropical landscapes of Darwin and Kakadu National Park to the central desert of Uluru and Alice Springs, the new town of Yolara near Uluru, to Canberra and the new Parliament House, then to Sydney. 1988, Glenn Murcutt's house for Sydney Ball; Richard Le Plastrier's house in a palm grove. I walked the northern shore of Sydney Harbor, sailed its length, flew over it in a helicopter. At Melbourne, Werribee Farm sewage treatment facility.

Europe: Denmark. 1964–66, 1973, and frequent visits in 1990–95, based in Lejre, a settlement from ancient times, Roskilde, a provincial town, and Copenhagen, but with field trips throughout the country. The pattern of visits provided a perspective on landscape change, especially the transformations between 1966 and 1973, a time of prosperity: by 1973 bicycles were dramatically diminished, and cars and parking lots had proliferated. 1990–95, cemeteries and gardens by G. N. Brandt and dozens of C. Th. Sørensen's gardens, parks, amphitheaters, campuses, and housing projects.

Europe: Finland. 1990, Helsinki and a small island (Möland) in the Archipelago. The landscapes of the city parks, the harbor and its fort, the inland lakes surrounded by dark firs gave context to the work of Saarinen, Aalto, and the Sirens. The planned, manicured environment of Tapiola seemed bland in contrast to the vitality of another planned development, Kottby, built in the 1920s for workers.

Europe: France. 1978, Saint Malo, a town destroyed in the Second World War and reconstructed with new buildings and ramparts in old style, Dinan, a provincial town in Normandy, Mont-Saint-Michel, Chartres, and Paris. 1992–97, Paris, as advisor to the Organization for Economic Cooperation and Development, exploring traces of various times: from ancient Rome (Amphitheater Lutèce) to the Renaissance (Hotel Sully and Place des Vosges), the nineteenth-century city of Haussmann and Alphand (Père Lachaise, Buttes Chaumont, the boulevards), to more recent landscapes at La Défense, Parc de La Villette, and Parc Citröen. The Île-de-France, landscape compositions of André Le Nôtre at Vaux-le-Vicomte, Versailles, Chantilly, Sceaux and Claude Monet's garden at Giverny. 1996, Verdun, to see the First World War landscapes.

EUROPE: GERMANY. 1966, Heidelberg, the Rhine, Munich and Dachau, East Germany, and Berlin. 1983, Munich, the Englischer Garten, housing projects of the early twentieth century, then Stuttgart to see an urban landscape planned to funnel fresh cool air off the hillsides in order to reduce air pollution. 1990, Hannover and its Herrenhausen. 1993, the autobahns, across former East Germany to conference in Potsdam, the gardens at Sansoucci and ruins and reconstructions in Berlin. 1996, Trier and its Roman ruins en route to Verdun.

EUROPE: ITALY. 1988, Redipuglia, via Trieste, then the Veneto and Carlo Scarpa's Brione Cemetery, Palladio's Villa Rotundo, near Vicenza, and the Villa Barbara at Maser. 1996, Hadrian's Villa and Villa d'Este in Tivoli, Boboli Gardens, Villa Medici and others in Florence, Villa Lante and Bomarzzo north of Rome.

EUROPE: NETHERLANDS. 1978, Amsterdam and the polderlands, from the long, narrow fields of early examples to the vast new polders.

EUROPE: SLOVENIA. 1988, Ljubljana, the works of Joze Plecnik—bridges, lampposts, and other artifacts, the Slovene countryside.

EUROPE: SPAIN. 1983, Andalusia, from Málaga to Antequera, and several other white hilltowns. Granada, to trace the flow of water through the gardens of the Alhambra and Generalife.

EUROPE: SWEDEN. 1990–96, the medieval university town of Lund, the city of Malmö, and the countryside of Skåne, Sven-Ingvar Andersson's house and garden at Marnas, the beech forest nearby, Per Friberg's house and garden, Malmö Eastern Cemetery by Sigurd Lewerentz. 1990, with Andersson to the park he designed in Ronneby and to Stockholm, Lewerentz's and Gunnar Asplund's Forest Cemetery, the beach park of Holger Blom.

EUROPE: UNITED KINGDOM. 1973, walks in the Wye River Valley near Hereford, along public footpaths on the British Ordinance Survey maps. 1978, Scotland, Glasgow, Glencoe, the Great Glen, Glen Loy and Glen Roy, Edinburgh. 1983, Stonehenge, Avebury, and the Ridgeway, Port Sunlight and Joseph Paxton's People's Park in Birkenhead, then Liverpool and London to compare the inner-city landscapes to those of American cities. London's residential squares, Hyde Park, St. James Park, Regent Street, and Regent's Park, Camdentown Garden Center and Urban Farm (vacant land reclaimed). 1987, Avebury and the Ridgeway, the Vale of the White Horse, Glastonbury, Hampton Court, Claremont, Rousham, Bowood and its adventure playground, Blenheim, Longleat and its maze and safari park, Stourhead, Hestercombe, Sissinghurst, and Hidcote; at Bath, from Roman Baths to eighteenth- and nineteenth-century parks and residential developments by John Nash.

NORTH AMERICA: CANADA. 1975–76, fieldwork for a study of the environmental resources of Toronto's Central Waterfront; 1985 and 1991, the waterfront and Don River Valley revisited.

UNITED STATES:

ARIZONA. 1984, Phoenix and Taliesin West. 1990, Phoenix, canals and dams of the Salt River Project, gardens by Steve Martino and John Douglas, South Mountain. 1995 and 1996, living and working at Taliesin West for several weeks. 1996, the Sonoran desert around Phoenix, the high desert in the Flagstaff volcano field, Grand Canyon.

CALIFORNIA. 1976, Berkeley, San Francisco, Marin County, and Point Reyes. 1986, Plazas and parks in San Francisco, Donnell Garden, by Thomas Church, in Sonoma. 1989, San Diego, Torrey Pines, Salk Institute at La Jolla. 1990, with Lawrence Halprin to see places he designed: the garden for his parents-in-law, the community of Woodlake, the San Jose Freeway, a garden under construction. 1994, Irvine and the new "edge-city" landscapes of Orange County, Disneyland, the Crystal Cathedral, SWA Group's Fashion Island in Newport Beach and South Coast Plaza in Costa Mesa, Noguchi's California Scenario, also in Costa Mesa. I participated in Halprin's community workshops on the future of Laguna Creek Wilderness Park. Study trips with colleagues in residence at the Humanities Research Center: a day-long journey up the Los Angeles River from Long Beach to South Central, Watts, and Pasadena; field trips to Laguna Beach, San Diego's Sea World, and the desert near Palm Springs. 1995, Death Valley, its hillsides of brown, green, orange, and white, Sunset Crater, salt flats. 1996, UCLA, Brentwood, and Culver City, Orange County and Laguna Beach revisited.

COLORADO. 1976, Denver, to inventory natural resources and hazards, the Platte River and Red Rocks Amphitheater, foothills along the Front Range west of Denver and Boulder, Rocky Mountain National Park, Vail. 1985, Platte River Greenway, Confluence Park, Harvard Gulch, and Boulder Creek—Denver's innovative flood control and storm drainage system. 1986, Colorado Springs and Garden of the Gods. 1989, Denver, Red Rocks, and Foothills Highway revisited, Fort Collins and the foothills, the High Plains and Pawnee National Grassland. 1990, from Denver's edge-city office parks and Harlequin Plaza, west into the mountains via Kenosha Pass to South Park, Fairplay, and Beaver Creek.

CONNECTICUT. From 1947, northwestern Connecticut: New Preston, Washington, and the Shepaug River Valley. 1978, Carl Andre's Stone Field in Hartford.

DISTRICT OF COLUMBIA. August 23, 1963, from Constitution Avenue to the Reflecting Pool, Lincoln Memorial and "I have a dream": the March on Washington. 1981, projects of the National Park Service's Ecological Services Laboratory: the Mall, Constitution Gardens, George Washington Parkway, Rock Creek Parkway. 1986, 1990, 1996, Vietnam Veterans Memorial. 1994 and 1996, the gardens of Dumbarton Oaks. 1994, at the Woodrow Wilson Center, an office high up in the Smithsonian Castle's flag tower, with a view of the Washington Monument, Lincoln Memorial, and Arlington Cemetery prompted reflections on prospects and axes; daily walks on the Mall in 1995–96 emphasized effects of scale.

FLORIDA. 1975, Sanibel Island, fieldwork for a comprehensive plan included nocturnal field trips to tag alligators and observe baby sea turtles. 1989, Amelia Island to see the product of a plan produced by Wallace McHarg Roberts and Todd twenty years earlier. 1989 and 1990, Disney World, including a "back-stage" tour of the nurseries. 1991, University of Miami, Coral Gables, Vizcaya, Fairchild Gardens, and Matheson's Hammock.

KANSAS. 1991, from Kansas City up the Kansas River Valley to the Konza Prairie, then zigged and zagged across the Great Plains on routes aligned with the midwestern grid.

KENTUCKY. 1991, Lexington, limestone and Bluegrass Country, Gainesway Stables designed by A. E. Bye, Pleasant Hill Shaker Community.

MAINE. 1976–80, week-long stays along the coast of Maine from Camden to Mount Desert Island.

MASSACHUSETTS. 1965–69 and 1977–86, Cambridge, Harvard Square, Harvard Yard, and the Charles River were home landscapes. 1969, walked the length of Boston's Emerald Necklace: Fens, Riverway, Ward Pond, Jamaica Pond, Arnold Arboretum, Franklin Park. 1971–76, second-growth woods of Amherst and Quabbin in central Massachusetts. 1979 and 1980, experiments by Peter Walker and Martha Schwartz: field of Necco wafers at MIT, roof garden, Bagel Garden. 1980–91, beaches, marshes, and dunes, bogs and woods of Cape Cod. 1982–85, Cambridge's Mount Auburn Cemetery, Boston's Neponset River, Roxbury, and Dorchester were sites for studio courses and research; Boston Harbor Islands, Beacon Hill, Boston Common, the Public Garden, Back Bay were subjects of lectures. 1993, Cambridge, Splice Garden with Martha Schwartz. 1997, the Fens, Roxbury, and Dorchester revisited.

MINNESOTA. 1985–86, St. Paul for State Capitol Competition.

MISSOURI. 1986, Washington University and St. Louis, the Arch and the Mississippi River. 1991, Kansas City, George Kessler's Park System, the Paseo.

NEVADA. 1995, Las Vegas and the Strip, Mirage Volcano, Hoover Dam.

NEW HAMPSHIRE. 1987, Mount Washington and the White Mountains.

NEW MEXICO. 1989, Albuquerque, Santa Fe, and landscapes significant to Native Americans, ancient and modern: Chimayo, Taos Pueblo, Aztec Ruins, Mesa Verde (Colorado), Chaco Canyon, and Acoma Pueblo.

NEW JERSEY. 1971, Alloway, Salem, and the coastal plain of southern New Jersey, Island Beach State Park, the Pine Barrens.

NEW YORK. 1967–97, New York City, weekend and day trips to Manhattan and Brooklyn. 1973–74, fieldwork on Long Island for new residential developments at Eaton's Point and Gardiner's Cove. 1975, Buffalo and Niagara Falls. 1995–97, the Adirondacks and its camps.

NORTH CAROLINA. 1976, the Blue Ridge Parkway, all the way to Asheville and the Smoky Mountains, an experience of road design as a form of art and narrative.

OHIO. 1953–65, Cincinnati and Wyoming, a suburb in the Mill Creek Valley, were landscapes of childhood and adolescence. A tributary of the Mill Creek flowed a few blocks from my home; from hilltop to valley was an economic transect from wealthy to poor neighborhoods. 1989, Columbus and Indian mounds at Newark.

OREGON. 1975 and 1995, Portland and urban redevelopment of 1960s, including Halprin's fountains and Pettigrove Park, Pioneer Square.

PENNSYLVANIA. 1969–77 and, since 1986, Philadelphia. 1970–73, field trips in the Delaware River Basin were an introduction to landscape architecture at University of Pennsylvania. 1987–98, working in West Philadelphia and Mill Creek, living in Chestnut Hill, the drive down the Wissahickon Valley and along the banks of the Schuylkill River is a daily route. 1992, farm country around Lancaster with a Mennonite farmer and my Danish father. 1995, Gettysburg, where smooth slopes and green lawns contrast with the rough, rocky slopes of Civil War photographs. Every year since 1995, I have been introduced to new sections of the city by my students, who trace the evolution of a neighborhood over time as part of their classwork. The choice of neighborhood is theirs.

SOUTH CAROLINA. 1989, Charleston and two former rice plantations along the Ashley River: Middleton Place and Drayton Hall.

TEXAS. 1973, fieldwork in pine-oak forest north of Houston for the Woodlands, a new town; in 1991, the result was disappointing. 1991, downtown Houston, River Oaks, Buffalo Bayou, Memorial Park, and the low-lying Fourth Ward, an African-American neighborhood of small frame houses, seen against distant downtown towers. 1987, Dallas, Fountain Square, Robert Irwin's Portal Park Slice, and downtown plazas.

VIRGINIA. 1976, Skyline Drive to the Blue Ridge Parkway. 1985 and 1989, Monticello and the University of Virginia, Charlottesville. 1996, Arlington Cemetery, John F. Kennedy Memorial, and Robert F. Kennedy Memorial.

WASHINGTON. 1988 and 1995, Seattle, to see Freeway Park, Gas Works Park, and Bloedel Reserve. 1995, Mill Creek Canyon Park, a landscape designed by the artist Herbert Bayer for stormwater management.

WISCONSIN. 1994, University of Wisconsin at Madison and the Driftless Region, including Frank Lloyd Wright's Taliesin in Spring Green and the Wisconsin Dells. 1997, further fieldwork at Taliesin.

Places: Maps, Archives, and Museums

Maps, photographs, and paintings, though one or more steps removed from the places they depict, help decipher traces and places that might not otherwise be seen: past settlement, rocks underground, an entire region, a place one has never been, significant details of light, color, texture. Examples of those studied in the original are discussed below; others are listed under Places: Published Sources.

MAPS. Historic maps make it possible to trace certain kinds of landscape change over time. Using a soil map of Iowa County from 1910, for example, I was able to observe that Frank Lloyd Wright sited buildings and planted groves at Taliesin on erodible, rocky soils, leaving the more fertile soils for crops and pasture. (Lounsbury, Clarence, et al. *Soil Map: Wisconsin, Iowa County Sheet.* [Washington, D.C.: Bureau of Soils, U.S. Department of Agriculture, 1910]. Appended to Whitson et al., see Places: Published Sources.) Insurance atlases of the nineteenth and twentieth centuries, such as those published by G. W. Bromley, depict streets, sewers, streetcar lines, buildings and their materials, structure, occupancy, and use (and sometimes even owners' names). They are drawn at a much finer-grained scale (e.g., 1 inch = 100 feet; scales vary) and contain far more detail than most other historic maps, and they cover entire cities. I constructed an understanding of the evolution of Boston's Dudley Street neighborhood and Philadelphia's Mill Creek through studying successive atlases; such atlases are available for many American cities.

Contemporary maps published by the U.S. Geological Survey for many of the places I studied are not cited individually here. These maps of landforms, waterways, roads and trails, buildings, woods, fields, marshes, orchards reflect an extraordinary amount of information; overlaid, they reveal correlations among landscape features otherwise difficult to detect. Nor have I cited here other contemporary maps and aerial photographs of places which I consulted, such as those produced by federal and state agencies like the Soil

Conservation Service, the Wisconsin Geological and Natural History Survey, and the Colorado Geological Survey.

ARCHIVES: PHOTOGRAPHS. Photographic archives were another source of records for tracing landscape change. Photographs and newspaper articles from the Urban Archives at Temple University document successive cave-ins on and around Philadelphia's Mill Creek from the 1930s on. By assembling hundreds of photographs of Taliesin North, I was able to reconstruct the way the landscape changed from the late nineteenth century, before Frank Lloyd Wright built there, to the construction of his home in 1911, until his death in 1959. Gathering these photographs required searching several archives: the Wood Collection and the John Howe Collection at the State Historical Society of Wisconsin, Madison; the Frank Lloyd Wright Archives at Taliesin West, Scottsdale, Arizona.

MUSEUMS: PAINTINGS. Landscape paintings often distill significant qualities of particular places: clouds and light in seventeenth-century Dutch paintings; colors and forms of eroded slopes in the mountains and hills of New Mexico in Georgia O'Keeffe's work; effect of wind on leaves and light brushed by Johan Thomas Lundbye, the nineteenth-century Danish painter. Exhibitions of works by the same artist or on a single theme permit insights difficult to glean from individual works. For example, an exhibit of O'Keeffe's paintings at New York's Metropolitan Museum of Art in 1988 permitted the comparison of depictions of New York and New Mexico; another, at Louisiana Museum in Denmark in 1994, of Claude Monet's paintings of Giverny from 1880 to 1926 showed the development of both his gardens and vision. "The Golden Age of Danish Painting," a show at the Metropolitan Museum of Art in 1994, featured nineteenth-century Danish landscape paintings and highlighted typical features Danes still value.

Places: Published Sources

There is a wealth of published sources on landscapes of particular places. A brief selection, arranged here by continent, includes books on gardens and urban design, geography and geology, culture and politics, as expressed in landscape. For classic readings, see Watts, *Reading the Landscape of America*, on natural landscapes; Hoskins and J. B. Jackson on vernacular landscapes of England and the United States, respectively. For design and politics: in European landscapes, see Mukerji (Versailles), Cosgrove (Italy's Veneto), Pugh (Rousham), Olwig (Danish heath); in North America, see Rosenzweig and Blackmar (Central Park), Greiff (Independence National Park), Gans (Boston's West End), White (Columbia River).

Regional guides are useful tools for reading the landscape of a particular place. State Geological Surveys often produce excellent contemporary guides; see, for example, Chronic, *Prairie, Peak, and Plateau*. Among the best general introductions to the natural and cultural history of a region's landscape are geological and soil surveys from the early twentieth century, which often summarize history of land use; see Whitson's soil survey (1914) of the county in Wisconsin where Wright's Taliesin is located.

Certain fiction and poetry are guides to reading local landscapes; Twain's description of the Mississippi River, Cather's of the American prairie, Heaney's and Montague's of Ireland are examples of a long tradition rich in description of particular places and their dialects. Knowledge of literature is essential to reading other places; Hunt and Woodbridge read dialogues among literary and garden texts in English gardens. Dialects provide clues to reading local landscapes: Basso and Munn relate Apache and Walbiri languages, respectively, to the landscapes they inhabit; Stilgoe, *Shallow-water Dictionary*, describes "estuary English."

Most sources describe places in words; others depict in paintings and photographs. Corner and MacLean, in *Taking Measures across the American Landscape*, combine telling aerial photographs and graphic interpretations. In *American Country Woman*, Lange investigates the relationship between people and place on the ground. Photographs can show landscape change and past practices: see Helphand, *Colorado*; paired images of New Mexico's and Boston's past and present in Jackson, *The Essential Landscape*, and Campbell, *Cityscapes of Boston*; and nineteenth-century photographs in Adams, *Atget's Gardens*.

ASIA

Ashihara, Yoshinobu. *The Hidden Order: Tokyo through the Twentieth Century*. Tokyo: Kodansha International, 1989.

Inoue, Mitsuo. *Space in Japanese Architecture*. New York: Weatherhill, 1985.

Itoh, Teiji. *Space and Illusion in Japanese Garden*. New York: Weatherhill/Tankosha, 1973.

Keswick, Maggie. *The Chinese Garden*. New York: St. Martin's Press, 1986.

Kuck, Loraine. *The World of the Japanese Garden*. New York: John Weatherhill, 1980.

Moynihan, Elizabeth B. *Paradise as a Garden in Persia and Mughal India*. New York: George Braziller, 1979.

Siren, Osvald. *Gardens of China*. New York: The Ronald Press, 1949.

Wescoat, James L., Jr., and Joachim Wolschke-Bulmahn. *Mughal Gardens*. Washington, D.C.: Dumbarton Oaks, 1996.

AUSTRALIA

Bell, Diane. *Daughters of the Dreaming*. Melbourne, Australia: McPhee, Gribble/George Allen and Unwin, 1983.

Benterrak, Krim, Stephen Muecke, and Paddy Roe. *Reading the Country*. Fremantle, Australia: Fremantle Arts Center Press, 1983.

Berndt, Ronald, and Catherine H. Berndt. *The Speaking Land*. Australia: Penguin, 1989.

Breeden, Stanley, and Belinda Wright. *Kakadu*. Brookvale, Australia: Simon and Schuster, 1989.

Flood, Josephine. *Archaeology of the Dreamtime*. Sydney, Australia: 1988.

Isaacs, Jennifer. *Arts of the Dreaming*. Sydney, Australia: Lansdowne Press, 1984.

——, ed. *Australian Dreaming: 40,000 Years of Aboriginal History*. Sydney, Australia: Lansdowne Press, 1981.

Layton, Robert. *Uluru*. Canberra, Australia: Australian Institute of Aboriginal Studies, 1986.

Munn, Nancy. D. *Walbiri Iconography*. Chicago: University of Chicago Press, 1986.

Myers, Fred R. *Pintupi Country, Pintupi Self*. Washington, D.C.: Smithsonian Institution Press, 1986.

Seddon, George. *Swan River Landscapes*. Nedlands, Australia: University of Western Australia Press, 1970.

Sutton, Peter, et al. *Dreamings: The Art of Aboriginal Australia*. New York: George Braziller, 1988.

Taylor, Jennifer. *Australian Architecture Since 1960*. North Ryde, Australia: Law Book Company, 1986.

EUROPE

Adams, Henry. *Mont Saint Michel and Chartres*. New York: G. P. Putnam, 1980.

Adams, William Howard. *Atget's Gardens*. Garden City, N.Y.: Doubleday, 1979.

Andersson, Sven-Ingvar, and Annemarie Lund. *Landscape Art in Denmark*. Copenhagen: Arkitektens Forlag, 1990.

Bermingham, Ann. *Landscape and Ideology: The English Rustic Tradition, 1740–1860*. Berkeley:

University of California Press, 1986.

Burl, Aubrey. *Prehistoric Avebury*. New Haven: Yale University Press, 1979.

Cosgrove, Denis. *Palladian Landscape*. State College: Pennsylvania State Press, 1993.

Crouch, Dora P. *Water Management in Ancient Greek Cities*. New York: Oxford University Press, 1993.

Daniels, Stephen. *Fields of Vision*. Princeton: Princeton University Press, 1993.

Grabar, Oleg. *The Alhambra*. Cambridge: Harvard University Press, 1978.

Gröning, Gert, and Joachim Wolschke. "Some Notes on the Mania for Native Plants in Germany." *Landscape Journal* 11, no. 2 (Fall 1992).

Hansen, Martin A. *Dansk Vejr*. Copenhagen: Hasselbalch, 1953.

Heaney, Seamus. "The Sense of Place." In *Preoccupations: Selected Prose 1968–1978*. New York: Farrar, Straus, Giroux, 1980.

———. *Selected Poems 1966–1987*. New York: Farrar, Straus, and Giroux, 1990.

Hoskins, W. G. *The Making of the English Landscape*. Baltimore: Penguin Books, 1970.

Hunt, John Dixon. *The Figure in the Landscape: Poetry, Painting and Gardening during the Eighteenth Century*. Baltimore: Johns Hopkins University Press, 1976.

———. *Garden and Grove: The Italian Renaissance Garden in the English Imagination, 1600–1750*. Princeton: Princeton University Press, 1986.

———. *Gardens and the Picturesque*. Cambridge: MIT Press, 1992.

———, and Peter Willis, eds. *The Genius of Place: The English Landscape Garden 1620–1820*. New York: Harper and Row, 1975.

Jashemski, Wilhelmina. *The Gardens of Pompeii*. New Rochelle, N.Y.: Caratzas Brothers, 1979.

Lambert, Audrey M. *The Making of the Dutch Landscape*. New York: Seminar Press, 1971.

Lazzaro, Claudia. *The Italian Renaissance Garden*. New Haven: Yale University Press, 1990.

Lund, Annemarie. *Danish Landscape Architecture, 1000–1996*. Copenhagen: Arkitektens Forlag, 1997.

Monrad, Konrad. *Golden Age of Danish Painting*. New York: Hudson Hills Press, 1993.

Montague, John. *Selected Poems*. Winston-Salem, N.C.: Wake Forest University Press, 1991.

Mukerji, Chandra. *Territorial Ambitions and the Gardens of Versailles*. Cambridge: Cambridge University Press, 1997.

Olwig, Kenneth. *Nature's Ideological Landscape*. London: George Allen and Unwin, 1984.

Prieto-Moreno, Francisco. *Los Jardines de Granada*. Madrid: Grefol, 1983.

Pugh, Simon. *Garden-Nature-Language*. Manchester, U.K.: Manchester University Press, 1988.

Ruff, Alan. *Holland and the Ecological Landscape*. Stockport, U.K., 1979.

Shepherd, J. C., and G. A. Jellicoe. *Italian Gardens of the Renaissance*. Princeton: Princeton Architectural Press, 1986.

Stechow, Wolfgang. *Dutch Landscape Painting of the Seventeenth Century*. London: Phaidon Press, 1966.

Taylor, C. *Fields in the English Landscape*. London: J. M. Dent, 1975.

Varnedoe, Kirk. *Northern Light*. New Haven: Yale University Press, 1988.

Watts, May Theilgaard. *Reading the Landscape of Europe*. New York: Harper and Row, 1971.

Weigand, T., and H. Schrader. *Priene*. Berlin: G. Reimer, 1904.

Whittow, J. B. *Geology and Scenery in Scotland*. Middlesex, U.K.: Penguin Books, 1977.

Woodbridge, Kenneth. *The Stourhead Landscape*. N.p.: National Trust, 1986.

NORTH AMERICA

Adams, Robert. *From the Misssouri West*. New York: Aperture, 1980.

Banham, Reyner. *Los Angeles*. Harmondsworth, U.K.: Penguin, 1973.

Basso, Keith H. *Wisdom Sits in Places*. Albuquerque: University of New Mexico Press, 1996.

Beard, Richard. *Walt Disney's Epcot Center*. New York: Harry N. Abrams, 1982.

Beardsley, John. *Gardens of Revelation*. New York: Abbeville, 1995.

Campbell, Robert, and Peter Vanderwarker. *Cityscapes of Boston*. Boston: Houghton Mifflin, 1992.

Capasso, Nicholas J. "Vietnam Veterans Memorial." In *The Critical Edge*, edited by Tod A. Marder, 189–202. Cambridge: MIT Press, 1985.

Cather, Willa. *My Ántonia*. Boston: Houghton Mifflin, 1954.

Chronic, John, and Halka Chronic. *Prairie, Peak, and Plateau*. Colorado Geological Survey Bulletin 32. Denver: Colorado Geological Survey, 1972.

Conzen, Michael, ed. *The Making of the American Landscape*. Boston: Unwin Hyman, 1990.

Corner, James, and Alex S. MacLean. *Taking Measures Across the American Landscape*. New Haven: Yale University Press, 1996.

Creese, Walter L. *The Crowning of the American Landscape*. Princeton: Princeton University Press, 1985.

Cronon, William. *Changes in the Land*. New York: Hill and Wang, 1983.

———. *Nature's Metropolis*. New York: W. W. Norton, 1991.

Engel, J. Ronald. *Sacred Sands: The Struggle for Community in the Indiana Dunes*. Middletown, Conn.: Wesleyan University Press, 1983.

Findlay, John M. *Magic Lands: Western Cityscapes and American Culture after 1940*. Berkeley: University of California Press, 1992.

Francaviglia, Richard V. *The Mormon Landscape*. New York: AMS Press, 1978.

Gans, Herbert J. *The Urban Villagers*, updated and expanded edition. New York: Free Press, 1982.

Garnett, William. *Aerial Photographs*. Berkeley: University of California Press, 1994.

Garreau, Joel. *Edge City*. New York: Doubleday, 1991.

Greiff, Constance M. *Independence: The Creation of a National Park*. Philadelphia: University of Pennsylvania Press, 1987.

Gutheim, Frederick. *The Federal City*. Washington, D.C.: Smithsonian Institution Press, 1976.

Helphand, Kenneth. *Colorado: Visions of an American Landscape*. Niwot, Colo.: Roberts Rinehart, 1991.

Hill, Mary. *California Landscape*. Berkeley: University of California Press, 1984.

Hogan, Pendleton. *The Lawn: A Guide to Jefferson's University*. Charlottesville: University Press of Virginia, 1987.

Iseley, N. Jane, and William P. Baldwin. *Plantations of the Low Country: South Carolina 1697–1865*. Greensboro, N.C.: Legacy Publications, 1985.

Jackson, John Brinckerhoff. *The Essential Landscape: The New Mexico Photographic Survey*. Albuquerque: University of New Mexico Press, 1985.

———. *Landscape in Sight: Looking at America*. New Haven: Yale University Press, 1997.

Jackson, Kenneth. *Crabgrass Frontier: The Suburbanization of the United States*. Oxford: Oxford University Press, 1985.

Kreisman, Lawrence. *The Bloedel Reserve*. Bainbridge Island, Wash.: Bloedel Reserve; Arbor Fund, 1988.

Lange, Dorothea. *American Photographs*. San Francisco: Chronicle Books, 1994.

———. *Dorothea Lange Looks at the American Country Woman*. Fort Worth: Amon Carter Museum, 1967.

Linden-Ward, Blanche. *Silent City on a Hill: Landscapes of Memory and Boston's Mount Auburn Cemetery*. Columbus: Ohio State University Press, 1989.

Longstreth, Richard, ed. *The Mall in Washington 1791–1991*. Washington, D.C.: National Gallery of Art, 1991.

Lopes, Sal. *The Wall: Images and Offerings from the Vietnam Veterans Memorial*. New York: Collins, 1987.

MacLean, Alex S. *Look at the Land.* New York: Rizzoli, 1993.

McPhee, John. *The Control of Nature.* New York: Farrar, Straus, Giroux, 1989.

Meyerowitz, Joel. *Cape Light.* Boston: Little, Brown, 1985.

————. *St. Louis and the Arch.* Boston: New York Graphic Society, 1980.

Novack, Barbara. *Nature and Culture: American Landscape and Painting 1825–1875.* New York: Oxford University Press, 1981.

O'Malley, Therese, and Marc Treib. *Regional Garden Design in the United States.* Washington, D.C.: Dumbarton Oaks, 1995.

Riley, Robert B. "Square to the Road, Hogs to the East." *Places* 2:4, 72–79.

Rosenzweig, Robert, and Elizabeth Blackmar. *The Park and the People: A History of Central Park.* Ithaca: Cornell University Press, 1992.

Scruggs, Jan C., and Joel L. Swerdlow. *To Heal a Nation: Vietnam Veterans Memorial.* New York: Harper and Row, 1985.

Schafer, R. Murray, ed. *The Vancouver Soundscape.* Vancouver, B.C.: A.R.C. Publications, 1978.

Stilgoe, John R. *Common Landscape of America.* New Haven: Yale University Press, 1982.

————. *Shallow-water Dictionary: A Grounding in Estuary English.* Cambridge, Mass.: Exact Change, 1990.

————. *Alongshore.* New Haven: Yale University Press, 1994.

Streatfield, David C. *California Gardens.* New York: Abbeville Press, 1994.

Thomas, Frank, and Ollie Johnston. *Disney Animation.* New York: Abbeville Press, 1981.

Thompson, George F., ed. *Landscape in America.* Austin: University of Texas Press, 1995.

Thompson, J. William. *Bryant Park.* Washington, D.C: Spacemaker Press: 1997.

Twain, Mark. *Life on the Mississippi.* Library of America, 1982.

Van Dyke, John C. *The Desert.* Salt Lake City: Peregrine Smith, 1980.

Van Valkenburgh, Michael, curator. *Built Landscapes.* Brattleboro, Vt.: Brattleboro Museum and Art Center, 1984.

Warner, Sam Bass. *To Dwell Is to Garden: A History of Boston's Community Gardens.* Boston: Northeastern University Press, 1987.

————. *Streetcar Suburbs.* New York: Atheneum, 1976.

Watts, May Theilgaard. *Reading the Landscape of America.* New York: Collier Books, 1975.

Westmacott, Richard. *African-American Gardens and Yards in the Rural South.* Knoxville: University of Tennessee Press, 1992.

White, Minor, ed. *Paul Caponigro.* New York: Aperture, 1967.

White, Richard. *The Organic Machine.* New York: Straus and Giroux, 1995.

Whitson, A. R., et al. *Soil Survey of Iowa County, Wisconsin.* Madison: Wisconsin Geological and Natural History Survey, 1914.

Worster, Donald. *Under Western Skies.* New York: Oxford University Press, 1992.

MIDDLE EAST

Al Khalil, Samir. *The Monument.* Berkeley: University of California Press, 1991.

Holod, Renata, and Hasan-Uddin Khan. *The Contemporary Mosque.* New York: Rizzoli, 1997.

Petruccioli, Attilio, ed. *The Garden as a City; Environmental Design: Journal of the Islamic Environmental Design Research Centre.* Rome: Carucci Editore, 1984.

————. *The City as a Garden; Environmental Design: Journal of the Islamic Environmental Design Research Centre.* Rome: Carucci Editore, 1984.

Landscape Authors

Interviews

In interviews with landscape authors—artists, engineers, landscape architects, architects, farmers and gardeners—I inquired about their home landscapes, working methods, sources of inspiration. Discussions sustained over many years with Poul Henriksen, Ian McHarg, Glenn Murcutt, Lawrence Halprin, and Sven-Ingvar Andersson gave me an insight into relationships among their experiences, ideas, and practices. Discussions with A. E. Bye, Richard Haag, Richard Le Plastrier, Adèle Naudé Santos, Mario Schjetnan, and James Wines gave me an appreciation for the great differences in approaches to landscape composition. Interviews with Taliesin Fellows, who worked alongside Frank Lloyd Wright, made it possible to reconstruct the evolution of the Taliesins.

Landscape Authors: Drawings and Unpublished Writings

Landscape authors reveal their thinking in plans, diagrams, and sketches; notations provide clues to working methods (pragmatics) and intentions (poetics and polemics). Most designers make successive studies, embodying reasoned steps and intuitive leaps. Faint pencil guidelines on C. Th. Sørensen's plan drawings reveal the complex, carefully plotted geometries of his gardens. Frank Lloyd Wright wrote notes on site plans and perspective drawings about ideas and instructions to workers for what should be planted and built, and how. Notations often cannot be deciphered in reproduction and must be studied in the original. The early, messy drawings frequently convey an author's thinking best. In studying landscapes designed by Wright, for example, the studies drawn in the act of designing are more informative than rendered plans and perspectives intended for presentations to clients or for exhibition. Although "unfinished" drawings are rarely included in exhibitions or reproduced in publications, the most important may be kept by designers as records, then eventually preserved in an archive.

I studied drawings and papers in many public archives and private collections. The Frank Lloyd Wright Archives at Taliesin West is the single largest collection of Wright's drawn work and unpublished correspondence; I also consulted the smaller, but important, collection in the State Historical Society of Wisconsin and the Lewis Mumford Papers at the University of Pennsylvania for the Wright-Mumford correspondence. The graphic work of the Olmsted Office is housed at the Olmsted National Historical Site in Brookline, Massachusetts; the papers of Frederick Law Olmsted, Sr. are in the Library of Congress. Most of Sørensen's drawings are at the Royal Danish Academy of Fine Arts, where he was professor for many years. Lawrence Halprin's archives are at the University of Pennsylvania. Most contemporary landscape authors maintain a collection of their own drawings; I looked at those of Glenn Murcutt, Sven-Ingvar Andersson, Adèle Naudé Santos, Laurie Olin, and Anuradha Mathur, among others. For published journals, correspondence, and professional reports, see below.

Landscape Authors: Published Accounts of Own Work

Frederick Law Olmsted, Frank Lloyd Wright, C. Th. Sørensen, Geoffrey Jellicoe, Lawrence Halprin, and Laurie Olin, all great landscape authors, have written about their work, intentions, methods, and sources. Just as their drawings are windows into the way they think and shape landscape, so are their writings. Professional reports, from author to client, tell the official account of what landscape authors intend. Some classics are published: Alexander (*Oregon*), Eliot, Olmsted (*Niagara*, Fein). Most are uncollected by libraries, however, and are difficult to locate: see, for example, Center for Environmental Design and Wallace McHarg Roberts and Todd.

Alexander, Christopher. *A Pattern Language Which Generates Multi-service Centers.* Center for Environmental Structure, 1968.

———. *Oregon Experiment.* New York: Oxford University Press, 1975.

Andersson, Sven-Ingvar. "En trädgård efter fem år." *Hem i Sverige* (1965:1), 24–29.

———. "Brev fra min hønsegård." *Arkitekten* (1967), 579–83.

———. "Häckar och höns—min torparträdgård." *Landskap* (1976/8), 180–84.

———. "Karlsplatz—Resselpark: En park- og byfornyelsesopgave i Wien." *Landskap* (1979/1), 16–21.

———. "Principper for bevaring af gamle haver." *Fortidsvern* (1986/1), 112–21.

Baron, Robert C., ed. *The Garden and Farm Books of Thomas Jefferson.* Golden, Colo.: Fulcrum, 1987.

Brownwell, Baker, and Frank Lloyd Wright. *Architecture and Modern Life.* New York: Harper, 1937.

Bye, A. E. *Art into Landscape; Landscape into Art.* Mesa, Ariz.: PDA Publishers, 1983.

Center for Environmental Design. *Landscape Development Plan: University of Pennsylvania.* Philadelphia: Graduate School of Fine Arts, University of Pennsylvania, 1977.

Church, Thomas. *Gardens Are for People.* New York: McGraw-Hill, 1955.

Cleveland, H. W. S. *Landscape Architecture as Applied to the Wants of the West.* 1873. Reprint, Pittsburgh: University of Pittsburgh Press, 1965.

Downing, Andrew Jackson. *A Treatise on the Theory and Practice of Landscape Gardening.* 4th edition. New York: Orange Judd Agricultural Book Publisher, 1865.

Eliot, Charles. "Report of the Landscape Architect." In *Report of the Board Metropolitan Park Commissioners.* Boston: January 1893.

———. *Charles Eliot: Landscape Architect.* 1902. Reprint, Freeport, N.Y.: Books for Libraries Press, 1971.

Fathy, Hassan. *Architecture for the Poor.* Chicago: University of Chicago Press, 1973.

Fein, Albert, ed. *Landscape into Cityscape: Frederick Law Olmsted's Plans for a Greater New York City.* Ithaca: Cornell University Press, 1968.

Goldsworthy, Andy. *A Collaboration with Nature.* New York: Harry N. Abrams, 1990.

Graham, Thomas E., ed. *Agricultural Social Gospel: The Gospel of the Farm by Jenkin Lloyd Jones.* Lewiston, N.Y.: Edwin Mellen, 1986.

Halprin, Lawrence. *Freeways.* New York: Reinhold, 1966.

———. *The RSVP Cycles: Creative Processes in the Human Environment.* New York: George Braziller, 1969.

———. *Cities.* Cambridge: MIT Press, 1972.

———. *Notebooks: 1959–1971.* Cambridge: MIT Press, 1972.

———. *Take Part.* San Francisco: Lawrence Halprin and Associates, 1972.

———. *Sketchbook of Lawrence Halprin.* Tokyo: Process Architecture, 1981.

———. *Lawrence Halprin: Changing Places.* San Francisco: San Francisco Museum of Modern Art, 1986.

———. *The Franklin Delano Roosevelt Memorial.* San Francisco: Chronicle Books, 1997.

Halprin, Lawrence, and Jim Burns. *Taking Part: A Workshop Approach to Collective Creativity.* Cambridge: MIT Press, 1974.

Harrison, Helen Mayer, and Newton Harrison. *The Lagoon Cycle.* Ithaca: Cornell Office of University Publications, 1985.

Hood, Walter. *Urban Diaries*. Washington, D.C.: Spacemaker Press, 1997.

Jekyll, Gertrude. *A Gardener's Testament*. New York: Charles Scribner's Sons, 1937.

——. *Home and Garden*. Suffolk, U.K.: Antique Collectors' Club, 1982.

Jellicoe, Geoffrey A. *Studies in Landscape Design*. Volumes I–III. London: Oxford University Press, 1960, 1966, 1970.

——. *The Guelph Lectures on Landscape Design*. Guelph, Canada: University of Guelph, 1983.

——. *The Landscape of Civilization: As Experienced in the Moody Historical Gardens*. Sussex, U.K.: Garden Art Press, 1989.

——. "A Philosophy of Landscape." In *Architect's Yearbook* 1:1 (1945), 39–42.

Jensen, Jens. *Siftings, the Major Portion of the Clearing, and Collected Writings*. Chicago: Ralph Fletcher Seymour, 1956.

Irwin, Robert. *Being and Circumstance: Notes Toward a Conditional Art*. Larkspur Landing, Calif.: Lapis Press, 1985.

Kiley, Dan. *Landscape Design: Works of Dan Kiley*. Tokyo: Process Architecture, 1982.

Lassus, Bernard, and Stephen Bann, intro. and trans. "The Landscape Approach of Bernard Lassus." *Journal of Garden History* 3:2, 79–107.

Leopold, Aldo. *A Sand County Almanac*. New York: Bantam Books, 1966.

Loudon, J. C. *The Suburban Gardener and Villa Companion*. London: Printed for the author, 1838.

Lynch, Kevin. *Managing the Sense of a Region*. Boston: MIT Press, 1976.

Mathur, Anuradha. "Recovering Ground: The Shifting Landscape of Dacca." In *Landscape Transformed*, edited by Michael Spens. London: Academy Editions, 1996.

McHarg, Ian L. *Design with Nature*. Garden City: Doubleday, 1969.

——. *A Quest for Life*. New York: John Wiley and Sons, 1996.

Neuhart, John, Marilyn Neuhart, and Ray Eames, eds. *Eames Design*. New York: Abrams, 1989.

Olin, Laurie. "Regionalism and the Practice of Hanna/Olin, Ltd." In *Regional Garden Design in the United States*, edited by Therese O'Malley and Marc Trieb. Washington, D.C.: Dumbarton Oaks, 1995.

——. *Transforming the Common Place*. Princeton: Princeton Archtitectural Press, 1996.

Olmsted, Frederick Law. "Parks, Parkways and Pleasure Grounds." *Engineering Magazine* 9:2 (May 1895), 253–60.

——. *General Plan for the Improvement of the Niagara Reservation*. New York, 1887.

Olmsted, Frederick Law, Jr., and Theodora Kimball, eds. *Forty Years of Landscape Architecture*. Cambridge: MIT Press, 1973.

Palladio, Andrea. *Four Books on Architecture*. 1738. Reprint, New York: Dover, 1965.

Pollan, Michael. *Second Nature*. New York: Atlantic Monthly Press, 1991.

——. *A Place of My Own*. New York: Random House, 1997.

Repton, Humphrey. *Theory and Practice of Landscape Gardening*. Edited by John Nolen. Boston: Houghton Mifflin, 1907.

Robinson, William. *Wild Garden*. 1870. Reprint, London: J. Murray, 1903.

Schwartz, Martha. "Back Bay Bagel Garden." *Landscape Architecture* (January 1980), 43–46.

Sørenson, Carl Theodore. *Parkpolitik*. Copenhagen, 1931.

——. *Haver: Tanker og Arbejder*. Copenhagen: Christian Ejlers, 1975.

——. *Utypiske Haver til et Typehus: 39 Haveplaner*. Copenhagen: Christian Ejlers, 1984.

Spirn, Anne Whiston. *The West Philadelphia Landscape Plan: A Framework for Action*. Philadelphia: Graduate School of Fine Arts, University of Pennsylvania, 1991.

——, and Michele Pollio. *"This Garden Is a Town."* Philadelphia: Graduate School of Fine Arts, University of Pennsylvania, 1990.

——, and Daniel Marcucci. *Models of Success: Landscape Improvement and Community De-*

velopment. Philadelphia: Graduate School of Fine Arts, University of Pennsylvania, 1991.

————, and Mark Cameron. *Shaping the Block*. Philadelphia: Graduate School of Fine Arts, University of Pennsylvania, 1991.

————, Michele Pollio, and Mark Cameron. *Vacant Land: A Resource for Reshaping Urban Neighborhoods*. Philadelphia: Graduate School of Fine Arts, University of Pennsylvania, 1991.

————, and Robert Cheetham. *West Philadelphia Digital Database: Atlas and Guide*. Philadelphia: Graduate School of Fine Arts, University of Pennsylvania, 1996.

Unwin, Raymond. *Town Planning in Practice*. 2d edition. London: T. Fisher Unwin, 1911.

Walker, Peter. *Minimalist Gardens*. Washington, D.C.: Spacemaker Press, 1997.

Wallace, McHarg, Roberts, and Todd. *Amelia Island, Florida*. Philadelphia: Wallace, McHarg, Roberts, and Todd, 1972.

————. *Woodlands New Community: Site Planning Guidelines*. Philadelphia: Wallace, McHarg, Roberts, and Todd, 1973.

Wright, Frank Lloyd. "Living in the Desert: Part One—We Found Paradise." *Arizona Highways* (October 1940), 12–15.

————. *Frank Lloyd Wright: His Living Voice*. Edited by Bruce Brooks Pfeiffer. Fresno, Calif., 1987.

————. *Collected Writings, Volume 1: 1894–1930*. Edited by Bruce Brooks Pfeiffer. New York: Rizzoli, 1992.

————. *Collected Writings, Volume 2: 1930–1932*. Edited by Bruce Brooks Pfeiffer. New York: Rizzoli, 1992.

————. *Collected Writings, Volume 3: 1931–1939*. Edited by Bruce Brooks Pfeiffer. New York: Rizzoli, 1993.

————. *Collected Writings, Volume 4: 1939–1949*. Edited by Bruce Brooks Pfeiffer. New York: Rizzoli, 1994.

————. *Collected Writings, Volume 5: 1949–1959*. Edited by Bruce Brooks Pfeiffer. New York: Rizzoli, 1995.

Zion, Robert. *Robert Zion*. Tokyo: Process Architecture, 1991.

Landscape Authors: Secondary Sources

Books about modern designers are often written by other landscape authors and by architectural and landscape historians. Andersson's and Høyer's book on Sørensen, Fromonot's on Murcutt, Jewell's on Walker, De Long's on Wright, Ambasz's on Barragan are appraisals by members of a younger generation of designers.

Abrioux, Yves. *Ian Hamilton Finlay*. Edinburgh: Reaktion Books, 1985.

Adams, William Howard. *Jefferson's Monticello*. New York: Abbeville Press, 1983.

————. *Roberto Burle Marx*. New York: Museum of Modern Art, 1991.

Adcock, Craig. *James Turrell: The Art of Light and Space*. Berkeley: University of California Press, 1990.

Ahlin, Janne. *Sigurd Lewerentz: Architect*. Cambridge: MIT Press, 1987.

Ambasz, Emilio. *The Architecture of Luis Barragan*. New York: Museum of Modern Art, 1976.

Andersson, Sven-Ingvar, and Steen Høyer. *C. Th. Sørenson: Havekunster*. Copenhagen: Arkitektens Forlag, 1993.

Andrews, Richard. *James Turrell: Sensing Space*. Philadelphia: Institute for Contemporary Art, 1993.

Balmori, Diana, Diane Kostial Mcguire, and Eleanor M. McPeck. *Beatrix Farrand's American Landscapes: Her Gardens and Campuses*. Sagaponack, N.Y.: Sagapress, 1985.

Brown, Jane. *Gardens of a Golden Afternoon; The Story of a Partnership: Edwin Lutyens and*

Gertrude Jekyll. New York: Van Nostrand Reinhold, 1982.

———. *Vita's Other World: A Gardening Biography of Vita Sackville-West.* New York: Viking, 1985.

Brown, Julia, ed. *Occluded Front: James Turrell.* Larkspur Landing, Calif.: Lapis Press, 1985.

Burkhardt, François, Claude Eveno, and Boris Podrecca, eds. *Joze Plecnik, Architect: 1872–1957.* Cambridge: MIT Press, 1989.

Chang, Chin-Yu, ed. *Lawrence Halprin.* Tokyo: Process Architecture, 1978.

De Long, David, ed. *Frank Lloyd Wright: Designs for an American Landscape 1922–1932.* New York: Abrams, 1996.

Eaton, Leonard. *Landscape Artist in America: Life and Work of Jens Jensen.* Chicago: University of Chicago Press, 1964.

Frampton, Kenneth. *Tadao Ando.* New York: Museum of Modern Art, 1991.

Fromonot, Françoise. *Glenn Murcutt.* London: Thames and Hudson, 1995.

Fuchs, R. H. *Richard Long.* New York: Thames and Hudson, 1986.

Grese, Robert. *Jens Jensen.* Baltimore: Johns Hopkins, University Press, 1992.

Hargreaves. Tokyo: Process Architecture, 1996.

Helphand, Kenneth. "Shaping the Israeli Landscape." In *Shlomo Aronson.* Washington, D.C.: Spacemaker Press, 1998.

Hazlehurst, F. Hamilton. *Gardens of Illusion: The Genius of André Le Nostre.* Nashville: Vanderbilt University Press, 1980.

Hobbs, Robert. *Robert Smithson.* Ithaca: Cornell University Press, 1981.

Hodge, Brooke. *Design with the Land: Landscape Architecture of Michael Van Valkenburgh.* Princeton: Princeton Architectural Press, 1994.

Holliss, Richard, and Brian Sibley. *The Disney Studio Story.* New York: Crown, 1988.

Howett, Catherine, ed. *Abstracting the Landscape: The Artistry of Landscape Architect A. E. Bye.* University Park: Department of Landscape Architecture, Pennsylvania State University, 1990.

Høyer, Steen, ed. *Sven-Ingvar Andersson.* Copenhagen: Arkitektens Forlag, 1994.

Jewell, Linda, ed. *Peter Walker.* New York: Rizzoli, 1990.

Joyes, Claire. *Claude Monet: Life at Giverny.* New York: Vendome Press, 1985.

Landecker, Heidi, ed. *Martha Schwartz.* Washington, D.C.: Spacemaker Press, 1997.

Nichols, Frederick D., and Ralph E. Griswold. *Thomas Jefferson, Landscape Architect.* Charlottesville: University Press of Virginia, 1978.

Rasmussen, Steen Eiler, Frans Lassen, Lisbeth Hertel, and Sven-Ingvar Andersson. *Karen Blixen's Flowers.* Copenhagen: Christian Eilers, 1992.

Riley, Terence, and Peter Reed, eds. *Frank Lloyd Wright.* New York: Museum of Modern Art, 1994.

Simo, Melanie Louise. *Loudon and the Landscape.* New Haven: Yale University Press, 1988.

SITE. New York: Rizzoli, 1989.

Spens, Michael. *Gardens of the Mind: The Genius of Geoffrey Jellicoe.* England: Antique Collectors Club, 1992.

———. *Jellicoe at Shute.* London: Academy Editions. 1993.

———. *The Complete Landscape Designs and Gardens of Geoffrey Jellicoe.* London: Thames and Hudson, 1994.

Spirn, Anne Whiston. "Frank Lloyd Wright: Architect of Landscape." In *Frank Lloyd Wright: Designs for an American Landscape, 1922–1932,* edited by David De Long. New York: Abrams, 1996.

———. "Constructing Nature: The Legacy of Frederick Law Olmsted." In *Uncommon Ground,* edited by William Cronon. New York: W. W. Norton, 1995.

———. "Texts, Landscapes, Life." In *Sven-Ingvar Andersson,* edited by Steen Høyer. Copenhagen: Arkitektens Forlag, 1994.

Steele, James. *Hassan Fathy.* London: Academy Editions, St. Martin's Press, 1988.

Stephensen, Lulu Salto. *Tradition og Fornyelse: Dansk Havekunst: G. N. Brandt.* N.p.: Frangipani, 1993.

Tankard, Judith B., and Michael Van Valkenburgh. *Gertrude Jekyll: A Vision of Garden and Wood.* New York: Abrams, 1989.

Thomas, Bob. *Walt Disney.* New York: Pocket Books, 1980.

Treib, Marc, and Dorothée Imbert. *Garrett Eckbo.* Berkeley: University of California Press, 1997.

Zaitzevsky, Cynthia. *Frederick Law Olmsted and the Boston Park System.* Cambridge: Harvard University Press, 1983.

Reading and Telling Landscape: General References

Rare is the source which integrates interpretations of natural, vernacular, and designed landscapes, even in the case of particular places. One must turn to many different disciplines for a full reading: meteorology, geology, ecology, zoology, anthropology, geography, history, art history, architecture, landscape architecture, urban design, among others. This selective bibliography of general references, together with those on particular places (Landscapes) and individual authors (Landscape Authors), is representative of the contributions of these diverse perspectives to reading and telling landscape.

Minnaert, Bloom, Dunne and Leopold, Daubenmire, and Forman provide introductions to reading meteorological, geological, botanical, and zoological features. Meinig's collection of essays on reading vernacular landscapes includes an essay on "axioms" by Pierce Lewis. Clay's guide describes landscape patterns as clues to past and present phenomena. White's review essay, "American Environmental History," is a guide to a vast literature on reading landscape; Cronon's "Stories" is an exploration of landscape meaning and historical narrative. Preziosi applies semiotics to the built environment. Panofsky describes the iconography of art, and Geertz presents an approach to meaning informed by ethnography; Cosgrove and Daniels integrate these approaches. For the use of photography in interpreting cultural landscapes, see Collier and Collier. Poets, in their close reading and use of imagery, are guides to landscape language: Rich, Applewhite.

There are fewer references on telling landscape. Many probing studies of landscape expression are by landscape authors themselves—Alexander, Lynch, Olin (see also Landscape Authors for descriptions of their own work)—and by those, like Schon, who have observed practitioners at work. Lakoff and Johnson describe how human thought processes and verbal language reflect relationships between body and landscape; Donald reviews research on human evolution and language development in terms of interactions among body, mind, and environment. A complementary perspective on these relationships is provided by studies of animals; see Griffin, Sebeok, Dawkins, and Haraway.

The published literature on landscape has expanded rapidly since 1980. Historically, there is resurgent interest in gardens and landscape at times when the relationship between nature and humankind is being reexamined and redefined; this is such a time. For those readers who wish to follow future developments and delve more deeply into landscape studies, the following journals contain articles on specific topics and present reviews of new books: *Landscape Architecture* (1910–), *Landscape* (1951–), *Landscape and Urban Planning* (1974–), *Environmental History,* formerly *Environmental History Review* (1977–), *Studies in the History of Gardens and Designed Landscapes,* formerly *Journal of Garden History*

(1980–), *Landscape Journal* (1982–), *Places* (1983–), *Topos* (1992–).

Abram, David. *The Spell of the Sensuous.* New York: Vintage Books, 1996.

Ackerman, James. "The History of Design and the Design of History." *Via* 4 (1980), 19–28.

———. *The Villa.* Princeton: Princeton University Press, 1990.

Alexander, Christopher. *The Timeless Way of Building.* New York: Oxford University Press, 1977.

———. *A New Theory of Urban Design.* New York: Oxford University Press, 1987.

———, Sara Ishikawa, and Murray Silverstein. *A Pattern Language: Towns, Buildings, Construction.* New York: Oxford University Press, 1977.

Anderson, Edgar. *Landscape Papers.* Edited by Bob Callahan. Berkeley: Turtle Island Foundation, 1976.

Andrews, Oliver. *Living Materials: A Sculptor's Handbook.* Berkeley: University of California Press, 1983.

Appleton, Jay. *The Experience of Landscape.* London: John Wiley and Sons, 1975.

———. *The Symbolism of Habitat.* Seattle: University of Washington Press, 1990.

Applewhite, James. "The Near Landscape and the Far: Nature and Human Signification." In *Southern Literature and Literary Theory*, edited by Jefferson Humphries. Athens: University of Georgia Press, 1990.

Arnheim, Rudolf. "Order and Complexity in Landscape Design." In *Toward a Psychology of Art*, 123–35. Berkeley: University of California Press, 1966.

———. *Visual Thinking.* Berkeley: University of California Press, 1969.

———. *The Dynamics of Architectural Form.* Berkeley: University of California Press, 1977.

Bachelard, Gaston. *The Poetics of Space.* Translated by Maria Jolas. Boston: Beacon Press, 1969.

Baljon, Lodewijk. *Designing Parks.* Amsterdam: Architectura and Natura Press, 1992.

Bateson, Gregory. *Steps to an Ecology of Mind.* New York: Ballantine Books, 1972.

———. *Mind and Nature.* Toronto: Bantam Books, 1980.

———. *A Sacred Unity.* New York: Cornelia and Michael Bessie Book, 1991.

———, C. Wilder-Mott, and John H. Weakland, eds. *Rigor and Imagination.* New York: Praeger, 1981.

Beardsley, John. *Earthworks and Beyond.* New York: Abbeville Press, 1984.

Berger, John. *Ways of Seeing.* London: Penguin Books, 1977.

———. *About Looking.* New York: Pantheon Books, 1980.

———. *Sense of Sight.* New York: Random House, 1985.

Berger, John, and Jean Mohr. *Another Way of Telling.* New York: Random House, 1983.

Bickerton, Derek. *Language and Species.* Chicago: University of Chicago Press, 1990.

Biedermann, Hans. *Dictionary of Symbolism.* New York: Meridian, 1992.

Bloom, Arthur L. *The Surface of the Earth.* Englewood Cliffs: Prentice-Hall, 1969.

Botkin, Daniel B. *Discordant Harmonies: A New Ecology for the Twenty-first Century.* New York: Oxford University Press, 1990.

Bourassa, Steven C. *The Aesthetics of Landscape.* London: Belhaven Press, 1991.

Braudel, Fernand. *The Structures of Everyday Life.* New York: Harper and Row, 1979.

Carr, Stephen, Mark Francis, Leanne Rivlin, and Andrew M. Stone. *Public Space.* New York: Cambridge University Press, 1992.

Cirlot, J. E. *A Dictionary of Symbols.* Translated by Jack Sage. 2d edition. London: Routledge, 1971.

Clark, Kenneth. *Landscape into Art.* New York: Harper and Row, 1979.

Clay, Grady. *Close Up: How to Read the American City.* Chicago: University of Chicago Press, 1973.

Cobb, Edith. *Ecology of Imagination in Childhood.* New York: Columbia University Press, 1977.

Collier, John, Jr., and Malcolm Collier. *Visual Anthropology: Photography as a Research Method.* Albuquerque: University of New Mexico Press, 1986.

Cooper, J. C. *An Illustrated Encyclopedia of Traditional Symbols.* London: Thames and Hudson, 1978.

Cosgrove, Denis, and Stephen Daniels, eds. *The Iconography of Landscape.* Cambridge: Cambridge University Press, 1988.

Cranz, Galen. *The Politics of Park Design.* Cambridge: MIT Press, 1982.

Cronon, William. "A Place for Stories: Nature, History, and Narrative." *Journal of American History* 78:4 (March 1992).

———, ed. *Uncommon Ground: Rethinking the Human Place in Nature.* New York: W. W. Norton, 1995.

Crowe, Sylvia. *Tomorrow's Landscape.* London: Architectural Press, 1956.

———, ed. *Space for Living.* Amsterdam, 1961.

Cuff, Dana. *Architecture: The Story of Practice.* Cambridge: MIT Press, 1991.

Cutts, Simon, David Reason, Jonathon Williams, Lucius Burckhardt, Graeme Murray, John Bevis, and Thomas A. Clark. *The Unpainted Landscape.* London: Coracle Press, 1987.

Daubenmire, Rexford. *Plants and Environment.* New York: Wiley, 1959.

———. *Plant Communities.* New York: Harper and Row, 1968.

Dawkins, Marian. *Through Our Eyes Only?: The Search for Animal Consciousness.* Oxford: Freeman, 1993.

Dewey, John. *Art as Experience.* New York: Capricorn Books, 1958.

Donald, Merlin. *Origins of the Modern Mind.* Cambridge: Harvard University Press, 1991.

Dubos, René. *Man Adapting.* New Haven: Yale University Press, 1965.

———. *So Human an Animal.* New York: Charles Scribner's Sons, 1968.

Dunlop, Storm, and Francis Wilson. *Weather and Forecasting.* New York: Macmillan, 1987.

Dunne, Thomas, and Luna Leopold. *Water in Environmental Planning.* San Francisco: Freeman, 1978.

Eiseley, Loren. *Immense Journey.* New York: Vintage, 1957.

———. *The Firmament of Time.* New York: Atheneum, 1969.

Eliade, Mircea. *The Sacred and the Profane.* New York: Harcourt Brace Jovanovich, 1959.

Evernden, Neil. *The Social Creation of Nature.* Baltimore: Johns Hopkins University Press, 1992.

Fairbrother, Nan *The Nature of Landscape Design.* New York: Alfred A. Knopf, 1974.

Feld, Steven. *Sound and Sentiment: Birds, Weeping, Poetics, and Song in Kaluli Expression.* Philadelphia: University of Pennsylvania Press, 1982.

Ferguson, George. *Signs and Symbols in Christian Art.* New York: Oxford University Press, 1961.

Fitch, James Marston. *Historic Preservation: Curatorial Management of the Built World.* New York: McGraw-Hill, 1982.

———. *Land Mosaics: The Ecology of Landscapes and Regions.* Cambridge: Cambridge University Press, 1997.

Frampton, Kenneth. "Towards a Critical Regionalism." In *The Anti-aesthetic: Essays on Postmodern Culture,* edited by Hal Foster. Port Townsend, Wash.: Bay Press, 1983.

Francis, Mark, Lisa Cashdan, and Lynn Paxson. *Community Open Spaces.* Washington, D.C.: Island Press, 1984.

Francis, Mark, and Randolph T. Hester, eds. *The Meaning of Gardens.* Cambridge: MIT Press, 1990.

Gans, Herbert J. *People, Plans, and Policies.* New York: Columbia University Press, 1991.

Geertz, Clifford. *The Interpretation of Culture.* New York: Basic Books, 1973.

———. *Local Knowledge.* New York: Basic Books, 1983.

Gerster, Georg. *Below from Above.* New York: Abbeville, 1986.

Girouard, Marc. *Cities and People: A Social and Architectural History.* New Haven: Yale University Press, 1985.

Glacken, Clarence J. *Traces on the Rhodian Shore: Nature and Culture in Western Thought to the End of the Eighteenth Century.* Berkeley: University of California, 1976.

Glazer, Nathan, and Mark Lilla, eds. *The Public Face of Architecture: Civic Culture and Public Spaces*. New York: Free Press, 1987.

Gleick, James. *Chaos: Making a New Science*. New York: Viking Penquin, 1987.

Golley, Frank. *A History of the Ecosystem Concept in Ecology*. New Haven: Yale University Press, 1994.

Gollwitzer, Gerda. *Bäume: Bilder und Texte aus Drei Jahrtausenden*. Munich: Schuler Verlagsgesellschaft Herrsching, 1980.

Goody, Jack. *The Culture of Flowers*. Cambridge: Cambridge University Press, 1993.

Gothein, Marie Luise. *A History of Garden Art*. 2 volumes. 1928. Reprint, New York: Hacker Art Books, 1979.

Gould, Stephen Jay. *Time's Arrow, Time's Cycle*. Cambridge: Harvard University Press, 1987.

Greenbie, Barrie B. *Spaces: Dimensions of the Human Landscape*. New Haven: Yale University Press, 1981.

Griffin, David. *Animal Thinking*. New York: Van Nostrand Reinhold, 1974.

Hancocks, David. *Animals in Architecture*. New York: Praeger Publishers, 1971.

Haraway, Donna. *Primate Visions*. New York: Routledge, 1989.

Harrison, Richard Pogue. *Forests*. Chicago: University of Chicago Press, 1992.

Hart, John Fraser. *The Look of the Land*. Englewood Cliffs: Prentice-Hall, 1975.

Harvey, David. *The Urban Experience*. Baltimore: Johns Hopkins University Press, 1989.

Hayden, Dolores. *Seven American Utopias: The Architecture of Communitarian Socialism, 1790–1975*. Cambridge: MIT Press, 1976.

———. *The Power of Place: Urban Landscape as Public History*. Cambridge: MIT Press, 1995.

Heidegger, Martin. *Poetry, Language, Thought*. New York: Harper and Row, 1975.

Helphand, Kenneth. "Defiant Gardens." *Journal of Garden History* 17:2 (Summer 1997), 101–19.

Helphand, Kenneth, and Cynthia Girling. *Yard, Street, Park: The Design of Suburban Open Space*. New York: John Wiley, 1994.

Hester, Randolph T. *Neighborhood Space*. Stroudsberg, Penn.: Dowden, Hutchinson and Ross, 1975.

———. *Community Design Primer*. Mendocino, Calif.: Ridge Times, 1990.

Hiss, Tony. *The Experience of Place*. New York: Alfred A. Knopf, 1990.

Hough, Michael. *City Form and Natural Process*. New York: Van Nostrand Reinhold, 1984.

———. *Out of Place: Restoring Identity to the Regional Landscape*. New Haven: Yale University Press, 1990.

Huizinga, Johan. *Homo Ludens: A Study of the Play Element in Culture*. Boston: Beacon Press, 1955.

Hurtwood, Lady Allen of. *Planning for Play*. Cambridge: MIT Press, 1968.

Huth, Hans. *Nature and the American*. Lincoln: University of Nebraska Press, 1990.

Jackson, John Brinckerhoff. *The Necessity for Ruins*. Amherst: University of Massachusetts Press, 1980.

———. *Discovering the Vernacular Landscape*. New Haven: Yale University Press, 1984.

———. *A Sense of Place, A Sense of Time*. New Haven: Yale University Press, 1994.

Jacobs, Jane. *The Death and Life of Great American Cities*. New York: Random House, 1961.

Jellicoe, Geoffrey A., and Susan Jellicoe. *The Landscape of Man*. New York: Van Nostrand Reinhold, 1982.

———, Susan Jellicoe, Patrick Goode, and Michael Lancaster, eds. *The Oxford Companion to Gardens*. New York: Oxford University Press, 1986.

Johnson, Mark. *The Body in the Mind*. Chicago: University of Chicago Press, 1987.

Kaplan, Rachel, and Stephen Kaplan. *The Experience of Nature: A Psychological Perspective*. Cambridge: Cambridge University Press, 1989.

Kassler, Elizabeth B. *Modern Gardens and the Landscape*. New York: Museum of Modern Art, 1964.

Kepes, Gyorgy. *Language of Vision*. Chicago: Paul Theobald, 1944.

———, ed. *The New Landscape in Art and Science*. Chicago: Paul Theobald, 1967.

———, ed. *Arts of the Environment*. New York: George Braziller, 1972.

Knuijt, Martin, Hans Ophius, and Peter van Saane, eds. *Modern Park Design*. Amsterdam: Thoth, 1993.

Kostof, Spiro. *The City Shaped: Urban Patterns and Meanings through History*. Boston: Little, Brown, 1991.

Krieger, Martin. "Up the Plastic Tree." *Landscape Architecture* (July 1973), 349–60.

Lakoff, George. *Women, Fire and Dangerous Things: What Categories Reveal About the Mind*. Chicago: University of Chicago Press, 1987.

Lakoff, George, and Mark Johnson. *Metaphors We Live By*. Chicago: University of Chicago Press, 1980.

Lang, Jon. *Creating Architectural Theory*. New York: Van Nostrand Reinhold, 1987.

Lasswell, Harold D. *The Signature of Power*. New Brunswick, N.J.: Transaction Books, 1979.

Lawlor, Robert. *Sacred Geometry*. London: Thames and Hudson, 1982.

Leveson, David. *A Sense of the Earth*. New York: Anchor Press, 1982.

———. *Geology and the Urban Environment*. New York: Oxford University Press, 1980.

Linenthal, Edward Tabor, *Sacred Grounds: Americans and Their Battlefields*. Chicago: University of Illinois Press, 1991.

Lippard, Lucy R. *Overlay: Contemporary Art and the Art of Prehistory*. New York: Pantheon, 1983.

———. *The Lure of the Local*. New York: New Press, 1997.

Lobeck, Armin K. *Things Maps Don't Tell Us*. New York: Macmillan, 1956.

Lowenthal, David. *The Past Is a Foreign Country*. New York: Cambridge University Press, 1985.

Lyle, John T. *Design for Human Ecosystems*. New York: Van Nostrand Reinhold, 1985.

———. *Regenerative Design for Sustainable Development*. New York: John Wiley and Sons, 1994.

Lynch, Kevin. *Image of the City*. Cambridge: MIT Press, 1960.

———. *What Time Is This Place?* Cambridge: MIT Press, 1972.

———. *Theory of Good City Form*. Cambridge: MIT Press, 1981.

———. *City Sense and City Design: Writings and Projects of Kevin Lynch*. Cambridge: MIT Press, 1990.

———. *Wasting Away*. San Francisco: Sierra Club Books, 1990.

———, and Gary Hack. *Site Planning*. Cambridge: MIT Press, 1993.

Maclean, Norman. *A River Runs Through It*. Chicago: University of Chicago Press, 1976.

Mandelbrot, Benoit B. *The Fractal Geometry of Nature*. New York: W. H. Freeman, 1983.

Marcus, Clare Cooper. *House as a Mirror of Self*. Berkeley: Conari Press, 1995.

———, and Carolyn Francis, eds. *People Places*. New York: Van Nostrand Reinhold, 1990.

McHarg, Ian L. "An Ecological Method for Landscape Architecture." *Landscape Architecture* 57:2 (January 1967), 105–07.

McKim, Robert H. *Experiences in Visual Thinking*. Monterey, Calif.: Brooks/Cole, 1972.

Meinig, D. W., ed. *The Interpretation of Ordinary Landscapes*. New York: Oxford University Press, 1979.

Minnaert, M. G. J. *Light and Color in the Outdoors*. New York: Springer-Verlag, 1974.

Moore, Charles. *Water and Architecture*. New York: Harry Abrams, 1994.

———, William J. Mitchell, and William Turnbull, Jr. *The Poetics of Gardens*. Cambridge: MIT Press, 1988.

Morrish, William, and Catherine Brown. *Planning to Stay*. Minneapolis: Milkweed, 1994.

Morrison, Philip, Phylis Morrison, and the Office of Charles and Ray Eames. *Powers of Ten*. New York: Scientific American Books, 1982.

Norberg-Schulz, Christian. *Concept of Dwelling*. New York: Rizzoli, 1985.

————. *Existence, Space, and Architecture.* New York: Praeger, 1971.

————. *Intentions in Architecture.* Cambridge: MIT Press, 1965.

Oelschlaeger, Max. *The Idea of Wilderness.* New Haven: Yale University Press, 1991.

Olin, Laurie. "Form, Meaning, and Expression in Landscape Architecture." *Landscape Journal* 7:2 (1988), 149–68.

Olwig, Kenneth. "Recovering the Substantive Nature of Landscape." *Annals of the Association of American Geographers* 86:4 (December 1996), 630–53.

Panofsky, Erwin. *Meaning in the Visual Arts.* Garden City: Doubleday, 1955.

————. "Ideological Antecedents of the Rolls-Royce Radiator." *Proceedings of the American Philosophical Society* 107 (1963), 273–88.

Penning-Rowsell, Edmund C., and David Lowenthal, eds. *Landscape Meanings and Values.* London: Allen and Unwin, 1986.

Prest, John. *The Garden of Eden: The Botanic Garden and the Re-creation of Paradise.* New Haven: Yale University Press, 1981.

Preziosi, Donald. *The Semiotics of the Built Environment.* Bloomington: Indiana University Press, 1979.

————. *Architecture, Language, and Meaning.* The Hague: Mouton, 1979.

Rapoport, Amos. *The Meaning of the Built Environment.* Beverly Hills, Calif.: Sage Publications, 1982.

Relph, Edward. *Place and Placelessness.* London: Pion Limited, 1976.

————. *The Modern Urban Landscape.* Baltimore: Johns Hopkins University Press, 1987.

Rich, Adrienne. *The Dream of a Common Language.* W. W. Norton, 1978.

Rieber, Robert W., ed. *The Individual, Communication, and Society.* Cambridge: Cambridge University Press, 1989.

Riley, Robert. "From Sacred Grove to Disney World: The Search for Garden Meaning." *Landscape Journal* 7:2 (1988), 136–47.

Rothman, Hal. *Preserving Different Pasts: The American National Monuments.* Urbana: University of Illinois Press, 1989.

Rowe, Peter G. *Design Thinking.* Cambridge: MIT Press, 1987.

Rowell, Galen. *Mountain Light.* Sierra Club, 1986.

Rudofsky, Bernard. *Streets for People.* New York: Van Nostrand Reinhold, 1982.

Schaefer, Vincent J., and John A. Day. *A Field Guide to the Atmosphere.* Boston: Houghton Mifflin, 1981.

Schafer, R. Murray. *The Tuning of the World.* New York: Alfred A. Knopf, 1977.

Schama, Simon. *Landscape and Memory.* New York: Albert A. Knopf, 1995.

Schapiro, Meyer. "Style." In *Aesthetics Today*, edited by Morris Philipson, 81–113. Cleveland: World Publishing Company, 1961.

Schon, Donald A. *The Reflective Practitioner.* New York: Basic Books, 1983.

Seamon, David, and Robert Mugerauer, eds. *Dwelling, Place and Environment.* New York: Columbia University Press, 1985.

Sears, John F. *Sacred Places: American Tourist Attractions in the Nineteenth Century.* New York: Oxford University Press, 1989.

Sebeok, Thomas A. *The Sign and Its Masters.* Lanham, Md.: University Press of America, 1989.

Seddon, George. "Reflections: Words and Weeds: Some Notes on Language and Landscape." *Landscape Review* 2 (1995), 3–15.

Shepard, Paul. *Man in the Landscape.* College Station: Texas A&M University Press, 1991.

Shelton, John S. *Geology Illustrated.* San Francisco: W. H. Freeman, 1966.

Short, Lester L. *Lives of Birds.* New York: Henry Holt, 1993.

Sonfist, Alan, ed. *Art in the Land.* New York: E. P. Dutton, 1983.

Sørenson, Carl Theodore. *Europas Havekunst.* Copenhagen: G. E. C. Gads, 1959.

Sorkin, Michael, ed. *Variations on a Theme Park*. New York: Hill and Wang, 1992.

Spens, Michael. *Landscape Transformed*. London: Academy Editions, 1996.

Spirn, Anne Whiston. *The Granite Garden: Urban Nature and Human Design*. New York: Basic Books, 1984.

———. "Urban Nature and Human Design: Renewing the Great Tradition." *Journal of Planning Education and Research* 5:1 (Autumn 1985), 39–51.

———. "Landscape Planning and the City." *Landscape and Urban Planning* 13 (1986), 433–41.

———. "The Poetics of City and Nature: Toward a New Aesthetic for Urban Design." *Landscape Journal* 7:2 (Fall 1988), 108–26.

———, ed. *Nature, Form, and Meaning: A Special Issue*. *Landscape Journal* 7:2 (Fall 1988).

———. "From Uluru to Cooper's Place: Patterns in the Cultural Landscape." *Orion* 9:2 (Spring 1990), 32–39.

Strain, Priscilla, and Frederick Engle. *Looking at Earth*. Atlanta: Turner, 1992.

Summerson, John. *The Classical Language of Architecture*. Cambridge: MIT Press, 1963.

Symes, Michael. *A Glossary of Garden History*. Princes Risborough, Buckinghamshire: Shire, 1993.

Taylor, C. *The Archaeology of Gardens*. Aylesbury, U.K.: Shire Publications, 1983.

Thomas, Keith. *Man and the Natural World*. New York: Pantheon Books, 1983.

Thompson, George F., and Frederick R. Steiner, eds. *Ecological Design and Planning*. New York: John Wiley, 1997.

Treib, Marc, ed. *Modern Landscape Architecture*. Cambridge: MIT Press, 1993.

Tuan, Yi-Fu. *Topophilia*. Englewood Cliffs: Prentice-Hall, 1974.

———. *Space and Place*. Minneapolis: University of Minnesota Press, 1977.

Tufte, Edmund. *Envisioning Information*. Cheshire, Conn.: Graphics Press, 1990.

Turnbull, David. *Maps Are Territories*. Chicago: University of Chicago Press, 1989.

Van Valkenburgh, Michael, curator. *Transforming the American Garden: 12 New Landscape Designs*. Cambridge: Harvard University Graduate School of Design, 1986.

von Frisch, Karl. *Animal Architecture*. New York: Van Nostrand Reinhold, 1983.

Wagstaff, J. M., ed. *Landscape and Culture*. New York: Basil Blackwell, 1987.

Walker, Peter, and Melanie Simo. *Invisible Gardens: The Search for Modernism in the American Landscape*. Cambridge: MIT Press, 1994.

Walter, Eugene Victor. *Placeways*. Chapel Hill: University of North Carolina Press, 1988.

White, Richard. "American Environmental History: The Development of a New Historical Field." *Pacific Historical Review* 54 (1985).

———. "Environmental History, Ecology and Meaning." *Journal of American History* 76:4 (March 1990).

Whyte, William H. *The Social Life of Small Urban Spaces*. Washington, D.C.: Conservation Foundation, 1980.

Williams, Raymond. *The Country and the City*. New York: Oxford University Press, 1975.

———. "Ideas of Nature." In *Problems in Materialism and Culture*. London: Verso, 1980.

———. *Keywords*. New York: Oxford University Press, 1983.

Wines, James. *De-Architecture*. New York: Rizzoli, 1987.

Wolschke-Bulmahn, Joachim, ed. *Nature and Ideology: Natural Garden Design in the Twentieth Century*. Washington, D.C.: Dumbarton Oaks, 1997.

Worster, Donald. *Nature's Economy: The Roots of Ecology*. Garden City, N.Y.: Anchor Press/Doubleday, 1979.

Zevi, Bruno. *The Modern Language of Architecture*. Seattle: University of Washington Press, 1978.

Acknowledgments

This book entailed many journeys, actual and metaphorical, in familiar landscapes and foreign terrain: physiographic, cultural, and disciplinary. I have had excellent and generous companions and guides.

For friendship, for conversations about the language of landscape extending over hours, days, and years, and for their work, I owe a special debt to Glenn Murcutt, Sven-Ingvar Andersson, Charlotte Kahn, and Bill Cronon.

I have described aspects of the language of landscape in dozens of lectures since 1985. These occasions permitted me to test ideas with diverse audiences and landscapes, provoked valuable feedback, and prompted many people to show me places that supported, extended, or challenged the ideas. Without the people and institutions that sponsored these trips and the native guides who shared their local knowledge this would have been a very different book.

I formulated the idea of landscape as language in dialogue with landscapes and architects of Australia in 1988 and gave my first presentation on the topic in Sydney and Melbourne the following year. I would like to thank the School of Architecture at the University of Sydney for appointing me the first Ethel Chettle Distinguished Fellow in 1988 and for inviting me back in 1989. The Royal Australian Institute of Architects sponsored a trip across Australia in 1988, and the University of Melbourne and Royal Melbourne Institute of Technology made possible my visits to that city. Glenn Murcutt, Rick Le Plastrier, Jennifer Taylor, and Peter Johnson persuaded me that the language of landscape encompassed buildings. Michael Ewing, John Richardson, Peter Stutchbury, and Paul Pheleros showed me their work, and David Jones, George Seddon, Jim Sinatra, Peter Towson, Peter Webel, James Weirick, and David Yencken commented and took me to see particular places. Helen Armstrong provided home, friendship, and discussion.

A trip to Japan refined my ideas. I am grateful to the City Bureau of the Japanese Ministry of Construction, and to Director Kazuo Majima and Deputy-Director Isao Naitoh, for sponsoring my trip and for providing two extraordinary guides from their staff: Toshiaki Funabiki, in Tokyo and Osaka, and Ayumi Rai, my companion in Kyoto, Kobe, Ise, and Toba. Both guides responded to a constant stream of questions with patience, openness, and thoughtfulness. The City Planning Association of Japan gave additional support. In Tokyo, Yoshinobu Ashihara, Shigeru Itoh, Akihiko Tani, Kazuhiko Takeuchi, Shunsaku Miyagi, Toshio Oyama, Akira Kobayashi, and alumni of University of Pennsylvania, especially Keiko Takayama, were all very helpful. I would like to thank the cities of Kobe, Kyoto, Ise, and the Mie Prefecture for their generous hospitality, especially my hosts and guides: in Osaka, Yasuko Tsuji and Takeshi Okada; in Ise, Mitsuo Mizutani, Michihiro Okunishi, Sigehiro Got, and Hisashi Inagaki; in Mie, Yasumasa Masuda and Kazuto Ikemura; in Kyoto, Kunihiko Ibuki, Satashi Uemuru, Shun-ichi Uchida, Sen'ichi Oyama, Makoto Suganuma, and Hisako Maeda; in Kobe, Osamu Maki, Osamu Nishi, and Toshihiko Inamatsu.

For many visits to Scandinavia since 1990, I would like to thank the following: in Denmark, the Royal Danish Academy of Art, Royal Danish Agricultural Institute, University of Odense, and Århus University; in Sweden, the Swedish Agricultural University at Alnarp; in Finland, Helsinki Technical University. For sharing ideas and places, I am grateful to Sven-Ingvar Andersson, Thorbjörn Andersson, Annelise Bramsnæs, Per Friberg, Jan Gehl, Jan Gezelius, Pär Gustafsson, Peter Holst, Steen Høyer, Leif Johannesen, Bodil Kjær, Ib Asger Olsen, Ken Olwig, Sonja Poll, Jørgen Primdahl, Henrik Pøhlsgaard, Tom Simons, Preben Skaarup, and Gunnar Sorte. Tove and Poul Henriksen, Birgitte Henriksen, Carl-Erik and Birgit Birn Henriksen, Sanne and Hans Andersen have made Denmark my second home.

Meetings at the Organization for Economic Cooperation and Development provided the occasion for many trips to Paris since 1992, and Chris Brooks, Josef Konvitz, and Françoise Fromonot guided me to particular landscapes in France. Dusan Ogrin invited me to Ljubljana in 1988, showed me the countryside of Slovenia, and pointed me toward Redipuglia. Hans and Ulrike Kiemstedt were my guides in both Hannover and Berlin; the University of Hannover and the Verbund für Wissenschaftsgeschichte in Berlin sponsored those trips. Guido Ferrara and the Italian Society of Landscape Architects invited me to Florence and organized visits to landscapes there; Giorgio Galletti showed me lesser-known corners of the Boboli Gardens.

Phyllis Lambert and the Canadian Centre for Architecture and the U.S. Library of Congress supported my research on Frank Lloyd Wright and made possible several trips to Taliesin North in Wisconsin and Taliesin West in Arizona. Jack Holzhueter gave me insight into Wright's family background. Bruce Brooks Pfeiffer, John deKoven Hill, and Cornelia Brierly shared their memories and knowledge of life with Wright, and Penny Fowler, Oscar Muñoz, Margo Stipe, and Indira Berndtson made stays at the Taliesins productive and enjoyable.

For other field trips in North America, I would like to thank the following organizations and guides: Arizona State University, John Meunier, Frits Steiner, Steve Martino, John Douglas, Ruth Zimmerman, Sharon Southerland, Dennis Siewert; University of Virginia, Warren Byrd, Reuben Rainey, Will Rieley; University of New Mexico, Jane Thurber and Steve Schreiber; University of Oregon, Kenny Helphand, Robert Melnick, Anne Bettman; University of Washington, Anne Moudon; University of California Humanities Research Institute, Michael Barbour, Mike Davis, Susan Davis; University of California-Berkeley, Clare Cooper Marcus, Michael Laurie; University of California-Los Angeles, Kate Hayles; University of California-Davis, Mark Francis, Rob Thayer, Kerry Dawson; University of Wisconsin, Bill Cronon, Arnold Alanen; University of Georgia, Darrel Morrison, Catherine Howett; University of Miami; Washington University; the Society of Soil and Water Conservation for a trip to Lexington, Kentucky; University of Colorado-Boulder, Society of Landscape Ecology, International Pedestrian Conference, Women's League of Voters of Colorado Springs, Thorne Ecological Institute, and the Colorado Chapter of ASLA for successive visits to Colorado's Front Range; American Collegiate Schools of Architecture Teachers' Workshop at Cranbrook Academy of Art; Dallas Institute; Garden Clubs of Houston. From 1973 to 1977, Wallace McHarg Roberts and Todd sent me to Houston, Denver, Montauk, Wye Island, Sanibel, and Toronto for fieldwork. Adèle Naudé Santos and Vince Healey showed me landscapes in San Diego and La Jolla. Kenny Helphand and Robert Melnick took me on a tour of the Rocky Mountains west of Denver.

I am grateful to Richard Haag, John Lyle, Martha Schwartz, Peter Shepheard, and Ken

Wright for taking me to places they designed and to A. E. Bye, Carol Franklin, Laurie Olin, Leslie Sauer, Mario Schjetnan, Adèle Naudé Santos, Carl Steinitz, Peter Walker, and James Wines for discussing how they work. Talks, trips, and workshops with Lawrence Halprin stimulated, provoked, and inspired.

Charlotte Kahn introduced me to Boston's inner-city landscapes and community gardeners. Hayward Ford continued my education in Philadelphia, and Ira Harkavy recruited me to work with teachers and students in Sulzberger Middle School. Glenn Campbell and Zakiyyah Ali have given me insight into children, life, and community in Mill Creek. I have worked with many research assistants on the West Philadelphia Landscape Project over the past eleven years; John Berg, Mark Cameron, Robert Cheetham, Martin Knox, Dan Marcucci, Michele Pollio, Sam Spirn, and John Widrick all worked on the project for two or more years and contributed in crucial ways, as did W. Gary Smith. The National Endowment for the Arts sponsored my study of urban vacant lands in 1985, and the J. N. Pew Charitable Trust, U.S. Department of Housing and Urban Development, Philadelphia Urban Resources Partnership, the Kellogg Foundation, and University of Pennsylvania's Center for Community Partnerships have supported the West Philadelphia Landscape Project.

A Noyes Fellowship at the Bunting Institute in fall 1985 enabled me to reflect and write about the poetics of landscape. A sabbatical in 1990–91 permitted me to develop the language of landscape within the context of the West Philadelphia Landscape Project, and a project fellowship from the National Endowment for the Arts in 1991 provided support for landscape photographs. A fellowship at the University of California Humanities Research Institute in 1994 provided a lively forum of colleagues who raised new questions to address. A fellowship at the Woodrow Wilson International Center for Scholars in 1995–96 gave me the time and space to bring the manuscript to near completion.

Linda Seidel, Ian McHarg, Narendra Juneja, Bob Hanna, and Peter Shepheard were teachers whose influence was formative. I have learned much from my students, and many research assistants have helped gather material: George Batchelor, Victoria Hoffman, Elizabeth Lardner, Paul Rookwood, Bill Hartman, Sylvia Palms, Christine Min, Marc Kushner, and Kamni Gill. Cathy Ford and Amy Freitag helped with the bibliography. Ann Donaghy typed my journals from 1989 to 1994.

I thank the following for permission to adapt publications of mine to which they hold copyright: Canadian Center for Architecture for my essay on Frank Lloyd Wright, and William Cronon and W. W. Norton for my essay on Frederick Law Olmsted. For permission to quote from Anthony Hecht's poem "The Gardens of the Villa d'Este," in The Hard Hours, I am grateful to Knopf, and, for the right to reproduce illustrations, to Bruce Brooks Pfeiffer and the Frank Lloyd Wright Foundation for the plan of Ocatilla; Ed Grushesky and the Philadelphia Water Department for the photograph of the Mill Creek sewer; the University of Chicago Press for the Bedolina petroglyph from David Turnbull, Maps Are Territories (originally published in J. B. Harley and D. Woodward, eds., The History of Cartography, volume 1, Cartography in Prehistoric, Ancient, and Medieval Europe and the Mediterranean [University of Chicago Press]); Dorothy McLaughlin for the photograph of Taliesin. And to Dee Mullin, a special thanks for locating and reproducing the photograph of Lovejoy Fountain. For generously providing their photographs and drawings, I would like to thank Alex MacLean, Lawrence Halprin, Glenn Murcutt, Laurie Olin, Sven-Ingvar Andersson,

Sonja Poll, James Wines, Alan Ward, and Lewis Watts. With the exception of the Wolf Tree, my own photographs are all 35mm Kodachrome slides, transformed by Kodak into digital files on CD-ROMs and converted to black-and-white images in Adobe Photoshop. Sam Spirn and Charles Neer converted the preliminary low-resolution images; I produced the final high-resolution images after expert coaching by Sam Spirn and Chung Kim.

Sven-Ingvar Andersson, Bill Cronon, David DeLong, Susan Frey, Frank Golley, Kathryn Gleason, Donna Haraway, Kate Hayles, Catherine Howett, Tom and Agatha Hughes, Charlotte Kahn, Michael Katz, Clare Cooper Marcus, Darrel Morrison, Ken Olwig, Jenny Price, Reuben Rainey, Dan Rose, Mark Rose, Carl Steinitz, Jennifer Taylor, Sam Bass Warner, Richard White, and Joachim Wolschke-Bulmahn commented on early versions of various chapters. Takamasa Miyazaki, Chiharu Takenaka, Keichi Fujiwara, Kinya Muriyama, and Anne Walthall read and responded to my descriptions of Japanese culture and landscape. Dolores Hayden, Kenny Helphand, John Dixon Hunt, Paul Spirn, and Isabelle Whiston read the entire manuscript. I am grateful to all for their insights. Judy Metro's immediate, enthusiastic response to the manuscript spurred the final phase of writing, and Lawrence Kenney's deft editing brought it to closure; Mary Mayer ushered the book gracefully through design and production.

For eighteen years, Jeannette Hopkins has challenged me to find and sustain my own voice and dared me to take risks. She has listened, read, questioned, provoked, and inspired through twelve years and countless drafts. She complained that the book would never be finished if I didn't stop traveling to far-off places, then insisted that the journal texts belonged in the book and defended them from translation into academic prose. I owe her a profound debt as editor and friend.

Landscapes have the advantage over libraries and museums that families, even small children, are willing to take vacations in them. My husband, Paul, partner of more than half a lifetime, was an enthusiastic companion on many trips, sent me off on other travels, and never questioned why this book was taking so long to write. My son, Sam, has grown up with the book: he was five when I began; now seventeen, he has been my research assistant for several years. Growing, he led me to see freshly and to feel landscape again from a child's perspective. Hundreds of swim meets, baseball, soccer, and basketball games were occasions to meditate on movement, geometry, and sport and to realize that muscles have memory.

My mother and father taught me to see the world in terms of questions and stories that guide actions and to believe that what you do is who you are. My Danish mother and father affirmed common meanings and values even as they coached me in a new culture. Both sets of parents showed me how to read landscape and to belong to a place through caring for it. This book is dedicated to them.

Index

memorials, 49–50, 59–60; Kongenshus, 28–31; Verdun, 50, 59, 61, 62; as elegy, 50, 275n8; Leopold Memorial Reserve, 52–53; National French Resistance Memorial, 59. *See also* Forest Cemetery; Redipuglia; Vietnam Veterans Memorial

memory, 98–99, 138–39, 196; landscapes of, 50–51, 59–63, 196, 253

Messiaen, Olivier, 148

metaphor, 15, 19–20, 27, 34, 200, 217, 226–29

metonymy, 223, 227–28

Mexico City, 106, 183

Michener, James, 154

Middleton Place (South Carolina), 68–69

Mies van der Rohe, Ludwig, 195, 232

Mill Creek (Philadelphia): design for, 3, 7, 23, 42, 213–15; as sewer, 10–11, 161–62, 185–88, 212; and abandonment of inner city neighborhoods, 92, 161–63, 175, 187, 265; reimagining, 267–72. *See also* Aspen Farms; Sulzberger Middle School

Miller, Wilhelm, 78

Minnesota State Capitol, competition, 252–53, 259

Mishima, Yukio, 235

Mississippi River, 27, 37, 49, 142

Mohr, Jean, on language of lived experience, 25

Monet, Claude, 35, 39

Mont-Saint-Michel, 47–48, 49, 54, 56, 110, 223

Mont Valérien (Paris), 50, 59, 60

Morrison, Darrel, 197

Morrison, Philip, 172, 174

Morrison, Phylis, 172, 174

mountains, 77, 143–46; as sacred landscape, 20, 33, 143, 165; in Japan, 134–35, 165

Mount Auburn Cemetery (Cambridge, Mass.), 230, 235

Muir, John, 52, 55

Mumford, Lewis, 196

Murcutt, Glenn, 3, 125, 195; and use of landscape, 21, 43–45, 197, 200, 245; method

of design, 43–45, 182, 202, 204–5, 206. *See also* Ball house; Bingie, Australia, house at

Muriyama, Kinya, 203

Mussolini, 20, 21, 59, 257

Nærum Garden Colony (Denmark): hedges at, 74–75, 222, 264; and Danish culture, 75, 158, 263; order and flexibility, 180, 193, 197

nature: cities as 3, 24, 156, 264–65; and shaping of landscape, 17–18; landscape as interpretation of, 24, 32; "native" nature, 31–32; and word for, 32, 273n7, 274n13; authority of, 244, 246–50, 259; and use of native species, 251; v. art, 252

Nazis, and political use of landscape, 17, 246, 249, 252

Netherlands, the, 158, 219

New York City, 158, 182–83, 232; Bryant Park, 51; Battery Park, 51–52, 224; Bronx River Parkway, 67, 90; Statue of Liberty, 218; Paley Park, 236; Jacob Javits Plaza, 255–56. *See also* Central Park

Niagara Falls, 53, 224, 262

Nicholson, Ben, 229

Noguchi, Isamu, 175

Norberg-Shulz, Christian, 122

Notre Dame cathedral, 58, 100

Nourlangie Rock (Australia), 124

Ocatilla (Arizona), 130, 180, 181

Ohio, 5, 205

Olin, Laurie, 51, 197, 250, 255

Olmsted, Frederick Law, 16, 196, 252; and wild landscape, 53–55, 70, 250, 277n43; Yosemite, 55, 70; Fens and Riverway, 70, 116, 196–97, 250–51, 281nn11,13; Niagara Falls, 224, 262. *See also* Fens and Riverway; Central Park

Oral Roberts University (Oklahoma), 220

Orange County, Calif., 42–43, 86, 87, 125, 175, 233, 263

time: in landscape, 50, 89–90, 140, 174–75; linear v. cyclical, 95; scale of, 174

Tokyo, 68, 76, 164, 166

topiary, 176–77, 191. *See also* Marnas

topographic maps, 91–92, 205, 207

trees, 17, 107, 140; wolf trees, 18–19, 77, 137, 138, 159; as metaphor, 20, 32, 100–101, 227; willow, 32–33; dogwood, 35, 104; at Ise, 55–56; as context, 133, 137–39; and wind, 177–78; at University of Virginia, 216; deformed beeches, 220–21. *See also* forest

Tschumi, Bernard, 200

Tuan, Yi-Fu, 94

Turrell, James, 142–43, 219, 245

Twain, Mark, 5, 16, 27, 36, 77, 142, 274n1

Uluru (Australia), 21, 143; and allusion, 77; as sacred place, 88, 111–12, 159; as performance space, 111–14, 118–19, 121; as landmark, 159, 219;

United States, 55; and orientation of houses, 75–76; and influence of English landscape, 78, 115, 228, 235; corporate headquarters, 78, 115, 257; national parks, 159; and natural garden movement, 251

University of California–Irvine, park, 106

University of California–San Diego, library, 200

University of Pennsylvania, 6–7, 41, 203; and Mill Creek, 72, 163, 214–15

University of Virginia, 21, 216, 217, 222

urban renewal, 67, 105, 171, 253–55, 259; and loss of past, 63, 175, 263

Urienborg, 225, 235

Utzon, Jørn, 200, 202

Van Valkenburgh, Michael, 201

Vaux-le-Vicomte, 90, 101, 182, 228

Venturi, Robert, 232, 252

Verdun, 50, 59, 61, 62; Fleury, 59

Versailles, 90, 121, 231; Hameau, 50; and allusion, 78, 218; and authority of power, 78, 220, 257; and geometry of design, 180, 182

Victory Arch (Baghdad), 220

Vietnam Veterans Memorial, 60–61, 77, 81, 85, 171; as elegy, 50, 275n8; and human context, 133, 147–48; as art, 256–57

Villa d'Este, 18, 236

Village Homes (Davis, Calif.), 75

Villa Lante, 236

Villa Rotonda, 222

Virgil, 78, 114

Vitus Bering Park (Denmark), 108, 195, 200

Vizcaya (Florida), 174, 230

Walker, Peter, 229, 257

Wallace, McHarg, Roberts, and Todd, 7, 208

walls: as memorials, 59, 81, 85, 147–48, 171; at Forest Cemetery 61–62; Berlin, 63, 227, 240–41, 242, 243; New England stone, 159, 160, 181

Washington, D.C.: Lincoln Memorial, 50, 85, 147, 220; Washington Monument, 85, 147; the Mall, 220, 227, 257; President's Park, 227, 236–37, 238–39. *See also* Vietnam Veterans Memorial

wastelands, transformed: the Fens, 24, 53–54, 69–70; Werribee Farm, 70, 71; Bloedel Reserve, 259–62, 263

water: and floodplains, 10–11, 90, 91, 92–93, 161–62; water systems, 22, 68–69, 88, 169–70, 227; in Murcutt's designs, 45, 200; and sacred springs, 58, 100; restoring quality of, 70, 184, 185–87, 212–13; as element of landscape, 85, 88, 100, 139–43; hydrologic cycle, 93–94, 226; needed for life, 124, 126; in Kyoto, 136; and rivers, 139–42; Halprin's studies of, 145, 198–99; in Priene, 169–70; and design of Fens, 196; as paradox, 230. *See also* Alhambra, the; fountains

Watts, May Theilgaard, 37

Welcome Park (Philadelphia), 81

Werribee Farm (Australia), 70, 71

Westminster Community Garden (Philadelphia), 210–11, 213

West Philadelphia, 210–15, 254; West Philadelphia Landscape Project, 73, 211–12, 215; Powelton/Summer-Winter Community Garden, 74; Spruce Hill Garden, 74; Garden of Eatin', 79; Gethsemane, 79; Sulzberger Middle School, 96, 162, 163, 214, 271; and City Planning Commission plan, 163; Westminster Community Garden, 210–11, 213. *See also* Aspen Farms; Mill Creek

Whitman, Walt, 139

Widrick, John, 73, 123, 212, 215

wilderness: as chaos, 18, 24; as sacred ground, 18, 55; human impulse to control, 31; constructed by Olmsted, 53–54, 69–70

Williams, Raymond, 248

Williamsburg, Va., 50, 253

wind, 177–78; and Danish heath, 28, 34, 81; and Murcutt's designs, 44–45, 182, 200, 245; and Venturi effect, 183, 219

Wines, James, 51

wolf trees, 18–19, 77, 137, 138, 159

Wordsworth, William, 37, 79

worship, landscapes of, 47–48, 54, 55–58, 222, 229. *See also* sacred places

Worster, Donald, 49

Wright, Frank Lloyd, 16, 196; and an American style of architecture, 78; and use of geometric form, 105, 109, 131, 181; and land as architecture, 127–28, 130, 132, 278n43; and nature, 127, 198, 247, 248; Japanese influence on, 127, 278n50, 279n53; and abstraction, 128, 198, 248; prow garden, 129, 131, 178, 198; Ocatilla, 130, 180, 181; and structure, 131–32, 180–81, 279nn55,59; and experimentation, 132, 178, 201, 203–4; Johnson Compound, 181

Wright, Ken, 22, 245

Wye Valley, 119–20

yellowwood tree, 10–11, 22–23, 272

Yosemite, 21, 49, 53, 55, 70